Hedin, Sven And

Southern Tibet

Mit einem englischen Part, Vol. 9

Hedin, Sven Anders

Southern Tibet

Mit einem englischen Part, Vol. 9

Inktank publishing, 2018

www.inktank-publishing.com

ISBN/EAN: 9783747726372

All rights reserved

SOUTHERN TIBET

DISCOVERIES IN FORMER TIMES COMPARED
WITH MY OWN RESEARCHES IN 1906—1908

BY

SVEN HEDIN

VOL. IX

STOCKHOLM 1922
LITHOGRAPHIC INSTITUTE OF THE GENERAL STAFF OF THE SWEDISH ARMY

CONTENTS

5

PART IV

EINE CHINESISCHE BESCHREIBUNG VON TIBET
VERMUTLICH VON JULIUS KLAPROTH. NACH AMIOT'S ÜBERSETZUNG BEARBEITET
HERAUSGEGEBEN VON ERICH HÄNISCH

DAS GOLDSTROMLAND
IM CHINESISCH-TIBETISCHEN GRENZGEBIETE
NACH DEM GROSSEN KRIEGSWERK VOM JAHRE 1781 DARGESTELLT
VON ERICH HÄNISCH
MIT FÜNF AUFNAHMEN DES VERFASSERS UND DREI KARTENTAFELN

PART V. GENERAL INDEX

JOURNEYS
IN EASTERN PAMIR

CHAPTER I.

THROUGH THE VALLEY OF THE GEZ-DARYA, 1894.

Three times I have travelled from *Fergana* to *Kashgar*. My first journey took place in December 1890 from *Osh via Terek-davan*, which was crossed on December 5th, *Irkeshtam, Ulugchat, Kanjugan, Ming-yol* and finally *Kashgar*. The second journey began on February 23rd, 1894 from *Margelan* and proceeded across the Pass of *Tengis-baï*, the *Alaï* valley, *Trans-Alaï*, the *Great Kara-kul, Pamirskiy Post, Mus-tagh-ata* and *Gez-darya* to *Kashgar*. The third time I again began from *Osh*, on July 31st, 1899 and took the road of *Gulcha, Taldik-davan, Tong-burun* or *Taun-murun-davan* which is the water-parting between the western and eastern *Kisil-su*, and finally the ordinary road by *Irkeshtam* to *Kashgar*.

As we, in this connection, are only concerned with such roads as have possibly been used by Chinese travellers of older times I will not describe these three roads, so much the less as this has already been done in my personal narratives. I will only stop for a moment at the last part of the second road, the one of *Gez-darya*, from which I have a few short annotations not before published.

From April 27th to May 1st or in five days I accomplished the journey from *Bulung-kul* to *Kashgar* which is 140 km. in length, giving 28 km. a day as an average. Unfortunately I travelled through the *Gez* valley under as unfavourable circumstances as possible. Studying the glaciers at the west side of the *Mus-tagh-ata*, I was attacked by a very violent iritis which made any kind of work impossible and compelled me to hasten to *Kashgar*. Half blind and with a bandage on my eyes I took the *Gez-darya* road which was the shortest. Of course it was impossible to make a map of the route.

The best orographical and morphological description of this region I have seen, is that of Dr. ARVED SCHULTZ.[1] Of his five names of places in the valley, *Gez, Kuruk, Atschik, Jul-tugai* and *Ui-tag*, I only heard three, *viz, Gez, Kuruk* and *Ui-tagh*. Of course there are many other names, though, by reason of my illness, I only noted a few of them.

---

[1] *Landeskundliche Forschungen im Pamir.* Hamburg 1916, p. 112 *et seq.*

After a minimum temperature of −8.6° in the night, we left *Bulung-kul* April 27th, and began to descend from 3,405 m. gradually the whole way down to *Kashgar*. Due north we had the beautiful peak of *Karagul*, 6.545 m. high, according to the map of SCHULTZ. We had to pass swampy ground and many pools full of water-plants; to our left were sand-dunes, climbing up the slopes of the hills. At 3 o'clock p. m. we passed *Tar-bashi*, or the »Beginning of the Narrow Passage», where the *Gez-darya* begins to break through the *Kashgar Range*. Here is a little fort with a garrison of a few Chinese soldiers and some native *karaulchis*. To the west and N. W. is the open plain stretching to *Chaker-agil* Lake. Turning to the right we entered the narrow passage, where the *Gez-darya* had a breadth of about 12 m. and a depth of 0.3 m., the half-clear water forming rapids. The valley is bounded by steep naked rocks, and its floor is full of gravel. The erosion terraces seemed to consist chiefly of gneiss. To the E. S. E. a magnificent peak was seen, obviously belonging to the *Charkum Range* which is an eastern ramification of the *Kashgar Range*. We camped at *Üch-kapa*, a *rabat* (or *robat*) or halting-place consisting of three clay huts of the shape of bee-hives. Dense fog filled the valley in the evening.

Here the minimum temperature was only at −0.1°. April 28th we continued. The valley is narrow and wild, the plateau-land has been succeeded by very accentuated relief. After a ride of 2 km. the road goes down to the right bank of the river which has to be crossed here. I estimated its breadth at 25 m., the average depth at 0.3 and the velocity at about 2 m. per second, which would give a volume of about 15 cub. m. per second. The bed was full of blocks and boulders. At highwater seasons one prefers to use a very narrow and dangerous path along the side of a nearly perpen-dicular mountain on the right bank. It is like a cornice and has a parapet of poles and osier, but is so steep that it seems enigmatic how a pony may climb it.

A second ford was easy, as the river was broad and shallow; this place is only a few hundred meters from the first passage. A little lower down the third passage is effected by the help of a very picturesque wooden bridge, which has been built across an enormous block in the middle of the river.[1] There are heaps of blocks and boulders everywhere. From the east, thick fog again came up the valley. A second bridge was well built at a narrow place, and a third one was called *Gög-agen-köpriu*. A little tributary from the S. E. had comparatively clear water and was crossed on a little wooden bridge. The erosion terraces of pebble and shingle are everywhere developed. Only the nearest part of the valley was visible, on account of the fog.

At *Chong-tash-bulak* there is some bush-vegetation. The road here runs along the base of a vertical terrace which partly had fallen down and looked very dangerous at places. At 4 o'clock p. m. we passed *Gez-bashi-köpriu*, a bridge near the little

---

[1] *Vide* photograph Vol. I, p. 233 of my personal narrative *Through Asia*.

fort of *Gez-kurgan*. At 6 o'clock we crossed the river on *Kara-moinak-köpriu*, and two hours later reached *Köuruk-karaul*, which obviously is the same as the *Kuruk* of Dr. SCHULTZ.

In the night of April 29th the minimum temperature was + 4.0°. A short distance below *Köuruk-karaul* we had a very difficult passage of the *Gez-darya*, which nearly cost the life of a pony. Light eastern breeze brought impenetrable yellow dust-fog up in the valley. The valley, which had been broad some distance, again becomes narrow. An hour later we crossed the river at an easy ford, and then again twice.

At *Konalya-tokai*, a place with bush vegetation, the river is very narrow and wild, forming a series of rapids; it is here crossed on a dangerous bridge 17 steps in length. The valley then becomes broader and its ground more comfortable. The mountains on the sides are steep and picturesque. In the midst of the valley a detached rock crops out. There is much vegetation; of grass, bushes, poplars and willows. From the belts of sand and gravel at the sides one gets an impression of the violence and force of the river during the highwater season. It is now divided into several branches, which often have to be crossed. The wind comes from the east and the mist conceals everything except the immediate vicinity. Human beings were nowhere seen. Only at *Ui-tagh*, where we passed the night, some Chinese soldiers were taking their rest in the *karaul-khaneh*.

In the night the temperature did not fall below + 5.6°. The dust-haze continued and obviously came from the east, for in this direction nothing was to be seen of the higher parts of the mountains whilst to the west the view reached farther. Leaving *Ui-tagh-kurgan* we passed three small miserable bridges during the first half hour. We met a caravan of 87 camels loaded with forage for *Bulung-kul* and led by Chinese soldiers. The valley becomes broader, its floor is sand and red clay with steppe vegetation.

At our last crossing of the *Gez-darya* the river flows in two branches, the first 13 m. broad and with 5 cub. m.; the second, 74 m. broad and with 33 cub. m. per second. After this passage the river is lost sight of to our left or west. The hills decrease in height and diverge. Passing through *Tash-malik* we ride between gardens, groves, fields and canals the entire way to *Sargon*. Here trees are planted on both sides of the road. Beyond *Sargon* we cross a level grass steppe. We camped in the large village of *Terem*.

On May 1st we rode through the large gardens of *Örtek* or *Örkesh*, and through the bazar of the little village of *Tokusak*. Having passed some more villages and cultivation, and having without the slightest difficulty crossed the *Kisil-su*, we reached *Kashgar* in the evening. The altitude at *Bulung-kul* being 3,405 m. and at *Kashgar* 1,304 m., the descent is in all 2,101 m. and the distance being 140 km., the rate of fall, as an average for the whole road, is as 1:66.6.

CHAPTER II.

EXCURSION TO EASTERN PAMIR, SUMMER 1894.

We now come to my second journey in *Eastern Pamir* during the summer of 1894. In my narrative, *Through Asia*, Vol. I, p. 258 *et seq.*, I have given a short description of this road from a picturesque and personal point of view. It here only remains to enter into a more detailed geographical description. On the other hand I have already, in the book just quoted, dealt at some length with the glaciers of the *Mus-tagh-ata* and will not return to them in this connection, especially as they have nothing to do with the object of these chapters which only describe roads that may have been taken by Chinese pilgrims.

The journey began in the evening of June 21st along the great caravan road to *Yangi-shahr*, after which we continued to *Gakchi* and *Boti*, villages belonging to *Tasgun*. By *Topagla, Ak-mesjid, Jigde-arik* and *Kolagli* we reached *Usun-sakal*, the last village of *Tasgun*, after which the *Tasgun-daryasi* is crossed on a bridge. Here is the boundary between the districts of *Tasgun* and *Yapchan*. To the latter belongs the river of *Khan-arik*, also called *Yupurga*. Through *Yapchan* flows a brook called *Yapchan-östäng*, which is said to be fed by springs. At *Yapchan* the altitude is 1,390 m.

Our next march followed the great caravan road by *Besh-kent*, a district of some 20 villages; the brook *Besh-kentning-östäng* is crossed on a bridge. Then follow *Tonghik* and *Mamuk*. At *Soghuluk* the altitude is 1,349 m., and at *Yangi-hisar* 1,380 m. Between the two last-mentioned places the following villages are situated: *Khancka, Seidlar* (or *Seidlik*), *Östäng-boi* with a brook, and *Chaka*.

The distance from *Yangi-hisar* to *Igis-yar*, which we accomplished during the night of June 25th, is 31 km. Here the highroad to *Yarkand* is left to the east and we continue on rising ground to *Igis-yar*. The latter place has an altitude of 1,736 m. or 356 m. above *Yangi-hisar*. The rate of ascent is therefore as 1:87.

Half an hour south of *Yangi-hisar* the *Mangshin-östäng* is crossed, carrying some 8 cub. m. of muddy water per second. On the brook *Sagan-östäng* is the village of *Kara-bash*, surrounded by low hills of sand, clay and gravel, continuing some distance to the east. Our road then crosses a steppe of sparse plants. To the right or west of our road is the region of *Tebes-östäng*. The largest villages were said to be *Yar-bag*, *Ötäsh* and *Bos-yulgun*. *Suget* is a village on the road. Some 8 km. due south of *Igis-yar* is an iron mine called *Kök-bainak;* the iron is found in layers of earth and clay. From *Kashgar* to *Igis-yar* we had travelled 94 km.

From *Igis-yar* our road runs S. S. W., S. W. and S. S. E. 47 km. to *Tokai-bash*, where the altitude is 2,668 m., or an ascent of 932 m., and a rate of 1:50.4. Leaving the square *karaul-khanch* or fort of *Igis-yar*, we soon entered the broad mouth of the valley to the S. S. W. From it comes a brook in two branches called *Tasgun*, watering several villages, gardens and fields on the plain of *Igis-yar*. The valley becomes narrower and has some forts and walls on the hills. Here the brook was called *Shahnas*, and higher up *Keng-kol*. Two mills are passed before we reach *Sar-unkur*. On a hill at the left or western side is a fort called *Kichik-karaul* or *Öräk*. Just above this point the left tributary *Ordulung* comes out. In one day's march it leads to *yeilaks* or summer grazing-grounds of Kirgizes. The mountains are greyish-brown, naked and weathered. The road is good, the valley rises gradually, its ground is grass-grown or sometimes gravelly and here and there poplar trees are seen. A little higher up the tributary *Kefsh-kakti* enters from the west. Such is also the case with *Gäjek-jilga*, which has a road to *Little Kara-kul*, and with which we should make nearer acquaintance on our return journey. The mountains opposite the junction are called *Kisil-tau*.

Leaving *Gäjek-jilga* at our right or north, we continue up the main valley of *Keng-kol* which becomes narrower and steeper. From the east enters the little right tributary of *Mahmud-terek-jilga*. At the opposite side of the valley there is a very steep massif called *Kis-kiya*. There still are groves of poplar trees.

At the point from which our direction becomes S. S. E. there is a new junction: from the left or west comes the *Chumbus* valley and from the right the *Keng-kol*, which we follow. There is a brook in each of them. *Arka-terek* is a tributary from the east. At *Tokai-bash* the *Keng-kol* River was 9.5 m. broad with an average depth of 0.2 m. and a velocity of nearly 3 m., giving a volume of 5.7 cub. m. per second. Here is a little rest-house of stone.

On June 27th we made a short journey south 12 km. to *Pokhtu*, where the altitude is 3,017 m. or 349 m. above the previous camp, the ascent thus being as 1:34. At the right side of the valley we notice three small tributaries, *Köturma*, *Mogur* and *Shilbile*. The rocks are crystalline: granites, syenites, porphyry, pegmatite, etc. From the left or S. W. comes the valley of *Käpch-kol* to the junction of *Tokai-bash*. A large part of the water comes from the *Käpch-kol*. The main valley is a series of picturesque landscapes with surprising, wild perspectives up the side valleys and here and there with wide grass-grown plains. *Besh-terek, Kara-dung* and *Pokhtu* are valleys from the S. W., the last-mentioned being the largest, nearly as large as the *Keng-kol* itself. Here a little *caravanserai* is built.

At *Pokhtu* the first snow falls at end of September. As early as March it disappears. The summer is the rainy season, and it rains a good deal. A few days before our visit the precipitation had been so considerable that the *Keng-kol* had been difficult to cross. The N. N. E. wind was said to be rain-wind and snow-wind. The Kirgizes of this region are *Kipchak*, though no tents were now pitched at *Pokhtu*. In the summer they wander to the *yeilaks* of the higher regions, in the winter they go down the valley.

On June 28th we had 25 km. S. S. W., and W. S. W. up through the valley of *Keng-kol* ascending 352 m. to the *aul* of *Keng-kol*, where the altitude is 3,369 m., the rise being 1:71. The first part of this distance the valley is narrow; the latter, somewhat broader. The rock seems chiefly to be crystalline schist and porphyry. There are considerable screes and erosion terraces the whole way. The road is very good on soft, grassy ground, where the brook meanders in all directions. Here and there, especially along the foot of the mountains and in the bed of the brook, there is gravel. Marmots are numerous.

From the left or west the following tributaries enter: *Momolai-unkur, Saribeles, Kara-agil* with three *yeilaks* called *Pokhtu, Seki* and *Sokutash;* then follow *Kisil-tiken, Tuiuk-yar, Kasim-Bek, Kuruk-köntöi* a double valley, *Ak-tö (Ak-tuya)* with a seldomly used road, *Chaltash* and *Shamaldi*, which enters a little below our camp. From the right or east and S. E., we passed *Sasik-teke, Yarik-bash, Yeshil* with a road to *Yeshil-davan, Kisil-tau* and *Kisil, Tegen-ächik* a narrow gorge with high mountains on the sides and a road to *Tegen-ächik-davan* and *Yarkand;* *Arselik* a valley with *yeilaks* and a road by *Arselik-davan* to *Charling; Yalpak-tash,* and finally *Kashka-su.*

From the *aul* of *Keng-kol* there is a road to *Kara-tash* and *Kara-kul* crossing the Pass of *Boora*. The *Keng-kol* River, which at the *aul* had not quite 1 cub. m. of water per second, is formed by the brooks of *Kashka-su, Tamgara* and *Boora,* of which the first is the largest, although it may be regarded as a right tributary of the *Keng-kol*. The road to *Kara-tash* passes several *yeilaks,* amongst them *Burgen* and *Merke,* which we should touch on our return journey. A road from *Yarkand* to *Tagarma* passes along the *Charling* and *Kashka-su. Tamgara* is also a right tributary. *Billauli* and *Boora-jilga* are left tributaries above our camp. The latter leads to the *Boora* Pass beyond which there is another *Boora-jilga.* which leads to *Kara-tash.* From the *aul* of *Keng-kol* one day's journey was reckoned to *Kara-tash.* and thence two days to *Kara-kul.*

The *aul* of *Keng-kol* at this time consisted of four tents with 21 inhabitants. They pass three months here every summer, and the winter they spend in the valley of *Ak-lö* or *Ak-tuya*. They had great flocks of sheep and goats grazing all around. There is not much snow in the winter. The last snow disappeared in the beginning of March; in the beginning of November new snow falls. The cold is not sharp. In January the wind is hard and the snow that falls at this season is called *sarik-kar* or yellow snow, obviously because it is occasionally covered by dust from the desert. The above-mentioned name of *Shamaldi* or »The Windy (place)» indicates hard winds. The summer is the rainy season, though the rain was diminishing now. Sometimes it rains several days without interruption, and the river cannot be crossed.

On June 30th we had 8.5 km. W. N. W. to the pass of *Kashka-su* 3,972 m. high, or a rise of 603 m. from the *aul* of *Keng-kol*, the rate being 1:14: from the pass we had 7.4 km. S. S. E. to *Chihil-gumbes* on the *Charling* River, where the altitude was 3,166 m. or a descent of 806 m. and a rate of fall of 1:9.2.

The uppermost part of the *Keng-kol* valley is called *Kashka-su*, not to be confounded with the *Kashka-su-jilga* that joins the *Keng-kol* near the *aul*. The valley is very narrow and gravelly between rocks of black schist in 70° E. N. E. From this valley flows the greatest part of the water of the *Keng-kol*. Near the pass of *Kashka-su* the same schist fell 72° N. N. E. The crest of the pass otherwise consists of soft rounded hills, whilst the surrounding ridges are wild and rocky. The grass was excellent round the pass, and large numbers of ponies were grazing here, belonging to merchants in *Yarkand*. The view is magnificent; deep-cut valleys at both sides, and far in the west, snow-covered ranges and peaks. »The struggle for the water-parting» is going on with energy, and the small feeders are cutting in their furrows from both sides towards the pass.

The descent is steep at the west side where the schist stands in 42° W. S. W. at the foot of the pass. The western valley is also deep and narrow and is called *Kashka-su*, as is the pass and the region. Its brook had little water. To the left is the tributary of *Koi-yoli* with an *aul* of six tents. To this place there is a shorter road across the same ridge as the one we had crossed, its pass being situated east of *Kashka-su*, but it is impossible for caravans. The rock was fine-crystalline and hard, falling 40° S. W. Below *Aidar* the black schist lay in 36° S. E. Along the *Charling* the rock was black slate and crystalline schist. The gravel and the blocks to a great extent consisted of granite or syenite. To the W. N. W. from *Kashka-su-davan* is *Tamgara-davan*, *Boora*. *Koi-yoli*, *Ucha*, *Aidar* and *Charling* were the only other names we heard. The river *Charling* which here was very small, only 3 or 4 m. wide, is also called *Charlung*. We camped at *Chihil-gumbes-karaul* on its right bank, where three families of 13 persons lived, and a few small

2. IX.

17

huts are built. Here is also the burial place of the region with three *gumbes* or tomb monuments. The Kirgizes of this place, and of *Keng-kol* and *Charling*, are Kipchak. One and a half hour's journey down the *Charling* is the *aul* of *Jilande;* still lower down is a place called *Togan-turuk;* one *tash* still further down are two *jilgas: Terek-öse* to the right with three inhabited huts, and to the left *Yauda-koli* with Kirgiz *yeilaks*. From *Chihil-gumbes* there are three roads: to *Keng-kol*, to *Yarkand* and to *Tagarma*. Merchants' caravans pass often between the two last-mentioned places. The climate is the same as at *Keng-kol*. The greatest part of the rain falls in the early summer.

On July 1st we had to cross the pass of *Ter-art*. From the camp we had 6 km. W. S. W. to the pass, the altitude of which is 4,040 m., the rise being 874 m. and the rate 1:6.9; on the other side we had 7.6 km. west and south, descending to 2,884 m. at *Pas-rabat*, or a descent of 1,156 m. at a rate of 1:6.6. On both sides the slopes therefore are very steep.

The eastern *Ter-art-jilga* had no water. The pass had the same rounded forms as *Kashka-su-davan*. The rocks consist of the same crystalline schists as hitherto, near the pass standing vertically N. W.—S. E. On the western side the road proceeds by an extremely narrow gorge with some water between erosion terraces. In its upper part the valley is gravelly, in the lower the ground is soft and grass-grown; willows appear here and there. There is a good deal of blocks. The brook gets an affluent from *Boramsal-jilga*. At 3 o'clock p. m. the valley got filled with light fog brought hither by the S. E. wind, and at 7 o'clock it began to rain. The valley becomes broader gradually. Along the base of the mountains are very mighty erosion terraces, which lower down are swept away along the left side, but on the right continue down to *Pas-rabat*. Their height above the floor of the valley is 50 m. and more.

We camped at the *karaul-khaneh* and *aul* of *Pas-rabat*, where three families of 13 individuals, Kesek Kirgizes, lived. In the vertical erosion terrace opposite the camp was a round grotto 4.3 m. above the floor, containing some horns of wild goats and some hay. West of the pass we only heard three names of *jilgas*, viz. to the left *Toshkan-jilga* and to the right *Teke-sekerik* with, in its higher regions, a road to *Boramsal-jilga* and *Kara-jilga-davan;* then to the right the large *Boramsal-jilga* with a road to *Kara-tash-davan*, situated somewhere N. W. The *Boramsal-jilga* may be regarded as the main valley, and the western *Ter-art* as a tributary to it. At *Pas-rabat* the *Tengi-tar* valley comes from the west and then the joined river is called *Pas-rabat* the whole way down to its junction with the *Taghdumbash-darya* or *Shinde* River. The *Tengi-tar* had near the confluence a breadth of 10 m. and a maximum depth of 0.4 m.

At the *aul* of *Pas-rabat*, which was called *Toil-bulung*, *Toile-bulung* or *Toyil-bulung*, the landscape is very picturesque, looking up the *Boramsal* valley with mountain ridges in its background, and the *Tengi-tar* with its foaming brook, and down the *Pas-rabat* valley. The mountain sides are mostly hidden by detritus, and living rock crops out only higher up. The valley is broad at the confluence and has excellent grazing-grounds. There is a burial place with several *gumbes*.

The climate is the same as described above. In the winter the snow is one foot deep or a little more. At the end of February and beginning of March the wind is hard. Sometimes it rains a week in the summer, and the rivers grow big; one has to cross them at noon, as they rise in the evening. At *Pas-rabat* the river freezes, but not higher up where warm springs come out. July 2nd I made a few measurements of the river below the point of junction. At 1 o'clock p. m. its breadth was 16.25 m., the average depth 0.41 m., the average velocity 1.05 m. and the volume 7 cub. m. per second. The temperature of the water was 10.5°, and of the air 17.3°. If the waterlevel at 1 o'clock is fixed as 0, the river had fallen 1.5 cm. at 3 o'clock and risen 3.5 at 5 o'clock; at 7 o'clock it had risen 16.0 cm. above 0, and the water had become very muddy. The average depth was now 57 cm. and the maximum 76 cm. The breadth was 17.25 m., the average velocity 1.45; the volume of water per second was thus a little above 14 cub. m. The temperature of the water was now 9.7°. At 8 o'clock the level stood 18 cm. above 0 and the temperature was 9.4°. At 9 o'clock the river had risen still 1 cm. and the temperature had fallen to 9.1°; the air having a temperature of 9.8°.

An important road from *Kashgar*, *Yangi-hisar* and *Yarkand* to *Tash-kurgan* passes by *Pas-rabat*; as a rule 5 or 6 persons pass by every day, sometimes 15 or 20.

On his journey 1906—1908, Dr. M. A. STEIN crossed my route at *Pas-rabat*, which he calls *Toile-bulung*. From *Buramsal-davan* to *Pas-rabat* he has the following names: *Buramsal* and *Tash-mazar*; from the latter place to the junction with the *Shinde* River: *Muktushtiya*, *Jashya*, *Kuruk Mazar*, *Yarghik-aghzi*, *Yughash-öghil*, *Bashi-Kara-tokai*, *Otra-Kara-tokai*, *Kara-tokai*, *Uchak*, *Momoluk*, *Unghurluk*, *Kichik Kara-su*, *Kara-su*, *Kokyer*, *Tikan-ynrt*, and finally the confluence, between which and *Tash-kurgan* he travelled in the narrow valley of the *Shinde* River. To the *Ter-art Pass* he gives an altitude of 2.936 m. or 52 m. more than my 2,884 m.; to *Pas-rabat* he gives 4,067 m. or 27 m. more than my 4,040 m. The difference between our observations is, therefore, very small.

On July 3rd we had a difficult journey of 19.5 km. west and W. S. W. to *Bulak-bashi* where the altitude is 3,722 m., being a rise of 838 m. at a rate of 1 : 23.3.

In the morning the river of *Pas-rabat* stood only 2 cm. above 0, and the water had a temperature of 7.5°. The rock is the same as hitherto, crystalline schist and granite or syenite. There is no lack of vegetation, grass, bushes and willow trees. The steep or nearly vertical erosion terraces reach high up on the slopes of the hills and have sometimes, because of the action of water, assumed phantastic forms. Grottos are often seen.

Leaving *Pas-rabat* we have first to our left or south three right tributaries, *Kichik-oljeke, Shagil-unkur* and *Chong-oljeke* with 5 or 6 tents and all with *yei-laks*. From the north come *Ak-taldu* and *Yam-bulak*. The latter, with a hut at its mouth, is considerable. A short distance from the junction the *Yam-bulak* is formed by two valleys. The left or southern one of these is the *Yam-bulak-jilga* proper which leads to *Yangi-davan* and *Tuge-boyun-davan*, beyond which a valley again joins the main valley. On this road one may also continue to *Chichiklik-davan*. This roundabout road, which is one day's march in length and probably very difficult, is used, even by caravans, in the winter when the *Tengi-tar* valley is impossible on account of ice and snow. By the right or northern valley is a road to *Little Kara-kul* and *Su-bashi* crossing *Tur-bulung-davan* and leaving the above-mentioned *Kara-tash-davan* to its right. In the entire region of *Yam-bulak* there are very good summer-grazings and 80 or 90 tents.

From the junction with the *Yam-bulak* valley the main valley is called *Tengi-tar*, and here begins the extremely narrow and difficult gorge which is filled with foaming water amongst heaps of large round blocks, where it sometimes looks hopeless for loaded ponies. The rock is here granite or syenite and the forms of the ridges and crests more cupola-shaped, not sharp-edged and wild as in the schist region. The volume of water is small, only 2 or 3 cub. m. per second, but still the wild rapids amongst the blocks are a great hindrance as it is impossible to see the holes between the big blocks. Nearly the whole way one has to ride in the water. At dry places there is always vegetation, amongst other plants wild *Rosa*-bushes and birches.

From the south enters *Gör-* or *Gur-jilga*, wild and narrow but leading to *yeilaks* where people occupying two or three tents now were said to pass the summer. A little higher up *Kara-jilga* comes from the same side; in its background we see a range with eternal snow.

Isik-bulak is a hot spring which in three small jets comes out from below a large block in the erosion terrace at the right or southern side of the *Tengi-tar* valley. The water is sulphurous and has coloured the stones around in yellow and brownish tints. Clouds of steam are surrounding the spring, which has a temperature of $52.8°$. The spring is situated 7 m. from the bank of the brook; 10 m. below the place where the spring water enters the brook the latter has a temperature of $19.0°$, and 10 m. above the same place $12.5°$. Two minutes higher up we pass a second spring of exactly the same character and with a temperature of $51.7°$; above it the brook had a temperature of $12.2°$. From the springs and down to *Yam-bulak* the brook never freezes; above them it freezes only at comparatively quiet stretches.

Some distance above the springs the *Tengi-tar* gorge is extremely narrow, only a few meters broad; here the deepest basins in the bed have been filled with stones for making the passage possible. The landscape is very wild and picturesque, and the foaming water of the brook fills the whole bottom of the gorge. At the left or northern side we climb a little mountain shoulder, *Tarning-bashi-moinak*, very steep, with a commanding picturesque view, and saving us from a difficult part of the gorge below. Its altitude is 3,441 m., whilst *Isik-bulak* had 3,278 m. *Tarning-bashi-moinak* or »The Threshold of the Beginning of the Narrow Passage» forms a boundary between two different types of valley. Here we leave the narrow and difficult gorge behind, and see in front of us to the west a comparatively broad and comfortable valley. The rock is here granite or syenite in a very weathered and rotten state. To the south rises at some distance a double peak with eternal snow, called *Kara-jilga-bashi*. The water from its melting snow reaches the *Tengi-tar* by *Kara-jilga*. The junction is called *Chil-ötök*. The main valley from the little *moinak* and westwards is called *Tar-bashi*. The morphological characteristics of the valleys are, therefore, clearly distinguished by the Kirgiz. So, for instance, is *keng* = broad, *kol* = a broad open valley. *Tengi* is a narrow gorge and *tar* is narrow. *Tar-bashi* is the Head or Beginning of the Narrow Passage.

We camped at *Bulak-bashi* where cold springs are numerous. From the south enters the tributary *Mus-aling* with a road 3½ *tash* in length to the Pass *Mus-aling-davan* and good *yeilaks*. The pass is difficult in winter on account of snow. On its southern side the road continues to the *Shinde* valley. At *Bulak-bashi* the snow reaches to the knees in winter. The last snow disappears in the beginning of April; in the beginning of November it again begins to fall. The winter is very cold, and all water freezes. The name *Mus-aling* or »Catching Ice» indicates that one has to melt the ice for getting water. Even the springs freeze. In the middle and end of May is the maximum of rain. The brook rises and falls regularly in the course of 24 hours if there is no rain. At 9 o'clock p. m. it has its maximum, at noon its minimum. At 3.30 p. m. we saw a curious phenomenon in the brook which had been small and clear so far. Now suddenly we heard a mighty roar from above and in a minute the brook increased to a large foaming and very muddy river. This, of course, was due to rain somewhere in the high regions. By far the greatest part of the water in the *Tar-bashi* brook comes from the *Mus-aling* valley; only a small quantity comes by the *Chichiklik* valley.

At *Bulak-bashi* we found six tents with 30 inhabitants of the Kesek tribe; they do not understand the Tajik language. Two of them were *bais* or rich men, possessing about 1000 sheep, 200 goats, 100 yaks, 30 ponies and 30 camels each. At *Bulak-bashi* is a *karaul-khaneh* with some watchmen who have to assist travellers and be responsible for the conveying of the Chinese post between *Yangi-hisar* and

Tash-kurgan. They are paid in wheat. From *Bulak-bashi* to *Yangi-hisar* are
six *karauls: Bulak-bashi, Pas-rabat, Chil-gumbes, Kashka-su-bashi, Tokai-bashi* and
Igis-yar. At each place are three watchmen or *karaulchis*.

The next day, July 4th, we made a short march of only 6 km. to the mouth
of *Kara-jilga* where the altitude is 4,175 m.; the ascent is 453 m. and the rate
1:13. The brook was now very small and its water quite clear. Only a half kilometer up the valley we passed the *aul* of *Oiman* consisting of six tents. At *Oiman-
agsi*, a little tributary from the south, 5 tents were pitched. The valley is broad,
its ground undulated, and the ascent was sensible. Through the openings of southern
tributaries we see the snow-covered ranges called *Kara-jilganing-bashi*. The southern
tributary, at the mouth of which we camped, was here called *Kichik-kara-jilga*.
I made a short excursion up in this valley, the floor of which has a steep ascent
and very good grass, where yaks were grazing. The marmots are numerous. The
brook increased in the afternoon and became muddy. The mountains on both sides
have soft, rounded forms and are covered with débris; only the snowy crest is of
solid rock.

At our camp of *Kara-jilga* there is much snow in the winter, more than
½ or ⅔ of a meter. It snows even in the summer, but only at night, and the snow
disappears in the day. There is not much rain. West and W. S. W. wind is
prevailing, especially in the spring and autumn. The Kesek Kirgizes of the place
only stay two months: when the permanent snow falls they wander down to *Toile-
bulung*. The road from *Yangi-hisar* to *Tagarma* has one of its difficult passages
here during the winter, but is always in use.

On July 5th we travelled 19 km. west and S. W. to *Kata-kok-moinak*,
where the altitude is 4,738 m.; it is an ascent of 563 m. or as 1:34. From
the pass we had 23 km. S. W., W. S. W. and N. W. to our camp *Shärnäp* in
Tagarma at an altitude of 3,236 m., or a descent of no less than 1,502 m. at a
rate of 1:15.

The minimum had been below zero, and thin ice covered the pools. The
valley becomes broader and more open. Small patches of eternal snow are seen at
both sides on the highest crests. From the north enters the *Salik-jilga* and from
the south the *Yukarke-kara-jilga* or the »Upper Black Valley». The latter has
snow-covered mountains in the background and a little clear brook which, as all
tributaries here, has cut its furrow down through the soft yellow clay filling the
floors of the valleys. Only the beds are full of gravel and blocks. The grass is
very good. In these higher regions the brooks have their maximum at noon and
decrease towards evening.

The width of the main valley increases, the mountains at the sides become
relatively lower and more rounded, those to the south being ramifications from the

snow-covered range. At the sides of the upper *Tar-bashi* valley only slopes falling
to the north, N. W. and N. E. had snow patches. In front of us we now also saw
a mighty snowy range, obviously the southern part of the *Mus-tagh-ata* massif. In
our neighbourhood everything was detritus; the floor of the valley is partly gravel,
partly grass.

Finally the *Tar-bashi* valley opens out into the wide round basin of the
Chicheklik Lakes. This arena is on all sides surrounded by partly snow-covered
mountains. To our right, or north, is *Yangi-davan*, from which comes down the
Yam-bulak road, which is used when the *Tengi-tar* is impracticable. In the midst
of the basin is a little lake, 500 m. in length, called *Chicheklik-kul;* here the altitude
is 4,458 m. Just east of it is a threshold perhaps some 20 or 30 m. above the lake,
being the water-parting between it and the uppermost *Tar-bashi* valley. This threshold
was called *Chicheklik-davan* by my guides. The whole region is called *Chicheklik,*
or, according to the Kirgiz pronounciation, *Chichekli.*

From the little lake an effluent goes to a still smaller lake close by and continues to the south from it, reaching the *Shinde* River under the name of *Chicheklik-su.*
Both the brook and the lakes have crystal-clear water, which gathers in the upper
lake from the surrounding hills. The lakes are at their largest in spring. In the
winter they are covered with ice. In the beginning and middle of July five Tajik
families with 2,000 sheep wander to the basin, passing three months there or until the
first snow comes. West of the *Kok-moinak* Passes we met a yak caravan on its
road thither. The snow remains six months and has a thickness of half a meter,
2 or 3 *garech* as the Kirgiz say, one *garech* being the distance between the tip
of the little finger and the tip of the thumb of an outspread hand. The winter is
cold; *burans* or snow-storms are common, both from west and east. There is not
much rain. A basin of this form is called a *tus-yeilak* or »even summer grazing».
Twenty tents were said to be pitched along the *Chicheklik-su* on its course down
to the *Shinde*. One gets the impression that the *Chicheklik* basin has once been
a »Firnmulde» filled with *névés* sending out glaciers to the south and east. The
Tar-bashi valley with its soft, rounded forms may easily have been the bed of a
glacier. Its floor consists of very fine material, and at the little *moinak* there were
blocks and débris which may have belonged to an end moraine. I found no striæ,
but hard rock was not easy to reach.

Having left the small lakes and crossed the *Chicheklik-su* where the altitude
was 4,420 m., we gradually ascended the *Kichik-kok-moinak* (also pronounced *kök*).
Everything is soft material and gravel of chiefly gneiss. The rounded heights are
grass-covered. To the east we have the snowy range of *Kugusu*. We have a fine
view of the lake basin from the pass. From the little trough-shaped depression
between *Kichik-* and *Kata-kok-moinak* several rills join in a brook running down

to the *Shinde*, perhaps joining the *Chicheklik-su* before reaching it. *Kata-kok-moinak* is also flat and comfortable with no living rock.

As the highway from *Tash-kurgan* to *Tar-bashi* and *Tengi-tar* crosses these two passes it is obvious that GOËS means them when he speaks of the mountains of *Ciacialith*. And probably HÜAN-CHUANG means the basin of *Chicheklik-kul* when speaking of the plain surrounded by the four mountains belonging to the eastern chain of the *Ts'ung-ling*. On STEIN'S *Map of portions of Chinese Turkistan and Kansu*, Sheet No. 3 I cannot identify his *Chichiklik Maidan*, at which he arrived from *Kara-kapa* along the brook that drains the *Chichiklik*. His *Chichiklik Dawan*, on the other hand, is in perfect accordance with my *Chichiklik-davan* as being the watershed between the little lakes and the *Tar-bashi*. If his *Chichiklik Maidan* is identical with my basin of *Chicheklik-kul*, our altitudes differ too much, for he has 4.573 m. and I have 4,458 m.

On the west side of *Kata-kok-moinak* we enter the valley of *Kok-moinakning-jilga* which gradually becomes more and more gravelly and narrow. During one hour's ride the valley was as narrow and difficult as the *Tengi-tar*, filled with blocks and water. At some protected places were still snow-patches and ice-sheets, across which we rode. *Kökuse* and *Yaslik* are tributary valleys, the latter from the south, the former with a road to *yeilaks*. Then the valley becomes a little broader and is called *Darshat*. Finally we reach its end, and see in front of us an extensive plain, *Tagarma*, with the snow-covered *Sarikol Range* in the background, and to the right parts of southern *Mus-tagh-ata*.

At the *aul* of *Kara-kechu* we crossed the stream of *Tegerman-su*, also called *Tagarma-su*. We left to our right the valley of *Tegerich*, and camped at *Shärnäp* on the *Tagarma* plain. The *Shärnäp-su* here comes down from the southern *Mus-tagh-ata*, which was said to be called *Kara-gorum* (*i. e. korum*).

From *Igis-yar* to *Tagarma* we had now crossed the *Kashgar System of Mountains* for the second time. On the first crossing we had followed one and the same river, *Gez-darya*, the whole way. Now, we first travelled in the drainage area of the *Keng-kol* up to the *Kashka-su Pass*, west of which we entered the drainage-area of the *Charling River*. West of *Ter-art* we kept sticking to the area of the *Pas-rabat* up to *Chicheklik-davan*, after which followed the drainage area of *Chicheklik-su*. West of *Kata-kok-moinak* we were in the area of the *Tagarma* brooks, which flow to the *Shinde* or *Taghdumbash-darya*.

Two years before the journey I have just described, Lord DUNMORE had travelled through the same region. Neither his text nor his small-scale maps allow us to follow his journey in detail. August 17th 1892 he left *Yarkand* and rode by *Yakarik (Yaka-arik)* and *Kara-Dawan*, obviously the same as the one crossed by YOUNGHUSBAND in 1890. Then he passed by *Kiaz Aghzay* at the junction of the

Kiaz (?) and the *Chahlung (Charlung, Chahrlung* or *Charling)*, which »ought to have been running from east to west», instead of west to east.[1] The next place we may identify is *Cheile Gombaz (Chil-gumbes)*, which also had been visited by Young-husband. From there he crossed a pass called *Tirak Pass (Ter-art)*. His altitudes are usually 100 or 150 m. too high. From *Chil-gumbes* to *Pas-rabat* he no doubt followed the same road as I have described above, for he says: »we followed for about two miles the course of the *Tikka Sikrik (Teke-sekerik)* river until we debouched into a broader valley, striking the *Bramsal (Boramsal)* river at right angles, running south-east. We followed that for about four miles, until its junction with the *Toilobolong (Toile-bulung)*, at a green spot called *Pahst Robat . . . .*» Later on he crossed the pass of *Yambulak* and arrived at the *Chichiklik Plain.* The *Kokmainuk Pass (Kata-kok-moinak)* he gives as 4,918 m. It is a pity that Major ROCHE, who accompanied him, did not make a map of the interesting road.

---

[1] *The Pamirs*, Vol. II, p. 3. London 1893.

CHAPTER III.

THE THIRD CROSSING OF THE KASHGAR RANGE.

The whole summer of 1894 was given up to wanderings and excursions amongst the glaciers of *Mus-tagh-ata*, and to an excursion to *Alichur Pamir* and *Yeshil-kul*. My experiences from this time are described in *Through Asia*, Vol. I, in *Petermanns Mitteilungen, Zeitschrift der Ges. für Erdkunde zu Berlin*, and elsewhere. In this connection we are concerned only with my different crossings of the *Kashgar System* of mountain ranges, and we have now arrived at the third crossing, beginning October 9th, 1894, and being my return journey from *Mus-tagh-ata* viâ *Igis-yar* to *Kashgar*.

I started from *Little Kara-kul* which is at an altitude of 3,720 m., and proceeded north-eastwards to the valley of *Ike-bel-su* and up this river, the southern feeder of *Gez-darya*, in a E. S. E. and S. E. direction, to the *aul* of *Tuya-kuiruk* at an altitude of 3,884 m. The distance is 18 km., the rise 164 m. and the rate of ascent 1 : 110. The place where we reached the river is called *Keng-shvär*. In the summer we had seen the *Ike-bel-su* as a very mighty river, now it had only 2 or 3 cub. m. of water per second. From the *Korumde Glacier* to the south it received a tributary of about 1 cub. m. per second. A part of the valley is called *Tokus-bulak*. Three northern tributaries are called *Shevakte, Chekanak* and *Teres-ösö*. *Tuya-kuiruk* is a wide open part of the valley where now four tents of Karateïts were pitched; the inhabitants are also *karaulchis*. At *Keng-shvär* were also four tents. The winter is cold but there is not much snow. The prevailing wind comes from the S. W. and is hard. The river is covered with thick ice in winter, but there is always some water flowing.

On October 10th our road goes 23 km. N. E., E., E. S. E., S. S. E. and S. E. up through the valley to *Tur-bulung*, where the altitude is 4,317 m., or a rise of 433 m. at a rate of 1 : 53.

Our camp of *Tuya-kuiruk* was at some distance south of the *Ike-bel-su*, so we had to return to its course, crossing heaps of old moraines and the brook that still carries half a cubic meter of water per second from the little *Tuya-kuiruk Glacier*

THE VALLEY OF IKE-BEL-SU, LOOKING EAST FROM KIYA, KENGSHEVÄR.
TO THE RIGHT KARA-TASH AND TUR-BULUNG. JULY 1894.

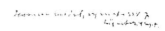

LOOKING S. S.W. FROM THE CAMP OF TEGERMEN-SU, SEPT. 24, 1894.

on the N. E. side of the *Mus-tagh-ata*. The valley of *Ike-bel-su* becomes narrower but the rise is regular and the road good, though full of gravel. During the summer the narrow furrow of the river is quite filled with foaming muddy water, and the road therefore sticks to the lower slopes of old rounded terraces and screes. The rock is green crystalline schist in 58° E. Living rock is very rare, everything being covered with detritus, gravel and blocks. The right side of the valley seems to consist, at least partly, of gneiss. On both sides the valley is bordered by dark, mighty ranges with snow on their crests and short rocky ramifications and mountain shoulders sloping down to the valley. The loose material of the screes reaches very high up on the slopes, and above their upper edges the living rock stands in nearly perpendicular teeth, crests and towers.

From the east, or E. N. E. enters the right tributary *Yalpak-tash*, a wild and narrow gorge between black picturesque rocks, and with a road to *Kara-tash-davan*. From this valley the *Ike-bel-su* received about 2 cub. m. of water per second; above the junction about 5 remained. At some places its bed is extremely narrow and the river must here be very deep and wild in summer. It has cut its bed through old moraines and heaps of gravel.

Tashning-tube is a triangular spot in the valley, where, on the slope of the left side, four tents were pitched. From the S. S. E. enters the wild and deep-cut valley of the left tributary, *Kok-sel*, bordered by imposing, snow-covered ranges. In its background we see an extended glacier landscape and here the considerable *Kok-sel Glacier* comes down, filling up nearly the whole *Kok-sel* valley with its tongue and snout. The glacier comes from the S. W. and turns to the north and even N. N. W. Higher up it seems to get contributions from small glaciers at its sides. From the *Kok-sel-jilga*, the *Ike-bel-su* gets a large portion of its water. The glacier is covered by nearly uninterrupted moraines, and only in the crevasses is the ice visible. The lateral moraines have not much place along the sides of the mountains. The end moraine is not large; it forms the S. E. border of the triangular spot.

From the junction of the *Kok-sel* and the *Tur-bulung*, the joint river is called *Ike-bel-su*. Our road goes up the *Tur-bulung* valley, ascending the very steep slopes of its right side in zigzags across screes of gravel, and living rock of gneiss. Farther on, at the round stone wall of *Ak-kalama*, the road again goes down to the floor of the valley which here is broader and has good grazing grounds. Steep, rocky mountains rise at both sides; at the left or south-western side a sharply defined black ramification separates the *Kok-sel* from the *Tur-bulung* valley. The watercourse of the latter forms a series of rapids and even small waterfalls.

The *aul* of *Tur-bulung* had four tents of the Naiman and Sart-Kipchak tribes. These people pass the summer at *Merke*, and had arrived at *Tur-bulung* ten days ago.

In another four days they intended to wander down to *Keng-shvär*, and later on to *Kara-kul* and *Sari-kol*. Sometimes they visit the regions south of *Tur-bulung-davan*. There is no direct road from *Tur-bulung* to the upper part of *Tegerman-su* at the S. E. side of *Mus-tagh-ata*. Between the two valleys is a very high and ice-covered pass and some small glaciers. Between *Kok-sel* and *Sar-agil*, a glacier on the southern side of *Mus-tagh-ata*, everything was ice and snow. Obviously a mighty ridge stretches to the east from the *Mus-tagh-ata* group. I was told that travellers from *Tur-bulung* to *Chicheklik* had no other practicable road than *via* the *Merke* valley, *Yam-bulak-davan* and *Yam-bulak-jilga*. The *Yam-bulak-davan* was said to be flat, but gravelly.

At *Tur-bulung* the winter is very cold and there is much snow and hard wind. Bears, wolves and foxes live in the mountains; there are *Ovis Poli*, wild goats and snow pheasants.

From *Tur-bulung* I made an excursion of 9 km. to the south up through the *Kara-jilga*. At its right or eastern side are two small hanging glaciers. The valley is comparatively broad and easy. In its upper parts two flocks of wild sheep were grazing; they fled southwards in the direction of *Chicheklik*. In the midst of the valley flows the brook from the *Kara-jilga Glacier*, which is fed from two sources. Above it and at the sides are snow and ice-covered peaks and ridges, and probably the »Firnmulde» from which it comes is in connection with the great snow and ice-masses of the *Mus-tagh-ata*. The surface of the *Kara-jilga Glacier* is quite black with moraines. At the point where we turned back to *Tur-bulung*, the altitude was 4,645 m. The ascent was, therefore, 328 m. and the rate as 1:27.

October 12th we travelled S. E., east and N. E. across the *Merke-bel* to *Merke*. From *Tur-bulung* we had 16 km. to the pass where the altitude is 5,198 m.; the ascent is therefore 881 m. at a rate of 1:18.2: from the pass we had 18 km. to *Merke*, where the altitude is 3,593 m.. or a descent of no less than 1,605 m. in a few hours, and at a rate of 1:11.2.

In the upper region of the *Tur-bulung* valley there are very good grazing-grounds to which the Kirgiz of *Merke* and *Keng-shvär* drive their sheep in summer. The uppermost part of the valley is troughshaped and here the brooks have cut down their furrows deep in the ground. Before reaching so far we had left to the south the left tributaries *Teke-yeilak* (pron. *yeilau*), *Kara-jilga*, described above and the little valley leading to *Tur-bulung-davan*.

On gravelly slopes we rode eastwards up through the trough which at an earlier period had been filled by ice and where now only gigantic old moraines were left. The whole pass of *Merke-bel* and both its western and eastern slopes consist of enormous moraines. Of the old glacier which has brought down the material, only a small rest is left on the southern side of the pass.

The ascent to the pass is not steep; we approach the saddle gradually. On the very top of the flat pass we have to ride about 2 km. on the snout of the glacier itself which, as well as the surrounding ground, was covered under 40 cm. of snow with a frozen crust. The pass is closed every winter. It is very flat and it is hard to tell exactly where it is. It was the highest pass I crossed in *Eastern Pamir*, or 5,198 m., even higher than *Ulug-art* (5,150 m.).

The mountains north of the pass had only small patches of snow; those to the south were quite covered with snow and ice. On the eastern side, where the valley slopes down at a much steeper rate, we rode for about an hour amongst enormous old moraines. The gravel is chiefly black and green crystalline schist. On the way down in the *Merke-bashi-jilga* we passed blocks of coarse-grained grey gneiss. Living rock was very rare; the mountain sides were covered with gravel and screes. The valley is comparatively broad and has good grazing grounds. To our right or south we pass the tributaries *Korum-jilga*, *Kara-jilga* and *Temir-jilga*. From the left we noted only *Kashka-su*. Now only one Kara-teït tent was pitched some distance below *Kashka-su*, where we camped. During summer many Kirgizes visit the valley. In the winter the snow and the hard S. W. wind drive them down to *Kara-tash* and farther.

On October 13th we travelled 16 km. N. N. E. down the valley to the entrance of the left tributary *Suget-jilga*, in which we ascended 2 km. to the *aul* of the same name, and where the altitude is 3,015 m. or a fall of 578 m. The *Merke River* now assumes the name of *Kusen-darya*, pronounced as *Ksen-darya*. The whole day it snowed heavily, and both at *Merke* and *Suget* the Kirgiz said it was the first serious snowfall of the winter season. The valley is narrow. The road sticks the whole time to its floor. Below the entrance of the watercourse of *Boramsal* the volume is about 2 cub. m. per second, in a very stony bed. Only twice the road passed by uncomfortable passages on the slopes of old terraces. Sometimes living rock is seen, always crystalline schist. Blocks of gneiss are numerous in and along the bed. The mountains at the sides are steep, black and wild, though now nearly everything became snowed over. From both sides enter a great number of small, short and steep *jilgas*.

From the right comes the large tributary, *Boramsal*, with a brook. Only from here the stream of the main valley is open; above this junction it was frozen. The *Boramsal* was now uninhabited. In its upper reaches there are good *yeilaks*. It has a road by *Boramsal-davan* to *Pas-rabat*. *Tamde-jilga* from the left is broad, but without importance. Near its mouth was an *aul* of four tents. Then follows, from the right, the large tributary of *Boora-jilga* with extensive grazing-grounds in its upper reaches, four tents, and a road by *Boora-davan* to *Keng-kol*, which it joins a short distance above *Kashka-su*. *Tora* is the name of a double *jilga* from the right without a road. *yeilaks* or tents. At the junction with the right tributary *Kismak-jilga* two tents were pitched, and higher up nine amongst the *yeilaks;* *Kismak-jilga* has a road to *Kismak-davan* and, on its S. E. side, to the *Chumbus-jilga* which joins the *Keng-kol*. *Kismak-davan* is flat and snow-covered. Finally from the right, or S. W., enters the *Suget-jilga* which is considerable and has groves of willows. Here a road goes to the pass of *Ike-bel-davan*, leaving *Kara-tash-davan* to the left and joining the *Yalpak-tash-jilga*, *Ike-bel-su* and *Keng-shvär*. *Ike-bel-davan* is said to be covered by ice and gravel, and practicable only on foot.

The *aul* of *Suget* consisted of five tents of Kara-teïts. They intended to remain here four months, nearly the whole winter, after which they would wander to upper *Merke*, where they pass the summer. There is a good deal of snow in the winter at *Suget*. but no hard wind. I got some information about the *Ulug-art Pass* farther N. W., and of the *Buru-kös-davan* which was said to be closed by snow 5 or 6 months every year. In 1895 I was to make a nearer acquaintance with the *Ulug-art*. The *Kusen-darya* was said often to be so swollen in the summer that it could not be crossed except at a few well-known fords.

From *Suget* we had 11.5 km. N. N. E. down the same valley to *Chat*, where the altitude is 2,876 m.; the descent is thus 139 m., and the rate as 1:83. The road is good, there is alternating grass and gravel; the valley is rather narrow, the snow gradually disappears, flocks of yaks are seen on the meadows. Only on the mountains the snow still remains. The rock is as hitherto black crystalline schist. The erosion terraces are well developed and pierced in vertical gorges by the tributaries. Below *Kara-tash-jilga*, which enters from the left, the main brook has about 4 cub. m. clean water per second in a bed full of gravel and blocks. From the right or east enters the *Khan-dösö-jilga*. Just below comes *Kara-tash* from the left; it has 8 tents higher up; and on the pass, *Kara-tash-davan*, two *karaul* tents. Below *Kara-tash* enters, also from the left, the *Kalmak-masar-jilga*, without habitations, and a road. The same is the case with *Bilauli-jilga* from the right. At *Chat* four tents were pitched inside of a wall of stone and earth. The people arrived a month ago and would soon move to *Suget*, where the wood is plentiful. The summer they pass at upper *Merke*.

The chief of *Chat*, Muhammed Tokta Bek, was Chong Bek or Grand Bek of *Kara-tash* and *Merke* with 70 tents, *Gäjek* with 40 tents, *Chimgan* with 60 tents, *Khan-terek* with 40 tents and *Kara-kul* and *Su-bashi* with 50 tents. Most of his subjects were Kara-teïts, though at *Chimgan* Yaman-teïts also were living.

At *Chat* there is not much snow in the winter. The cold is not bad and the wind not hard.

Before reaching *Chat* we had left to our left side, or W. N. W., the continuation of the main valley which we had been following ever since *Merke-bel*. All the water from *Merke*, *Boramsal*, *Kara-tash* and other valleys pierces here the mountains in a wild deep-cut gorge, sometimes bounded by vertical rock walls and so narrow that a passenger can touch both sides at the same time. In the summer this road is impossible, as the gorge is filled to 1½ m. or more. Only in the winter it can be used on the ice, and if the gorge is not quite filled with snow. If at the same time the *Gäjek-davan* is closed by snow, the Kirgiz of the region may be cut off for some time. When I asked what they did under such conditions they answered: »yatamis», we sleep. Still, at some broad places in the *Khan-terek* valley there were said to be pitched some 30 or 40 tents at the time of our passage. The watercourse of *Khan-terek* continues down to *Kamper-karaul, Tebes* and *Yangi-hisar*.

Two *tash* from the entrance to *Khan-terek's* gorge the latter receives a left tributary called *Chimgan*. It is large and of importance, as 50 or 60 tents are pitched in its lower part during the winter; in its upper part during the summer. Even some barley is grown in this valley, where there is a good deal of *tokai* or forest. It has a road to *Tur-bulung* and *Ikc-bel-su*, and in its upper part are two glaciers. A right tributary to the *Chimgan* is called *Teres-öső*, and has a bad and difficult road up to *Kara-tash-davan*, practicable only on foot or with yaks. There are no inhabitants in *Teres-öső*.

On October 15th we travelled 9 km. E. N. E. to *Gäjek-davan*, 3,975 m. high, thus being an ascent of 1,099 m. and at the rather steep rate of 1:8.2. On the other side we had 14.3 km. E. N. E. in zigzags to the mouth of *Sarik-kis-jilga* and up in its valley to the *aul* where we camped at an altitude of 2,762 m., or 1,213 m. below the pass.

To begin with, the *Chat-jilga* is comparatively broad and has good grazing-grounds. On both sides the mountains are snow covered. From the north or right side of the valley enters the *Yaman-jilga*, uninhabited, with small *yeilaks* and a bad roundabout road to the lower part of *Gäjek-jilga* east of the pass. Opposite it is *Yöruluk-jilga*, uninhabited and with a footpath to *Chumbus* and *Keng-kol*. *Kisil-teken*, a right tributary, has no road, *Taigan-üshtü*, a left tributary, is also without importance. *Sor-kisil-teken* and *Kisil-bulak* enter from the right or north. At *Kisil-bulak*, where springs crop out, three valleys meet; between the two from the N. E. is a thin ridge of schist across which our road goes. This place is called *Teke-sekerik*, and from here the valley is an extremely narrow gorge gradually leading to rounded hills of yellow clay and sand and black fine gravel of schist. There is some grass, and the place is called *Sarik-ot*.

From *Gäjek-beles* nothing could be seen, as all the valleys were filled with impenetrable fog. From the pass our road goes very steeply down in hundreds of zigzags on a sharply modelled ramification from the range of *Gäjek-beles*, and situated between the *Belden-jilga* to the right and *Sar-yalang* to the left. At the foot of this precipitous slope the altitude is 3,602 m., or a descent of 373 m. At this base we have to our right the mouth of *Belden-jilga,* and a little beyond it *Topchu-murum-jilga.* The next right tributary is *Musde-jilga,* coming out at a widening of the main valley called *Kara-su.* From here the *Gäjek* valley is for some distance a narrow gorge, where only very short and insignificant tributaries enter. At the point where *Yaman-jilga* opens from the left, the valley again suddenly becomes broad. A little lower down we notice *Kara-gai-jilga* from the same side.

The valley then remains broad and open; its brook had about half a cubic meter of water per second. The whole landscape was snow covered. There are bushes and grass. The road is good. The prevailing rock is black crystalline schist. To the left we have the *jilga* of *Arka-terek* and a little lower down to the right, *Sarik-kis.* We rode up 3 km. to the *aul* of *Sarik-kis* in this valley. Looking south from the *aul* we had to our left a little steep *jilga* with a path across the *Yapchan-davan* to the valley of *Chumbus;* to the right another little *jilga* with a road to *Kuru-bel* and *Gäjek-beles.* Between both is a mighty massif.

The *aul* of *Sarik-kis* consisted of 5 tents and 20 persons of the Kara-teït tribe. They pass the winter here and go in summer to the upper *yeilaks* of their valley.

October 16th we travelled 3 km. north to the junction of *Sarik-kis* and the *Gäjek* valley, and thence 36.5 km. E. N. E. and N. E. to *Igis-yar.* The descent is 1,026 m. and the rate 1 : 38.5. After 14.5 km. in the *Gäjek* valley we reach the junction with the *Keng-kol,* from which we followed the same road as before by *Igis-yar-karaul* to *Igis-yar.*

The three following days I only noted the time and principal names. October 17th: left *Igis-yar* at 12.50 p. m., reached *Aktam,* a garden, at 2.58 p. m.; *Shanas,* a village, at 3.45 p. m.; *Teter,* a large village, 4.30 p. m. and *Tebes* or *Teves,* a village, at 5.15 p. m. October 18th: left *Tebes* at 11.23 a. m., crossing several small branches and canals irrigating *Tebes* and several villages north of it; at 1.28 we reached the village of *Yingis-kerik;* at 2.15 p. m. we crossed a low ridge stretching eastwards to *Yangi-hisar* which we now leave to our right; at 2.30 p. m. we reached the village of *Agus* north of the ridge; at 3 o'clock p. m. the village of *Hergusa* between small detritus hills; and 6.30 p. m. *Kone-sak* a large village. Between *Hergusa* and *Kone-sak* the country is very desolate. October 19th: left *Kone-sak* at 9.45 a. m.; at 11.30 a. m. we crossed at *Akto,* a branch of the *Khan-terek-su* on a bridge; at noon we reached *Chahr-shanel* on the *Gez-su;* at 1 o'clock p. m. *Kosala;* an hour later we crossed the *Gez-darya* and 2.12 p. m. the *Khan-arik;* at 2.50 p. m. we reached *Tasgun;* at 4.30 p. m. *Yangi-shahr* and at 5.45 p. m. *Kashgar.*

In these three days we covered 90 km. in all.

CHAPTER IV.

ACROSS THE ULUG-ART IN 1895.

In the beginning of Vol. II of my book *Through Asia*, London 1898, I have sacrificed only a few pages to the description of my journey in the eastern parts of the *Pamirs*, accomplished during the summer of 1895. On p. 682 of the work quoted I say: »The length to which this book is growing precludes me from describing this present expedition with anything approaching the same circumstantial minuteness. Perhaps I may be permitted on another occasion to relate the results of my 1895 journey in the southern regions of the *Pamirs*.»

Although twentysix years are gone since the journey alluded to was undertaken, the promise just mentioned has never been fulfilled, nor has the map drawn during the journey been worked out. When Dr. B. HASSENSTEIN after my return transformed my field maps into the excellent sheets of *Eastern Turkestan, North Tibet*, and parts of *Mongolia* and *Northern China* which were published in *Petermanns Mitteilungen*, Ergänzungsband XXVIII, 1900, it was decided that the field maps from the *Eastern Pamirs* should be left for a later occasion. And this occasion did not come. My years were filled with new journeys, new maps and new projects, and the *Pamir* sheets were always put aside as being of inferior importance.

During my studies of the remarkable journeys of the great Chinese pilgrims, my interest in the southern parts of the *Pamirs* has again been awakened, and I have believed it advisable to look up my old diaries once more in the hope that my own experiences may to a certain degree facilitate the solution of the dark points of the Chinese itineraries. In my personal narrative quoted above, I have briefly described the northern part of my journey in the *Eastern Pamirs* and the return journey to *Kashgar*. This part has very little to do with the Chinese pilgrimages. Still, for completeness' sake I will make a résumé of it again before dealing at some length with the southern portion of the same journey. In this connection I will, of course, only deal with the geography. The meteorological observations and absolute altitudes, have been published by Professor NILS EKHOLM, in Vol. V, Part I^a, of my *Scientific Results of a Journey in Central Asia 1899—1902*,

4. IX.

Stockholm, Lithographic Institute of the General Staff of the Swedish Army 1905, pages 42—50.

The field maps have been worked out by Colonel H. BYSTRÖM, who has checked them when necessary and possible, with later material. Still, it should be remembered that the original sheets presented to Colonel Byström were drawn by a beginner, for as early as the summer of 1894 I had made some maps of the glaciers of the *Mus-tagh-ata* and in the spring of 1895 I had surveyed in the *Takla-makan Desert* on my way from *Khotan-darya* by *Aksu* to *Kashgar*. Therefore, no doubt, my topographical field work in the *Pamirs* was imperfect. In certain parts, later expeditions may have brought home more accomplished topographical material. But it has not been accessible to me, and in the absence of better material I decided to publish my own maps, which also have the advantage of serving as a direct illustration of my geographical observations.

The journey was accomplished from July 10th to October 3rd 1895. Of this lapse of time, however, only fifty-nine days were spent for the journey itself, as I was a guest of the Anglo-Russian boundary commission at *Mihman-joli* from August 19th to September 13th. The length of the journey measured on Colonel Byström's map, will be 1,241.5 km. Though the topographical details of this journey are not quite reliable, still I give in the following description the distances and the rate of rise and fall of every day's march. As the first sheet of my original map has been lost, Colonel Byström, in his construction in two sheets in 1:500,000 of my survey, has made use of Russian and British maps for the stretch *Kashgar-Tokusak*, which I travelled June 10th, 1895. On his map, the northern sheet of the *Pamir* map in my Atlas, this distance comes to 23.8 km., and the direction is S. W. *Kashgar* being at 1,304 m. and *Tokusak* at 1,359 m., the rise is 55 m. and the rate 1:433.

The *Kisil-su* is crossed and the whole road goes through villages, fields and gardens. Many *ariks* or irrigation canals are passed, all of them bringing water from the *Kisil-su*.

On July 11th our road proceeds nearly westward 29.5 km. to *Upal*, where the height is only 60 m. above *Tokusak*, or 1,419 m.; the rise being therefore as 1:492. Nearly half the way went through gardens and fields belonging to *Tokusak* and its neighbouring villages. The rest of the way crosses a sandy plain, sometimes interrupted by red loess-formations, which are also common in *Tokusak* and *Upal*. The brook of *Upal* comes from *Ayag-art*, a valley leading to a pass, and situated north of *Ulug-art*. *Upal* is said to have 2,000 *uilik*, houses or families, which seems to be exaggerated. Wheat, barley, rice and melons are the principal products. The rice plantations were said to be partly irrigated by an *arik* from *Gez-darya*, south of our route.

The rainy season had just set in and it rained the whole day and part of the next. In the afternoon a *sil* came down through the bed with enormous quantities of red, muddy water, completely destroying the bridge and fifteen houses. The *sil* water is said to continue to the *Kisil-su* and to join this river near the bridge on the road between *Kashgar* and *Yangi-shahr*. The winter is cold, but there is not much snow.

The third day's march July 13th, took us 40 km. S. W. to the entrance of the mountains. In this distance we rose nearly to double our former altitude or from 1,419 m. to 2,672 m., *i. e.* 1,253 m. and at a rate of 1:32.

For a short distance the road follows the willow avenue of *Upal* with *ariks*, fields and grey mud walls on the sides, after which one comes out on a gradually rising steppe. To our right and westwards are pointed out the parts of the *Kashgar Range*, where the two passes *Ayag-art* and *Kasig-art* are situated, said to be easier than *Ulug-art* which we are going to cross. In our neighbourhood, to the right or N. W. of our road, is a comparatively low mountain ridge starting from the vicinity of *Kasig-art*, and bounding *Upal* on the north. In this ridge there is said to be a Chinese watch-place called *Upalat-karaul*. To the left or south of the route the steppe gradually rises in the direction of *Tash-melik*. Between *Upal* and *Tash-melik* there is another *karaul* called *Yulug-bash-karaul*.

Steppe plants are growing here and there, though sparse. Immediately to our left there is a cañon-shaped furrow in the ground, 5 m. deep and 70 m. broad. In its bottom flows a little brook fed by springs and irrigating some small fields lower down. The brook of *Upal*, which is to our right, is also fed by springs and grows, as we had seen, enormously after rain, but only for a few hours.

The furrow to our left gradually becomes broader, 200 m., and 400 m., and deeper; 10 or 12 m. Our road goes down to its bottom, where abundant grass is growing and flocks of sheep grazing. At its sides rise nearly perpendicular walls of loess, pebbles and shingle. After a while we again leave the furrow and continue on the partly barren, and gradually rising ground, on which a few steppe plants grow.

By and by the rise becomes steeper and the ground more gravelly. In the front, the lower regions of the mountains become visible, whilst the higher snow-covered parts remain hidden in clouds. Several small furrows, formed by the last rain, are crossed. Suddenly we enter the mouth of the valley leading to *Ulug-art*. It is bounded by comparatively mighty ramifications from the mountains, and the appearance is therefore quite another than at *Igis-yar*, where one gradually passes between small hills and ridges before one is in the valley itself. In the very mouth of the *Ulug-art* valley the ground consists of a flat gravelly fan on which the brook forms a real delta of small branches.

The road runs on the top of a terrace 30 m. high and consisting of pebbles and shingle, and originally worked out by the brook at an epoch with more copious precipitation. On the terrace there is a place called *Kirk-sheit* with two *gumbes*

or small grave-towers, and several tombs. At this place the road goes down from
the terrace to the bottom of the valley.

Now the living rock makes its appearance at both sides, though here and
there hidden by fragments of the old terraces. It is green crystalline schist, sometimes pierced by quartzite veins. The dip and fall is first 38° N. 10° E., then
28° N. 10° E. The valley is fairly broad and rises regularly without undulations. It is
full of round stones. There is some vegetation, amongst other things wild roses. At
the right or southern side is the *karaul* called *Uruguma*, where the whole year round
two watchtents were pitched, inhabited by Kirgizes of the Tavur tribe. The tents
had a beautiful situation, surrounded by a grove of poplar trees *(terek)* and willows
(suget). On the hills in the vicinity, the *artcha* or juniperus, and the *kara-gai* or
spruce of Tian-shan were growing. Bear, wolf, wild goat and partridges were common.
The winter is cold; the snow at the most reaches to the knees of a wanderer. The
rainy season had begun a few days ago. The brook of the valley loses itself in
patik-yer or swampy ground, and only one *arik* reaches *Upal*. The valley is windy,
and the wind comes both from the plains in the east and from *Sarikol* in the west.

From *Uruguma* a road goes south to *Buru-kös-davan*, a high, steep and
difficult pass which rarely is used. Our road, westwards, goes to *Ulug-art*, which
is easier and is chiefly used by Kirgiz and Chinese who travel to and from *Muchi;*
in the summer the natives of *Bulun-kul* and *Chaker-agil* travel this way if the
Gez-darya road is impassable by reason of much water in the river. As a rule the
Ulug-art may be traversed only during two months in the year; from June 15th
to August 15th. In the winter it is quite buried in snow, and it is snow-covered
also during a great part of the summer. A little *jilga* or side valley near *Uruguma*
was called *Bustan-archa*.

The next day, July 14th, we continued up through the valley of *Ulug-art* to
an *aul* or tent-camp at an altitude of 3,614 m., and July 16th only 40 minutes
to another *aul* a little higher up and at an altitude of 3,762 m. The distance in all
was 27 km., the rise 1,090 m. and the rate of the ascent as 1:25.

At the camp of *Uruguma* the living rock was green schist in 23° S. 60° E.
at the right side of the valley. A little higher up at a *yeilak* or summer grazing
ground with a few *terek* trees, the same rock lay in 31° S. 40° E. Still higher up
the rock was black schist with quartzitic veins, and the dip was 73° S. 60° W. Where
we left the *Ayag-art* valley the green schist lay 29° S. The valley is fairly broad,
partly between wild rocky mountains; and its bottom is covered with round gravel.
The brook is split into several branches, now with perfectly clear water. Sometimes
it is bounded by steep terraces of pebbles and shingle.

At a few places there are *terek* trees and *archas*. The Kirgiz were complaining
that the Chinese spoiled the rare wood by using it for fuel in *Upal*. The valley

LOOKING N. E. FROM THE UPPER AUL OF ULUG-ART, JULY 16, 1895.

Under and slope has 3th and a fa and 16 inch

LOOKING WEST FROM THE UPPER AUL TOWARDS THE ULUG-ART, JULY 16, 1895.

Ubag art pass of and V fat ifa unter of 10 inch

THE RIDGE SOUTH OF THE ULUG-ART. LOOKING S. 40° W. FROM THE UPPER AUL,
JULY 16, 1895.

THE ROAD UP TO THE UPRANG PASS; LOOKING S. 30° E. JULY 31, 1895.

41

becomes broader and the lower slopes of the mountains more and more covered with earth and detritus. Both to the north and south the valley is bounded by mighty mountain ridges covered with snow, from which short and steep side-valleys enter.

A little beyond half way we have three valleys in front of us. The one to the left or S. W. is *Kichik-Buru-kös;* the one in the middle *Ulug-art,* coming from the pass of that name; and the one to the right or N. W. comes from *Ayag-art, Yaman-sara, Chimgan* and *Chicheklik.* The brook from *Kichik-Buru-kös* is dark grey, nearly black, whilst that of the two other valleys is yellowish grey. As the water earlier in the day had been clear, it obviously had rained in the course of the day. Mighty terraces are seen in all three valleys. In the background of the *Yaman-sara* valley, high snowy mountains were to be seen.

A very heavy rain mixed with hail and snow began, and continued the rest of the day. The lower *aul* of *Ulug-art,* at which we camped, was situated on the top of the right side terrace which was very high and steep, affording a splendid view of the valley and its brook gradually rising after the rain. The whole landsape was now white from snow and hail.

The *aul* consisted of two *kara-ui* or tents; one inhabited by Kipchaks, the other by Naimans. They only pass the summer here; in the winter they, and all other Kirgizes of the region, go down to places where the valleys open into the plain. In the direction of the pass, six tents were said still to be pitched. In the winter it is impossible to live here on account of the great amount of snow. The summer has a kind of regular valley-wind blowing at day-time from the pass, and during the night from the plain.

At *Kichik-Buru-kös* three tents were pitched, and at *Chong-Buru-kös* near *Urugund* there were four. In the *Yaman-sara* valley they estimated twelve or thirteen tents of the Naiman tribe. Through the *Yaman-sara* valley a road leads up to *Chicheklik* and *Ayag-art.* The latter was said to be very comfortable and easy; it leads to the *Alai* valley, whereas the *Ulug-art* leads to *Sarikol.*

As the snowfall continued, the Kirgizes said that the *Ulug-art* might become closed for the season. The road of *Yaman-sara* could be used in this case. But the pass *Chicheklik* in its upper reaches was said to be very difficult even for men on foot. So far as I could make out, this pass has to be crossed before one comes to the *Ayag-art. Chimgan* is a *yeilak* and valley on the road to *Ayag-art.*

However, a Kirgiz warned us regarding *Ayag-art,* as the valley going down from its western side joins the *Markan-su,* which, in case of sunshine, becomes very swollen, and has to be crossed five times. Also it has a very strong current. The importance of *Ulug-art* lies in its possibility in the summer when other passes leading to *Markan-su* and *Gez-darya* may be difficult. Finally a Kirgiz promised to take us over *Ulug-art,* and we therefore, July 16th, rode a little bit up to the *Upper*

Ulug-art aul with six tents on the top of the terrace, and also with a beautiful view. The inhabitants were of the Kipchak tribe and pass the winter at *Bustan-terek* and *Chimgan*. The Bek of the Kirgizes of *Ulug-art*, *Yaman-sara* and *Ayag-art* was said to have his tent at *Bustan-archa*.

Like *Terek-davan*, the *Ayag-art* was said nearly always to be passable.

Between the two *auls* the rock was hard and quartzitic, and was situated 19° N. 60° E.

On July 17th we had to travel 11.6 km. to the west in order to reach the pass of *Ulug-art*, and thence 24 km. W. S. W. to the next camp at the mouth of the valley *Tuyuk-dur*. The upper *aul* of *Ulug-art* was at an altitude of 3,762 m., the pass is 5,150 m. high; the ascent is therefore no less than 1,388 m., which is indeed a stiff climb in such a short distance; the rate is as 1:8.4. The camp of *Tuyuk-dur* on the *Sarikol* side of the pass was at 3,796 m.; the descent was therefore, 1,354 m., and the rate of the fall as 1:17.8. As could be expected, the slope down to the depression of the *Tarim Basin* is twice as steep as the slope to the high valley of *Sarikol*, or rather to the northern continuation of the *Sarikol* proper.

The one day of crossing *Ulug-art*, »The big pass», was one of the hardest I have ever had in Asia. Eight Kirgiz from the upper *aul* accompanied us with two ponies and some provisions. The winding path leads up through a narrow, deep-cut gorge with a very steep ascent. In its bottom a little brook from the pass flows amongst round gravel of gneiss and crystalline schist. On both sides the gorge is bounded by steep terraces of pebble and shingle, the tops of which are more level or rounded, covered with some grass and moss amongst gravel, and here and there with swampy ground kept wet by melting snow at the sides. Wild rocky cliffs raise their heads above them. The sides of the terraces fall very steeply, sometimes perpendicularly down to the brook, the water of which is perfectly clear. On some of the grassy slopes of the valley, Kirgiz shepherds were tending camels and sheep.

At 6.30 a. m. the pass became hidden by dark clouds. An hour later it again became visible, but at 9 o'clock the whole region disappeared in impenetrable clouds and it began to snow heavily. The weather remained extremely unfavourable for nearly the entire remainder of the day.

At the southern side of the valley two small glaciers were visible. They were very steep and formed, as it were, cascades and falls of ice. At their perpendicular ice-fronts, rudimentary front moraines had been formed. Small brooks came down from their snouts, joining the brook in our valley. At the northern side of the latter only small apophyses from the ice-covering of the highest regions were seen.

The ascent finally becomes extremely steep and we enter the trough or »Mulde» at the eastern side of the pass, crossing the little brook every two or three minutes.

The last bit, one climbes in hundreds of zigzags on a little extremely steep ridge full of gravel, which now was covered by 1 or 2 feet of snow. Living rock was here rare. The dip and fall near the pass was 35° E. Everything is crystalline schist in varieties. The ascent up to the pass was impossible for loaded animals, and the loads had here to be carried by Kirgizes.

At 11 o'clock we finally reached the pass, 5,150 m. high. Here is a little stone pyramid with some poles and rags, called *Hasret Ulug-art-masar*. The saint of the pass is Lord of the weather and has the power to let travellers have a happy passage; therefore his name is mentioned every minute during the climb. The snowfall was very lively and nothing of the no doubt magnificent landscape was to be seen. The temperature was −0.6°.

It took us one hour and a half to get the luggage up and to examine the descent to the west. For if the ascent had been difficult the descent was indeed dangerous. To begin with the slope is gradual, but suddenly one stands at the edge of a precipice in wild projecting rocks between and around which one has to slide down with the help of both feet and hands. The rocks lay in 21° N. N. E. Everything was covered with icy snow two feet deep, in which steps had to be hewn with an ax. Every pony had to be assisted by two men with ropes. The boxes had to be allowed to slide down through the snow.

The lower part of the slope from the pass consisted of gravel and blocks without living rock, all snow-covered, and had a gradient of 35½°. One of the ponies lost his equilibrium and rolled down about 200 m., broke his back and died. The rest of the little caravan came down without damage. *Ulug-art*, however, proved to be the most difficult pass I had so far traversed in the *Pamirs*.

An impenetrable snow storm concealed everything around, and only the details in our neighbourhood were visible. The most important feature of the landscape is a comparatively large glacier immediately to our left, of which we get a birdseye view. It originates in the high regions south of *Ulug-art* and its tongue turns N. W. and west, following the upper part of the pass-valley. It is completely snowed over. We descend to its right side where a small triangular lake with grey muddy water has been dammed up between two small mountain ridges and the glacier, the ice of which falls perpendicularly down into the pool. The latter seems chiefly to be fed by a little brook coming from a rudimentary glacier at the right side of the valley. The latter glacier is surrounded by wild, picturesque rocky peaks, from which gigantic and steep screes of gravel and blocks fall down to the little lake and the side of the large glacier. Probably because of the last days' rain and snow the scree along the lake had been destroyed. We had, therefore, to proceed wherever we could and at some 50 m. above the surface of the little lake. This passage was difficult and dangerous, especially as loose blocks could easily come down along the steep slope.   The luggage had therefore again to be carried by Kirgizes some 400 m.

Occasionally small peaks of crystalline rock cropped up from the gravel, dipping 10° and 15° S. S. E.   We march along the right side of the large glacier, the magnificent curve of which is seen coming out from between two rocks and fills the whole upper part of the main valley.   Our path sticks to the right side of the valley, where we sometimes have to enter small gorges and often cross the brooks from rudimentary glaciers to our right.   The largest ice formations of the valley are situated at its southern side, where obviously the highest mountains are situated and which is the shady side.

A second little glacier lake is of the same form and size as the first.   Its water had a tint of green though it was very muddy, probably from the fine material brought thither from the ground moraine.   The clear ice of the glacier falls perpendicularly down into the lake on the surface of which ice blocks were swimming. The right lateral moraine is clearly to be seen, though it is narrow and small.   The middle moraine is well developed.   The glacier tongue seems to slope 4° towards the valley.   Our path goes up and down over the screes sloping from the mountains at the right side of the valley.

A third lake was larger than the two first ones, about 2 km. in length, and it had also a nearly triangular shape.   Leaving this lake and the snout of the glacier behind us, we continue on the floor of the valley where the descent becomes more and more gradual.   The front moraine of the glacier was pierced by a brook from the surface and sides of the glacier, though it did not contain much water on account of the cold and cloudy weather.

At the left side of the valley we have now four small glaciers.   The second one is the largest, and its snout reaches down to the bottom of the valley.   It has a small frontal moraine and brook, and its perpendicular front has dark stripes of solid material.   The higher regions of the mountains south of our valley are covered with ice, and their slopes are snow-covered the whole way down.   The mountains to the right have no glaciers, and only their highest parts are snow-covered.   On both sides the rocks are high and wild, and mighty screes slope down to the bottom of the valley covering the living rock.   The bottom of the valley is full of gravel, and the joined brook has cut down its erosion bed through the deposits of detritus. The right terrace is mightier than the left one.   Only at one place was some grass seen.   We had to continue until the valley became broader.   The mountains at the sides diminished in height, and finally snow patches were seen only on the highest peaks and ridges.

From the right or north a tributary joined the *Ulug-art* valley.   Its name is *Tuyuk-dur*.   It is uninhabited and has neither vegetation nor fuel; only a brook coming from a glacier, and in its background considerable snow-covered mountains are seen. It is *tuyuk* or uninhabitable, barren. At the junction of the two valleys we camped on the gravelly ground. The gravel was crystalline schist, gneiss and porphyry in several varieties. The dip some distance above this place was 39° S. 50° W.

On July 18th we travelled W. S. W. 16.4 km. to *Muchi*, where the altitude was 3,440 m. or 356 m. lower than *Tuyuk-dur* camp. The rate of the descent is thus as 1:46.

The valley is covered with gravel in which only sparse steppe-plants grow. The ground falls gradually to the W. S. W. where in the distance the *yeilaks* of *Muchi* are visible as dark patches. To our right the mountain range continues with steep screes, and the valley of *Muchi* is seen to the W. N. W. bounded by considerable but not steep ranges. Finally the country opens out and we ride on nearly level ground where the brook of *Muchi* is crossed; its water is not clear, its current is slow and its bed full of gravel. The volume of water was about 2.5 cub. m. per second. The brook of *Muchi* comes from the W. N. W. Travelling up in this direction through the *Muchi* valley one comes to *Kara-art*, on the watershed between *Gez-darya* and *Markan-su*. On the other side of the pass *Kara-art* one comes to *Ui-bulak*, *Kisil-art* and *Alai*. The northern-most part of the *Sarikol* valley, in the vicinity of *Kara-art*, more than one day's journey from the pass, is called *Kiyak-bash* or *Kiyak-bashi*. It has a *karaul* of 10 tents. From the west the valley *Kara-sok* enters; it has a road to *Kisil-jiyik*, but is *tuyuk* in its upper part leading to an impossible pass beyond which is the *Great Kara-kul*. From the S. W. enters the valley *Aramut-jilga*, which also is considerable and has a road to *Rang-kul*. Another valley in the west is called *Oi-balgan* and leads to a pass of the same name with a road to *Rang-kul*. The brooks from all these valleys join the *Muchi*.

At *Muchi* the cold is said to be very severe in winter, but the amount of snow is not very great. In spite of the rainy season the *Gez-darya* was said to be low, and therefore most people bound to *Kashgar* preferred it to *Ulug-art*, which was regarded as a very bad road. West wind was said to predominate.

At *Muchi* Naiman Kirgizes were living, at *Ayag-art* Chal-teit. The *Kara-sok* valley is during the winter visited by Naiman Kirgizes, in the summer it is uninhabited, though it has *yeilaks*. Naimans are also to be found in the *Aramut* valley. On the road to *Kara-art* there were no Kirgizes. At *Muchi* some 50 or 60 tents were pitched, and sheep, yaks, ponies and camels were grazing.

The next day, July 19th, our road turns to the S. E. and east for 12.4 km., in the very gradually falling valley of the *Muchi-su*, sinking only 25 m. to *Kün-times*, where the altitude is 3,415 m.; the rate is thus 1:496.

5.   IX.

The road follows the lower slopes of the terraces at the right side of the valley, avoiding the swampy ground along the river. To our right we leave the mouth of the *Aramut-jilga* with snowy mountains in its background. The living rock was the common crystalline schists with quartzite and pegmatite veins, situated in 15° S. 40° W. Then we cross the river to its left bank. The quantity of water was about the same as the day before, or 2.5 cub. m. per second. The current is slow and noiseless, the water transparent only to 12 cm. The river was so small on account of the cold and cloudy weather. After warm sunny summer days it grows rather big and is sometimes difficult and even impossible to cross. At high water the swampy patches at the sides of the river are also inundated. Even now their ground was so swampy that the animals sank deep in it, and we had to ride on solid ground higher up the left side. Here the road is situated on the screes of gravel and on the top of the terrace. At several places the grass is very good, and yaks and camels were grazing.

The valley suddenly becomes very narrow, as a gorge, and remains so for about a half kilometer. This picturesque corridor is bounded by very steep walls of wild rocky cliffs. The river fills nearly the whole bottom, and sometimes one has to ride in the water amongst blocks. Occasionally there is space left for the path at the left side. The water had now a temperature of 16.6°. The schist lay in 72° S. 40° W.

The narrow passage comes to an end, and is followed by a great open widening with good grass. Then there is a second, shorter gorge and a second very large widening of the *Muchi* valley. Hitherto we had only passed small *jilgas* or side valleys, but now we approached the more considerable transverse valley by which the brook of *Ulug-art*, after piercing the mountain range to the north of our road, comes down and joins the *Muchi-su*. In this transverse valley there are also considerable erosion terraces. The brook of *Ulug-art* was here divided into two branches of clear water. Just at the mouth of the valley there is a flat extensive fan which forces the *Muchi-su* towards the right side of the main valley.

Just east of the fan there is a large plain with good grass, and large flocks of sheep and goats were grazing amongst the *auls* pitched here. About midway we had passed the Chinese fort of *Muchi*, where 31 Chinese soldiers and a few Kirgiz and Kashgarliks were living in black tents. The *lansa* of the place was said to possess 80 ponies.

The place where we camped at the junction of the two valleys was called *Kün-times*, or properly *Kün-tegmes*, i. e. »the sun does not reach», for this part of the valley remains in shadow during the winter. Sixteen tents were said to exist here in three *auls;* eight at our camp, and two, each with four *kara-ui*, a little lower down. Their inhabitants are Naimans. In the winter they wander some distance down the valley, but are as a rule rather stationary. The winter is cold with little snow. At the end of October the mountains are white with snow. The summer had so far been cloudy and chilly, and the *Muchi-su* therefore was unusually small. After strong sunshine it may grow so big that it cannot be crossed. As was said before, it carries the water from the valleys *Kara-art, Kara-sok, Oi-balgan* and *Aramut*. In the spring there are winds from the west and W. N. W. Three *beks* were said to be the administrative chiefs of these northern parts of *Sarikol;* the one of *Muchi*, Imet Bek, commanding from *Kara-art* to *Kün-times;* the one of *Bulun-kul,* Jan Mohammed Bek, from the latter place to *Chaker-agil.* and south of him Togdasin Bek of *Su-bashi.*

On July 20th we travelled 34.6 km. E. S. E. and S. E. sinking 96 m., or from 3,415 m. to 3,319 m., being at a rate of 1 : 360. Some short distance below the camp we crossed the river, which now carried about 3.5 cub. m. per second, but increased in the course of the day, partly from the arrival of water from melting snow and ice, and partly from the addition of small tributary brooks. In the higher regions of the mountains to our left was a great deal of snow; the southern mountains were hidden by clouds.

Having passed the two *auls* of four tents each, we have to our right two tributary valleys which join before reaching the main valley; the western one called *Kok-tash* has no road and no *yeilaks*, whilst the eastern one has *yeilaks* but no road. To our left opens the valley *Orta-sai* with a rocky path to *Ulug-art*. A little farther on to the right we pass two insignificant *jilgas, Kichik-bulung* and *Kum-jilga,* both without roads or human dwellings. To the left the valley *Bereden-sai* is comparatively large, but without importance. *Küüshden-sai* is a large, sharply modelled *jilga* with glaciers in the background and surrounded by snowy mountains. At the mouth of the last-mentioned valley is an uninhabited place called *Igis-yarning-robat,* where a clay-cupola serves as a shelter for wanderers. Opposite to it, at the right side of the main valley, against which the river is pressing, our road crosses a little projecting rocky promontory, *Tash-kiya,* of mica-schist and gneiss in 29° S. 60° W., and farther on 26° W. At this place where the fan of *Küüshden-sai* makes the valley narrow, the river forms small rapids, and grows to a volume of 9.6 cub. m. per second.

At *Tash-kiya* the grass-grown plains of the valley come to an end, after which the whole floor of the valley is filled with the gravel from the screes at the base of the mountains. Farther on *Tumanchi-jilga* comes out from the right; it is considerable, but uninhabited and without a road. At its mouth the main valley is again broad and provided with grazing ground. From the left enters the large *jilga* of *Buru-kös,* which has an enormous scree of gravel between mighty terraces of pebbles and shingle. By this valley a nearly never used path leads to the pass of *Buru-kös,* beyond which we had passed a few days before. At the sides of the southern *Buru-kös* very considerable snow-mountains were seen which, towards our valley, gradually go over into ramifications and ridges with erosion furrows and small valleys between; their more rounded slopes, where living rock is rare, consist of detritus and débris, and have at their base the mighty erosion terraces which here and there are pierced by small valleys with delta-shaped fans. The terraces may be some 60 or 70 m. high, and are shaped, by the action of water, into pillars, towers and picturesque formations. Their horizontal stratification is very well visible from different layers of sand, fine gravel, and coarser material.

At the right side we pass *Chapgen-jilga* with seven tents. To the left is *Peigadung-jilga*, comparatively large, and at its mouth is a square Chinese wall, where formerly a Chinese *lansa* was stationed. Below *Buru-kös* the whole valley is filled with gravel from the screes. But from *Peigadung* the grazing-ground predominates the whole way, with good tussock-grass. The region is very swampy. The river is often divided into several branches. An *aul* of 4 tents was passed and another of 9; before reaching them we had counted 18 tents. Our road goes along the right side of the valley; on the top of its terrace there was a burial place with a *gumbes*. Opposite this place, and below or S. E. of *Buru-kös,* five short and steep side valleys are situated; in the background of three of them glaciers were seen. Finally we turned around a promontory and camped on a meadow at the eastern shore of the lake *Chaker-agil-kul* where an *aul* was pitched.

At the lake 6 tents were situated, though 60 were reported for the whole district of *Chaker-agil.* The inhabitants are of the Naiman-tribe. I was told that distinction was made between three different kinds of Naiman Kirgizes: Mirza Naiman at *Muchi,* Kichik Naiman at *Chaker-agil,* and Yerde Naiman at *Bulung-kul.* The Kirgizes now dwelling at the lake pass the winter in the *Kalema-jilga* which enters the basin of the lake from the west and where the grazing is good. In the upper reaches of the *Kalema* there is no ice but a good deal of snow. If the weather is sunny and warm a considerable amount of water comes down and fills the little lake, which then gets an effluent to *Gez-darya.* At my visit the lake had no outflow on account of the cold weather. The lake is in winter covered with ice as thick as a man's arm. The winter is very cold, but there is rarely more than four fingers of snow; the place is very windy, especially in spring and autumn. The winds come both from the *Gez* valley and from the *Kalema* valley. Many of the mountain slopes round the lake seemed to be covered with a thin layer of wind-driven sand.

The day of July 22nd was spent on an excursion around the oblong little lake of *Chaker-agil* which is only 4,200 m. in length and 2,100 m. at its broadest place. At its eastern shore there is a belt of sand dunes, not more than 5 m. high and directing their steep lee sides to the west, showing that eastern winds are prevalent, at least during the warm season. Here two sandy peninsulas project into the lake, one of them ending with a little island.

West of the second peninsula there is a bay with a grassy shore. The lake is shallow here. At the southern shore the mountains have a comparatively steep fall down to the lake, though they always leave a belt of nearly level ground between their base and the shore, partly occupied by grass, partly by dunes. In the former case the ground is swampy.

Kum-jilga is a little valley from the south; it has no road, and is inhabited only during the winter. In its mouth there are several sand dunes. West of this valley a rocky promontory falls steeply to the very shore; it consists of weathered crystalline schist in 26° S. 30° W. Beyond it there are several capes of detritus sloping 34° to the shore. Wild geese and ducks are common. An eagle was seen.

Farther west the mountains fall away and leave room for a narrow meadow. At the western-most part of the lake are excellent grazing-grounds with swampy soil. A considerable number of yaks and camels were grazing here. Along the shore reeds grow. In the background the great valley of *Kalema* opens, and in its upper reaches the snow-covered crest of the *Sarikol Range* is visible. *Kalema* is visited in the winter. Because of the chilly weather its brook, which enters the western-most part of the lake, was now nearly dry. There is no trafficable pass across the *Sarikol Range* in the upper part of *Kalema*. At the lower part of the *Kalema* valley the *Sor-kum-jilga* enters from the south and the *Kara-jilga* from the north. Through the latter a short-cut road crossing a little pass, leads to *Muchi*.

Along the western half of the northern shore, reeds grow in a narrow belt. From the northern mountains several promontories go down to the shore with bays between them. They chiefly consist of horizontally stratified pebbles and fine yellow clay. On a little island surrounded by reeds and situated near the northern shore there is a saint's tomb called *Kindik-masar*. The island consists of detritus. Opposite it is a fine meadow where the little valley *Kindikning-bele* enters; it has a road to *Muchi* across an easy pass.

A little farther east a rocky promontory stands opposite the one at the southern shore, and consist of some igneous rock in 40° S. 60° W. Between the two rocky capes the deepest part of the lake seemes to be situated. At 4 o'clock p. m. the water had a temperature of 14.9°. It is perfectly clear and fresh. The colour of the lake is blue, green, violet in the most beautiful nuances. Algae and aquatic plants grow in a belt along the shore, especially where reeds protect against winds and waves. The northern shore seems to have a steeper slope down into the lake than the southern.

Along the eastern half of the northern shore are terraces of pebble and shingle sloping steeply to the lake but level on their surfaces. At their base there is a strip of swampy ground with grass. The lake seems to have been formed by the action of the prevailing eastern wind which has dammed up the broad mouth of the valley which morphologically is the continuation of the *Kalema*. It is the threshold of sand brought thither by the wind that has given origin to the lake basin. Signs of glacial action are not visible here, and the blocks seen at some places have fallen down from the rocks above. As pointed out before, the slopes of the hills, especially those south of the lake, are covered with a thin layer of sand.

CHAPTER V.

JOURNEY IN SARIKOL, 1895.

On July 23rd our road went S. E., south and S. S. E. 22 km. to *Usun-tal*, where the height is 3,359 m. The rise is 40 m. or as 1 : 550. At first, however, the ground sinks until we reach the neighbourhood of *Gez-darya*, where the rise begins, and is, therefore, considerably steeper than the rate mentioned above. The lake had risen a little as the sun had been working the last two days, and the effluent carried 0.135 cub. m. per second. The sand dunes continued along the base of the southern mountains, even covering the lower part of the slopes. The sandy plain is perfectly barren; only along the base of the eastern mountains was grass seen.

The *Gez-darya*, which we reach just opposite the little fort *Tar-bashi*, was here very broad and formed pools and swamps. A hard eastern wind was blowing carrying much sand with it. Along the base of the hills there are many fresh springs with crystal-clear water and much algæ. Near *Bulung-kul* mica-schist in 49° S. 35. W. cropped out. Here the sand gives place to meadows surrounding the springs. The largest spring had at 1 o'clock a temperature of 7.6°, whilst the river had 14.5° and the air 18.9°.

Some small brooks from the *Sarikol* mountains, *Chugutai*, *Kum-jilga*, and others, form an extensive swamp, with treacherous, muddy ground. The lake *Bulung-kul* was more like a swamp containing a number of pools. At its eastern shore is the fort of the same name, commanded by a certain Jan Darin. Our road then turns S. S. E. along the left bank of the *Gez-darya*, and the valley is called *Usun-tal*. The crystalline schist lay in 66° S. The mountains bounding the valley on the east are called *Ak-tau*. There is a glacier opposite *Bulung-kul*, and east of it the brook from this glacier has formed a large fan falling 6° towards the valley. South of it are two other, larger glaciers with moraines and brooks piercing the considerable terraces at the base of the mountains. Finally we crossed the *Gez-darya*, which carried no great volume of grey, muddy water and easily could be crossed. The floor of the valley then partly consists of gravel and partly of meadows. In a heavy rain we pitched our camp at the base of the eastern mountains.

On July 24th we continued S. S. E., south and S. S. W. 24 km., rising 389 m.
or to 3.748 m. at our camp in the *Su-bashi* valley; being a rate of 1:62. Here
I return to regions of *Eastern Pamir* which I had visited the summer before, 1894,
when studying the glaciers of the *Mus-tagh-ata*. As I have described my experiences
on this mountain more in detail in my book *Through Asia*, I will here quickly
pass this region.

We travelled the ordinary road by *Yeri* and the *Ike-bel-su* glacier, the
moraines of which reach even the mouth of the *Kuyunde* valley, and are pierced
in a deep gorge by the river. The brook from *Basik-kul* was now very insignificant. The water of this lake had a temperature of 18.5° at 1 o'clock, whilst *Kara-
kul* had 15.1° two hours later and at 8° in the air. We passed between both lakes
in rain and wind.

In the *Usun-tal* valley we had seen only one tent. South of *Little Kara-kul*
there were several *auls* with numerous flocks. In spite of the rain the *Su-bashi*
brook was very small. Beyond the little fort of *Su-bashi* we reached the *aul* of
Togdasin Bek, now counting 5 tents. A tent-dweller told us that the weather had
been rainy for ten days and that in the nights it had snowed. The mountains were
snowed over, as for instance *Koch-korchu*, *Tur-bulung* and *Kamper-kishlak*. The
glacier brooks had dwindled and were frozen over higher up. The last winter had
been very cold, but with little snow. A hard south wind had been constantly blowing.
All high passes were now more or less covered with snow, as *Kara-tash*, *Merke*,
Kok-moinak and *Chichekli*. The *Gez-darya* was unusually low.

On July 25th we travelled along the whole western side of the *Mus-tagh-ata*
group. The first 16.7 km. took us S. W. and W. S. W. to *Ulug-rabat-davan*, 4,237 m.
high, a rise of 489 m. and a rate of 1:34. From the pass we had 24.3 km. south
and S. S. E. to *Gäjäk* with an altitude of 3,499 m., or a fall of 738 m., being a
rate of 1:33.

The whole *Mus-tagh-ata* was now covered with snow all the way down to
the snouts of the glaciers, and there were hardly any black rocks visible in the snow
masses. At *Kara-su-karaul* two Chinese soldiers and eight Tajiks were stationed.
In the upper part of the *Kara-su-jilga* several Kirgiz tents were pitched. A brook
comes down from this valley. The largest watercourse we passed was the one from
Kok-sel on the *Mus-tagh-ata* which carried some 8 cub. m. per second. Passing
Korumde-jilga and *Kayinde-masar*, we camped at the *aul* of *Gäjäk* where 4 tents
were pitched.

Togdasin Bek calculated that 280 tents were under his jurisdiction, of which
70 were at *Su-bashi* and *Kara-kul*; 45 tents at *Kara-kul* and *Keng-shevär* (or
-*shvär*) were said to be under a special *bek*, Alim Kul Bek. *Muchi*, *Chaker-agil*
and *Bulung-kul* were believed to possess 70 tents together.

From *Ulug-rabat* to *Tagharma* my Kirgizes calculated 130 tents, 40 of which were situated at *Kara-su*, *Kayinde* and *Gäjek*. From *Muchi* to *Bulung-kul* the inhabitants belonged to the Naiman tribe; the subjects of Togdasin Bek were mostly Kara-teït. The Kirgizes of *Gäjek* were Sari-teït and those of *Tagharma* partly Sari-teït, partly Kesek.

The next day, July 26th, our journey continued 36 km. S. E. and south to *Tash-kurgan*, descending from 3,499 to 3,152 m. or 347 m. which is as 1 : 104. It should, however, be noticed that from the junction of the *Kara-su* and *Taghdum-bash* Rivers the ground rises to the south.

One road goes down through the valley of *Gäjek* at the side of which high erosion terraces rise, and where also blocks are seen occasionally; old moraines also prove that the action of the glaciers has reached so far down. Just below the *aul* the glacier brook of *Aftab-urui* and its valley join the main valley. The glaciers of *Aftab-urui* are situated between those of *Kok-sel* and *Shevär-agil*. To our right, in the *Sarikol* Mountains the transverse valley of *Shilbile* opens; it has no road and no practicable pass.

Our valley finally opens out into the *Tagharma* plain which slopes towards the S. E. To our right or S. W. is the mighty *Sarikol Range* with its snow-covered peaks and crests and its many transverse valleys. At the base of its rocky sides are large screes of detritus gradually falling towards the plain. We are following the very edge of the gravelly ramifications from the *Sarikol* mountains. *Kara-su*, as the joint river from the *Ulug-rabat-davan* is called, turns to the east, south and S. E. Now, early in the morning, the river was small, only a few cubic meters, but it increased in volume in the course of the day and after receiving several affluents from all the valleys which are directed to the *Tagharma* plain.

To the right we have the mouth of the valley *Berdesht* with its brooks. By this valley a road goes to the plateauland of *Pamir* in the west, crossing a pass in the *Sarikol Range*. Then follows the little valley *Kichik-Shilbile* with *yeilaks* but no road and no pass, *Kongus-tube* with *yeilaks* and a peak in the background, *Sari-tash (= Sarik-tash)* with a brook, and *Gellang-kol* with a more considerable brook; all situated in the *Sarikol Range*.

To our left we have extensive grazing-grounds. The following names were given: *Kok-yer* with an *aul* of five tents; *Serala*, a little fort with Chinese garrison on the left side of *Kara-su*; *Daulet* with a *karaul* and some Tajik tents. At a greater distance to the left is *Besh-kurgan* with a Chinese garrison. Sometimes Tajik huts are seen, built of sun-bricks. Barley and wheat are grown, and the fields are irrigated from *Sari-tash* and *Gellang-kol*. Only the Tajiks cultivate the fields. *Shosh-davan* farther S. E. may be regarded as an ethnological boundary between the Kirgizes and the Tajiks. The boundary is, however, not an absolute one, for, as we have seen,

6. IX.

there are Tajiks on the *Tagharma* plain, and there are Kirgizes in *Taghdum-bash Pamir*.

The next valley from the *Sarikol* side is the *Cherbasin-jilga*. All the water-courses of the *Tagharma* basin by and by join the *Kara-su* and flow to the gorge of *Tengi* by which they pierce the little range of *Shosh-davan*. At the end of this they join the *Taghdumbash-darya* and go down to the junction with the *Raskan-darya*. Before reaching the *Tengi* passage, the *Kara-su* gives rise to a swampy region with soft and unreliable ground called *Birgaul*. Here is the *aul* of the same name with four tents at one place and four at another. To the south the landscape is magnificent. To our right we leave the little pass *Shosh-davan* with a road to *Tash-kurgan* and forming the southern boundary of the *Tagharma* plain.

S. E. of *Cherbasin* the side valleys, *Shosh*, *Meidan* and *Shinde* come from the *Sarikol* Mountains. The last-mentioned is large and has a comfortable road to the *Ak-su* or *Murgab*. The *Shinde* valley comes from the S. S. W. and represents a characteristic feature in the landscape.

About 2 km. S. E. of *Birgaul* our road enters the *Tengi* gorge in which the *Kara-su* takes its winding course between the mountain-sides, sometimes leaving narrow belts for meadows. The rest of the floor of the valley is covered with gravel, and erosion terraces of pebble and shingle are as usual developed. Crystalline schist is prevalent, at the left side in $25°$ S. $80°$ E. At its end the *Tengi* gorge becomes broader and finally it joins the *Taghdumbash-darya*. The joint river, continuing eastwards, pierces the *Kashgar Range* in the narrow and wild gorge of *Shinde-jilga* which is said to be quite filled up by the river, allowing a passage only on the ice in the winter. Just at the junction of *Kara-su* and *Taghdumbash-darya* the *Dershet* valley enters from the N. E., and in the background the mountains round *Chicheklik-davan* are visible.

From the junction our direction becomes south, and the ground rises slowly. We are now in the broad valley of *Taghdumbash-darya*, which is much bigger and has clearer water than the *Kara-su*; the latter being fed by the muddy brooks from the glaciers. To our right, or west, we have the hills and screes from the ramification of *Shosh*. In the distance *Tash-kurgan* is visible on its terrace in the valley. The road is good and hard, and along the banks of the river there are excellent grazing-grounds.

We pass by the Tajik village of *Chushman* consisting of 45 small clay houses with groves of willows and cultivated fields. There are also flocks of sheep, goats and cattle. The Tajiks are regarded as more well-to-do than the Kirgiz. Sometimes the ruins of forts and houses are seen. The river is divided into several winding branches of clear, greenish-blue water. The brook from the large *Shinde* valley is considerable and flows in a delta of branches across its fan down to the *Taghdum-bash-darya*. *Tisnep* is a large village said to consist of 200 clay huts within a wall of sun-dried bricks, and surrounded by fields.

Immediately to our right we have now one erosion terrace on the top of which the fortress and village of *Tash-kurgan* are built, reminding one of the situation of the little Russian fort of *Pamirskiy Post* on the *Murgab*. The fortress is at a short distance from the village, and its walls rise perpendicularly from the level surface of the terrace. These walls of *Tash-kurgan* had been very much damaged, and nearly all the houses of the village were destroyed by the earthquake which took place July 5th to 20th, and of which we experienced a shock at 8.10 a. m. on the 27th. All the inhabitants and the Chinese garrison were now living in tents outside of *Tash-kurgan*.

July 28th our road continued S. S. E. in the broad and open valley of *Tagh-dumbash-darya*. The distance was 32 km. and the rise 255 m., *Yergol*, our next camp, being situated at an altitude of 3,407 m.; the rate of ascent was 1 : 125. The *Taghdumbash* valley S. S. E. of *Tash-kurgan* is like a plain of the same kind as *Tagharma*. It consists of solid material and deposits brought down by the river and filling up the space between the mountains. The *Tagharma* is the result of the same kind of action carried out by the *Kara-su*. Both rivers, therefore, form alluvial plains before they break their way through the mountains.

To begin with we rode a few kilometers eastwards to the village of *Toglan-shah*, crossing the *Taghdumbash-darya* which here was divided into seven large and several small branches, carrying 50 or 60 cub. m. per second together. At this place the water was not clear. Between the branches there was excellent grazing-ground.

From *Toglan-shah* our direction becomes S. S. E. To our right or on the west we see the village of *Khosgun* situated near the mouth of the *Khosgun-jilga*, by which a road leads to a pass in the *Sarikol Range* that only can be crossed on foot. It is a short-cut road to *Aktash* on the upper *Ak-su*; the *Khosgun* road obviously enters the upper part of the *Shinde-jilga*. The mountains from which the *Khosgun* valley comes are considerable and snow-covered.

Farther south we have to our left, or east, the transverse valley of *Ograt* with a road to *Ograt-davan* in the *Kashgar Range* and, farther eastwards, to the villages of *Kochkar* and *Tong* and finally *Yarkand*. The pass is said to consist of two thresholds with a small lake or pool between. On our road is a village called *Togolak-gumbes*, surrounded with barley fields. A little farther south is *Yergol* with good grass. The river here flows in *one* bed. At the right or eastern side of the valley we passed several small *jilgas*. Sometimes the *Kashgar Range* grows into snowy groups, but glaciers are not seen. As a rule the vegetation is sparse, the floor of the main valley being covered with gravel for the greatest part. In the valley of *Ograt* good grass and a brook were seen.

Our road, July 29th, to *Hojet-Bai*, was 32.3 km. in length, to the south, S. S. E. and S. S. W. For *Hojet-Bai* I got on altitude of 3,633 m., which would mean a rise of 226 m. at a rate of 1:143.

The road proceeds on the top of the right terrace until the latter is pierced by the brook from *Tagh-ash-jilga* in the *Kashgar Range*. Opposite it is a considerable valley in the *Sarikol Range* called *Korumde*, and farther south another, *Sarik-tash*. The ground is then gravel until we reach *Rang* with good grazing grounds and barley fields. A brook from *Er-jilga* in the east irrigates the fields. *Kosh* is also a *jilga* of the *Kashgar Range* without a brook. At the plain of *Deftar* the ground is cultivated by Tajiks. Here enters a brook of some 7 cub. m. per second from the two large valleys in the east *Saidi-kol* and *Senkar*. The latter leads to the village of *Marian* with a hundred Tajik huts. In the *Sarikol Range* we pass the valley of *Pisläng*, which in its upper reaches is formed by two valleys; the northern one leading to *Ak-tash*, the southern to *Beïk-davan*. At the opening of *Pisläng* there is a Tajik *karaul*.

South of the *Senkar* brook we ascend the top of the considerable right terrace on the edge of which we ride for about two hours. *Taghdumbash-darya* has cut down its bed in a deep gorge bounded by the terrace and the mountains at the western side of the valley, where five transverse *jilgas* open, the largest called *Kara-jilga*. Finally we go down from the terrace to the junction of *Taghdumbash-darya* and *Hunserab*. Near the confluence both rivers are close to one another, and the gigantic terrace stands like a fortress between them. *Shiralji* is a peak to the east belonging to the *Kashgar Range*.

The *Taghdumbash-darya* comes from the W. S. W., the *Hunserab* from S. S. E., in which direction the eternal snow of the southern mountains shines. At the time of this march the valley was not much inhabited. We had seen more people in the *Kara-kul* region. Signs of the earthquake were visible at several places in the valley, and some huts had fallen to pieces. The erosion terrace was pierced by cracks; one of them was very long and 8 cm. broad; its inner edge was 12 cm below the outer.

Our next march, July 30th, to *Kara-su* which is a right tributary of the *Hunserab*, was directed to the S. E. and S. S. E. 23.3 km., the ground rising at a steeper gradient than hitherto, or to 3,939 m., *i. e.* 306 m. higher than *Hojet-Bai*; the rate is therefore, as 1:76.

We travel on the right or eastern side of the *Hunserab River* leaving the upper *Taghdumbash-darya* in the west. The erosion terraces are at some distance from the river; between them the ground is covered with gravel and is level, though gradually rising to the south.

Westwards from *Hojet-bai* there is a road to *Kara-chukur, Beïk, Min-teke, Vakjir* and *Kok-turuk.* East of *Hojet-Bai, Shiralji-jilga* comes out from the vicinity of the *Shiralji Peak;* it is inhabited by Tajiks during the winter. *Kutas-soïdu* is a *yeïlak* (summer grazing ground) or *shevär* (pronounced *shvär*, meadow along the river) now inhabited by Vakhanliks. *Kichik-Sasik-teke* and *Chong-Sasik-teke* are small valleys in the mountains to the west of our valley. Another on the same side is called *Yetim-dube.* Opposite the latter we pass along the rocks of the right or eastern side of the valley, where excellent grass grows on both sides of the river. The place is usually simply called *Masar*, though its name is properly *Sultan-Seïd-Asan-masar.* On the right bank of the *Hunserab* there was here an *aul* of ten black tents inhabited by Kesek Kirgizes. Their yaks and sheep were grazing in the neighbourhood. Above this place there is a small Kirgiz cemetery with cupola-shaped tombs, and still higher up is a small *jilga, Masarning-bashi.*

At the western side a large tributary valley, *Parpak*, opens, the *yeïlaks* of which were used by Tajiks and Vakhanliks; the same is the case with the valley *Teshik-tash.* A projecting rock at the right or eastern side of the valley consists of hard greenstone in 14° S. 30° W., and is called *Burgu-toase.* The living rock crops up from amongst the gravel and the blocks.

Next, to the east, we pass the mouth of the large tributary *Ilik-su* (also pronounced *Ileg-su*) with a pass and a two days' narrow and difficult road to *Raskan-darya.* Some passages on the eastern side of the gorge were said to be filled by blocks amongst which a river flows; the road is passable only when there is little water in the rivers, as now was the case. In the mouth of *Ilik-su* were very good pasturages; its brook had now nearly no water at all, though it may be large after sunny days.

Our road is comfortable, as the ground is hard; consisting of dust and sand with tussocks and grass; sometimes it is gravelly. *Sar-arik* is a region on the left side of *Hunserab* where the grass is particularly good. The valley is comparatively broad. It is still a long way to the black and white crests and peaks in the south. In nearly all directions are magnificent, snow-covered mountains. Those to the south belong to the *Kara-korum*, and on their far side is *Kanjut.* The road across the pass of *Hunserab* was said to go to a place in *Kanjut* called *Gircha*, to which also the *Min-teke* road comes down.

In the lower part of the right tributary, *Kara-su*, where we camped, the grass was good but no inhabitants were seen; only in the upper reaches of the valley Vakhanliks were said to camp. The *Kara-su* valley also leads to a pass. As a rule travellers to *Yarkand* take the road of *Tash-kurgan.* The narrow passage east of *Ilik-su* mentioned above is two and a half days in length and was said to have been very much destroyed by the last earthquake, heaps of blocks and gravel having fallen down from the mountain sides into the gorge; only on foot or with yaks was the passage possible. Even in this narrow gorge there are widenings with grass and bush vegetation from which fuel used to be obtained for the Chinese chiefs.

Regarding the climate, the winter was said to be very cold and the snow about half a meter deep. The summer is more windy than the winter, and it blows as a rule from the west. Even during the summer the greatest part of the precipitation comes as snow. In the winter all the watercourses are frozen, except just below the spring. The nomads passing the summer in the upper *yeilaks* of the valleys here about, wander in the winter down to *Hojet-Bai, Kutas-soidu* and farther north. The inhabitants are for the greatest part Tajiks, living in *ak-ui* or white tents of felt.

On July 31st we travelled S. E. and south 12 km., rising 283 m. or to 4,222 m. at Camp *Uprang;* being a rate of 1 : 42.

Leaving *Kara-su,* in the upper reaches of which 15 Tajik tents were said to be pitched, we continued on the right or eastern bank of the *Hunserab.* At the western side of the valley we passed the *jilga Kashka-su* with five Tajik tents and three of Naiman Kirgizes. The main valley is fairly broad, with undulated and grass-grown ground. From *Kashka-su* a brook comes down to the *Hunserab,* piercing the erosion terrace at the left side of the river. On the lower slopes of the western mountains there was an *aul* of five Tajik tents called *Därvase. Bugos* is a *yeilak* on the river with two tents and a little brook. The space between *Kara-su* and the main river in its lower part is occupied by detritus hills and terraces; higher up by a snow-covered ramification from the *Kashgar Range.*

Örtäng-tus is a widening of the valley with five scattered Tajik tents. *Korum* (pronounced Gorum) is a considerable valley from the west with four Tajik tents. From the east *Ak-jilga* comes in with a brook. Here we leave the bank of *Hunserab* and ride across dry slopes to *Uprang,* an important valley with an *aul* of four Kipchak tents. A little beyond the *aul* and a gravelly ridge we camped at the *Uprang* brook where the grass was good. At 5 o'clock p. m. the brook carried about 2.5 cub. m. per second of clear water. At 7 o'clock, when the water from melting snow and ice had reached so far down, the brook was three or four times larger and its water muddy. On the first occasion it had a temperature of 15.1°, on the latter 11.2°. The bed was filled with gravel and blocks of granite, gneiss, red porphyry, fine-grained crystalline schist, etc. The brook makes a considerable contribution to the *Hunserab.*

The passes of *Uprang, Ulutör* and *Hunserab* may be said to mark the southern boundary of *Taghdumbash Pamir.* My Tajik and Kirgiz friends regarded *Deftar* as the northern boundary of the same district. According to them *Rang* and *Tash-kurgan* therefore did not belong to *Taghdumbash.* The whole valley up to the north was called *Sarikol (Sarik-kol)*. Seventy or 80 tents of Tajiks were said to be located at *Taghdumbash*. Stone huts are not used in these high regions. The inhabitants live under exactly the same conditions as the Kirgizes and have yaks, ponies, sheep and goats, and, of course, dogs; but no camels. Their language is Persian, although they also have a perfect command of Kirgiz.

Regarding roads the following particulars were given to me. Across the pass of *Hunserab* a road goes in five days to *Kanjut*, though the great amount of water in the rivers makes it very difficult during the summer. The *Uprang-davan* which is high and difficult, can be crossed only on foot or with yaks. On its eastern side there is a road to *Raskan-darya*, which only at the end of September can be crossed. The valley going down eastwards from *Uprang-davan*, is also called *Uprang*, and has at its mouth a Chinese *karaul* of 11 men. Here, as lower down, we were told that nomads travelling to *Yarkand* in summer always take the road by *Tash-kurgan* and *Chicheklik*. The pass of *Ilik-su* was not regarded as difficult, but the gorge at its eastern side, which has a brook going to *Raskan-darya*, had been destroyed by the earthquake. It is inhabited only at one or two places, where wheat is grown. Even if a traveller from *Ilik-su* succeeds in reaching the *Raskan-darya* he cannot continue, as the river cannot be crossed during the summer. If he continues upwards along the left bank of the river a four days' journey to a place called *Kok-jilga*, he has to cross *Raskan-darya* three times. This can be done only in the winter. By the *Sankar-jilga* and its pass, which is comparatively easy, one arrives by *Marian* to *Tong* and *Raskan-darya*. In one word, the latter river blocks all the road to the east.

At the part of the *Uprang* valley where we camped, the winter is said to be very cold and the snow sometimes to reach to a man's knees. If much snow falls the nomads go down to *Masar*, otherwise they remain in the region. The strongest and most frequent winds are said to come from the *Hunserab Pass*, and from the same direction come also the snow clouds. At *Uprang* rain is rare, and nearly all precipitation falls as snow. Not lower down than at *Masar* the greatest amount of precipitation in summer is rain.

The view from our camp at *Uprang* was fascinating in its grandeur; to the N. N. W. the broad valley of *Taghdumbash* bounded by its snow-covered ranges, the *Sarikol Range* to the west and the *Kashgar Range* to the east, and to the south the magnificent snowy peaks and crests of the northern *Kara-korum*.

August 1st was sacrificed for a visit to the Tajiks living in the mouth of the *Korum-jilga*. As members of the Iranian race they have finer and more distinguished faces than the Kirgiz, and as a rule they are better dressed and adorn their women and horses with bright colours and ornaments. But as pointed out before, their conditions of life are otherwise the same as those of the Kirgiz.

The water of the *Uprang River* began to rise at about 3 o'clock p. m.; at
9 o'clock it had some 10 cub. m. per second. The *Hunserab* was much bigger and
proved to be not quite easy to cross. The temperature of the water in the rivers of
course changes in the course of the day. In the *Uprang-su* it was 8.5° at 10 o'clock a. m.;
13.5° at 1 o'clock p. m.; and 6.1° at 9 o'clock p. m. The water also became more
muddy towards the evening.

On August 2nd we continued our march to the S.S.W. and south up in the valley
of *Hunserab* for 20.2 km. and camped in the valley of *Ulutör* at an altitude of
4,589 m., being an ascent of 367 m. and a rate of 1:55. The road sticks to the
right or eastern bank of the river. Along the river there is a *shevär* or meadow
called *Räng*, uninhabited, as is the whole valley. At the right or eastern side the
tributary *Terskei-tametuk* enters, and at the left or western side *Köngöi-tametuk*.
Both are comparatively large *jilgas* with considerable brooks, and in the background
of both mighty, snow-covered ranges are seen. Glaciers are not visible in their
upper parts, only eternal snow. They are to the greatest extent filled with *korum*
or gravel, but have grazing-grounds in their lower parts. The limpid brook of
Terskei-tametuk forms at its junction with the *Hunserab* a delta, the two largest
branches of which are separated from each other by a rounded ridge.

The bed of the main river is broad, though only partly filled with water in its
several branches. The whole bed is filled with rounded gravel. *Ak-jilga* is a large
tributary valley from the S. E. with a considerable brook. A little farther on we
leave to our right or in the west the main valley of *Hunserab*, and continue due
south into the valley of *Ulutör (= Ulug-tur)*. After a while we reach a point where
two valleys join, both with glaciers in the background; we follow the western one.
In its upper part we pitched our camp.

The whole day's march had taken us through excellent grazing-grounds abun-
dantly watered. Yaks and camels were often seen grazing. Wild sheep, wild goats
and *ular* or mountain partridge were common. In every little valley there is a brook,
and innumerable rills from melting snow flowed down across the undulated meadows,
often making the ground soft and treacherous. The brooks from *Terskei-tametuk*
and *Ak-jilga* had absolutely clear water, proving that they come exclusively from
melting snow. *Hunserab* has muddy greyish water, proving that it is chiefly fed by
glacier brooks. Opposite *Ak-jilga*, spongy ice-floes were seen in the *Hunserab*, and the
Ulutör River was partly freezing during the night, though the minimum temperature
was only a little below zero. A great part of the ice-floes, which obviously had come
down from higher regions, did not disappear in the course of the day, though the
temperature of the air was at 16.2° at 4 o'clock p. m.

At both sides of the *Ulutör* valley the mountain slopes are covered with
detritus and grass, having steep, but rounded forms. Above them the hard living

rock appears in wild rocky peaks and crests. In the background to the south three glaciers are visible, surrounded by eternal snowpeaks and presenting a magnificent spectacle especially at sunset. We follow the *Taghdumbash-* and *Hunserab* Rivers to some of their uppermost sources like the branches of a tree. *Taghdumbash-darya* has thus a considerable drainage area; the southern boundaries we are now studying in the mountains which, under the name of *Kara-korum*, may be regarded partly as an eastern continuation of the *Hindu-kush*, and the northern boundary of which we touched in the *Ulug-rabat Pass*. The whole southern part of the *Mus-tagh-ata Group* falls within its boundaries and contributes, together with thousands of brooks from the *Sarikol-*, *Kashgar-* and *Kara-korum Ranges* to the mighty river which in the *Shinde* gorge pierces the *Kashgar Range* and flows to the junction with *Raskan-darya*.

CHAPTER VI.

THE ULUTÖR, HUNSERAB AND UPRANG PASSES.

August 3rd was devoted to a short visit to the snouts of the glaciers in the upper part of the *Ulutör* valley. The distance to the highest point reached was 4.5 km. and the rise to it 260 m. As its own height was 4,849 m.; the rate of the ascent was thus as 1 : 17.3.

The ground is, as hitherto, extremely soft; covered with grass, moss and the same flowers and plants as those described on *Mus-tagh-ata*.[1] The rills and brooks from melting snow which disappear in the gravel of the screes at the base of the mountains, reappear in the central part of the valley and make everything wet. Sometimes there are, amongst the grass, small pools containing algæ. From the easternmost of the three principal glaciers in front of us descends a brook, the ice-sheets of which have been accumulated one upon another to a thickness of 2 m., forming comfortable bridges for crossing the brook, the bed of which is filled with gravel and blocks of granite. Great erratic blocks are strewn about, not always easy to distinguish from those which have fallen down directly from the neighbouring rocks. Old moraines are not visible, the ground is soft and grass-grown, only here and there belts of gravel occur.

We direct our course to the middle glacier, which seems to be the largest. In its lowest part it seems to be 30 or 40 m. thick. Its whole right or eastern side is nearly vertical and covered with a thin light grey layer of fine material, in which also a horizontal structure is clearly visible. The right lateral moraine on the top of the glacier is very insignificant, and the strand moraine of the same side is only rudimentary, 1 or 1.5 m. high nearest the glacier. It is partly swept away by the right glacier brook. The ice-wall at the right side is carved out to a height and depth of 2 or 3 m.; therefore an over-hanging vault of ice is formed. The ice below the vault is quite black and contains solid material, obviously from the ground moraine. From the surface of the glacier small brooks and rills flow in cascades with a temperature of 0.5° at a distance of 3 m. from the glacier.

---

[1] *Cf.* Professor OSTENFELD and Professor WILLE in Vol. VI.

64

Looking S. 55° E. from the Pass of Ulu-tōr, Aug. 3, 1895.

Looking E. S. E. from the Uprang Pass, Aug. 7, 1895.

The snout of the glacier is very broad and blunt, even broader than the rest of the tongue in its lower part. This curious form is due to the fact that the snout reaches the very foot of the hills at the opposite side of the valley, and, therefore, even is forced to run uphill for a short distance. On account of the constant pressure of the ice from behind the snout is much broken up, forming heaps of ice blocks. The right part of the snout, which is directed downwards to the valley, is cupola-shaped and has a rudimentary moraine on its top.

We continued westwards along the snout, wandering on the slope of the hill at the northern side of the valley. It consists of nothing but blocks of all sizes, and falls 33° towards the snout. Here we find that the snout has also a blunt apophysis to the west, formed by the obstruction created by the northern hill base. The glacier is seen coming directly from the south, where its »Firnmulde» and the extensive troughs of its *névés* are surrounded by gigantic snow ranges and peaks. From a high observation point on the slope we see the dark middle moraine of the glacier, which partly touches the moraine of the left side. The moraines consist of gravel, the blocks being rare. A short distance above the snout, transverse and longitudinal crevasses are well developed, but lower down they are pressed together. Some of the crevasses are of enormous size. Nearly the whole surface of the glacier is dirty.

The western glacier comes from its own »Firnmulde» to the S. W. and forms an »S», the end of which is directed towards the snout of the middle glacier, though it does not quite touch it. The ice masses of the middle glacier rise considerably above those of its western neighbour. The latter has a considerable left moraine on its top consisting of finer material; of granite, crystalline schist, and porphyry in many varieties. Living rock is difficult to reach, cropping out from the gravel higher up. The surface of the S. W. glacier is more level, and it describes a fine double curve in its rocky passage. From the N. W. a small glacier approaches it without joining it.

Between the snouts of the two glaciers and the slope of the northern hills, a little lake, hardly frozen, has been formed. The brooks from the melting ice of the two glaciers make their appearance at the eastern corner of the middle glacier. The water from the western glacier has, therefore, to flow under the snout of the middle glacier. The joined brook comes out of the latter as from a grotto some five meters high. As the day was cloudy there was not much water, perhaps 5 or 6 cub. m. per second.

The third or eastern glacier is more even and falls regularly to the valley. Its surface was covered with long dark belts of fine material hardly to be regarded as moraines; its front moraine was very insignificant, but its »Firnmulde» and *névés* considerable. Beyond the rocks and crests between which these glaciers come down, one sees in the distance gigantic peaks and snowfields. The three glaciers seemed to be smaller than the largest of the *Mus-tagh-ata, Yam-bulak-bashi, Tergen-bulak, Kamper-kishlak* and others, all of which have so large and well developed moraines.

Between the eastern and the middle glaciers there was a little hanging glacier with a mountain ridge on each side. Its snout is visible at considerable height above the valley. Its front is vertical, and below it a front moraine falls in regular and steep slopes towards the valley.

At the glaciers we were indeed at the southern boundary of *Taghdumbash Pamir*. The drainage areas which were our nearest neighbours were to the south the *Indus*, to the east the *Raskan-darya*, to the west the *Panj*, to the N. W. the *Ak-su*, and beyond the *Ulug-rabat* the *Gez-darya*. We were in a region from which the water flows to the *Indian Ocean*, to *Lop-nor* and to *Lake Aral*.

The following information may be of some interest. In the upper reaches of the *Ulutör* valley no roads were said to exist and no passable passes known; the glaciers we had visited had no names. In the winter three Kirgiz tents are pitched at the confluence of the *Hunserab* and *Ulutör*, above which place nobody lives. In the cold season nearly all go down to *Kara-jilga*, *Ilik-su*, *Masar* and other places. The Tajiks have their own Tajik *beks* under the Chinese administration. The Kesek Kirgizes of *Masar* pass only two or three months every summer in *Taghdumbash Pamir*. The rest of the year they spend along the *Raskan-darya*. When returning to this river they take the road of *Ilik-su* and have from its pass a journey of three days to *Raskan-darya*, the left bank of which they follow upwards to *Kok-tash* where the valley is broad and the grass good. Only in spring and autumn, and, of course, in the winter, this road may be used. At *Kara-chukur* about 100 Kirgiz tents were said to exist. The tent-dwellers belong to the Kipchak, Teït, Naiman and Kesek tribes. Their chief, Kasim Bek, who also had jurisdiction of the Kirgizes in the upper *Taghdumbash*, was subject directly to Mi Darin, the Commandant of *Tash-kurgan*.

In the region of *Ulutör* and *Hunserab* the winter is very cold and snow falls to a depth of about two feet. The prevalent winter wind comes from the *Hunserab Pass*, i. e. the west; the prevalent summer wind from *Taghdumbash*, i. e. the north. The ice we found in the *Ulutör* brook and other watercourses at the same altitude, had remained from the last winter. In the autumn the brooks freeze, extensive ice-sheets are formed, and one layer accumulates above another. Finally everything is frozen. The ice-sheets remain during the spring and begin to melt when the warm weather comes. The year of my visit, 1895, very much ice was left even so late as the beginning of August, and it probably would not melt altogether before the autumn cold began. During warm and sunny summers all the ice melts.

As is known, the *Uprang*, *Ilik-su*, *Sänkar* and *Kandahar Passes* all lead to *Raskan-darya*. From the *Hunserab Pass*, as mentioned above, a road goes to the village of *Gircha* in *Kanjut*. The principal road to the country in the south goes by *Min-teke*. The two passes are not difficult, and there is no ice or snow to be

A VIEW IN THE DIRECTION OF KANJUT FROM THE HUNSERAB PASS, AUG. 5, 1895.

THE SOUTHERN GLACIER OF THE HUNSERAB PASS, AUG. 5, 1895.

crossed. But the narrow valleys south of the passes are filled with gravel and water, and can be used only on foot during the summer.

August 4th we left the camp of *Ulutör* and returned north to the confluence of the *Ulutör* and *Hunserab* where the altitude was 4,388 m. The distance is only 6 km. The descent 461 m. and the rate 1:13.

The next day I undertook with two Kirgizes an excursion to the pass of *Hunserab*. The distance from our camp was 7.4 km. due west, and the ascent up to the threshold 421 m. As the latter had an altitude of 4,809 m., the rate is, therefore, as 1:17.6.

The *Hunserab Pass* proved to be one of the easiest and most comfortable I had so far crossed in the *Pamirs*. Between two mighty ranges with short snow-covered ramifications towards the valley and small glaciers between the ramifications, the broad, soft and grass-grown *jilga* of *Hunserab* gradually rises towards the threshold. Swampy ground is formed by small brooks from the sides. All the glaciers visible come to an end at an altitude above that of the pass; they are very small and their moraines insignificant. At the foot of the hills are screes and heaps of detritus, the rest of the country between the ranges having soft rounded forms. Hard rock is not within reach. A flock of 13 wild sheep fled into the valley *Ak-sai* coming in from the south and leading to small glaciers. The brook from the latter joins the brook from the pass, and where both meet there is a light grey plain of gravel, or a *sai*, surrounded by green hills.

The pass itself is more like a flat, green, somewhat convex plain with a very gradual ascent on both sides, where small pools of water stand. To the S. W. a deep-cut sharply modelled passage is seen between black rocky ranges covered with eternal snow. To begin with, the slope down to the *Kanjut* side is also gradual, but becomes more and more steep and the road finally is very difficult as it proceeds in a narrow gorge filled with water. This valley is also called *Hunserab*. North and south of the pass, glaciers come down without reaching the pass itself. The northern one has a brook which just at the glacier front freezes into ice-sheets. On the pass there are some blocks of grey and greenish granite of the same kind as lower down was found *in situ*.

The valley leading to *Kanjut* is seen S. 61° W.; three days journey lead to *Gircha* and six to the *khan-ui* or the residency of the late Safdar Ali Khan.

From the pass of *Hunserab* we returned by the same way as we had come down to our old camp in the lower part of the *Uprang* valley at 4,222 m. Just below the confluence of *Hunserab* and *Ulutör* the living rock was granite in 24° N. 30° E., though not quite clear. The granite forms two ridges between which there were several signs of nomads' visits and fireplaces of stone. This grazing-ground is called *Yeryi (Yer-ui?)*. Opposite this place, at the right side of the valley, there are two *jilgas Kichik-Akayu* and *Chong-Akayu* or properly *Ak-ayik,* as a nearly »white bear» had been seen there once upon a time.

The passage of the *Hunserab* was very easy now, as the river had dwindled to a brook with quite clear blueish-green water. The day had been cold and the sky cloudy. Therefore, no water came down from the glaciers, only from the snow-fields in the neighbourhood and from springs. The grass, the moss and the screes serve as filters in which the solid material remains. After warm sunny days the activity of the glaciers is lively, and the brooks bring down fine material ground under the ice, and the river grows mighty and muddy. The glaciers of these parts of the mountains are small, though the *névés* are considerable. The glacier we had seen at the southern side of the pass came from the same »Firnmulde» as the western-most one of *Ulutör.*

We camped in a big tent belonging to the Kipchaks of *Uprang* who had large flocks of yaks, sheep and goats in the vicinity, and a few camels higher up. The weather was full winter. Snow had fallen during the night, though in the valley it disappeared before noon. All the mountains remained white the whole day. In the evening it snowed again, and the entire valley was covered with one inch of snow.

As mentioned above, the rate of the ascent from our camp at the confluence of *Hunserab* and *Ulutör* to the pass of *Hunserab* was 1:17.6. From our *Uprang* camp, which was 21.7 km. from the *Hunserab Pass,* and up to the *Uprang Pass,* a distance of 14.3 km., the ascent was nearly the same, or 1:18; the camp being at 4,222 m. and the *Uprang Pass* at 5,013 m. To the latter an excursion was undertaken August 7th.

The valley is fairly broad and is bounded by mighty, partly snow-covered mountain ranges. The crests consist of living rock; the slopes and bases of screes and gravel below which the undulated meadows, crossed by innumerable rills, fill up the rest of the valley. A large number of yaks were grazing here. The last bit of the ascent is steep and gravelly, though not at all difficult. At the left or southern side of the pass two broad and short glacier-tongues, or rather apophyses from the same ice-stream, go down to the pass. The brook springing from them is the source of the *Uprang River.* The snouts reach 20 or 30 m. below the altitude of the pass.

The *Uprang-davan* is an extended cupola-shaped threshold, though smaller and less flat than the *Hunserab Pass.* On its sides are high snow and ice-covered mountain crests. The trough at the western side of the pass, by which the last ascent is made, had a good deal of snow and ice with several small brooks going down to the *Uprang River.* The latter is partly deep-cut in soft, vertical schist.

On the eastern side of the pass the ground falls much more steeply, and the road is seen going down between rocky, wild ramifications and mountain shoulders to the S. 65° E. Then the road makes a turn to the right before it continues to

Chummek my pān Sommuk | hu not tel Taghdumbash Pamir, Aug, 1895

LOOKING N. W. FROM CAMP UPRANG TOWARDS TAGHDUMBASH PAMIR, AUG. 1, 1895.

LOOKING S. 50° E. FROM THE PASS OF ULU-TÖR, AUG. 3, 1895.

the valley of *Raskan-darya*. The first day's march is said to be easy, but then one comes to a steep, deep-cut gorge full of gravel, blocks and water foaming with rage. This road is very rarely used, and my Kirgizes had not travelled it. In the background to the E. S. E. a mighty snow-covered range is seen, the same that forces the road to make a curve to the right or south.

At the southern side of the pass was living rock in knolls rounded by weathering and destruction. It was a fine-grained crystalline schist in 53° S. 35" E. Amongst the gravel we found a light reddish specimen resembling feldspar; at other places, just below and west of the pass the schist lay in 12° W. S. W. and 26° N. N. E. It is strongly folded. In the bed of the river there were also stones and blocks of granite.

The view from the *Uprang Pass* was occasionally hidden by snow drifts; however, to the N. N. W., in the direction of the *Taghdumbash Pamir*, one got the impression of a very extensive plateau-land crossed by mountain ranges. To the east the view is hidden by high rocky ranges, in which the erosion has given rise to the most accentuated forms and vertical lines.

On August 8th I made a visit to the *Kara-su* valley and camped at an altitude of 4,315 m. The distance is 9 km. and the direction north, N. E. and east. About halfway a little pass is crossed, on the northern side of which there is an arena-shaped valley with excellent grazing-grounds where large flocks of sheep were grazing. The place is called *Turuk*. The same crystalline rock as before stood here in 73° S. Thence the road goes down to the *Kara-su*, which now carried only a few cub. dm. of perfectly limpid water in a deep-cut furrow. The ground consisted of a layer of mould two feet thick pierced by innumerable roots and forming, as it were, a grass-topped carpet on the gravel.

The valley is broad, with snowy crests on both sides. In the background to the east snow-covered mountains are also seen. There is a path leading to a threshold in the upper reaches of the *Kara-su* valley. It may only be used by men on foot, and therefore only hunters take this road. On the other side there is a *jilga* going to *Raskan-darya*. In this region the passes are called *bel*, not *davan*. At the *bel* of *Kara-su* there are only rudimentary glaciers. In the valley there are several *auls*, or 13 tents in all.

Some additional information was given here. The Kirgizes and Tajiks were said to live in enmity toward one another which chiefly is caused by the difference in race and religion; the Kirgizes belonging to the Sunna, the Tajiks to the Shia, sect. As nomads they live under exactly the same conditions, but there is a great difference in the fact that the Tajiks as a rule pass the winter in stone or mud houses in villages, as *Marian*, *Däftar* and *Tash-kurgan*, and only pass the summer in tents in the higher valleys. They are, therefore, only half nomads. Their flocks of yaks, sheep, and goats, on the other hand, always graze in the valleys and are watched by shepherds.

At *Kara-su* the winter is cold and much snow falls, though less than in other high valleys in the vicinity. The snow always is deepest at the *terskei* or shady side of each valley, the *köngöi* or sunny side being more exposed. The prevailing winter winds come from *Parpak* and *Hunserab, i. e.* from N. W. and S. W., the same as in *Tibet.* The summer is less windy. All precipitation falls as snow. The Tajiks of *Kara-su* belonged to the Vakhanlik tribe which seems to mean that they originated from Vakhan. They pass the winter in *Marian* and *Tash-kurgan.*

The *Sänkar* or *Sängar Pass* leads to *Marian* and is said to be difficult. *Ogri-art,* »The Thieves' Pass» (pronounced *Ograt*), is easier and leads to *Ütshe* or *Uche,* across a first-class pass in the *Kashgar Range.* The pass of *Kara-su* is called *Taldi-bel,* as willows *(tal)* grow on its eastern side in a gorge which lower down joins the valley from the eastern side of *Ilik-su* before it reaches *Raskan-darya.* The valley of *Ilik-su* is said to be very narrow, though at some wider places grow *tokai* or forests of *tal* (willow) and *kayin* (birch). The amount of running water is not very great, but the road is difficult on account of *korum,* gravel and blocks.

It would be a mistake to imagine the *Kashgar Range* as *one* range. The orography is not so simple as that. To do so would be to make the same mistake as to regard the Transhimalaya as one range. The *Sänkar* road to *Yarkand,* for instance, is said to cross five passes, most of them difficult, and to take 12 days. The *Kashgar Range* is in reality a very complicated *system of ranges.*

The *Raskan-darya* is also known as the *Serafshan* or »Gold-rolling River».

August 9th we travelled from the *Kara-su* camp into the *Ilik-su* valley, the distance being 12 km. and the direction N. W. and N. E. Having crossed the brook twice and left *Turuk* to the south, we began to climb the southern slope of the ramification from the *Kashgar Range,* separating the *Kara-su* and *Ilik-su* valley from each other. Here two small mountain shoulders at our right are called *Sarik-tash* and *Kara-tash.* The slope becomes more and more steep and is covered with detritus of schist and quartzite.

Finally we reach the secondary pass, *Otra-bel,* with an altitude of 4,467 m. It is vaulted and easy though covered with detritus. The view is interesting. To the north at the right side of the valley of *Ilik-su* is a hill called *Bash-yurt,* or, according to other information *Bos-yurt,* at the base of which there are good *yeilaks.* North of it is the large *jilga Ish-tur* leading to a pass of the same name and a passage to *Raskan-darya.* Still farther north we see the valley leading to the pass *Sarik-bel.* Opposite us, always at the right or northern side of the *Ilik-su* valley, is the tributary valley of *Kalta-aul* without a road or pass but with good grass and a brook. Just below us we have a bird's-eye view of the *Ilik-su* valley, energetically eroded, narrow in its upper part, broad in its lower, and having a brook surrounded with grazing-grounds.

LOOKING EAST FROM ILIK-SU, AUG. 11, 1895.

VAKJIR, LOOKING S. E., AUG. 15, 1895.

We camped at the *aul* of *Ilik-su* at an altitude of 4,133 m. There we found six Tajik tents. The inhabitants had arrived in the middle of May. During the winter they live at *Masar* and lower down, for the cold is sharp in the *Ilik-su* valley and the considerable amount of snow makes it difficult for the sheep to find grazing and for the men to find fuel. A great part of this snow is said to be due to the S. W. wind which sweeps heaps of snow up into the valley. At *Masar*, on the other hand, the broad, open valley is swept free of snow by the wind. In the summer there is very little wind. Rain is rare; the precipitation falls as snow.

The Tajiks of *Ilik-su* have large flocks of yaks, sheep and goats, but no camels. Most of them are perfect nomads, as they dwell in tents even at *Masar* and not in *tam-ui* or stone houses as do several other Tajiks. The household and the flocks are looked after by the women, just as in the Kirgiz *auls*.

The black schist near our camp lay in 87° N. 30° E.

The following day I made an excursion with yaks up to the pass of *Ilik-su*. The distance is 6 km. Just above the camp the valley becomes narrow, but there is still grass and grazing flocks. The ascent is increasingly steep; as an average it is as 1:7.5, for the camp is at 4,133 m. and the pass at 4,935 m. The grass disappears and there is only gravel. A part of the valley is a narrow gorge with relatively low hills at the sides. To the right the hills are hidden by detritus, to the left the living rock stands in 68° N. 46° E. At one place there is a little threshold of solid rock across the valley where the brook forms a cascade. Finally the valley is transformed into a trough with snow-patches. This we leave to our right and the path climbs the extremely steep rocks at our left where the schist forms steps. Everything is covered with slabs and flakes of schist, where only mountain ponies and yaks are able to climb.

This difficult passage leads directly up to the pass of *Ilik-su*, which forms a vaulted platform smaller than those of the other passes. A rudimentary glacier is seen at the southern side of the threshold. From this glacier a little brook starts to the east. The eastern slope down from the pass is said to be easier than the western, which is an exception to the rule we had found with the other passes. It soon enters a narrow gorge now supposed to be very difficult from blocks which had fallen down from the sides during the earthquake. This gorge is joined by the one from *Taldi-kol*. There are small patches of *jangal* or forest, and at one place wheat and barley are grown. The name of this place is *Uruk*, and it is situated near *Raskan-darya*. From *Uruk* there is no road along the river; it is a *cul de sac*. From the pass three mountain shoulders are seen eastwards, and at greater distance a mighty snow-covered range.

8. IX.

CHAPTER VII.

ACROSS THE VAKJIR PASS TO CHAKMAKTIN-KUL.

Having visited five of the high valleys at the southern edge of *Taghdumbash Pamir* and climbed three passes, I left this region and continued my journey westwards to the *Vakjir Pass* and *Chakmaktin-kul*.

On August 11th we travelled 25 km. N. W. and west, descending from 4,133 m. to 3,628 m., or 505 m., a rate of 1:49.5. We again passed *Masar* with its Kirgiz *aul* of 10 tents of the Kesek tribe, though a few Kara-teït and Chal-teït also were said to live here. Some of them pass the winter at *Uruk* on the *Raskan-darya*, watching yaks. The shepherds and their sheep pass the winter at *Masar*, as the animals cannot be taken across the *Ilik-su Pass*. Even if they could make the journey they would be torn in the bushes and *jangal* on its eastern side.

At *Masar* we crossed the *Hunserab* which here was 40 m. broad and half a meter deep and of a moderate velocity. The water was quite clear and bluish green. Then we ascended the 50 m. high left erosion terrace, the surface of which was undulated and consisted of gravel and meadows watered by small rills from the south. From *Sasik-teke* a brook comes down.

Having marched a few kilometers between the southern mountains and some small detached hills, we entered the mighty valley of the upper *Taghdumbash*. Just in the corner where the river turns to the north a mighty mountain group is visible during a very long part of the march. From the southern mountains a little narrow valley comes out; it has eternal snow in its background and perhaps some little glacier, as its name is *Mus-jilga*. A similar valley opposite it is called *Koshin-ghir*, or as others would have it, *Kashik-unkur*. Both have grass and brooks in their lower parts, but no roads. At the next brook we camped at a place called *At-yeilak* (pronounced *At-yeilau*). Our Kirgizes said that the mountains south of the *Vakjir Pass* were called *Mus-tagh*; the name *Hindu-kush* they had not heard.

On August 12th our road proceeded W. S. W. 18.6 km. on the right or southern bank of the *Taghdumbash River*. The next camp being at 3,855 m., the rise is 227 m. and the rate 1:82.

Just south of the road some big blocks are called *Chadir-tash*, after which the high and steep tributary valley of *Toro* comes in from the south with snowy mountains in its background. A glacier is not visible in its upper part, but at its mouth there are extensive and mighty old moraines of granite and several erratic blocks. A part of the gorge itself is also filled with moraines. The moraines below the mouths of the southern tributaries press the *Taghdumbash River* against the left or northern side of its valley, where the mountains have a steep fall to the river. These mountains were called *Ak-tau (Ak-tagh)*. Opposite *Toro* there is a valley *Teke-sekerik* with no road and no pass.

From the north enters the broad and mighty valley of *Beïk*, also called *Paik*. Opposite it, on the right bank of *Taghdumbash-darya*, was an *aul* of four tents; two Kesek, one Bostan and one Teït. At the same place was a Chinese *karaul* of three tents. All these tent-dwellers remain here the whole year round watching the roads to *Ak-tash* and *Taghdumbash Pamir*. The winter is cold with much snow and hard western winds.

From the south open two considerable tributaries both called *Sarik-jilga*, both with old moraines, meadows, some bush-vegetation, brooks and a snowy range in the background. Between these we pass the *aul* of six tents belonging to the Kirgiz chief of the region, Kasim Bek. Near the camp we passed living rock, a hard crystalline variety in 64° S. 60° W. Here the river is divided into several branches crossing very good grazing-grounds. At our camp a lonely tent was pitched, and at the left side of the river there was a larger Kesek *aul* with great flocks. The inhabitants pass the winter somewhat lower down in the valley. Their shepherds wander with the flocks to the vicinity of *Vakjir*, where the grass is said to be good and the snow is swept away by the continual wind. At our camp in the region of *Kara-chukur* the snow used to reach a man's knees. The cold is less intense here than at *Masar* and *Ak-tash*. The two *Sarik* valleys were now inhabited by Kirgiz. It is difficult to count the number of tents, as many of them are hidden in the small valleys. The natives themselves estimated that in this upper part of the *Taghdumbash* were 100 tents, about half of them Kesek and half Sarik-teït, but there were a few tents of Naïman and other tribes.

At *Kalik, Min-teke* and generally all along the southern mountains, the amount of snow is very considerable. In the middle of November the snowfall begins in earnest, and is at its maximum in the middle of January. The hard winter is reckoned as being four months long, and the autumn is three months. As early as the middle of October there is not much water left in the river which is completely frozen in the winter; only springs then have running water. As a rule the river is difficult to cross in summer; 1895 was an unusual year, as the river could be crossed nearly everywhere. The greatest part of its water is said to come from *Vakjir; Tegermen-su*,

Min-teke, Kalik and other valleys contribute with their brooks. The name used here was *Taghding-bash*, not *Taghdum-bash*. It is also pronounced as *Taghden-bash* or *-bashi;* and by the Kirgiz as *Daghdum* or *Daghdam-bash*.

The Chinese power extends to *Vakjir*. A few days beyond this pass is the first Afghan post. At *Ak-tash* the Russian territory begins.

On August 13th our journey continued nearly west 27.6 km., and the ground ascended 227 m. or to 4,082 m., the rate thus being 1 : 121. The first half of the march the road sticks to the right bank where a little gravelly threshold is crossed, swept by the river. Beyond it there was an *aul* of 4 tents. The valley *Olauche* is to the south. Its neighbour to the west is called *Dastar* and has a brook of about 2 cub. m. per second. *Kashka-su* is the next tributary on the same side, and opposite it we pass the three *jilgas, Kosh-tube*.

From the gravelly terrace the road goes down to the considerable brook of *Min-teke* some 20 m. broad and 0,4 m. deep on an average, flowing across a good grazing-ground. The valley of *Min-teke* is broad and large. The road up to the pass was said to turn to the right; to the left a tributary valley called *Kachenai* enters the main valley. In the background a mighty snow-range rises.

Opposite *Min-teke*, to the north, we have the valley *Tamgetuk* with a brook in a widespread delta. Then follow at the southern side three considerable valleys, all called *Kara-jilga* by reason of the black schist cropping out here. Opposite the first of them we notice the valley *Otash*. The main valley then turned N. W. for a while, after which we passed the northern tributaries *Sari-tash (= Sarik-tash)* and *Kisil-dung*, both with brooks. *Sari-tash* leads to a pass which can be used on foot or with yaks.

A little beyond *Min-teke* we cross the *Taghdumbash River* to its left bank where there is now sufficient space for the road. The river flows here in two branches crossing a swampy meadow and with resp. about 7 and 22, or about 30 cub. m. of water per second. A considerable part of this volume comes from the *Tegirmen-su*, a northern tributary with a short-cut road to *Ak-su* and *Kisil-rabat*. The volume amounted to about 4 cub. m. per second. We camped in the angle between both rivers, which now were muddy after a clear day. In the afternoon the *Tegirmen-su* had a temperature of 10.2°, the *Taghdumbash* 11.6°. The latter, or main river, is also called *Kara-chukur* in its higher course.

From this place to the *Vakjir Pass* no Kirgizes live in the summer. In the winter some of them ascend a little higher up. Much snow falls, but usually it is blown away by the hard west winds. If it snows much and no wind blows, the snow accumulates and many sheep are lost. During such unfavourable winters the Kirgiz try to reach *Tagharma* early. The west wind prevails in winter, the summer is somewhat windy. Northern wind brings clouds and precipitation; western wind usually clear weather. As a rule the river is so big in summer that it can be crossed only with difficulty. During summers when the river is very big, all the Kirgizes live on the right or southern bank. The winter grazing is regarded as particularly good in this region, and many signs of winter camps were seen.

On August 14th our march was 27.6 km. to the west, S. W. and west, rising from 4,082 to 4,606 m., or 524 m., being a rate of 1:53.

At 10.30 a. m. the main river had a temperature of 5.3°; *Tegirmen-su* 5.8°. Both had dwindled considerably and their water was nearly clear. At the confluence the tributary forms a large delta. The first two tributaries from the south were called *Yelang-jilga* and *Kona-yelang-jilga;* they are high and steep and without importance. The same is the case with *Kara-kokde* from the north. To the south the *Kalik* represents a broad and mighty tributary with large brook; to the left is the *Kalik Pass*, to the right a glacier and a road joining the one in the next *jilga,* and proceeding to *Kosh-bel.*

Beyond the northern tributary, *Balta-aling,* we cross the river which here was 32 m. broad and at the most 0.45 m. deep, with a very gravelly bed. At the point where our direction becomes S. W. we pass the large left tributary *Kok-turuk,* which from the north receives the tributary *Kipchak-jilga.* The first leads to *Kok-turuk-davan,* said to be high and full of gravel *(korumluk).* To the south we see the tributary *Kosh-bel* with a brook and a road to the pass *Kosh-bel* by which *Kanjut* is reached. In the mouth of *Kosh-bel* there were several erratic blocks and flattened moraines.

Again we cross the river. *Kamar-utuk* is a place with sheepfolds of stone. Here a little granite knoll crops up. There was a grotto in the mountain, obviously a place where shepherds live in summer. From the south the large *Chong-jilga* enters; it has a brook coming from glaciers, and eternal snows are visible on the ranges in the background. From the north comes a nameless valley with a glacier in its upper part. Again turning S. W. we camp on a meadow. South and S. E. of this place there are several hanging glaciers with rills and small brooks.

Farther up in the valley and to the left a large glacier is visible and the *Vakjir Pass* seems from here to be very easy. The valley is the whole way up broad and rich in grass, only occasionally interrupted by gravel and erosion terraces. Swamps are numerous. The most common animal we saw was hare. Wild sheep and wild goats are rare, and so is also the wolf. Bear is fairly common. The *ular* is said not to be found in this part.

On August 15th we crossed the *Vakjir Pass.* The direction is S. W. and W. S. W. From the camp we had 8.3 km. to the pass, the altitude of which is 4,936 m., or 330 m. above the camp. The rise is 1:25. To the next camp, *Duldul-achur,* we had 19 km. and descended, from the pass, 813 m., as the height of the camp was 4,123 m. Here the rate of fall is 1:23.4.

Approaching the *Vakjir Pass* the valley assumes the form of a trough with soft ground, full of swamps, small pools, moss and grass, and small brooks and rills coming down from the sides, especially from the south. To the left (south) a fine glacier-tongue becomes visible; it has a large end-moraine and two brooks. The ascent is not steep. Gradually one reaches the pass, the eastern part of which forms a nearly level platform. Here is a little oblong lake of greenish, ice-cold water, from which a little brook flows N. E. in its stony bed.

Leaving the lake, or rather pool, to our right we continue S. W. and have to our left a second glacier-tongue, broader than the first. From its N. E. corner a brook comes out, giving rise to the oblong pool and before its outflow in it forms a flat delta of hard fine deposits. A little higher up along this brook there is a gravelly wall, probably an old moraine, crossing the bed of the next brook, which, therefore, forms another pool, smaller than the first mentioned. Here is the real source of the *Taghdumbash-darya*.

The formation of small lakes on the very top of high passes is a comparatively common phenomenon. On *Hunserab* we had seen swamps, probably the rests of old lakes or pools, dammed up by the moraines of the neighbouring glaciers. On *Ogri-art* there is said to be a pool, and I met the same phenomenon on many of the Tibetan passes.

A very short distance S. W. of the pools we rise to the saddle of the *Vakjir Pass* proper, a very easy, vaulted protuberance. Granite blocks and gravel are common, and living rock at some distance.

The ground is, as usual on the high passes, wet from melting snow and ice. At the right or northern side, there is another glacier. The snouts seem to end about 10 or 20 m. above the pass. From the northern glacier the water flows to the S. W. to the *Panj*, and this therefore is one of the sources of the *Amu-darya*. Here is the *Taghdumbash par préférance*. We are standing at the very »Head of the Mountains». To the east every drop of water runs to *Taghdumbash-darya, Raskan-darya, Yarkand-darya, Tarim* and *Lop-nor;* to the west to the *Panj, Amu-darya* and *Lake Aral.* The Indian water-parting is not far to the south.

From the pass the view is magnificent in all directions. The road down to the S. W. is at its beginning uncomfortable, as it passes amongst blocks of moderate and large size. Here and there are small stone pyramids by which the track is marked in snowdrifts and in mist. Then the slope becomes steep for a shorter stretch where gravelly and soft grassy ground alternate.

To our left a splendid perspective opens; a considerable glacier fed from three snow accumulations or »Firnmulden». It has a well developed medial moraine turning to its right side. From its snout several brooks flow down, forming a dark grey river in the valley filled with glacial clay, the finest material ground beneath the weight of the ice-mass. Farther W. S. W. there is quite a series of small glaciers ending high above the valley, and sending their brooks to the main river. This is, according to Lord CURZON, the real source of the *Amu-darya*, a view that is no doubt correct.[1]

Most of the small glaciers have large end-moraines. A little farther on the river flows in a deep-cut, sharply eroded bed, its depth being some 30 m. The solid rock is granite in 87° W. Tributaries enter also from the north. The first one we passed had quite yellow water, and a deep-cut bed with living rock at its right side, *viz.*, black schist in 86° N. W. This tributary was a wild foaming water-course, not quite easy to cross. At its bank was a stone-cairn; its name was *Tash-köpriu*, indicating the existence of a bridge once upon a time. The next tributary from the left, coming from a large valley with a great glacier in the background, had black water, which did not get mixed with the grey water of the main river until some 400 meters farther on.

Our road goes high above the main river on its right or north side, where several tributaries in gravelly valleys and deep-cut beds are crossed. At an altitude of 100 or 150 m. above the present valley one sees a sharply drawn line in the rocks, marking an old stand of the valley. The erosion of the tributaries seems to be stronger towards the side which is nearest the main valley, *i. e.* the right side of those coming from the south, and the left side of those from the north.

During a short stretch the main bed is broad and open, and here the river flows in several arms. But soon it again becomes as narrow as a gorge. On its sides the soft rounded slopes of the valley gradually rise to the screes and rocks of the mountains bounding it to the north and south. The relief is more wild and grand here than on the *Taghdumbash* side of the pass.

From the left another large tributary, *Divane-su*, comes, originating from a big glacier, at the side of which a magnificent pyramidal peak is seen covered with snow and ice. The main valley broadens out, as does the river bed between its erosion terraces. On a meadow between softly rounded hills we pitched our camp. The living rock was black schist with veins or layers of quartzite.

The next day, August 16th, we continued down the valley to the west and N. W., and finally N. E. up to *Chakmaktin-kul*. The distance was 39 km. in all. We began from 4,123 m. and ended at the lake for which I found 4,114 m. From *Bozai-gombaz* to *Ak-tash*, Colonel BYSTRÖM has entered upon the map of my journey published in the atlas to this work, the altitudes which are to be found on the English map published in 1896 under the title: *Map of the country on both sides of the Boundary Line drawn by the Joint Commission for delimiting the Russian and*

---

[1] *Vide supra.* Vol. II, p. 208 *et seq.*

Afghan territories on the Pamirs 1895, Scale 1:253,440 or 1 Inch = 4 Miles. I need
not to say that the altitudes found with instruments of precision by the English surveyors are perfectly exact, whereas mine, which were found only by boiling-point
thermometer and three aneroids, are too much dependent upon the atmospheric
pressure for the time being, to be reliable. My altitude for *Chakmaktin-kul*, therefore,
e. g. is more than 100 m. too high. My result was 4,114 m., whilst the English
map gives only 3,993 m. It is only the stretch from *Bozai-gombaz* to *Ak-tash* of
my itinerary that can be checked by help of the English map. For this stretch
Colonel BYSTRÖM has borrowed all the topographical detail and entered it on his
map of my journey. He has done the same with the names, many of which are
identical with those I heard.

However, we left *Duldul-achur* and travelled down the valley of the *Vakjir-
darya*. After a ride of one hour we passed a *rabat* consisting of two small stone
huts and a cemetery. The place is called *Chahr-tash*. An hour westwards the schist
falls 53° N. 30° W., and farther on 27° N. 30° W. The débris is granite and schist.
We had only small brooks to cross, most of them in well eroded furrows. The bed
of the main river is broad, and between its erosion terraces the river is divided
into several branches. In spite of its width the bed is fairly deep-cut. From the
edges of its terraces the soft grassy slopes gradually rise to the base of the black
rocks. The glaciers decrease in size and number and finally come to an end. The
place where we were nearest to the river was called *Kur-utuk*.

Around the last promontory from the mountains, to our right the road turns
to the N. W., north and N. E. in more than a right angle. The river makes a sharp
bend to the S. W., and is given the name *Panj* or *Pändsh*. Where the *Vakjir*
valley joins the great valley in which the uppermost *Ak-su*, the *Chakmaktin-kul* and
the uppermost *Panj* are situated, a wide, open plain is formed, at the N. W. side
of which several tributary valleys enter. Our road does not proceed on the floor
of the valley but sticks to the slopes of the mountains to our right at a considerable
height above the valley. Here we soon enter a landscape of ravines between hills
of loose, horizontally stratified clay, generally grey, but at one place red. Here and
there the ground is swampy from springs. Approaching the lake one gets the impression of seeing a nearly flat water-parting in the valley; or rather, that S. W. of
the S. W. end of the lake there is a hardly noticeable convexity of the clay ground
separating the drainage area of the *Ak-su* from that of the *Panj*. From our road
it was, however, difficult to tell whether such is the case or not, for we are still at
a certain height above the floor of the valley. At that point of our road where
one could think of a water-parting in the valley, I read a height of 4,151 m., or
37 m. above the surface of the lake. Some 8 km. from the S. W. end of the lake
we passed a little brook from a tributary *jilga* to our right or S. E., which, divided

into several arms, seemed to run into the lake, or at least into the marshes in its
S. W. prolongation. From the next little tributary valley another brook went in the
same direction. These brooks are not entirely easy to cross, as the ground around
them is very swampy and treacherous. Such is also the case with the several springs
we had passed on the slopes. To a certain degree the Kirgizes are right in saying
that the lake is formed by springs.

Finally we turn to the north, crossing the valley and a brook from the northern
mountains which reaches the south-western end of the lake in two branches. Just
east of the second and at about 1 km. N. W. of the end of the lake, we camped.

From here one finds that the shores of *Chakmaktin-kul* are very low and flat and
that the lake fills a good deal of the broad valley. Only on the S. W. shore are there some
very flat undulations of the clay ground. From the background to the N. E. is the broad
opening of the valley by which the uppermost *Ak-su* runs in the direction of *Ak-tash*.
The mountains were snow-clad, the weather cold and windy. In the evening it rained.

There are discrepancies between the names I heard and those of the English map.
Colonel BYSTRÖM has adopted the English version, as the surveyors from India travelled
slower than I and had the best guides that could be found. For the distance from *Bozai-
gombaz* to the S. W. end of the lake, the English map has four valleys from the N. W., *viz:*
Ak-jilga, Ak-jilga, Achik-tash and *Burguluya*. For the same valleys I heard the names:
Ak-jilga, Burgut-uya, Ak-sai and *Kul-kur-jilga*, the last-mentioned being the one which
runs in two branches into the lake and at which we camped. However, I accept the
English version and call it *Burgut-uya* or »The Eagle's Nest». According to the English
map this little river is of great interest for it effects a very remarkable bifurcation. At
the point of issue from its mountain valley the river divides into three branches, the
two eastern of which go to the lake, whereas the western and principal one turns to
the S. W. and goes to the *Panj*. I saw only the two first-mentioned, as I came from
the south. The route entered on the English map and obviously used by the surveyors,
follows the N. W. side of the valley and therefore crosses all three branches. As the
surveyors crossed the watercourses and saw them with their own eyes their statement
must, of course, be correct. Colonel BYSTRÖM has drawn the hydrography on the
map of my journey in accordance with this statement. Under such conditions the small
swampy brooks which I crossed at the S. E. side of the valley, which came from the
southern mountains and which I then supposed were running to the lake, were in reality
either tributaries of the western branch of the *Burgut-uya* or ended in marshes at
its left bank. This could not be made out from my route.

In his excellent work: *Landeskundliche Forschungen im Pamir*, Hamburg 1916,
Dr. ARVED SCHULTZ has adopted the following view:[1] Am See Tschakmaktin-kull

---

[1] Op. cit., p. 80.

9. IX.

(»Feuerstein-See«), in 3,995 m. Höhe (4,023 franz. Gen.-St.-K.), findet eine Bifurkation eines Baches statt, der einerseits nach S. W. zum Wachan-darja, anderseits nach N. O. zum Ak-su abfliesst. This is the version of the English and Russian maps. In a note SCHULTZ adds: Die französische Generalstabskarte 1:1,000,000 stellt die Bifurkation nicht dar, sondern zeigt W.-lich des Tschakmaktin-kull einen Riegel, der auf einem 4,230 m. hohen Pass übergangen werden soll. W.-lich von diesem Riegel sammeln sich dann erst die von der Wachan-Kette abströmenden Bäche, um sich nach 8 km. in den Quellfluss des Pändsh, Wachdschir, zu ergiessen. Die Darstellung der Bifurkation auf der russischen Gen.-St.-Karte 1:420,000 halte ich für richtig.

The Russian and English maps, therefore, agree with one another. The Russians seem, however, to have had this view even before the Anglo-Russian Boundary Commission, for on a rather simple map on the scale of 40 versts to an inch, Дорожная Карта Туркестанскаго военнаго округа, for 1893, the hydrography of *Chakmaktin-kul* is drawn exactly as on the English map of 1896. The *Burgut-uya* is there with its bifurcation to the lake and to the *Vakhan-darya* or Upper *Panj*, and from the N. E. end of the lake the *Ak-su* has its origin.

In the days of HÜAN-CHUANG, some 1,300 years ago, the situation may have been different insofar that the bifurcation then probably was easier to see, for the precipitation may have been greater than nowadays. The lake cannot have been much larger, as the valley is nearly flat. But if it has been larger, it may have delivered a direct effluent to the *Panj*, and the bifurcation would thus have taken place in the lake, and not as now in the *Burgut-uya* brook.

On August 17th we continued 8,8 km. N. E. along the northern shore of *Chakmaktin-kul*. The colour of the lake is a beautiful greenish blue. The ground is mostly soft and level with sparse grass; sometimes it consists of coarse sand. Occasionally low undulations hide the view of the lake. A few granite blocks are seen. Somewhat more than halfway we crossed a little brook from the valley *Gäsä*, which on the English map has no name. The shore-line forms a few capes into the lake where also a little island is seen. Wild geese were not seen here but they appeared in considerable numbers in the lake. The camp of the day was pitched near an *aul* of three tents and a *karaul* a short distance from the N. E. end of the lake. Here a brook comes down from the northern side of the valley. Its name was said to be *Ak-sai-echkele*. On the English map this valley is called *Ak-sai*, and is, not far from the lake, joined by another valley called *Ichkele*. Some distance up in the western valley, the *Ak-sai*, the living rock was some kind of granite in 60° N. 30° W. The lake is said to get the largest quantity of water from the *Burgut-uya*, though here the greatest part of the water also was regarded as coming from springs. This year, 1895, the supply of water was less than usual. Other years the lake has been larger. By the *Burgut-uya* one reaches, across a difficult pass, the *Sor-kul* or WOOD'S lake. No other of the tributaries opening to the lake has a road. In the upper parts of some of the south-eastern there are small glaciers.

Between our camp and the lake there were some small hills of sand and gravel only a few meters high, surrounded by soft, swampy ground with springs. At 4 o'clock p. m. the temperature of the air was 10.1°, of the lake 14.3° and of a spring near the shore 13.6°. In the *Ak-sai* brook 3 km. from the shore we found 7.3°. The water of the lake was found to be perfectly clear and as fresh as spring water; it contains algæ. In the winter the lake is covered with very thick ice, from which the snow is quickly swept away by the hard, regular S. W. wind. The Kirgiz ride across the lake on yaks and camels. As early as the middle or end of October the lake freezes and remains frozen for seven months. During the summer the wind comes from all sides; rain is rare, the precipitation falls as snow.

The next day we had a rest. Hard W. S. W. wind was blowing, but the sky remained perfectly clear and blue and the mountains of *Kisil-rabat* and *Ak-tash* were visible in every detail.

The *aul* of *Ak-sai* remains here the whole year round. In the district of Upper *Ak-su* 100 tents were estimated. During the winter several tents are pitched in the small valleys round the lake. The inhabitants were said to be Teït Kirgizes of the *uroks:* Durbölen-orus, Alapa, and Kochkor. On *Great Pamir* there were 100 more tents of the same tribe and especially of the *urok* Gader-shah.

***

CHAPTER VIII.

TO THE KANDAHAR PASS.

The next day, August 19th, I travelled N. E. and E. N. E. 47.7 km. to *Mehman-yoli* where the Anglo-Russian Boundary Commission was then stationed and where I stayed until September 13th. According to the English map, the altitudes of the two endpoints are 3,993 and 3,896 m. The valley of the uppermost *Ak-su* therefore, in a distance of 47.7 km., falls only 97 m. or at a rate of 1:485.

From the southern part of the N. E. end of the lake the *Ak-su* has its effluence and flows in an undecided bed from pool to pool and from swamp to swamp towards the N. E. and E. N. E. in its broad and open valley which to the north is bordered by the range that was baptised »Range of Emperor Nicholas the 2nd» by the British Commissioners, and to the south by the range called by the natives *Mus-tagh*. The river gradually increases as it gets tribute from nearly all the small valleys at both sides. To the left or north I noted seven names for tributary valleys, whereas the English map has eight. In the following table my names are in the first series, the English in the second:

Echkele	Ichkele
A nameless jilga	Mulk-ili
Andemin	Kara-jilga
Kara-jilga	Andimin
A nameless jilga	Tas-tere
Yaman-ang	Kizil-chur
Shoro	Sari-tash
Orta-bel	Jilga to Yaman-shura Pass
A nameless jilga	A nameless jilga
Gunche-Bai	Jilga to Urta-bel Pass
Six small nameless	Two nameless jilgas
jilgas.	Gunzhibai-jilga
	Mahomet-jilga
	Tash-jilga
	Yul-beles.

Where my *Kara-jilga* enters the *Ak-su*, the main valley was called *Andemin;* a name that was also attributed the third valley to the left. Where *Yaman-ang* joins the main valley the region at the base of the mountains was called *Tash-sera,* obviously the same as the *Tash-tere* of the English map. Which of the two versions is correct I cannot tell, for both words, sera, serai (house), and tere (skin), are Kirgiz words. Below *Tash-sera* the valley on both sides of the *Ak-su* was called *Kara-dumur.* My next valley is *Shoro.* The names of *Yaman-ang* and *Shoro* are again to be found in the name *Yaman-shura* of the English map. Below the mouth of my *Orta-bel* valley, the *Ak-su* valley was said to be called *Bosala.* The English map has no valley with the name of *Orta-bel,* only a pass somewhat farther N. E. My *Gunche-Bai* is the *Gunzhibai-jilga* of the English map, which has a *Mulk-ile* valley as the second one from the S. W. and corresponds to my first nameless *jilga.* Below it the same map has a little lake called *Bish-utek.* Having left the *Gunche-Bai* valley behind, I passed a place in the main valley called *Turduning-guri* or Turdu's Tomb. At nearly the same place the English map has a *Turdunin-kul* or Turdu's Lake; probably both names are right.

As to the tributary valleys from the right or southern range, the *Mus-tagh,* the English map has only entered three *jilgas* near *Mihman-yoli,* all three called *Kara-jilga.* I have four *jilgas* belonging to the first half of the road, namely: opposite *Echkele, Yar-turuk;* opposite my *Andemin, Yer-kapchal* with a road to *Kok-turuk;* opposite my *Kara-jilga, Yer-kapchal* No. 2; and opposite *Shoro, Kara-jilga,* which is identical with the first *Kara-jilga* of the English map. By the *Kara-jilga* which is No. 4 to the left or north in my series, a road was said to pass to *Sor-kul.*

There is, therefore, a certain confusion regarding the names and especially regarding their localisation. Nearly all the names are identical, though the same names in both cases are often given to two different valleys. It is so much the more difficult to tell which version is the right one since the Kirgizes themselves do not always agree in their information.

At any rate I found that a brook with two heads flowed out of the *Chak-maktin-kul* to the N. E., being the source of the *Ak-su,* whereas not a drop of water flowed to the S. W. All the Kirgizes affirmed that the water supply of this summer was less than usual. During summers with great precipitation the lake increases in size and the source of the *Ak-su* increases in the same proportion. The size of the lake must under all conditions be insignificant, as the water constantly flows out to the N. E. It therefore seems impossible that conditions could ever be such that any part of the superfluous water of the lake could flow to the S. W. But a traveller coming from the S. W. and following the course of the *Vakhan-darya* and seeing its water flowing towards the S. W., will very likely get the impression that it comes from the lake, and he will be persuaded that this is the case if he does not particularly examine the hydrographical problem.

On August 21rst I visited together with Dr. Alcock of the British Commission, the hot sulphurous springs of *Bakhmir-masar* situated 6.2 km. E. S. E. of the head-quarters camp. The water proved to have a temperature of 39.65°.

On September 13th I rode with General Gerard and General Pavalo-Shveikovskiy to *Ak-tash*. a march of 19.5 km. to the N. E., during which I had not the opportunity of continuing my map. Colonel BYSTROM has borrowed this part of the itinerary from the English map. For the whole march one sticks to the valley of the *Ak-su*. The most important place passed on this road is the *aul* of *Kisil-rabat* with the left tributary of the same name.

On September 14th I left *Ak-tash* and travelled N. N. E., E. S. E. and N. E. for 28.9 km. The first 18.5 km. to the pass of *Lakshak* rise from 3.801 m. to 4,645 m., or 844 m., being a rate of 1:22. The last 10.4 km. descend from the pass to the next camp which was at 3,988 m., or a fall of 657 m., and at a rate of 1:15.8. These figures give an idea of a profile of the *Sarikol Range* in the southern part of its stretching.

At *Ak-tash* camp we crossed the *Ak-su*, the bed of which was easy and shallow; the stream was very slow. At both sides of the river, cracks from the earthquake were visible. One has then to cross a secondary little threshold, *Naisa-tash* in a ramification from the *Sarikol Range*, standing between the *Ak-su* and the eastern *Shinde* brook, which carried very little water. From the left or south comes a little tributary called *Kugechege*, with a limpid brook but no road. At the left side of the *Shinde* valley the rocks are steep and clean-washed by the brook. At the right side is an erosion terrace. A little east of *Kugechege* the rock was hard crystalline schist, which also was true at *Sari-jilga*, a little tributary from the south. At the *Ak-sai-jilga* from the north the same rock lay in 51° S. 10° W., and was impregnated with white veins.

The valley is not narrow, though we generally ride in its deepest part, some-times crossing the brook. Here and there grass grows; the rest is gravel. Beyond *Ak-sai* and *Mus-jilga* the valley becomes narrow and its slope steep. The pass is easy; it is an even saddle, called *Lakshak-bel*. The eastern slope is covered with fine detritus material. There is no snow and no glaciers. The living rock lay here in 81° N. 60° E. On the eastern side the way down is at first steep, then gradually falling. In a very deep and narrow gorge the eastern brook, which also is called *Shinde*, turns to the N. N. E. Here the road runs on the hills at the right side of the narrow passage. The living rock is here porphyry in different varieties, as a rule steeply falling to the north. Curious formations such as rocky teeth and towers are not rare. At one place in the valley one such formation stands like a pillar 8 m. high. Finally the black schist appears again.

Where the valley becomes a little broader there is a *karaul* of two Tajik tents from *Tash-kurgan*. A short distance east of the pass a little southern valley is called *Kichik-khan-yoli*. Lower down, near the camp, are two other valleys from the south, *Khan-yoli* and *Ak-chirak*. All three are said to lead to passes by which there are roads to *Ak-tash*. This seems to be correct, for on the English map there is a valley called *Khan-yoli* south of the same range.

We camped at *Keng-shevär* near a *karaul* of 8 Tajik guards and 2 Chinese soldiers. During the winter this *karaul* moves lower down to the N. E. in the valley as the snow makes it impossible to find grazing or fuel. The snow is usullay 2 feet deep. Sometimes the pass is closed by snow, and numbers of horses get lost on it. One or two months in the winter it is not used. Instead of it one takes the *Berdesh* or *Berdesht* road to *Tagharma*. There is a good deal of traffic, as Afghans, Badak-shanis and Vakhanliks take this road. Here, as at so many other places, S. W. wind was said to blow in winter. Sometimes the snow is blown away from the pass by hard winds, but usually the snow is covered with a hard frozen crust.

On September 15th our road proceeds N. N. E. and N. E. for 30 km. to *Tash-kurgan* where the altitude is 3,152 m. We therefore descend no less than 836 m., or at a rate of 1:35.9. The *Lakshak-bel* is thus 1,493 m. above *Tash-kurgan*.

In the morning the whole country was snowed over. Not far below *Keng-shevär* the valley becomes gravelly and the road uncomfortable. This place is called *Kara-korumning-bashi* or »the Beginning of the Black Gravel». At the left side the rock is gneiss in 40° N. 30° E. At *Kara-korum* one has to cross a scree of gravel and blocks. Opposite, at the left side, is the little tributary of *Girde-kul*. Between both, the brook has cut its furrow very deep. The valley is deep and narrow and sometimes has erosion terraces. The brook carries about 1 cub. m. per second of water but gradually grows larger. The water is clear as crystal. There are heaps of gneiss blocks of all varieties; fine-striped green, coarse-striped grey, etc. At *Yar-utck* from the left we again cross a scree. The gneiss is then striped in white and black. Pegmatite is common. Then granite appears, generally reddish and falling steeply to the north.

Here the rocks are nearly perpendicular at both sides and only a narrow gorge is left between them when fresh fallen blocks are numerous after the earthquake. The passage is disagreable, as one often has to ride under overhanging blocks which may come down at any moment. Constantly we cross the brook that meanders between the blocks. Finally the valley opens. At its left side the granite had a fall of 55° S. 55° E. It was white with small black crystals.

Now we see the *Tash-kurgan* valley in front of us; broad and mighty. In the distance the fortress is visible. Leaving the *Shinde* valley behind us we still follow its brook, which by and by divides into several branches and into ariks or irrigation canals going to the fields of wheat, barley, etc., between which the road runs. We camped near the fort on the top of the left erosion terrace.

As I had travelled the *Pas-rabat-Tengi-tar-Keng-kol* road the previous summer, I decided now to take the road of the *Kandahar Pass*. I was told that the latter in older times had been very much frequented, but that nearly all traffic nowadays preferred the *Pas-rabat* road. However, it proved to be difficult to get a guide in *Tash-kurgan*. Everybody pretended to be busy with the fields and the harvest, but the real reason was that they were afraid of the Chinese. Finally we got a man who, before we reached the highest pass, dropped behind and was lost to sight.

To the highest threshold of the *Särghak Pass* we had, September 16th, a distance of 18 km. The rise is 880 m., as the altitude of the pass is 4,032 m. The rate is 1:20.5. On the eastern side we had 6.2 km. to the village of *Bäldir*, the altitude of which was found to be 3,117 m., or a descent of 915 m. at a rate of 1:6.8 which may be said to be very steep.

We passed between fields, small gardens and a few groves of willows, and crossed the *Taghdumbash-darya*, which now was only one-third of its volume of six weeks ago and had perfectly clear water. At its eastern side we soon entered a narrow gorge with, at its right side, rocks of mica-schist in 77° N. 10° E. There was no water. The ascent is steep, and after a while the broad *Taghdumbash* valley was seen below us with its green vegetation patches and its river. Here we climbed steeply on the left hills of the gorge, a difficult passage that had to be improved with axes and stones. It leads to a first pass which is 3,427 m. high and situated in mica-schist in 62° N. 15° E.

East of this pass the ground becomes more rounded and open, and we ascend to the second pass having an altitude of 3,823 m. The landscape then becomes curious. It is a series of flat, cupola-shaped undulations, consisting of hard detritus dust. Living rock is rare, plants are seen occasionally; it is like a highland steppe. Sometimes the ground is nearly level and one does not see any steep slopes in the vicinity. Dry erosion furrows cross this highland in zigzags. The road goes up and down these furrows, crossing flat ridges or following their crests or sides.

The third pass had an altitude of 3,938 m. In its neighbourhood the mica-schist cropped up in sharp ridges and peaks laying 69° S. 10° W. After a while we reach the fourth and highest pass, 4,032 m. in altitude. The view from here is magnificent. To the south we see the snow-covered highest part of the range we are just crossing, and east of it the valley of *Ütshe* or *Üche*, to the left side of which our range stretches long, irregular ramifications. On these our road proceeds in innumerable zigzags down through small erosion valleys, up through other valleys. Finally an extremely steep slope leads down to a very narrow gorge, the floor of which has a gradual fall. It contained no running water, only a few pools. At the mouth of this valley the same rock as before stood in 41° S. 20° W.

Here we enter the valley of *Ütshe*, where a ploughed field at an abandoned hut gets its irrigation-water from a little brook. A few minutes later we camp at the little village of *Bäldir*, where only one household lived. The Yus-bashi of the place had some 50 households spread in the valleys around under his dominion. He owned cattle, sheep, goats and donkeys. In the winter he settles down on the *Ütshe River* at its confluence with the *Shinde River*, which is the continuation of the *Taghdumbash-darya*. At the confluence is the village *Bäldir* proper. The name was said to apply to the whole region as well. The name of the pass was *Särghak*. Another pass, *Chosh-bel*, was said to have a road joining the *Ütshe* valley lower down. Higher up the river was a place called *Ütshe*. Wheat and barley are grown. The winter is cold, but there is little snow and not much wind. During the warm season the usual wind comes from the region of *Mus-tagh-ata*. The high mountains are a protection against other winds. A good deal of rain falls, more at *Ütshe* than at *Bäldir*. Wolves, foxes and wild goats live in the region. At the confluence there are groves of willows and poplar trees.

From our camp we could get a vague idea of the confluence to the N. 10° E. There the *Taghdumbash-darya* is called *Shinde*, and in a deep-cut, wild gorge the river cuts through the range we have just crossed. From the village *Bäldir* proper at the confluence, there is no road in any direction except the one from Upper *Bäldir* and *Ütshe*.

The next day, September 17th, we made a short march of only 9 km. S. E. up the valley to *Ütshe* where the altitude is 3,237 m., a rise of 120 m. at a rate of 1 : 75. The brook, about 2 cub. m. of perfectly clear water per second, is often crossed. The valley is of moderate size, not broad. In its background, S. E., a mighty, snowy range is visible. Along the right side are considerable erosion terraces, often with a vertical side.

Tar-bush is a little village of two or three huts in a broader part of the valley. The houses, built of clay and stone and with a roof of wood, are like the Persian, and often have a *bala-khaneh*. In the fields the harvest had just been gathered.

Above the mill *Khan-kelide*, the valley becomes narrower and has mighty erosion terraces on the top of which our road sometimes runs. Sometimes the solid rock consisting of crystalline schist in 59° S. 10° W. is visible. Still higher up the valley widens out into a regular plain with nearly level, swampy ground and several small villages of a few houses of clay and stone, and some black tents. Great flocks of yaks, sheep, goats, white cows and donkeys were grazing amongst the excellent grass. The brook crosses this plain which is called *Tang-ab*. Mighty mountains rise all around.

The little village where we camped is called *Vacha*; above it is *Ütshe*. The population is Tajik. At *Vacha* they lived in black tents. During the winter several

10. IX.

of the families settle down in the clay houses. The information regarding the climate
was the same as at *Bäldir*. To the S. W. of *Vacha* is the pass *Ogri-art*, which
is said to be even easier than the *Särghak*.

From *Vacka* we continued S. W. and east on September 18th, 18.8 km.; rising
553 m. or to 3,790 m. at the next camp, the rate of ascent being 1 : 34.

From the right or east the tributary *Shar-tisak* enters, and opposite it, from
the west, *Küncsi-jilga*. The region in the main valley is called *Karak* or *Grag*.
The next right tributary is *Hunserab*, and higher up *Ak-jilga*, with a road joining
the one in *Shar-tisak*, which is said to lead to *Kisil-tagh* and to be used by
merchants. Then the main valley is called *Sherab*. It is well inhabited. Fields,
irrigation canals, houses, groves, gardens, peasants, flocks and donkeys are seen in
all directions. We pass a *guristan* or cemetery with a little mosque and a few
gumbaz. Along the river there is some bush vegetation. Erosion terraces have
been formed the whole way. Higher up, the valley becomes narrow and there is
no population. It is formed by two valleys; *Langar* from the S. S. W. and *Shuïdun*
from the S. S. E. By *Langar* there is a road to *Marian* and *Raskan-darya*. In
the corner of the junction a *masar* or saint's tomb is seen on an isolated rock,
below which some *gumbaz* have been built.

About half the brook comes from *Langar* where soft green schist falls 37° S. 20° W.
Leaving the *Shuïdun* we enter the little eastern tributary *Chakarga* and pitch our
camp at a little rest-house called *Rabat-Kandahar*. The grass is good.

Our road goes up the *Shuïdun* valley, which partly is very narrow. From
the S. S. W. enters the valley *Marian-taugak* with a road to *Marian*. Above it
the valley again becomes broader. Again we pass a cemetery and a *masar*. The
Shuïdun valley is said to lead to a little pass *Bichan-art* or *Pchan-art*, which is
flat and easy and leads to the village of the same name. Beyond the latter is the
pass *Kara-vatrak*, high and difficult and with a road to *Boramsal* and *Raskan-
darya*, which here was called *Pil* or *Tong-darya;* and finally to *Chup* and *Asghan-
sai* above *Kargalik*. South of *Rabat-Kandahar* is the village of *Marian* not very
large and situated in a narrow valley. It could be reached by a road crossing a
pass to the south. This pass is obviously situated in a range joining the range of
Kandahar-davan with the one of *Ogri-art* and *Särghak*. The latter is to be
regarded as a special range parallel with and west of the one of *Kandahar-davan*.
The western range is the southern continuation of the one with *Kata-kok-moinak,
Kichik-kok-moinak* or *Chichiklik-davan* and *Mus-tagh-ata*, and still farther north,
the *Ulug-art-davan*. This range is the real *Kashgar Range*.

In the morning of September 19th, after a night temperature of −0.5°, the
whole country was white with snow two inches deep. We had 12.5 km. to the
Kandahar Pass which is 5,062 m. high, a rise of 1,272 m. at a rate of 1 : 10. The

next camp, *Kochkur-Bek-Bai*, was at 3,331 m. In a distance of 11 km. we had therefore to make the enormous descent of 1,731 m. The rate here was steep, or as 1:6.3.

Regarding the pass in front of us, its name is usually pronounced as *Kanda'r* or *Kanda'ar*. During the winter it is often impracticable on account of snow. Even at the *Rabat* there is much snow, and flocks grazing in the high valleys are sometimes lost. The region is regarded as *sarhad* or cold. The earthquake of which we had heard so much, had been felt the whole way to *Tong*. In the district of *Ütshe-Tang-ab* nearly all houses had been destroyed and only lately rebuilt. Here the shock had been very strong. In *Tong* only two or three houses had been damaged.

From the *Rabat* the ascent is steep, but regular and without difficult passages on the top of ridges and slopes. Near the pass a pool is formed every summer; it had now dried up. The snow made the ascent easier by covering the sharp-edged gravel. On a few short stretches the ground is nearly horizontal. The last bit of the ascent is very steep.

The Pass of *Kandahar* is of quite a different type than other passes we had crossed. It is sharp as a knife. At the very crest the green schist stands nearly vertical, or falling 70° N. 50° E. On the eastern side the descent is difficult and could hardly have been accomplished with laden ponies. Our luggage was carried by yaks. One has to glide down through one foot of snow on an extremely steep slope between projecting rocky teeth. It is like the *Ulug-art*. The difficult passage is, however, short, and was made in 15 minutes. Then the slope is less steep, and the gravel was covered with more snow than on the west side. It snowed even now and continued until we reached the camp.

The gravel is followed by soft wet slopes, good *yeilaks* and finally a valley, narrow between rocks and with a brook. To the right opened the tributary *Lab-dilush* without a road but with *yeilaks*. The rock was the same green schist falling N. 20° E. and nearly vertical. We camped in the narrow valley at a *rabat* consisting of a stone wall under a block, and called *Kochkur-Bek-Bai*. Here we met the Bek of *Tong*, who said that the flocks of his district in the late summer grazed on these high *yeilaks*; when the snow began they were brought back to *Tong*. *Kandahar-davan* is, if possible, also used in winter by the *Tong* people, as it is the only pass to *Sarikol* in the neighbourhood. If it is closed one has to take the long roundabout road by *Yarkand* and *Tagharma*.

CHAPTER IX.

BY TONG BACK TO KASHGAR.

On September 20th we made a very short march, *viz.* 6.6 km. north and N. N. E., descending 294 m. or to 3,037 m. at the camp in the forest of *Tersek*. The rate of fall was 1:22.4. From *Kandahar Pass* to this camp we thus descended no less than 2,025 m.

It snowed heavily the whole night till 11 o'clock a. m. There seems to be a good deal of precipitation in the autumn on the eastern side of the *Kashgar System*. We had had the same experience the previous year. At *Tersek* the snow used to reach to the knees in winter, at *Kotshkur-Bek-Bai* it was two feet deep. In the summer it often rains and sometimes the river cannot be crossed. Even so soon as the latter half of September all precipitation falls as snow, and influences only indirectly the amount of water in the brook. The spring flood is therefore considerable. There is very little sunshine in winter.

Opposite the camp of *Kotshkur-Bek-Bai* a few Tajik families lived in huts, watching their flocks. A short distance from the camp the valley becomes as narrow as a gorge with gravel and numerous blocks. The brook had about 5 cub. m. of clear water per second and had often to be crossed. The road runs partly some distance up the side of the valley, and partly on the top of the erosion terraces. It goes up and down in zigzags. From the left comes the tributary of *Topeïcherab* leading to *yeïlaks*, but without a road. *Tersek* is a narrow valley from the right. Here a luxuriant forest of willows, birches and bushwood begins in the main valley. Here we camped. Some Tajiks who had accompanied us with their yaks, returned from here with fuel. The rock is the ordinary green crystalline schist.

On September 21st we continued N. E. and east down in this valley, the name of which, as of the whole district, is *Tong*. The distance is 20.3 km. to the next camp, *Langar*, where the altitude was 2,420 m., or a fall of 617 m., and a rate of 1:33.

The road is not good; to begin with it is gravelly and has erosion terraces. Wide places with grass and groves are passed occasionally. The rock is the same

crystalline specimen; syenite or granite. From the left comes the valley *Chirakunch.*
A little farther on an enormous block has fallen down and stands upright in the
middle of the valley, resembling a gigantic morel when seen in fore-shortened perspective. It is called *Naisa-tash.* The mountains at the sides are very steep, reminding one of the houses at the sides of a street. The view to the sides is therefore completely hidden, and only from the mouths of the tributaries can one get an
idea of the landscape. The brook is small and has to be crossed constantly.

Karik-atti is a wide part of the valley. *Marab* is a left tributary with a
road to *Almalik,* a region with *yeilaks* situated between the *Tong* and *Shinde*
valleys. *Chucherak* is a large open part of the valley with several habitations. From
the left comes the tributary *Guchman.* *Achema* is a wide place with a hut in a
poplar grove *(Populus euphratica). Juniperus* is also seen. *Kirgak* is a valley from
the right, *Khan-geli-unkur* from the left. By the large left tributary *Chupan-cherab,*
a road goes to the village of *Kugosh.* The next two valleys from the left are
Tichman, with a road to *yeilaks,* and *Kader-kapan.* The tributaries from the left
or north are nearly always larger than those from the right. Finally we reach
Langar, a little village surrounded by fields in which the harvest was piled in cocks
awaiting dry weather. Wheat and barley are grown. At some places the fields
were ploughed with wooden ploughs.

At *Langar* a side-valley nearly as large as the main valley comes in from
the right. It is called *Kichik-östäng* in contradistinction to the main valley, which
here is called *Ulug-östäng.* The brook of this valley is smaller than that of the
main valley. By *Kichik-östäng* a road goes in two days to the pass *Chupan-cheran,*
and thence in another two days to the valley of *Boramsal* where *kishlaks* or winter
grazing spots are found; thence it crosses *Bichan-art* to *Marian.* *Chupan-cheran,*
therefore, seems to be a pass in the same range as the *Kandahar Pass* and with
the same water-parting importance as it. *Bichan-art,* on the other hand, probably is
a secondary pass somewhere in a ramification from one of the two ranges we had
crossed thus far. *Chupan-cheran* is said to be very difficult and gravelly, and is
usually crossed on foot. In the winter it usually is closed by snow. For travellers from
Langar to *Marian,* the road by the *Kandahar Pass* is shorter than the road by
Chupan-cheran. The valley of *Kichik-östäng* has habitations only at its mouth. At
Langar two *masars* are built; those of *Sultan Bamafil Vali* and *Sultan Bamafil
Mujerat.* At the first there are two very small mosques; the brook flows between them.

The *Tong* is a wild and picturesque transverse valley which has cut down
its furrow through the eastern part of the range we crossed in the *Kandahar Pass.*
The landscape is magnificent and fascinating. The earthquake had been strongly
felt everywhere, and we were told of one or two men who had been killed by blocks
falling down from the rocks above.

As shown above, several of the geographical names in the valley are Turki in spite of the Tajik population. The natives explained this by the fact that their neighbours to the east were Jagataï Turkis', and to the west Kirgizes, and that there was much communication between the two. Yakub Bek and other rulers had also been of Turkish origin. The Tajiks all speak Turki quite fluently, though Persian is their own language. The pass of *Arpa-talak* was regarded as the boundary east of which only Sunnites live. In the village of *Tong* there were six Shiah families. There is no enmity between the two sects, and they often intermarry. The Tajiks had a memory of having come from the *Sarikol.*

They preferred the rule of Yakub Bek to that of the Chinese, as he was a Mohammedan and a *padshah.* But the taxes were much heavier in his days. To the Chinese they had only to deliver a certain amount of fuel and hay. In the valley of *Tong* there were no Chinese officials. On the other hand, merchants often visit the valley with different wares. Chinese travellers to *Tash-kurgan* usually prefer the road of *Kok-moinak.*

The inhabitants of the valley are sedentary and live to a great extent from agriculture. Most of the day's march we had passed along fields of wheat or barley, watered from *ariks* at the sides of the river. Rain is common during the summer. The wind is not hard, as the valley is protected by the high mountains all around. In the winter there is much snow and it is cold, but there is any amount of fuel. Of ordinary animals they mentioned wild goat, wolf, fox, marmot, *ular* or snow-pheasant; but no bears. The *palank* or panther was said to attack even the yaks.

From *Langar* the *Tong* valley runs 13.4 km. N. E., S. E., and N. E. to our next camp *Kandalaksh,* descending to 2,102 m. or 318 m., being at a rate of 1:42. To begin with, the valley assumes the direction which is the medium of the directions of the two component valleys *Ulug-* and *Kichik-östäng.* Where the two valleys meet, the rock is granite (or perhaps syenite) in 40° N. 60° E.

The whole way down the valley is inhabited, and we pass along a series of villages; *Topabin, Sheik-masar, Barkhun, Belangedek, Turdideh, Sháravian, Sarikyar, Purkshman* and finally *Tong* proper with the large, comfortable house of Mohammed Kerim Bek, the chief of *Tong,* whom we had met on his way to *Tash-kurgan.* The title and function of Bek is here hereditary.

All the villages are surrounded by fields where the harvest had been just brought in safety, and by gardens and groves. The houses are built of stone, earth and clay. There are cows and donkeys; the yaks have disappeared, and no camels are seen. The villages with the picturesque surroundings and luxuriant verdure between the high grey mountains present very pleasant and fascinating perspectives. The road runs along the river, past the irrigation canals, stone walls, houses, fields of wheat, barley, maize, »porchak», peas, melons, etc., and groves of walnut, apricot, and apple trees. Everything is said to grow here except grapes.

The name *Tong*, pronounced *Tung*, signifies »narrow passage», though *tong* also means »frozen». We continued a little farther to the village of *Kandalaksh* and were received in the house of the *ming-bashi*, who had to provide us with *suchis* or watermen for the passage of *Raskan-darya*. Most of them lived in this village.

In *Tong* and *Kandalaksh* the river was called simply *Darya*, or sometimes *Tongning-daryasi*. The name *Raskan*, or *Raskam* as it is pronounced in *Tong*, is in use higher up the river, where also the name *Sarafshan* is heard. The *Tagh-dumbash-darya* or *Shinde River* joins the main river a long way lower down. In the summer the latter is swollen to enormous size and cannot be crossed. People who have to go to *Yarkand*, therefore travel only in autumn, winter or early spring. In the winter the river is said to be covered with very solid ice. Three days journey is calculated for a man on horseback to *Yarkand*. From *Tong* there is no direct road to *Kashgar*; one has to take the road by *Yarkand*, or by *Yaka-arik* and *Kök-rabat* as I did.

The *Tong River* is also said to be very swollen during the summer and occasionally cannot be crossed. They say it is a *yava-su* or wild water. After strong rains the bed becomes filled with muddy water in a few hours. As a rule the amount of rain is not very great. More than half a foot of snow rarely falls in the winter.

At *Tong* a tributary valley enters from S. S. W. It has a road leading to the village of *Kichik-Tong* of some 30 houses. This road crosses a pass which is very difficult and can only be used by men on foot. It was already said to be covered with snow. *Kichik-Tong* is said to be at the same distance from *Raskan-darya* as is *Tong*, and in a valley of the same size as the *Tong* valley which also joins the *Raskan-darya*. The river of *Kichik-Tong* obviously comes from a pass of the same importance as *Kandahar-davan*, and in the same range as it.

On September 23rd we had 4 km. eastwards to the river, and then on and along the river 2 km. N. N. W. to the next camp. At the river I found an altitude of 1,994 m., and, at the camp, *Kuruk-langar*, which is situated some 25 or 30 m. above the river, 2,013 m.

Riding down to *Raskan-darya* we passed the villages *Kengerabun* and *Kurug-bagh*. The *Tong River* is crossed several times amongst large blocks in its bed. At the mouth, to the left, the crystalline schist stands in 55° S. 50° W. The *Tong* valley is much narrower than the *Raskan* valley, and the roar and rush of the tributary is much louder than that of the compact and mighty mass of the main river. Both to the south and the north the *Raskan* valley presents magnificent views. The river has cut down its furrow deep between wild, steep mountains, the ramifications and slopes of which are seen in picturesque perspectives both upwards and downwards. The water has a greenish colour but is not quite clear. The temperature was 13.2° at noon. The highwater seemed to have stood 3½ m. higher than the actual level. A little below the confluence there is a small tributary from the right or east called *Kaurele*, with a path leading to *yeilaks* where cattle graze.

The passage is made by the help of on ordinary hand-barrow supported by 12 *tulums* or airfilled goat-skins. The raft is called *sal*. A swimming pony lead by a man swimming on a *tulum* tows the raft across the river, the current of which sweeps it down a long way before it gets over to the right bank. At the left bank the river is shallow for a short distance, after which the depth suddenly becomes three or four meters. At the right side the mountains fall steeply down into the river which here is foaming. Lower down at the landing place the current is again quiet. From the landing place the strong current again crosses the bed to the left side, where the watermasses some hundred meters lower down foam in violence against the rocks. It may be a question of one's life to reach the right side before one is dragged into the whirls lower down. A man had been drowned there a short time before our passage. A Chinese official who came to *Tong* one month before us got so frightened upon seeing the river that he returned and took the road of *Kok-moinak*.

When returning, the raft is driven a long way down in the direction of the dangerous place, from where it has to be towed up by a pony along the left bank. The river now diminished in size every day, and was said to be so low in the end of October that it could be forded on camels. The place where we crossed the river was also a *kechik* or ford.

On the right side the caravan is again loaded and we continue along the river. Here the rocks again fall directly into the river, and the road runs as a cornice above the water. It has been improved with stones and poles, but it is so narrow that the loads have to be carried by men. Farther on one crosses a ridge of sand at the foot of which there are two or three huts called *Kumlik*. At the next corner we enter the tributary valley by which the road goes up to *Arpa-talak-davan*. In the very mouth and at its left side is the village *Kuruk-langar*, inhabited by ten Tajik families and having a very picturesque situation in its luxuriant groves and gardens, and surrounded by magnificent, wild rocky mountains. The houses are built of stone or of sundried bricks, and most of them have open balconies made of the Tian-shan spruce, willow or poplar tree. The name, »The Dry Station», is said to indicate that the valley is dry if no rain falls. Now it had only a little rill. In some years of drought the wheat harvest is lost. As a rule there is not much precipitation in summer. The amount of snow in the winter is also insignificant, though all the mountains around are snow-covered.

In the end of December the *Raskan-darya* freezes and the ice remains for 2½ or 3 months. Only at that time is there direct communication over the ice with

Kichik-Tong, and farther to *Boramsal* and the valley of *Chep* or *Chup* which is a right tributary of the *Raskan-darya*. From *Chep* a direct road leads to *Karga-lik* across a difficult pass in the same range as the one of *Arpa-talak*; it can be traversed only on foot or with yaks. The journey to the mouth of the *Chep* valley is three days long; passing *Kichik-Tong*. From *Kuruk-langar* to the confluence of the *Taghdumbash-darya* there is no road and no inhabited valleys. At the end of May the highwater comes, and the river remains high for three months. Hard wind is never experienced, as the place is protected by mountains on all sides. A saint's tomb at *Kuruk-langar* is called *Ulug-masar*.

On September 24th we travelled up the valley of *Arpa-talak* and camped after 13.8 km., at *Sugetlik* where the altitude is 2,974 m. or 961 m. above *Kuruk-langar*; the rise is 1:14.4. The ascent is regular, though sensible. The road is more comfortable than in the *Tong* valley, as there is less gravel and more soft ground. *Tokai* or forest is more rare, the valley winds in all directions; in its middle there is a little brook.

From the left side, or south, enters the valley *Ghar-masar*, where the crystalline rock stands in 74° S. 35° W. A broad part of the valley is called *Kara-sai*, and east of it a *masar* has the curious name of *Panja-baskan* or »the five fingers pressed (to the ground)». Here all Mohammedan travellers touch the ground with their right hand. From the left comes the valley of *Katle*; at its mouth is a village of the same name. *Ushmuk* is a widening, and *Topusgan* is the next. By the right tributary *Kadas*, a road goes to the pass *Dukan-unkur* in a western ramification of the range of *Arpa-talak*. The pass can be used only on foot or with yaks, and its road leads to a tributary of *Raskan-darya*. *Sultan Sarik Ata-masar* is a saint's tomb on a rock to our right, and opposite it is a northern tributary called *Kurunluk*. A little above this place one valley is formed by two valleys; the one from the N. E. called *Shuras*, without a road, the other from the S. W, *Arpa-talak* (or *Arpa-tailak*), coming directly from the pass. The latter is comparatively broad and has a good deal of barley under cultivation. *Kitlekh* is a tributary from the right with a village and fields. We camped at the village *Sugetlik*, where the green schist fell 63° S. 30° W.

At *Sugetlik* is a new junction of two valleys; the one from the N. E. is *Su-getlik*, the one from the S. E. is *Arpa-talak*. On September 25th we travelled up the latter. At *Sugetlik* the altitude was 2,974 m. The pass is 3,834 m. high, the ascent, therefore, 860 m. in a distance of 7.8 km., or as 1:9. The direction is S. E. On the eastern side we had 15.8 km. S. E., E. N. E. and N. N. E. to *Unkurluk*, where the altitude was 2,393 m.; here the fall is 1,441 m. and the rate 1:11. These figures show that the ranges of the *Kashgar System* are rather accentuated.

The valley up to the pass is narrow but comfortable. Leaving it we ascend softly rounded slopes with very good grass. The slopes falling to the north were

II. IX.

snow-covered from the snow-fall the day before. Over such ground we finally reached the easy pass, on the soft saddle of which only one little knoll of solid rock cropped out; crystalline schist in 76° S. 38° W. The view is interesting in both directions. To the west we see the mighty snow-covered range we crossed in *Kandahar-davan;* to the east several ranges are visible, lower and more diffuse the farther away they are situated, and finally disappearing in greyish-yellow haze.

The slopes to the east are like those to the west, though quite dry and without snow. There was a very rich vegetation of *Juniperus (archa)*, both on the slopes and in the valley. A part of the slope is called *Dobe-davan*, and lower down we pass a nearly level place with good grass, called *At-yeilak*. *Yangi-yeilak* is situated to our left high on the top of a mountain group, visited only by wild goats. *Gudere-yeri* is a village of a few huts and fields.

At *Igis-arik-karaul* there is a little square walled fort, a village and some trees. Here the large tributary *Agach-yeilak* enters from the right, leading only to grazing grounds. Our road enters a narrow passage of the valley; the ground is partly gravel, partly grass; a little brook meanders between the mountains.

Kisil-kor is a valley from the right with a road to the pass of *Ögrum-davan*, on the other side of which it continues to the large villages of *Chupan* and *Kargalik*. At *Kisil-kor* the black schist stood in 56° S. 40° E. *Böche* is a right tributary without a road. At the village of *Vastala* the valley becomes much broader. *Kichik-yar*, from the right, has a road to the pass *Kichik-art* on the eastern side of which is a grazing-ground called *Böghe*. From the latter a road goes to *Damsir*. At *Un-kurluk* we camped.

At *Unkurluk* only barley is grown; the corn was now threshed with oxen. Wheat is rarely grown in this region; maize only farther down. As a rule the fields are sown only every second year. The spring was said to be the rainy season, though much precipitation falls in winter. The snow is generally one foot deep. The brook freezes hard. The inhabitants move in winter to their villages lower down. The prevailing wind during the cold season comes from the east. The brook is swollen during one month in summer. The inhabitants are Turki, with the exception of two Tajik families at *Igis-arik-karaul*. *Arpa-talak-davan* therefore is an ethnological boundary. The Turki language is pronounced in a softer way than in *Kash-gar*. *Unkurluk, e. g.*, is pronounced as *Ungniluk*. From the pass and downwards the valley is called *Asboi*. Lower down it is called *Üch-bäldir*, and joins the *Yar-kand-darya*.

The earthquake was strongly felt, but no houses were damaged. Water in pans on the fire splashed over from the effect of the shock.

We were approaching lower regions and on September 26th descended 686 m. during a march of 21.2 km. to *Damsir*, where the height was only 1,707 m.; the rate of fall was thus 1:31. The valley is very winding. The road runs through the villages *Koshkur-agil, Sciat, Kush-utek, Kayinlik, Tukus, Ma-raskan, Yilanlik* and *Baku*, most of them situated at the mouths of tributaries with the same names. The last part of the valley is comparatively narrow, but at *Üch-bäldir* it is very broad and has many villages, habitations, fields, gardens and groves. The most important cereal seems to be maize, just now ready for the harvest. The brook is here spread in several canals. From here the whole valley is called *Üch-bäldir*. From the left we notice the tributary *Kelik*, with a few villages at the confluence. Then there is again a narrow passage, and below it a widening with several large villages. This region is called *Kisil-kiya* from the red sandstone at the sides. We camped at the village *Bälde* in the district of *Damsir*. Here the valley is broad, the mountains lower than before, and there is everywhere land under cultivation.

Maize, barley and turnips are the most important products. Usually a field is first sown with barley, and after it is ripe turnips are planted on the same ground. The fields are sown annually. The ordinary trees are poplar, willow and apricot. *Bälde* is inhabited by ten families, all Turki. *Bälde* and *Damsir* may be reached only by three roads; the one over which we had arrived, the one from below which we were to travel downwards the next day, and the road by the left or western tributary *Pouian*, the mouth of which is situated a little lower down. The last mentioned road passes by the village of *Kendelik*, crosses the two passes *Tokus-art* and *Kisil-art* and reaches the *Yarkand-darya* just below the confluence of the *Raskan-darya* with the *Taghdumbash* or *Shinde River*, where the village of *Koserab* is situated; here the river is crossed on rafts and the road continues to *Charlung* and the regions we had visited the previous year.

There is not much snow in winter; at the most it is 2 dm. deep. The summer is said to be the rainy season. North wind brings rain; south wind clear weather. The harvest depends exclusively on the rain; lower down the fields are irrigated from the river. In some dry years the maize harvest is lost. Of wild animals the inhabitants mentioned wolf, fox and hare.

The day's march had crossed the same crystalline rocks as before, at *Unkur-luk* the schist stood in 68° S. 40° E.; at *Kush-utek* the rock was porphyry in 53° S. 70° W.; the sandstone lay in 47° N. 80° E. and was soft and rotten; a little below the sandstone followed a white kind of rock, possibly limestone in 40° N. 80° E.

On September 27th we had our last day in the mountains, travelling 30.5 km. down to *Kachung*; descending 161 m. or from 1,707 to 1,546 m.; a rate of 1:190. Red sandstone and conglomerate prevail, with sides eroded by rains. The situation is 44° N. 50° E. The hills decrease in altitude and the valley becomes broader. *Tashna* is a village to our left. The whole valley is full of gravel, and the marks of the highwater are visible at the sides. At *Kusherab*, 1,567 m., we leave the mountains and get a glimpse of the desert plains to the N. E. This large village is situated at some distance from the great river, and the intervening space is inundated in flood time. The river is even now magnificent: its water is not so clear as at *Tong* and not so muddy as below *Yarkand*. The temperature of the water at noon was 15.6°. On both sides of the bed are low, flat hills of loose material.

At *Kusherab* we crossed the river on a ferryboat 14,3 m. in length. The river had here a breadth of 78 m. and a velocity of a little more than 1 m. per second. The greatest depth was 3.14 m., and the average depth about 1.60 m. The volume of water would be about 125 cub. m. per second. From *Kusherab* to *Yarkand*, ferryboats function at six other places. During the highwater period, or for three months, the ferryboat of *Kusherab* cannot be used on account of the great force of the river. Only *suchis* with *tulums* are able always to cross it. Lower down where the current is slow, the ferryboats operate the whole summer.

At the left or northern side the road ascends a terrace some 10 m. high consisting of fine yellow alluvium eroded by the present river: at some places it is vertically carved out by the water and great blocks of earth occasionally fall down into the river.

Chamsal is a large village with extensive cultivation, gardens and fields, and roads zigzagging between grey clay walls. *Kachung* is another large village on the left bank, with broad irrigation canals from the river which here is divided into several branches. On the right bank as well there are large villages, one of them called *Chimdu*.

Kachung had 200 families. The whole population is Turki. On the road to *Yarkand* only two villages were said to be inhabited by Tajiks, viz., *Tokusmak* and *Kaltala*. Wheat, rice, maize, melons, apricots, apples, pears, and peaches are grown. Often two harvests, wheat and maize, are brought in from one field. Poplar, willow and mulberry are the most common trees. The inhabitants have great flocks of cattle and sheep. There is a direct road to *Kargalik*, crossing the river with *Kachung's* own ferryboat. To *Yarkand* is one day on horseback. In *Kachung* there is no bazaar. In the winter the river is frozen and can be crossed everywhere. It is generally called *Darya-i-Sarafshan*, and gold is obtained from the sand in the bed. The name *Yarkand-darya* is in use only in and below *Yarkand*.

September 28th we travelled 25.8 km. N. N. E. and north to *Yaka-arik* where the altitude is 1,364 m., a fall of 182 m. or as 1:142. We had still two hours' ride before we left the last cultivation of *Kachung* behind. To our left we have the whole way an old rounded erosion terrace corresponding to a similar one along the right bank and at a considerable distance.

The country is then desolate until we reach the village of *Tumshuk-serai-karaul* with a burial place and a little mosque. A direct road runs from this village to *Charlung* which often is used by Chinese officials. Then follows again a wide desolate space or *sai* to *Yaka-arik*, a large village irrigated by an *arik* from the river. From this place there is no direct road to the mountains. *Yaka-arik* is the common name of a group of villages, amongst others *Langar* and *Tokmakla*. The large irrigation canal continues to *Kok-rabat*.

To the last-mentioned village we had, the next day, a ride of 19.8 km. to the north and N. W. The ground falls 71 m. or to 1.293 m.; a rate of 1 : 279. The entire distance takes us through villages, of which *Choglik* and *Sai-langar* are the largest. Before reaching *Kok-rabat* we enter the great caravan-road from *Yarkand* to *Kashgar*. Here we were on well-known tracks, and I will only mention the names of the places we passed during the last four days from *Kok-rabat* to *Kashgar*, September 30th: the ruins of *Abdullah-Khan-rabat*, *Ak-rabat*, with a well 36.3 m. deep and a constant temperature of 15.5°; *Ötekchi*, an abandoned rest house; *Kisil*, a village — its only road to *Sarikol* runs by *Igis-yar*, the same I have described above. At *Kisil* and several other places on this road I was told that the prevailing wind in summer came from the N. W. and often was very strong, whereas nearly no wind blew in winter. A ruined place below *Kisil* is called *Teter-mesjid*.

October 1st we passed through the villages *Kuduk*, *Kosh-gombaz*, *Toplok* and *Kelpin;* and camped in the village of *Karavash*, belonging to *Yangi-hisar*. Just south of the village is a large river-bed with a dam forcing the water to flow by a canal at the left bank. The river then runs to the villages *Khoja-arik*, *Mangshin*, *Sagan* and *Momoluk*, from which a road goes to *Ordan-Padshah* and *Hasret-Begim*. The water of the river-bed was said to come from the valley *Kampan*, inhabited by Kipchak Kirgizes, and to pass by *Lai-bulak* and *Kaghui*. The water of *Yangi-hisar* itself comes from *Khan-terek*.

October 2nd we continued by *Seidlar* and *Sogoluk* to *Yapchan*, and the last day by *Tasgun* and *Yangi-shahr* to *Kashgar*. Our road from *Kok-rabat* to *Kashgar* was 142 km. in length. In Yakub Bek's time the distance between *Yarkand* and *Kashgar* was reckoned as 27 *tash*, now it is 54 Chinese *potai*.

The whole journey from *Kashgar* through *Eastern Pamir* and back to *Kashgar* was 1,241.5 km. in length.

OSTTÜRKISCHE NAMENLISTE

MIT ERKLÄRUNGSVERSUCH

VON

A. v. LECOQ

EINLEITUNG.

I. HERKUNFT DER GEOGRAPHISCHEN NAMEN OSTTURKISTANS.

Noch heute ist die Rechtschreibung, Aussprache und Bedeutung vieler Ortsnamen *Ost-turkistans* schwankend, unsicher und selbst rätselhaft. Denn während Namen wie *Aqsu* und *Qara-tasch* jedem Geographen bekannte allgemein-türkische Wörter wiederbringen, können andere der verschiedensten Herkunft sein. Entweder sind es Wörter aus der Sprache der *Qara-Kirgisen*[1] oder aus dem *Arabischen, Persischen, Mongolischen, Mandschuischen, Ti-betischen* und *Chinesischen*; ferner ist an die iranischen Dialekte der *Pamir-Tadschik* und schließlich auch an die verschollenen *alten Landessprachen* zu denken[2], besonders die häufig recht fremdartigen Namen von Ortschaften am Südwest- und Südrand unseres Gebiets ge-hören vielleicht in diese letzte Kategorie.

In den Bergen nach *Kaschmir* hin wird man ferner mit *Kaschmiri* und *Schina*[3]-Wörtern zu rechnen haben, selbst das isoliert dastehende *Burischeski* von *Hunza-Nagyr* und von *Yasin* kann vielleicht zur Erklärung mancher Namen dieser Gegenden herangezogen werden; über die frühere Verbreitung dieser Sprache sind wir nicht unterrichtet.

Aus dieser Zusammenstellung ergiebt sich, wie schwierig es ist, den Versuch der Er-klärung solcher Ortsnamen zu unternehmen; es gehören dazu ganz gewaltige Sprachkennt-nisse auf den verschiedensten Gebieten, wie sie augenblicklich kaum in einer Person vereinigt sein dürften. Darum soll hier nur das den türkischen Sprachen zuzuweisende Material behandelt werden.

---

[1] Hierzu muß bemerkt werden, daß die Sitze der Qara-Kirgisen sich keineswegs auf die Gebirge um den Südwest-, West- und Nordrand Ostturkistans beschränken, sondern sich im Norden beinahe bis Tschugutschaq (ostt. *čöräk*, چورك = Pfanne, flaches Tal), in Tarbagatai, im Osten fast bis in die Gegend von Qómul (چومل sic!) erstrecken: wir trafen im Jahre 1904 qarakirgisische Nomaden, deren Gefährten ein unglückliches Gefecht mit Choschot-Mongolen bestanden hatten, bei der Station Yamatu (Strecke Tschugutschaq-Manas); und im Jahre 1908 fiel ein Sohn unseres Hauswirts SABIT (ṭābit) aus Qara-chódscha in einem Gefecht chinesischer Truppen gegen auf-ständische Qarakirgisen in der Gegend von Bári-köl (Barkul der Karten). Auf dieser ganzen, ausgedehnten Strecke hat man also mit Namen zu rechnen, die qarakirgisisch sein können und bei unserer geringen Kenntnis der be-treffenden Dialekte schwer zu erklären sind. Die Qarakirgisen heißen in Ostturkistan oft *qazaq*, genau wie die Qazaqkirgisen.

[2] Es handelt sich vermutlich um das *Sakische* und andere *iranische* Dialekte, sowie um *indische* Dialekte im Süden; im Westen und Norden hätten wir mit dem *Soghdischen*, daneben von *Kutscha* bis *Turfan* mit dem *Tocharischen* zu rechnen. Vgl. meinen Aufsatz, Die vierte deutsche Turfan-Expedition; Túrán, Budapest 1918, S. 7 ff.

[3] Die Sprache der Dard. Vgl. FRED. DREW, The Jummoo and Kashmir territories, London 1875, A. H. FRANKE, A history of the Western Tibet.

12. IX.

2. SVEN HEDINS VERDIENST UM DIE ERFORSCHUNG DER OSTTÜRKISCHEN NAMEN.

Der erste und einzige Gelehrte, der den verdienstlichen Versuch der Erklärung der Ortsnamen Ostturkistans gewagt hat, ist SVEN HEDIN, der im Jahre 1900 eine etwa 20 Seiten starke enggedruckte Liste von Ortsnamen unseres Gebiets veröffentlicht hat[1]. Diese umfangreiche Pionierarbeit hat natürlich gewisse Schwächen, da der schwedische Autor die Vokale zunächst als Schwede hörte und nach den Regeln der *schwedischen* Sprache niederschrieb. Die Aussprache des schwedischen *o* und *u* z. B. weicht von der deutschen Aussprache dieser Vokale ab; der Name der Stadt *Kurla* würde in dieser für Deutsche richtigen Schreibung von einem Schweden, so viel ich weiß, eher *Kürla*, die Notierung *Korla* dagegen *Kurla* gesprochen werden; demgemäß schrieb Sven Hedin *Korla*.

Der Umstand wieder, daß bald für ein Werk in deutscher, bald für eines in englischer Sprache geschrieben wurde, veranlaßte eine gewisse Unsicherheit im Gebrauch mancher Konsonanten, z. B. *s* und *j*. Da Sven Hedin auch kein geschulter Phonetiker ist, müssen die von seinen Begleitern oft sicher im breitesten Landdialekt hervorgesprudelten Namen ihm große Schwierigkeiten gemacht haben. Daß es nicht leicht ist, solche aus Bauernmund kommenden Wörter sogleich richtig zu erfassen, beweist z. B. der einigermaßen spaßhafte Irrtum M. A. STEINS, eines namhaften, in der Sanskritphonetik geschulten Philologen, der *dändän uilïq* (Ort der Zähne- oder Elfenbein-Ochsen) gehört und notiert hat, wo sein Gewährsmann, der Steinschen Übersetzung gemäß, nur *dändän öilük* (Ort der Elfenbein-Häuser) gehört haben kann. Wer weiß, ob mir nicht auch ähnliches zugestoßen ist!

Im ganzen genommen, scheinen mir aber SVEN HEDINS Aufzeichnungen, wenn man sich in seine Art der Umschrift eingelesen hat, die brauchbarsten zu sein, die von Geographen Ostturkistans geliefert worden sind, und man ist ihm für die auf diesen Stoff verwendete Mühe den größten Dank schuldig.

3. INNERE EIGENTÜMLICHKEITEN DER OSTTÜRKISCHEN NAMEN.

Was die Namen selbst angeht, so zeugt eine Kategorie unter ihnen in beredter Weise von der trübseligen Eintönigkeit des Lebens dieser Hirten, Bauern und Karawanenführer. Ortsnamen wie *čiräy saldï* (er hat die Lampe hingestellt), *gürünč qaldï* (der Reis ist [liegen] geblieben) oder *ïštan astï* (er hat die Hosen aufgehängt) bezeichnen Örtlichkeiten, an denen irgendein unter den Hirten, Karawanenleuten usw. bekannter Mann dieses oder jenes getan, oder wo sich dieses oder jenes zugetragen hat. Mir ist nur ein einziger Name dieser Art bekannt geworden, der sich auf ein geschichtlich einigermaßen bedeutendes Ereignis bezieht. Der sich über mehrere Kilometer ausdehnende Lagerplatz am Aufgang zum *Qara-qoram-Passe* (auf der Turkistan- oder Nordseite) trägt den Namen *daulät bäg öldï* = der König ist gestorben. Hier soll nämlich im Jahre 1533 der Herrscher von Mogulistan Sultan Sa'ïd Chän auf der Rückkehr von einem Raubzug gegen *Lädāk* an der verderblichen Höhenluft (p. *dämgïrï*, l. *tütäk*, *ïz*, vulg. *yäz*) gestorben sein. An beinahe derselben Stelle ist 1906 mein Reisegenosse, der britische Hauptmann J. D. SHERER, durch dieselbe Krankheit in Todesgefahr geraten. Das *Tarikh-i-Rashidi*[2] verlegt zwar den Ort des Todes des Sultan Sa'ïd an den

[1] Petermanns Mitteilungen, Ergänzungsband XXVIII 1900, S. 350—370.

[2] Ausg. N. ELIAS, London 1895, S. 446.

nördlicher gelegenen *Sügät-Pass*, aber dieser Pass ist ziemlich niedrig, es gibt dort keine „böse" Höhenluft, und außerdem widerspricht die Angabe der Überlieferung. Nebenbei bemerkt, kann es nicht allein die Höhe sein, die den Aufenthalt an manchen Stellen so gefährlich macht; so gilt z. B. der *Sasser-Pass* und seine nächste Umgebung in dieser Hinsicht als gefährlicher als der höhere *Qara-qoram.*

Die Dörfer im Kulturland werden häufig nach den Tagen benannt, an denen dort der wöchentliche Markt abgehalten wird; also Montagsmarkt, Dienstagsmarkt usw. Das Vorhandensein eines Rasthauses, eines Heiligengrabes, Brunnens usw. verleiht dem dabei gelegenen Ort oft seinen Namen; man muß aber stets daran denken, daß jedes erdenkliche Ereignis, wichtig oder lächerlich trivial, jeder Einfall, mag er uns noch so unverständlich sein, die Veranlassung zur Benennung eines Ortes gegeben haben kann.

4. ÄUSSERE EIGENTÜMLICHKEITEN.

Die Rechtschreibung der osttürkischen Wörter ist schwankend. Es gibt einige Leute, die nach arabischer Weise die Schreibung der Vokale im Wort vermeiden, andere, die alle Vokale unter allen Umständen einsetzen; die meisten schreiben aber ohne Plan bald so, bald so, wie die Wörter eben aus ihren Federn fliessen. Anderseits ist das *Kirgisische* keine Buchsprache und wird daher nicht geschrieben; allerdings sind mir einige kirgisische Wörter von Osttürken niedergeschrieben worden.

Seltsamkeiten wie der türkische Name der Stadt *Qômul,* (aus mong. *Chamil*) vermag ich nicht zu erklären: in den Briefen und Schriftstücken des Wang von Qōmul wird stets *q(o)mül* قومول geschrieben, statt wie zu erwarten wäre *qômul* قومل oder evtl. *qômül* قومول.

Finales *a* wird in „schweren" Stämmen gern durch alif ﺍ, in leichten durch hä ﻩ wiedergegeben; manche Schreiber machen es aber umgekehrt oder nach Belieben, ja, es kommt vor, daß auslautendes kurzes *ä* (ﻩ) durch *yä* ﻯ ersetzt wird; so schreibt man z. B. *süpürgä,* سوپورگى, Besen, Bürste, zuweilen سوپورکى bei Beibehaltung der Aussprache *süpürgä.*

Langes auslautendes *ä* wird besonders von den auf ihre persisch-arabische Schulung stolzen Schreibern von *Chotän, Yärkänd* und *Käschgar* in persischer Weise durch ein angehängtes *r* differenziert, um zu verhüten, daß jemand es als *ä* spreche. So zeigen die seit der Revolution geprägten Kaschgarer Kupfermünzen die chinesische Bezeichnung der kleinen Kupfermünze *dä-tsien,* türkisch früher *dä-čän* (چن ﺍﺩ), nunmehr als *där-čän* (چن ﺩﺍﺭ), eine Unart, die auch auf den Namen der Stadt *Kučä* übertragen worden ist. Besonders englische Reisende, denen ja ein *r* zur Dehnung des *a* in der eigenen Sprache nicht fern liegt, haben zur Verbreitung dieser falschen Schreibweise in europäischen Werken viel beigetragen.

Der Buchstabe *fä* ﻑ wird fast immer statt des *pä* ﭖ verwendet.

Eine Eigentümlichkeit besonders der westlichen Dialekte hat einen Zwiespalt in die Schreibweise des Namens des bekannten Passes *Qara-qorum-Qara-qoram* eingeführt. In vielen zweisilbigen Wörtern, deren erste Silbe ein *o (ö)* und deren zweite Silbe ein *u (ü)* enthält, verändern die westlichen Dialekte, augenscheinlich von Maralbaschi an nach Westen, das *u (ü)* der zweiten Silbe in *a (ä)*. So z. B. *qotuz* (Yakochse) *qotaz, sögüt* (Weidenbaum) *sögät* und *sügät, qorum* (Steinschotter) *qoram, özüm* (ich selbst) *özäm* usw.; einige so veränderte Wörter, wie z. B. *qotaz,* haben sich allmählich im ganzen Lande eingebürgert, andere aber, wie *öyäl* für *öyul* (Sohn), auf die westlichen Landschaften beschränkt.

Da nur die *u*-Formen in unsern alten Texten auftreten, dürften die *a*-Formen eine spätere Entwicklung sein.

5. BESONDERE BEMERKUNGEN ZUR NAMENLISTE.

Es hätte eine Menge Raum beansprucht, die vorkommenden Namen hier allesamt in alphabetischer Ordnung aufzuführen; ALBERT HERRMANN hat es daher vorgezogen, die zusammengesetzten Namen zu zerlegen und ihre einzelnen Wörter separat je einmal aufzuführen. Dies erklärt, daß einige Wörter, wie *ạ̈γ̇z* (Mund, Mündung), *ạ̈ṅgiz* (Stoppelfeld), mit dem Possessiv-Suffix *i* versehen auftreten.[1]

Auch dieser Versuch, osttürkische Namen zu erklären, wird noch zahlreiche Mängel aufweisen. Er ist gemacht worden in der Hoffnung, daß spätere Reisende in dem interessanten Lande sich veranlaßt sehen werden, nachzuprüfen und zu ergänzen und ihrerseits Namen zu sammeln, die sie sich von ihren Gewährsmännern in einheimischer Schrift aufzeichnen und erklären lassen sollten. Manche solcher Erklärungen werden ja nur Volksetymologien sein, andere werden aber sicherlich geeignet sein, unsere Kenntnisse in dankenswerter Weise zu bereichern.

BEMERKUNGEN ZUR SCHREIBUNG UND AUSSPRACHE.

Vereinfachte Aussprache	Umschrift und Aussprache	Arabische Schrift	Aussprache
	‛	ع	Der arabische Kehllaut ‛*ain*, von den Osttürken nicht gesprochen.
Ch, ch	č	چ	deutsches *tsch* in *Kutsche*, engl. *ch* in *church*.
I, j	ǰ	ج	*d* mit nachfolgendem *j*, wie in *Budget* oder engl. *pigeon*.
Gh, gh	γ	غ	in der Kehle geschnarrtes *gh* oder *r*, genau wie der Berliner das *g* in *sagen* spricht.
H, h	ḥ	ح	scharf geröcheltes *h*; meist in arab. Wörtern, von den Osttürken wie gewöhnliches *h* gesprochen.
K, k	k	ك	unserem k entsprechend.
	q	ق	tief in der Kehle hervorgebrachter *K-Laut*.
Kh, kh	χ	خ	deutsches *ch* in *Rache*, schottisches ch in *loch*.
ng	ṅg	ڭ	gutturales *n*, *ṅ*; das *g* ist als Konzession an die Schreibweise der Osttürken hinzugefügt.
S, s	s	س	scharfes (stimmloses) *s*, wie in *reissen*, engl. *son*.
	ṣ	ص	emphatisches *s*, nur in arab. Wörtern (wie *s* gesprochen).
Sh, sh	š	ش	deutsches *sch* in *schön*, engl. *sh* in *shoe*.
T, t	ṭ	ط	emphatisches *t*, nur in arab. Wörtern (wie *t* gesprochen).
Y, y	y	ى	deutsches *j* in *Jäger*, engl. *y* in *yellow*.
Z, z	z	ز	weiches (stimmhaftes) *s* in *reisen*, engl. *z* in *zone*.
	ẓ	ض	

Abkürzungen: a. = arabisch, ch. = chinesisch, kirg. = kirgisisch, mandsch. = mandschuisch, m. = mongolisch, p. = persisch, p. t. = turkisiertes persisch, vulg. = vulgär.

---

[1] Wie das grammatische Verhältnis der einzelnen Wörter in ihren Zusammensetzungen ist, zeigt z. B. der Name *Marat-baš-i* = Kopf des Hirsches.

OSTTÜRKISCHE NAMENLISTE.

Vereinfachte Umschrift	Umschrift und Aussprache	Arabische Schrift	Erklärungsversuch
Abad (Awad)	äbäd (p. t.)	آباد	Wohnort
Abdal	abdāl (p.)	آبدال	Derwisch; Abdal = ein besonderer Volksstamm in Ost-T.
Abtab	âb-tâb (p.)	آبتاب	Glanz
Ach	ač	آچ	hungrig, Hunger
Achan s. Azghan			
Achik	ačiq	آچیق	bitter
Achur	äχur, für äχor (p.)	آخور	Stall
Adam ölturgan	ädäm öltür-gän (a. t.)	آدم اولتورکان	(er, sie, es) hat Menschen getötet
Aftab s. Ab-tab			
Aghil	âγîl (vulg. ëγîl)	آغیل	Hürde
Aghin	aγïn	آغین	Strom
Aghzi	aγzi	آغزی	Mündung (eig. *seine* M.)
Ägin	ägin	اکین	Ackerfeld
Ahsak s. Aksak			
Ai	âi	آی	Mond
Aidar	aidar (kirg.)		Männerzopf
Aidin	äidïn	آیدین	Licht, Glanz
Aighin	aiqïn	آیقین	weit, geräumig
Aighir	aïγïr	آیغیر	Hengst
Airilghan	airïl-yan	آیریلغان	Teilung, Trennung (wörtlich; getrennt)
Airish	airïš	آیریش	Trennung
Ak	aq	آق	weiß
Akin	aqïn	آتین	ein Wasserlauf
Aksak	aqsaq	آتساق	hinkend
Ala	älä	آلا	bunt
Alakan	alaqan	آلاقان	Hand
Aling	al-ïng	آلینك	nimm!
Alish	alïš	آلیش	Auslauf eines Kanals (cf. ëlïš)

115

Vereinfachte Umschrift	Umschrift und Aussprache	Arabische Schrift	Erklärungsversuch
Ållik	ällịk	الّيك	Fünfzig
Al-monchuk	äl mònčuq	آل مونچوق	wörtl. rotes Kleinod, Perle
Altin	altín	آلتين	unten
Altmish	altmĩš	آلتمیش	sechzig
Altun	altun	آلتون	Gold
Altunchi	altun-či	آلتونچی	Goldarbeiter
Ambal	ambal (für amban, mandsch.)	آمبان	chin. Verwaltungsbeamter
Ambar	ambār (p.)	انبار	Magazin, Scheuer
Andere	ān-dārä (p. t.)	ان دره	breites Tal (?)
Ang	äng	انك	Wild
Angetlik s. Hanghirtlik ?			
Ara	ára	آرا	mittlere
Aral	arál	آرال	Insel
Aralchi	aral-či	آرالچی	Inselbewohner
Archa	arča	آرچا ,آرچه	Wacholder
Arghan	arġan, arγan	آرغان	ein dicker Strick
Arik	aríq	آریق	Kanal
Arka (Arga)	arqa	آرقا	Rücken; was hinter einer Sache liegt
Arpa	arpa	آرپا	Gerste
Arslan	arslan	آرسلان	Löwe
Art	art	آرت	Pass
Artish	artĩš (artuš)	آرتیش	Juniperus excelsa
Ashkan	aš-qan (für ač-qan)	آچقان	er (man) hat überschritten dawan ačmaq, einen Paß überschreiten (wörtl. öffnen)
Asma	ásma	آسما	aufhängen (?)
Astin	astīn	آستین	unter
At	ạt	آت	Pferd
At alghan	ặt al-γan	آت آلغان	man (er) hat das Pferd genommen

116

Vereinfachte Umschrift	Umschrift und Aussprache	Arabische Schrift	Erklärungsversuch
Ata	ata	آتا	Vater
Atti	àt-tì	آتدى	er hat geschossen
Ayagh	ayāγ	ایاغ	Fuss; in Zusammensetzungen = unterer
Ayalik	āya-lïq	آيالىق	Handfläche
Ayiklik	āyïq-lïq	آبىقلىق	Bärenort
Azghan	azγan	آزغان	Rose
Bagh	bāγ (p.)	باغ	Garten
Baghchi	bāγ-čī (p. t.)	باغچى	Gärtner
Baghir (Bagir)	baγïr (mit Suff. baγri)	باغير	Leber; übertragen Herz
Baghlaghan	baγla-γan	داغلا غان	(er) hat gebunden
Baghrach (Bagrash)	baγrač	باغراج ؛ باتراج	Topf
Bai	bai	باى	reich
Bain s. Payin			
Bakhmal s. Makhmal			
Bala Koidi	bala qoi-dï	بلا قويدى	er (sie) hat das Kind gesetzt, (gelegt, gestellt)
Bäldir	bäldir (kirg.)		Name einer Sumpfpflanze
Balik	balïq	بالىق	Fisch; Stadt
Balta	balta	بالتا	Axt
Barkhun	barχun für barγan	بارخان	Düne
Bashi, Bash	bāšī	باشى	Kopf, Haupt (mit Suffix!)
On bashi	ön bāšī	اون باشى	Dorfschulze (Haupt über zehn Leute)
Basik	basïq	باسىق	niederer
Baskak	basqaq	باسقاى	Schafseuche
Baskan	bas-qan	باسقان	bedrückt, überschwemmt
Baste	bas-tï	باستى	hat gesiegt; hat gedrückt
Bazar	bazār (für bāzar [p.])	بازار	Marktort
Charshamba bazar	čāršämbä bazār (p.)	چيارشنبد بازار	Marktort für den vierten Wochentag
Doshamba bazar	dōšämbä bazār (p.)	دوشنبه بازار	Marktort für den zweiten Tag der muhamm. Woche

Vereinfachte Umschrift	Umschrift und Aussprache	Arabische Schrift	Erklärungsversuch
Yakshamba bazar	yäkšämbä bazar (p.)	يكشنبه بازار	Marktort für den ersten Wochentag
Bedächi (Bedachi)	bédä-či	بيمده چى	Händler mit Luzerneheu
Bedelik	béde-lik	بيده ليك	Luzerneklee
Begim	bägim	بيكيم ، بكيم	„mein Fürst". Im östl. Turkistan Anrede und Titel der Fürsten. Im westl. Turkistan und Indien Titel der Fürstinnen.
Bel	bél	بيل	Gurtgegend (Kreuz) des menschlichen Körpers, Einschnürung, Paß
Belchi	bél-či	بيملچى	Paßführer
Beles	bäläs (kirg.)		Hügel
Besh	bäš	دش	fünf
Beshuk s. Böshük.			
Bir	bir	بير	Eins, einer
Bish s. Besh			
Boghaz	bôyáz	بوغاز	Futter; Kehle, Engpaß
Boghu s. Bughu			
Boinak	boinaq (= moinaq)	بوينات	Kamelhals; Halsband
Bora	bôrä (p.)	بورا	Borax (vulg. Matte)
Bora tûshken	bôrä tûš-kän (p. t.)	بورا توشكان	(der Borax) die Matte ist gefallen
Böri (Bore)	bôri	بورى	Wolf
Böshük (Beshuk)	bôšük	بوشوك	Wiege
Bostan (Bustan)	bostän für bostän (p.)	بوستان	Garten
Boyuluk s. Buyaluk			
Boyun, Boyan	boyun (boyan)	بويون	Nacken
Boz	boz	بوز	grau
Bozai	bozai	بوز اى	Kalb
Bugas s. Boghaz			
Bughu	buyú	بوغو	Maralhirsch
Bughuluk	buyu-luq	بوغولىق	Ort der Maralhirsche
Büghür	bügür	بوكور	die Krümmung, der Buckel (Name eines Fleckens)

Vereinfachte Umschrift	Umschrift und Aussprache	Arabische Schrift	Erklärungsversuch
Buka	buqa	بوقا	Stier, Bullochse
Bulak	buláq	بولاق	Quelle
Bulanghan	bulan-ɣan	بولانغان	man hat geraubt
Bulung	buluñg	بولونك	der Winkel, die Ecke
Buran	buran	بوران	Sturm
Burkut (Burgut)	bürküt	بورکوت	Adler (*A. chrysaëtos*)
Burun	burun	بوروون	Nase (resp. Bergsporn)
Buya	büyä	بویه	*Sophora*-Pflanze
Buyaluk	büya-luq	بویه‌الوق	Ort der Buya(*Sophora*)Pflanzen
Buzrugvar	buzruk-var		ein sehr tantalisierender Name. *buzruk* ist eine in O. Turkistan geläufige Entstellung des pers. *buzurg* بزرك *groß* das öfter auftretende *var* entzieht sich meinen Nachforschungen.
Chäch (Chäsh)	čäč, vulg. čäš	چچ	Korn auf dem Dreschplatz
Chadir	čädir	چادر	Zelt
Chaghan	čaɣan (m.)	چاغان	weiß
Chak	čaq	چاق	Maß; Zeitpunkt
Chak saldi	čäk sal-dí (p. t.)	چك سالدی	er hat das Los ausgeworfen (etwas ausgelost)
Chakan	čaqán	چاقان	Streitaxt
Chakir	čaqir	چاقر	Habicht
Chakirga	čakirgä	چکرکه	Heuschrecke
Chakka	čakka, čaqqa	چکه, چقه	Kleine Kupfermünze
Chakma	čaqma	چاقما	Rille (durch Überschwemmung gewaltsam zerrissener Kanal usw.)
Chakmak	čaqmaq	چاقماق	Feuerzeug (Stahl und Stein)
Chakmaktin	čaqmaq-tin	چاقماق تین	vom Feuerstein her
Chal	čal	چال	Wurzel
Chalchik	čalčïq	چالچیق	Kamel- (oder Wurzel-) Loch
Chapan kaldi	čapan qal-dï	چاپان تالدی	„der Rock ist zurückgeblieben"

13. IX.

Vereinfachte Umschrift	Umschrift und Aussprache	Arabische Schrift	Erklärungsversuch
Chapgin	čapqïn; čapqun	چاپقين . چاپقون	Schneesturm
Chapkan	čapqan	چاپقان	Wildwasser
Char	čar (p.)	چهار	vier
Chärchi	čär-či	چرچى	Wanderhändler
Charkhchi	čarχ-či (p. t.)	چرخچى	Garnwinderadmacher
Charkh asti	čarχ as-tï (p. t.)	چرخ آستى	er (sie) hat das Spulrad aufgehängt
Charkhlik	čarχ-lïq (vulg. čaylïq, čaqalïq p. t.)	چرخليق	Ort der Garnspulen
Charuklar	čaruq-lar	چاريقلار , چاروقلار	Sandalen, Bauernstiefel
Chat	čat	چات	Kreuzweg, Vereinigung zweier Flüsse
Chatkal	čatqal	چاتغال , چاتغال	niederster Teil eines Tales, Land zwischen zwei Flußläufen
Chav	čaw	چاو	Ruhm
Chayan	čayan	چايان	Skorpion
Chehel	čähäl, (vulg. čil) (p.)	چهل	vierzig
Chekanak s. Chikanak			
Cheke	čäkä	چكه	Sand
Chelek (Chilek)	čäläk, čiläk	چلاك	Holzgefäß, Eimer
Chep (Chup)	čäp (kirg.)	چپ	Brustwehr, Verhau
Cherik	čerik	چريك	Heer; Soldat
Chibugh (Chibu)	čibuγ	چمبوغ	Zweig; Pfeifenrohr
Chibuklik (Chivighligh, Chivegglik)	čibuq-lïq, vulg. čiwïγ-lïγ	چمبوق ليق	Ort, wo Reisig (junge Bäumchen) steht
Chichäklik	čičäk-lik	چيچاكليك	Blumenort
Chigh	čïγ	چيغ	Riedgras
Chighelik	čïgä-lik	چيكه ليك	Ort des „wilden Hanfs" (Asclepias Spec., liefert Fasern)
Chigherik	čïγ ärïq (vulg. ärïq)	چيغ آريق	Kanal, an dem Čïγgras (Arundinella nepalensis) wächst
Chigitlar	čigit-lär	چيكيت لار	Baumwollsamen (Plur.)
Chikanak	čïqanaq	چيقاناق	Ellenbogen
Chilgha s. Jilgha			

Vereinfachte Umschrift	Umschrift und Aussprache	Arabische Schrift	Erklärungsversuch
Chilan	čilän (p.)	جیلان	*Zizyphus*
Chimen	čämän, čimän (p.)	چمن	Rasenplatz, Wiese
Chindelik	čindälik	چیندد لیك	(von heute) in vier Tagen
Chira	čira	چیرا	im Osm. und Kasan. eine Kiefer, ein Kieferspahn
Chivilik	čibin-lik (vulg. čiwillik)	چیبینلیك	wo es Fliegen gibt; Fliegennetz
Chok	čoq	چوق	viel
Choklik	čoq-liq	چوقلبق	Beamtentitel bei den Kalmücken (wenn in Sariqol: Messerort)
Choka	čökä	چوكد	Eßstäbchen (die Form čoqa kommt nach Radloff ebenfalls vor; mir ist sie nicht begegnet)
Chokan (Chaukan)	čoqan, čauqan, ǧugan	چوكان	jungverheiratete Frau
Choku (Chokka)	čoqu (kirg.)		Scheitel
Chöl	čöl	چول	Wüste
Cholak	čolaq	چولاق	Krüppel
Chong	čoṅg	چوڭك	groß
Chöp (Chupp)	čöp (kirg. u. Ferghana)	چوف , چوپ	Heu, Gras zu Pferdefutter
Chopan	čopan (auch p.)	چوپان	der Hirt
Chorgha	čorǧa	چورغا	der Auslauf (e. g. einer Teekanne)
Chörgülme (Chugulme)	čörgülmä (?)	چورگولمد	Das im Kreise gehen, sich drehen
Chörgültmek (Chugultmæk)	čörgültmäk	چورگولتماك	veranlassen, daß etwas hin und her geht, sich dreht
Chubuk	čubúq (čibuq)	چیبوق	Rute, Stab, Zweig
Chuchuk	čüčük	چوچوك	süß
Chukur	čuqur	چوقور	tief, steinig
Chulak s. Cholak			
Chupan s. Chopan			
Churga s. Chorgha			
Chürge	tüšürgä, vulg. čürgä	توشورکد	ohne Etymologie
Daban, davan	daban (vulg. dawan)	دابان	Paß
Dafdar s. Däptär			

Vereinfachte Umschrift	Umschrift und Aussprache	Arabische Schrift	Erklärungsversuch
Dā-khan	dāhkan, dihkan (p.)	دهكان	Bauer, Grundbesitzer
Dāplär	dāplär, für dāftär (p.)	دفتر	das Heft (Schreibheft)
Dārvase	dārwāzä (p.)	درواره	Thor, große Pforte
Darya	dārya (p.)	دربا	Fluß
Dashı	dāšt (p.)	دشت	Wüste (Steppe)
Davan s. daban			
Daulet (Dovlet)	daulät, vulg. auch dölät, dövlät (a.)	دولت	Macht
Debe s. Döbe			
Divane	dıwānä (p.)	ديوانه	religiöser Bettler
Döbe (Debe)	döbä	دوبه	Hügel
Döng (Dung)	döñg	دونك	Hügel
Dönglik	döñg-lik	دونك ليك	Hügelort
Donkuz s. Tongguz			
Dost	dōs(t) (p. t.)	دوست	Freund
Dovlet s. Daulet			
Dua	duʾā (a.)	دعا	Gebet
Duga s. Tögä			
Duldul	duldul (a.)	دلدل	Name des Maultiers Alis
Dung s. Döng			
Dungsatma s. Satma			
Dutar	dū-tar (p.)	دوتار	Gitarre
Echkü (Echke)	äčkü	اچكو	Ziege
Egiz	‹giz	ايكيز	hoch
Egri	ägri	اكرى	krumm
Elish	alīš (vulg. ‹līš)	آليش	Verkauf, s. auch älīš
Engizi	äñgizi	انكبزى	Stoppelfeld (eig. sein St.)
Er	är	اير	Mann
Eshek	äšäk	ايشاك	Esel
Eshme	{ äšmä\ išmä	اشمه\ ايشمه	Wanderhändler\ Seilerei

Vereinfachte Umschrift	Umschrift und Aussprache	Arabische Schrift	Erklärungsversuch
Eski	äski	اسكی	alt
Ezitgo	ēzïtqà (von azïlmaq)	آزدتقا	Fata morgana
Faiz	faiẓ (a.)	فيض	arab. Name; Überfluß; Gnade (nur in Compositis)
Fakhtalik s. Pakhtalik			
Gäjek s. Käyik?			
Gao (Go)	gao (p.)	كاو	Kuh
Gerem	gërám		unterirdisches Gelaß
Gez	gäz (p.)	كز	Pfeil
Ghalbir (Gallbe)	ɣalbïr (p.)	غلبير	Sieb
Ghar	ɣār (ar.)	غار	Höhle
Ghärip (Ghereb)	ɣärïp (a.)	غريب	Wanderer, arm
Ghaz	ɣāz	غاز	Gans
Ghazlik	ɣāz-lïq	غاز ليق	Gänseort
Ghunach	ɣunač	غوناچ	das Füllen
Gilim (Gilem)	gilïm (p.)	كليم	Teppich
Gög s. Kök			
Gör	gör (p.)	كوز	Grab
Gul	gül (p. t.)	كل	Blume
Gul terighan	gül tërï-ɣan	كل تاريغان	man hat Blumen gepflanzt
Gulcha	gülča (p.)	كلچه	„wie eine Blume", meist fälschlich gulča = yulča geschrieben, was „Bergziege" bedeutet
Guma	gúma (p.)	كوما	Name einer Medizinalpflanze (*Pharnaceum Mollugo*)
Gumbaz, Gumbez	gumbaz (p.)	كنبذ	Kuppel
Gusari (Gusar)	guzari ? (p.)	كذری	Markt am Wege
Gyn s. kün			
Hallal	halāl (a.)	حلال	rituell rein, erlaubt
Hanghirtlik	hańɣïrt-lïq	هانكغير تلیق	Ort der Fuchsenten (*Casarca rutila*)
Härrälik	härä-lik (p. t.)		Sägenort

123

Vereinfachte Umschrift	Umschrift und Aussprache	Arabische Schrift	Erklärungsversuch
Hasa	hasa vulg. für hasar = hïsar (s. d.)		
Hashiklik	hašiq-lïq (für ášïqlïq ?) (o.t.)	عاشیق لمق	Ort der Knöchel (zum Hazard-spiel), aber auch Ort der Ver-liebten
Hazret	hazrät (a.)	حضرت	Majestät, Heiligkeit (Titel)
Haule Haulu	hawlï (griech. αὐλή)	دولی	Hof, Gehöft
Hisar	ḥïsar (a.), vulg. hasa	حصار	Fort
Igerchi	ëgär-či	ایكارچی	Sattelmacher
Igis s. Egiz			
Igri	ägri	اكری	krumm
Ike	ïkä (für ïkï)	ایكی	zwei (?)
Ilek	ïläk	ایلاك	angeblich: Zusammenfluss von zwei kleinen Wasseradern
Ilkichi	yïlqï-či; ïlqï-či	بیلقی چی	Pferdehirt
Inchkä	inčkä	اینچكه	dünn, schmal
Irkeshtam	ir-käš-tam	ایركشتام	Mann vorbeigehen Wand (kirgis. Erklärung)
Ishak s. Eshek			
Ishiklar	išik-lär	ایشیك لار	die Türen
Ishmä s. Eshme			
Ishtan asli	ïštan as-ti	ایشتان استی	er hat seine Hose aufgehängt
Iskender aitu-si	iskändär aitu-sï (? ?)	اسكندر آیتوسی	Rede, Wort Alexanders des Großen (??)
Islik	is-lik	ایسلیك	Qualmort
Issik	ïssïq	ایستق	heiss
Issingän (Isängän)	issïñ-gän	ایسیٹكان	erhitzt, heiss
Jaka s. Yaka			
Jam	ǧam (p.)	جام	das Trinkgefäss
Jangal	ǧäñgal (p.)	جانكال	Gestrüpp
Jaz s. Yaz			
Jilande s. Yilan-de			
Jigde	ǧigdä	جیكدد	Elaeagnusbaum

Vereinfachte Umschrift	Umschrift und Aussprache	Arabische Schrift	Erklärungsversuch
Jigdelik	ğigdä-lik	جمكدد امك	*Elaragnus*-Ort
Jılgha	ğïl;a	جبلغا	Schlucht
Jikik l. Yikik	yïqïq (?)	يبيق	zerstört
Jul s. Yul			
Kabuk asti	qabuq (qawaq, qawuq) as-tï	تادوق آستی	er hat den Kürbis (aber *qabïq* auch - Rinde!) aufgehängt
Kabirgha (Kovurgha)	qabïrγa, vulg. qowurγa	تادبرغا	Rippe
Kachdi	qač-dï, qač-tï	تاجتی	er ist davongelaufen
Kächik	käčïk	كچيك	die Furt
Kächiklik (Kichilik)	käčïk-lik	كچيك امك	Ort der Furten
Kadir	qadïr (?) (a.)	قدر	Macht, Kraft
Kaichi (Kachi)	qai-čï	تايجچی	Schere
Kak	qäq	قاك	getrocknete (Früchte u. dgl.)
Kakle s. Keklik			
Kakskal	qäqšal	تاقشال	trocknes Holz, toter Wald (= kötäk)
Kala	kala, kalla (p.)	كلَد	Rindvieh, Kühe; Kopf
Kala askan	kala (kalla) as-qan (p. t.)		er hat die Kuh, (den Kopf) aufgehängt
Kala s. auch Kara			
Kalamuch s. Much			
Kaleghach	1. qälïγäč vulg. für qarlo-γäč 2. vulg. für qara aγäč	تار‌بوغاچ ترا آغاچ	Schwalbe Ulmenbaum
Kallasti	kalla as-tï (p. t.)	كلَه آستی	er hat die Kuh aufgehängt
Kalmak	qalmaq	تالماق	die Mongolen
Kalta	qalta	تالتا	Tasche; kurz
Kama	qäma	تاما	Fischotter
Kaman	kämän (p.)	كمان	Bogen (Waffe)
Kamar	qamar	تامار	Nase
Kamisch	qamïš (vulg. qömuš, qëmïš)	تاميش	Schilfrohr
Käm pullik	kam pullïq (p. t.)	كم ڤلليق	Jemand, der wenig Geld hat

125

Vereinfachte Umschrift	Umschrift und Aussprache	Arabische Schrift	Erklärungsversuch
Kanat	qanat	قنات	Flügel
Kanjigha Kanjurgha	qangїγa qangurγa	قانجورغه	der Sattelriemen
Kapak askan	qapaq as-qan	قاپاق آستقان	man hat den Deckel aufgehängt
Kapan	qapan	قاپان	Wage
Kapchal	qapčal		unübersteiglicher Ort (?)
Kaper	käpir für käfir (a.)	كافر	Ungläubiger
Käptär asti	käptär as-tї	كفتار آستى	er hat Tauben aufgehängt
Kara	qara	قرا : قره	schwarz, dunkel
Kara aghach s. Kaleghach			
Karaghai (Karghai)	qarayai	قرا غاى	Nadelholzbaum (Kiefer)
Karangghu	qaraṅγu	تارانكغو	Dunkel
Karaul	qaraul	تارأول	Wachthaus
Karchigha	qarčїγa	تارچىغا	Habicht
Karghalik	qarγa-lїq	تارغاليق	Krähenort
Karghasi asti	qarγa-sї(nї) as-tї	تارغا آستى	er hat seine Krähe aufgehängt
Kargha yakti	qarγa yaq-tї	تارغا ياتتى	die Krähe hat sich genähert
Karlogach s. Kaleghach			
Kar yaghdi	qar yaγ-di	تار ياغدى	(hier) hat es geschneit
Kar yakak	qar yaγ-qaq	تار ياغقاق	wo es immer schneit
Kash	qaš	تاش	Nephrit; hohes Uferland
Kashik (Kasig)	qašїq, (kirg. qasїq)	تاشيق	Holzlöffel
Kash-chi	qaš-čї	تاش چى	Nephritarbeiter
Katik	qatїq (qattїq)	تاتيق	hart
Katta	katta (West-Turkistan)	كتّه	groß
Kayindi	qayїndї (kirg.)		Birkenort
Käyik	käyik	كيك	Antilope
Kayinlik	qayїnlїq	تايين ليق	Birkenort
Kayir	kayir		Salzsteppe im Gebirg (Sojonisch)

Vereinfachte Umschrift	Umschrift und Aussprache	Arabische Schrift	Erklärungsversuch
Kaz s. Ghaz			
Kazalik	qazā-lïq	تضالبق	Schicksalsort
Kazan	qazan	قازان	Kessel
Kaya	qaya	قايا	Felsen
Kazuk kakti	qazuq (qozuq) qāq-tï	قازوق ئاقتى	er hat den Holznagel einge-schlagen
Kechik (Kechu?)	käčik	كچيك	Furt
Keklik	käklik	ككلبك	Steinhuhn
Kema s. Kime			
Kenderlik	kändär-lik (?)	كندرلبك	Hanfort; Schürzenort (?)
Keng	käṅg	كينك	weit
Kent	känd (p.)	كند	Ortschaft
Kepek	käpäk	كفاك	Kleie
Kerik	kerik (kirg.)		weit
Ketmen	kätmän	كتمان	Hacke (Werkzeug)
Ketmenlik	kätmän-lik	كتمان لبك	Ort der Hacken
Khadalik	χāda-lïq	خادد لبق	Ort der Ruder
Khalpat	χalpat (χalifät, a. t.)	خليفة	Schulmeister; Geistlicher.
Khan	χān	خان	König. Fürst
Khane	χānä (p.)	خانه	Haus
Top-khane	tōp χānä (p. t.)	توپ خانه	Artillerie
Khanika	χāniqäh (a.)	خانقاد	Derwisch-Kloster
Khaniya	χāniyä (p.)	خانيه	dem Kaiser gehörig
Khitai	χïtāi	خطاي	Chinese
Khoja	χṓğa	خوجه	der Chodscha (in Ostturkistan χṓğa = Fürst)
Khosgun s. Kuzghun			
Khosh (Khush)	χōš (p.)	خوش	gut
Khurjin (Khurjun)	χurǧïn, χurǧun (a. ?)	خرجين	großer Sattel-Quersack
Kichik	kičik	كجيك	klein

14. IX.

Vereinfachte Umschrift	Umschrift und Aussprache	Arabische Schrift	Erklärungsversuch
Kichilik s. Kächilik			
Kigiz	kigiz	كيكيز	Filzteppich
Kilich	qilič	تيليج	Säbel
Kime	kimä	كيمه	Boot
Kir	kir	كير	Schmutz
Kirchin	qirčin	قيرچين	Pest (?)
Kirghak	qiryaq	قيرغاق	Rand
Kirighat	qïrïγ ät	قمرع ات	entweder: 40 Pferde, oder: ver-letzte (gebrochene) Pferde
Kirik, Kirk	qiriq (qirq)	قيريع ,قرق	vierzig
Kishlak	qišlaq (t.)	تيشلاق	Winterlager
Kismak	qismaq	تيسماق	Zange (auch: enger Ort)
Kiya s. Kaya			
Kiyak	qiyaq	قيان	Riedgras
Kizilji Khanim	qizilği χanïm	قيزيلجى خانيم	„meine Fürstin Kizilği"
Köbrük	köbrük (köwrük)	كوبرك	Brücke
Kobuzak	qobuzaq (qabuzaγ)	توبوراق , تابوراغ	Baumrinde
Kocha	kóča (t. p.)	كوچا	Gasse
Kochkach s Kuchkach			
Kochkar	qočqar	توچقار	Widder
Kodai	qodäi	توداى	Schwan
Koghun	qoγun	توغون	Netzmelone
Koghush	qoγuš	توغوش	Seufzer
Koi	qoi	قوى	Schaf
Koichilik	qoičf-liq	توىچى ليق	Schafhirtenort
Koighan	qoi-γan	توىغان	hingestellt
Koilugh	qoï-luγ = qoillq	توىلوغ	Schafort
Köküll (Kököl)	kökül (p. ?)	كوكول	Locke, Zöpfchen
Kök	kök	كوك	blau; grün
Kol, Koli	qol, mit Suffix: qoli	تول ; توىى	Schlucht

Vereinfachte Umschrift	Umschrift und Aussprache	Arabische Schrift	Erklärungsversuch
Köl (*nicht* Kul)	köl	كول	Teich, See
Kolchak	qolčaq	قالچاق	Handschuh; Armschiene
Konak	qonaq	قوناق	der Gast; die Mohrenhirse
Kön	kön	كون	gegerbtes Leder
Kone	köhnä (p.)	كهنه	alte
Konalgha	qonalya (für qonalɣu)	قونالغو	Nachtquartier
Konchi	kön-či	كونچی	Schuster (oder Gerber)
Kongghuz	qoŭgyuz	قونكغوز	Käfer
Könglek (Köinek)	köŋläk, vulg. köinäk etc.	كوڭلاك	Hemd
Köntäi	köntäi (kirg.)		hohl (vom Baum)
Korum	qorum (qoram)	قوروم ، قورام	Geröll
Korumduk	körümdük (?)	كوروممدوك	Brautgeschenk
Kosh	qoš	قوش	doppelt; ein Paar
Koshlash	qošlaš	قوشلاش	Verdoppelung (Doppelgespann?)
Koshun	qošun	قوشون	Heer
Kötäklik (cf. Kötek)	kötäk-lik	كوتاك ليك	Baumstumpfort; toter Wald
Kotan	qötan	قوتان	Viehstall
Kotaz	qötaz	قوتاز	Yakochse
Kötek	kötäk	كوتك	Baumstumpf
Kötürmä	kötürmä	كوتورمه	Traglast?
Köuruk s. Köbrük			
Kovurgha s. Kabirgha			
Koyuk (Kuyuk)	qoyuq, quyuɣ	قويوق	dickflüssig
Köyük	küyük (in Chotan: küyäk)	كويوك	angebrannt
Közä, Kuza	közä für p. kûza	كوزه	Krug
Kozuk-kakti	qozuq (= qazuq) qāq-ti	قازوق قاقتی	„er hat den Pflock eingeschlagen"

Vereinfachte Umschrift	Umschrift und Aussprache	Arabische Schrift	Erklärungsversuch
Kucha	kučä	كوچا	die Stadt Kutschä; vielleicht vom soghd. qöčä Mund (sc. des Passes). (Das von den Engländern in die Literatur eingeführte Kuchar [mit fin. r] geht von den West-Turkistanern aus, die die Länge des a durch ein angehängtes Dehnungs-r hervorheben. An Ort und Stelle schrieb man ursprünglich Kučä; die Form Kučár ist eine Neuerung der West-Turkistaner.)
Kuchkach	qušqač	تورشقاچ	Sperling
Kuduk	quduq	توودوق	(Zieh-)Brunnen
Kusruk	quiruq	تويروق	Schwanz
Kulak	qulaq	تولاق	Ohr
Kulan	qulan	تولان	Wild-pferd (oder -esel)
Kulan urgi	lies: qulan öl-di	تولان اولدی	(hier) starb das Wildfüllen
Kulchak s. Kolchak			
Külük	külük	كولوك	das Lachen; der Held; das Reitpferd
Kum	qum	توم	Sand
Yakaking Kum	yaqa käng qum	ياقا كيڭك توم	die weite Sandfläche am Rande (des Kulturgebiets)
Kumluk	qum-luq	توم لوق	Sandort
Kumush	kümüš	كموش	Silber
Kumushluk	kümüš-lük	كموش لوك	Silberort
Kunchikish	kün čīq-īš	كون چيقيش	Sonnenaufgang, Osten.
Kün (Gyn)	kün	كون	Sonne, Tag
Kün-tegmes (Küntimes)	kün täg-mäs	كون تكماز	die Sonne erreicht nicht (diesen Platz)
Kurbanchik	qurbančīq (a. t.)	توربانچيق	kleines Opfer
Kurchin s. Kirchin			
Kurghan, Kurgan	qurʁan	تورغان	Festung
Kurla	kurla	كورله	ohne Etymologie. Wohl ein alter Name
Kurpe	körpä	كورپه	Tischdecke

Vereinfachte Umschrift	Umschrift und Aussprache	Arabische Schrift	Erklärungsversuch
Kuruma	*lies:* körünmäz	كوزونماس	was nicht gesehen wird = unsichtbar
Kurunluk	qurun-luq (für quran-)	قوزون لوق	Waffen-Ort (?)
Kuruk	quruq	قوزوق	trocken
Kus	küz	كوز	Herbst
Kusc	quzï	قوزى	Lamm
Kush	quš	توش	Vogel: Beizvogel, speziell der Adler (qara quš)
Kush ovasi	quš uwasï (uyasï)	توش اوواسى	Adlernest
Kuslıchi	quš-čï	توش چى	Beizjäger, der Adler zur Jagd abrichtet
Kutas s. Kotaz			
Kuyantilik	quyan (qoyun) tilik	توبان تيليك	Hasenspur (??)
Kuyundi	qoyundï	توبوندى	Hasenort
Kuza (s. Közä)	közä (p.)	كوزد	irdenes, langhalsiges Gefäß
Karghalik Kum Kuza	qaryaliq qum közä	تارغاليق توم كوزد	Közä (aus sandigem Ton gebrannte Gefäße) für den Markt von Karghalik
Merket Kum Kuza	märkit qum közä	مركت توم كوزد	ebensolche für den Markt von Märkit (Route Yarkänd-Maratbaši)
Kuzghun	quzyun	توزغون	Rabe
Kyll	kül	كول	Asche
Lachin	lačin	لاچين	Wanderfalk (*Falco peregrinus*)
Lai	läi (p.)	لاى	Lehm
Lailik	läi-lïq	لاى ليق	Lehmsumpf-Stelle
Langar	läügär (p.)	لنكر	Rasthaus
Latta	latta (p.)	لتـه	Lumpen
Leshkär	läškär (p.)	لشكر	Heer
Mahalla	mahalla (a.)	محلّه	Bezirk (Stadtviertel)
Maidan	maidän (p.)	ميدان	ebener weiter Platz
Maklımal (Bakhmal)	maymal (a. p.)	بغمل	Samt (und was daraus hergestellt wird)
Malik aulaghan	mälik awla-yan	ملك آولاغان	„der König hat gejagt"

Vereinfachte Umschrift	Umschrift und Aussprache	Arabische Schrift	Erklärungsversuch
Mamugh (Mamuk)	mamuγ	ماموغ	Baumwolle
Mandalik (Mandarlik)	mandä-lïq	مائدليق	Manda- (Clematis sp.) Ort
Manglai	mañglai	مائكلاى	Stirn
Maral	maral	مارال	Hirsch (-kuh)
Mäsälik	mäsä-lik	مسه ايك	Stiefelort
Mayaklik	mayaq-lïq	مايائ ليق	Schafmistort
Mazar	mazar (a.)	مزار	heilige Grabstätte
Kambar mazar	qambar mazär (a.)	قنبر مزار	Grabheiligtum des h. Kambar
Okur-mazar	öqur (für äγur) mazäri (p. a. l.)	آخور مزارى	Pferdestall-Heiligengrab. Nach der Legende befand sich hier ein Stall des Pferdes von Hazrät 'Ali, Muhammeds Schwiegersohn; auf einer der nahestehenden, merkwürdigen, steil aus dem ebenen Boden emporragenden Felsklippen findet sich ein Hufabdruck dieses Pferdes.
Sultan Kara-sakal-atam	sultan qära saqäl atäm	سلطان قرا ساقال آدام	Grabheiligtum Vater Schwarzbart-Sultan (wahrscheinlich auf eine buddhistische Legende zurückzuführen!)
Sultan ming bash ata maz	sultan miñg baš ätä mazäri	سلطان مينك باش آدا مزارى	Grabheiligtum Sultan Vater der tausend Köpfe (sicher auf eine buddhistische Legende zurückzuführen)
Tungan-mazar	tuñgan mazar	تونكان مازار	tunganisches Grabheiligtum
Mazar-aldi	mazar al-dï	مزار آلدى	er hat das Heiligengrab genommen
Märdeklik	märdäk-lik (p. t.?)	مردك ايك	Pilzort
Meshed	mäshäd (a.)	مشهد	Heiligengrab
Mesjid	mäsğid (a.), vulg. mätčit	مسجد	Moschee
Gungning mächiti	gung nïïg mäčïti (ch. a. t.)	كونك نيمنك مسجدى	Moschee des Gung (chin. = Herzog)
Mian	miyan (p.)	ميان	inmitten
Ming	miñg	مينك	tausend
Mis	mis (p.)	ميس	Kupfer
Moghal s Mughal			
Moinak s. Boinak			

132

Vereinfachte Umschrift	Umschrift und Aussprache	Arabische Schrift	Erklärungsversuch
Moji	mōǧi	موجی	(ohne Etymologie)
Momoluk	mama-luq (?)	مامالوق	Mutterbrust-Ort (?); Großmutter-Ort (?)
Moyak s. Mayaq			
Muji s. Moji			
Much	muč für murč, richtig murič (p.)	مرج	Pfeffer
Mughal	muγāl	مغل	Muγal (Mongole)
Mukhtar	muχtar (a.)	ختار	ausgezeichnet
Muz	múz	موز	Eis
Muz-aling	muz aling	موز آلینك	vorn verschneit (?)
Muzde	muzdäh (p. t.)	موز ده	Eisgau
Muz astï	muz as-li	موز آستی	er hat Eis aufgehängt
Nagarachi	naqara-či	نقاره چی	Paukenschläger
Naiza	naiza (p.)	نیزه	Lanze
Nishandar	nišāndār (p.)	نشاندار	Fahnenträger; mit Zeichen versehen
Ochak	očaq	اوچاق	Dreifuß, Feuerstelle
Ogri	öγrï	اوغری	Dieb
Oi	oi	اوی	Grube; Niederung, Tal
Oi s. Ui			
Öi (Oi)	öi, mit Suffix öyi	اوی ، اویی	Haus
Abdul Baki öi	'abdu-l-Bāqi(nïng)öyi (a.t.)		Haus des Abdu'l Baqi
Ak öi, kara öi	aq öi, qara öi	آق اوی ، قرا اوی	weißes Haus = weiße Filzjurte der Kirgisen, schwarzes H. = schwarze do. der Kirgisen und Kalmücken
Imam Nasirning öyi	imām nāṣïr nïng öyi	امام ناصرنینك اویی	Haus des Imām Nāsir
Islam ning öi	islām nïng öi (für öyi)	اسلام نینك اوی	Haus des (Hrn.) Islam
Ming öi	mïng öi	مینك اوی	tausend Häuser. Aus dem Persischen (hazar sönf) übernommener Ausdruck für die Reste nicht islamischer, hier speziell buddhistischer Kultstätten

133

Vereinfachte Umschrift	Umschrift und Aussprache	Arabische Schrift	Erklärungsversuch
Seit oi	seit öi	سيد اويى	Haus des Sayyid
Urusning öi	urus nïng öi	اوروس نينك اوِى	das Haus des Russen
Yangi sudake öi	yangï sū-daqï öi	يانكى سوداقى اوِى	das Haus am neuen Wasser (neuen Kanal)
Oiman	oiman	اويمان	Tal, Niederung
Okchi	oq-čï	اوقچى	Pfeilmacher
Onbesh	onbäš	اون بش	fünfzehn
Orda	örda; ördü	اوردا ,اوردو	Palast
Ordam Padshah	ördam pädšah (für ördam-i-padšah?)	اوردام پادشاد	„mein Palast König", bekannter Wallfahrtsort
Ördeklik	ördäk-lik	اوردك ليك	Entenort
Örkech	örkäč	اوزكاچ	Kamelrücken; Krümmung
Orta	örta	اورتا	Mitte
Örtäng	örtäng	اورتانك	Posthaus
Örtek	örtäk (für ördäk)	اوردّاك	Ente
Örük (Öräk?)	örük	اوروك	Aprikose, Pflaume; Heerlager
Ösängke-Kaosh	lies: üzängü-qöš	اوزانكو قوش	hufeisenförmiger Lauf zweier zusammenfließender Ströme
Östäng	östäng	اوستانك	Bewässerungskanal
Östäng chapan qaldi	östäng čapan qal-dï	اوستانك چاپان تالدى	Graben, (wo) der Rock dageblieben ist
Ot	öt	اوت	Gras, Kraut; Feuer
Otlak	öt-laq (f. ötlïq, -luq)	اوتلاق	Wiese
Otak	otaq	اوتاق	Hütte
Ötäk, s. Ötük			
Ötäsh	ötäš (ötüš)	اوتوش	Durchgang, Pass
Ötök s. Ötük			
Ötük	ötük; ötäk	اوتوك ,اورتاك	Stiefel
Ötekchi	ötäk-či (f. ötük-či)	اوتوكچى	Schuhmacher
Otra	otra	اوترا	Mitte

Vereinfachte Umschrift	Umschrift und Aussprache	Arabische Schrift	Erklärungsversuch
Pakalik	paqa-lïq	فاتالیق	Frosch-Ort
Pakhtak	páχtak (a. p. t.)	داختاك	die Kaschgharer Ringtaube (*Turtur Stoliczkae*)
Pakhtalik	paχta-lïq	داختالیق	Baumwollort
Panja	pänǧä (p.)	پنجاد	fünfzig
Parcha	pārčä (p.)	پارچه	Stück
Parpak	parbaq		vielästig
Pas	päs[t] (p.)	پست	niedrig, eben
Pashalik	paša-lïq (f.pädšah-lïq) (p.t.)		Königsort; Königtum
Patalchi (?)	padä-čï (?)	فاداچی	Kuhhirt
Patkaklik	patqaq-lïq	فاتقاق لیق	Sumpf
Payin (Bain)	päyin (p.)	پادین	unten, unterer
Pavan	palgän, palwän für päh- läwan (p.) ?	پهلوان	Held
Peiga	päigä	فیكه	Wetllaut
Pialma	pialma	غیالما	(ohne Etymologie)
Puchakchi	pïčäq-čï	غیمچاق چی	Messerschmied
Pushang	pušäng	غوشانك	Hebebaum
Pyazlik	pïäz-lïq (p. t.)	پیازلیق	Zwiebelort
Rabat	rabät, rïbät (p. a.)	رباط	Herberge
Rang	räng (p.)	رذك	Farbe
Saghraghu	saγraγu	ساغراغو	taub
Saghizlik	säγïz-lïq	ساغیزلیق	Harz- oder Teerort
Sai	säi	سای	Steinwüste
Sail	seid (a. t.)	سید	Sayyid
Sakrighu s. Saghraghu			
Säkirtmä	säkirt-mä	سیكیرتمه	steiler Ort (wo man springen muß)
Salkanche	salqïnča, vulg. salqänčä	سالقین چه	ziemlich kühl
Saltjelek	salja-lïq		Zeckenort
Säman	saman	سامان	Stroh

15. IX.

Vereinfachte Umschrift	Umschrift und Aussprache	Arabische Schrift	Eklärungsversuch
Samsak	sänısaq (für sarĭmsaq)	ساريمساق	Knoblauch (auch Mannesname)
Sängär (Singer)	säügär (p.?)	سنكر	die Schanze
Sang	säng (p.)	سنك	Stein
Sang-uya s. Zan-guya			
Sap	sap (kirg.)		Reihe
Sap-örük (Sap-urik)	sap örük	ساف (صاف) اوزوك	Alles voll Aprikosen!
Sara	= sahra (a.)	حدرا	das platte Land (spr. sara)
Särdekchi s. Zardakchi			
Särgak	särgäk	سركك	jemand, der wenig schläft
Sarigh (Sarik, Sari-, Sar-, Sor-)	särĭɣ, särĭq	ساريق ، ساريغ	gelb
Suyi sarik	suyi sarĭq	سويى ساريق	sein Wasser ist gelb
Sarik buya	särĭɣ büyä	ساريغ دويا	eine Pflanze (Sophora spec.)
Sar-unkur	sär-ünkür	سار اوزككور	Milanen-Höhle?
Sasik	säsĭq	ساسيق	slinkend, verfault
Satma	satma	ساتمه	halbunterirdische Hütte
Savätl asti	sävät (für säpäd, p.) as-tĭ	سبد آستى	(er) hat den Korb aufgehängt
Savughluk	säwuq-luɣ	ساوقلوغ	kalter Ort
Sayyad (Seﬂat)	sayyad (a.)	صياد	Jäger
Schechellik	šäɣĭl-lĭq (vulg. šäɣĭllĭq)		Kiessteppe
Seﬁdlar	säyyidlär, säidlär (a. t.)	سييدلار	die Sayyids
Seinek s. Singek			
Sekitma s. Säkirtmä			
Seksan	säksän	سكسان	achtzig
Sel	säl	سل ، سيل	Wildbach
Shahid (Sheit)	šähid (a.) vulg. šeit	شهيد	Märtyrer
Shahidlik (Shaidlik)	šähid-lik (a. t.)	شهيدليك	Märtyrerort
Shaptulluk (Shaftulluk)	šaptul-luq (p. t.)	شافتول لوق	Pfirsichort
Shamal	šamal (a.)	شمال	Norden
Sham-aldi	šäm al-dĭ (ar. t.)	شمع آلدى	er hat das Licht genommen

Vereinfachte Umschrift	Umschrift und Aussprache	Arabische Schrift	Erklärungsversuche
Shäshak s. Shishkak			
Shahr	šähr (p.)	شهر	Stadt; Ort
Sheitlar	šait-lar (vulg. für šähıdlär a. t.)	شهيدلار	die Märtyrer für den Glauben
Sherab	šäräb (ar.)	شراب	Getränk, Wein
Shahid-ulla (Shitala) (?)	šähid ullah (a.)		Blutzeugen Gottes, Märtyrer
Shibär (Shvär)	šibär	شبباز	Grasplatz (?)
Shishkak (Shäshkak?)	šišqaq (čičqaq)	چيچقاق	cacator
Shor	šor (p.)	شور	Salz
Tola-shor	tola šör (t. p.)	تولا شور	(der Boden ist mit) viel Salz (bedeckt, das die Erdrinde krustenartig in die Höhe hebt und weiten Strecken das Aussehen eines Schneefeldes geben kann)
Shorchuk (Shorchik)	šörčuq, šorčiq (p. t.)	شورچوق	Salzloch
Shur s. Shor			
Shvär s. Shibär			
Sil s. Sel			
Silik (Sillik)	silik (t.)	سيليك	rein, glatt
Singek öldi	siügäk öl-dı	سينكاك اولدى	die Mücke ist gestorben
Singer s. Sängär			
Soghuluk	soγul-luq	سوغوللوق	Ort, wo die Zwiebel wächst
Soghun	soγun (söγan)	سوغون	Zwiebel
Sok, Soug	söq, sö-uq; sawuq	سوغوق	kalt
Sokushghan	soquš-γan	سوقوشغان	man hat gekämpft
Sokku	soqqu	سوقّو	Mörser
Sollak	lies: su-luq (su-laq)	سولوق	Ort, wo Wasser steht
Sorun	{ entweder sörün { oder sorún	سوزون سوزون	kühl Ehrenplatz
Su	sū	سو	Fluß, Wasser
Sügät (Sögät, Suget)	sügät, sögüt	سوكت	der Weidenbaum (Salix daphnoides)

137

Vereinfachte Umschrift	Umschrift und Aussprache	Arabische Schrift	Erklärungsversuch
Sulagh	suláɣ	سولاغ	Tränke
Sumbe	sümbä		Ladestock
Supa	süpä für suffa (a.)	صُفّة	Bank, Estrade, Terrasse
Süzük (Syssuk)	süzük	سوزوك	klar (rein)
Tagarma	Taɣarma	تاغِرما	Etymologie fehlt
Tagharchi	taɣar-čı	تاغارچى	Sackmacher
Tagh	täɣ	تاغ	Berg, Gebirge
Tagh-tövän (Takhtuven)	taɣ töwän	تاغ توبان	Fuß des Berges
Tailak tutghan	tailaq tut-ɣan	طايلاق توتغان	man hat das zweijährige Kamel eingefangen
Takir	täkir	تكير	rund
Takla Makan	taqla makän (at. ?)		diese Bezeichnung der großen Wüste war meinen Leuten aus Turfan vollkommen unbekannt; sie nannten sie nur čöl oder gobi. Die Leute aus Andigan, die Inder, Afghanen und Kaschmirer in Kučä, Yarkänd und Chotän kannten den Namen T. M. dagegen, und in diesen Städten ist er auch bei den Eingeborenen gangbar. Ob er mit Scherbenort zu übersetzen ist, steht dahin. Vielleicht ist es ein dzungarischer Name
Tala	tala	تالا	Ebene
Talak	talaq (a.)	طلاق	Ehescheidung
Talashte	talaš-tı	تالاشتى	er hat sich mit jemand geprügelt, gezankt
Tälbäk s. Tilpäk			
Taldi (Taldık, Taldu)	tal-dı	تالدى	mit Weiden besetzt
Talkan	talqan	تالقان	geröstetes, geschlagenes Korn, (manchmal vorher zum Keimen gebracht)
Tallik (Talluk)	tal-lıq	تال لیق	Weidenbaum-Ort
Tam	tam	تام	Mauer
Tamasha	tamäšä (p.)	تماشا	Unterhaltung, Schauspiel
Täng	täng	تڭ	die Hälfte (des Weges)

Vereinfachte Umschrift	Umschrift und Aussprache	Arabische Schrift	Erklärungsversuch
Tangle Kessdi	täñglä (vulg. täñgnä) käs-dı	تاڭكلا كسدى	(er) hat einen Holztrog geschnitzt
Täpis (Tebes, Tebis)	täpis	تغيس	das Ausschlagen (Pferd)
Tar	tar	تار	Engpaß
Tangitar (s. auch Teng)	täñg-i-tar (p.)	تذلك تار	finsterer Engpaß
Tarashillik	taraš-līq (?)	تارِاشلِيق	Abfälle beim Hobeln, Sägen u. dergl.
Tärim (Terem)	tärim	تيريم	Stoppelähren, Stoppelfeld (?)
Täris	täriz	تريز	widrig
Tasghun	tasɣun; tazɣīn	تاسغِين	Hochwasser im Wildbach
Tash	taš	تاش	Felsen, Stein
Tasmachi	tasma-čı	تاسماچى	Riemenmacher
Tatlik	tat-līq	تاتلِيق	süß
Tätur	tätür	تتور	verkehrt
Taushkan s. Toshkan			
Tavekkel	tawaqqal	für a. توغّل	fern, abgelegen
Tayik	tayīq	تايِغ	Seichtwasser
Tebes s. Täpis			
Tegirman	tägirmän	تكيرمان	Mühle
Tekke, Taka, Teke, Tike	täkä, tikä	تيكا	Wildschaf, Wildziege
Temir	tämir, tämür, tömür	تمور	Eisen
Temirlik, Tömürlik	tämir-lik	تمورليك	Eisenort
Teng (s. Tangitar)	täñg (p.)	تذلك	enger Paß
Tengiz	täñgiz	تيمكيز	die See, das Meer
Ter	tär	تيِر	Schweiß
Teräk (Terek)	tėräk	تيِراك	die Pappel (Populus alba)
Terem s. Tärim			
Teres s. Täris			
Teret	tärät (verdorbenes a.)	طايارة	Waschort (Closet)
Tersek s. Tirsek			

Vereinfachte Umschrift	Umschrift und Aussprache	Arabische Schrift	Erklärungsversuch
Tetir, Tätir s. Tötürä			
Tevven s. tübän			
Tezak s. Tizak			
Tez yortghan	tez yort-ɣan	ديمز يورتغان	(das Pferd) hat schnell getrabt
Tikän (Tigen)	tikän	تيكان	Dornstrauch
Tike-sekerik	tikä säkirik	تيكا سيكبريك	Bocksprung
Tilpäk (Tälpäk)	tilpäk	تيلپاك	Sonnenhut aus Filz
Tirsek	tirsäk	تيمرسالك	Ellenbogen
Tizak	tizäk	تيمرالك	Pferdemist
Tögä (Tuge)	tögä	توكا : تيمود	Kamel
Töge toidi	tögä toi-di	تيمود توبلدى	das Kamel wurde satt
Töge tyschkek	tögä tüš-käk (sc. yär)	توكا (تيمود) توشكاك	Ort, wo Kamele lagern, hinfallen usw.
Togan-turuk	toɣan turuq	توغان تورزوق	Falkenständer
Toghdagh	toɣdaɣ	توغداغ	die Trappe (Vogel)
Toghlan	toɣlan	توغلان	rollen (Verbstamm)
Toghraghu	toɣraɣu	توغراغو	das gelbe Harz der *Populus euphratica*
Toghrak	toɣraq	توغراق	Pappel (*Populus euphratica*)
Chong aralning toghrighi	čoṅg aral niṅg toɣräɣi	چوڭك آرال نيڭك توغراغى	*Toghraq*-Pappel (auf) der großen Insel
Mupte-tograk	mupti (für a. mufti) töɣraq	مفتى توغراق	der Toghraq-Baum des Mufti
Toghri	toɣri	توغرى	gegenüber
Tögörmen s. Tügärmän			
Toi boldi	toi bol-dı	توى بوالدى	(hier) wurde das (Hochzeits)-Fest begangen
Tokach	toqač	توقاچ	Art Weizenbrot
Tokachlar	toqač-lar	توقاچلار	Plural, Weizenbrote
Tokachi	toqač-či	توقاچچى	Bäcker
Tokai, Toghai	toqai, toɣai	توغاى	Waldwiese (in manchen Dialekten Krümmung eines Flusses)

Vereinfachte Umschrift	Umschrift und Aussprache	Arabische Schrift	Erklärungsversuch
Tokchi s. Tughchi?			
Tokhi	toχï	توخی	Huhn
Tokmakla	toqmaqla	توقماقلا	mit Keulen schlagen (Verbum!)
Tok	toq	توق	satt
Toktek s. Toghdagh?			
Tokum	toqum (für taqïm)	تاقیم , توقوم	Pferdegeschirr; Filzdecken, die man unter den Sattel legt
Tokuz	toquz	توقوز	neun; steht auch für: sehr viele
Tokuzak	toquz aq	توقوز آق	vielleicht: neun Wasserläufe
Tola	tóla	تولا	viel
Toldurma (Toldema)	toldurma		Anfüllung (Gastmahl)?
Tolgash	tolγaš	تولغاش	Krümmung, Zickzack
Tölkölik s. Tülkilik			
Tollak	toluq, tolïγ (?)	تولوق , تولوغ	erfüllt von —, voll
Tömürlik s. Temirlik			
Tong	toñg	توڭك	gefroren
Tongluk	toñg-luq	توڭكلوق	gefrorener Boden
Tongguz	toñggúz	توڭككوز	Schwein
Tongguz atti	toñgγuz at-tï	توڭككوز اتتی	er hat ein Schwein geschossen
Tonggus baßte	toñgγuz bas-tï	توڭكغوز باستی	Wildschweine haben (hier) Spuren eingedrückt
Tonguzluk	toñgγuz-luq	توڭكغوزلوق	Ort der (Wild)schweine
Topa	töpá	توفا	Stauberde
Topchu	topču, topča für topčï	توفچی	Knopf
Topluk	töp-luq	توف لوق	Kanonenon
Toppschak	topčaq	توفچاق	gutes Pferd
Torbachi	torba-čï für töbra-či (p. t.)	توبرد چی	Macher von Futtersäcken für Pferde
Torchi	tör-či	تورچی	Netzfischer; Netzjäger
Torgeyak	torγa-yäγ (yäk)	تورغا یاغ	Fett, in kleine Stücke zerschnitten

Vereinfachte Umschrift	Umschrift und Aussprache	Arabische Schrift	Erklärungsversuch
Torpak öldi	torpaq öl-dí	توُرپاق اوُلدى	das zweijährige Kalb ist gestorben
Toruk	turuq, toyruq	توُرروق · توُغَرروق	braun (von Pferden)
Toshkan	tošqan	توُشقان	Hase
Tötürü (Tötöru)	tötürü	توُتوُررو	umgekehrt, verdreht
Tozakchi	tuzaq-čï	توُزاقچى	Fallen- (Schlingen-) Steller
Tübä (Tube)	tübä (vulg. döbä)	توُبه	Hügel, Gipfel
Tübän	tübän, tüwän, töwän	توُبان	unten
Tübenki (Tüvenki)	tübän-ki	توُبانكى	der untere
Tugarak s. Toghrak			
Tuge s. Tögä			
Tügärmän (Tägürmän)	tügärmän, tägürmän	تِكوُرمان	Mühle
Tughchi	tuy-čï	توُغچى	Standartenträger
Tuiuk	tuyuq, tuyoq	توُيوق	unzugänglich; Verhau
Tukhu s. Tokhi			
Tülkilik	tülki-lik (tilki-lik)	توُلكوُليك	Fuchsort
Tumanchi	tuman-čï	توُمانچى	Hebelmacher (?)
Tümen	tümän	توُمان	zehntausend i. e. ein Distrikt, der 10000 Mann stellen kann (oft nicht zutreffend!)
Tumshuk	tumšuq	توُمشوق	der Vorsprung (wörtl. Maul, Schnauze. Übertr. Sporn eines Gebirges; etwas, das irgendwo hineinragt oder -springt)
Tumshughi	mit Suffix tumšuγï	توُمشوغى	sein Vorsprung etc.
Tunnur	tönúr (für tänúr)	تَنوُر ,تاَنوُر	Ofen
Tura	turá	توُرا	Festung (Turm)
Turuk	turuq	توُرروق	Wohnort
Turun	turun, torun	توُرزون	Kamelfüllen
Tüschken	tüš-kän	توُشكان	(er) hat sich niedergelassen, ist abgestiegen, hat gelagert, ist gefallen usw.
Tut	tut (a.)	توُت	Maulbeerbaum, Maulbeere

Vereinfachte Umschrift	Umschrift und Aussprache	Arabische Schrift	Erklärungsversuch
Tütür s. Tötürü			
Tüvenki s. Tübenki			
Tuyuk-dur	tuyuq dur	دویوق دور	es ist ein Verhau
Tuz	tuz	توز	Salz
Tuzluk	tus-luq	توزلوق	Salzort
Tyschk	tüšük	توشوك	Loch
Ucha	uča	اوچا	Nacken, Rücken, Schulter
Uchak s. Ochak			
Üch	üč	اوچ	drei
Uchme	üǧmä, im Osten ǧüǧäm	اوجما, اوجمه; جوجم	Maulbeere
Ui	ui	اوی	Ochse
Üi s. Öi			
Ulugh	ûluγ	اولوغ	groß
Ulughjat (Ulugchat)	ûluγ ǧât (čât)	اولوغ جات (چات)	die große Kreuzung zweier Täler am Zusammenfluß zweier Flußarme
Umbesh s. Onbesh			
Unkur	ûñkür	اونككور	Höhle
Unkurluk	ûñkür-lük	اونككورلوك	Höhlenort
Uprang	ûp räñg, äb räñg (p.)	آب رنك	wasserfarben
Urugumá	viell. uruγ-umaq	اوروغ اوماق	Samen (und) Geschlecht
Ürük s. Örük			
Ushak	ušaq	اوشاق	klein; kleine Kinder; Diener
Utuk s. Ötük?			
Uttera s. Otra			
Uya	uya, auch uva	اویا, اووا	Nest
Uye s. Öi			
Ya	yâ	یا	Bogen (Waffe)
Yaghash	für yaγač	آغاچ	Baum, Holz

16. IX.

Vereinfachte Umschrift	Umschrift und Aussprache	Arabische Schrift	Erklärungsversuch
Yailak	yailaq	ياىلاق	Sommerlager
Yaka	yaqa	ياقا	wörtl. Kragen, übertragen = Rand (n. b. der Wüste)
Yäkän	yäkän	يكان	Binsen
Yäkänlik	yäkän-lik	يكانلبك	Binsenort
Yalaghan s. Yalghan?			
Yalang	yalañg	يالانك	entblößt
Yalghan	yalγan	يالغان	Lügner
Yalghuz	yálγuz	يالغوز	einsam
Yalpak	yalpaq	يالفاق	flach
Yam	yam	يام	Postpferd
Yaman	yaman	يامان ، يمان	schlecht, böse
Yan	yán	يان	Seite
Yandag s. Yantak			
Yandash-kak	yandaš qáq	يانداش قاق	Tümpel (aber auch: trockene Gegend) des Freundes
Yangi	yañgi	يانكى	neu
Yantak	yantaq	يانتاق	Kameldornpflanze *(Alhagi camelorum)*
Kancha yantak	qanča yantaq	تانچا يانتاق	einige K.-Pflanzen
Yapchan	yapčan	يافچان	bekannter Ortsname, ohne Etymologie
Yapkaklïk	yapqaq-lïq	يانقاق لىق	Ort der yapqaq-Pflanze *(Eurotia ceratoides)* nach Hedin (y. wörtlich = Verschließer)
Yar	yär	يار	die Klippe, Lößklippe
Yardang	yärdañg	ياردانك	Lößkegel
Yaka yardang	yaqa yardañg	ياقا ياردانك	Lößkegel am Wüstensaum
Yarghik	yarγïq (für yarγaq)	يارغاق	Pelz, Regenmantel
Yarik	yaríq	يارىق	gespalten
Yavash	yawaš	ياواش	ruhig, milde
Yeilak s. Yailak			
Yaz	yaz	ياز	Sommer

Vereinfachte Umschrift	Umschrift und Aussprache	Arabische Schrift	Erklärungsversuche
Yer	yär	ييـر	Land, Ackerland
Yesi	yásí (vulg. yesí)	يـاـسى	flach
Yigde s. Jigde			
Yilan	yilän	بيـيلان	Schlange
Yilan-de	yilan-däh (p. t.)	بيـيلان دد	Schlangengau
Yilanlik	yilan-líq	بيـيلانليق	Schlangenort
Yildizlik	yíldíz-líq	يولـلدوزليق	Ort der Gestirne
Yoghan	yöγan	يوغـان	groß, dick
Yol	yol	يول	Weg (oder: türk. Meile)
Yokarki (Yukaki)	yoqqärqı	يوقّـارقى	oberer
Yul	yui	يول	Bach
Yulghun	yulγun	يولغون	Tamariske
Yumalak (Yumulak)	yumalaq	يـومالاّى	rund (aber auch = Schafmist)
Yurt	yurt	يورت	Land, Heimat
Yurung	yūruñg; yürüñg	يوروـنك	hell
Vash	wahš (a.)	وحش	wildes Tier
Zan-guya	zän gūyä (p.)	زن كوبا	die Sängerin (?)
Zardakchi	zärdäk-čī (p. t.)	زردكچى	Möhrenhändler
Zeman	zämän (a.)	زمان	Zeit

ZUR
GEOLOGIE VON OST-PAMIR

AUF GRUNDLAGE DER VON SVEN HEDIN
GESAMMELTEN GESTEINSPROBEN

VON

BROR ASKLUND

MIT ZEHN TAFELN UND EINER GEOLOGISCHEN ÜBERSICHTSKARTE

VORWORT

Im Auftrag von Dr. SVEN HEDIN wurde diese Untersuchung im Frühjahr
1921 begonnen. Als Material standen mir 232 Gesteinshandstücke, sowie Dr. HEDINS
Tagebücher zur Verfügung. — Die Gesteinshandstücke und die aus ihnen hergestellten
Dünnschliffe werden in der Mineralogischen Abteilung des Naturhistorischen Reichs-
museums (Naturhistoriska Riksmuseet) zu Stockholm aufbewahrt.

Im Laufe der Untersuchung erwiesen sich einige Gesteinshandstücke als fossil
führend; deshalb wurden sie an das Geologisch-Paläontologische Institut und Museum
der Universität Berlin übersandt, wo sie durch die liebenswürdige Vermittlung von
Professor Dr. W. JANENSCH dem Assistenten des Instituts, Dr. W. O. DIETRICH, über-
geben wurden, dessen Untersuchungsergebnisse in diese Veröffentlichung aufgenommen
worden sind.

Infolge der großen Flächenausdehnung des Untersuchungsgebietes und des Mangels
an eingehenden Arbeiten, die Anknüpfungen an schon bekannte Verhältnisse hätten ermöglichen können, hat diese Schrift nur den Charakter eines Beitrags für künftige
Forschung. Durch die Einheitlichkeit des Materials jedoch kann sie von ziemlich großer
Bedeutung für diese werden.

Bei dem Versuch, ein Altersschema aufzustellen, habe ich mich soweit als möglich
auf die Angaben zu stützen gesucht, die früher durch STOLICZKA und BOGDANOWITSCH
gewonnen wurden, sowie auf LEUCHS' ausgezeichnete sachliche Zusammenfassung im
»Handbuch der regionalen Geologie»; doch deuten Dr. DIETRICHS Untersuchungen an,
daß kretazeisch-tertiäre Gesteine im Pamir eine bedeutendere Ausbreitung haben, als
früher bekannt war. Die Alterseinteilung muß, was dieses Material betrifft, in recht weiten
Grenzen gehalten werden, und ich habe Vorsicht in allen kühneren Analogieschlüssen
walten lassen.

Dr. HEDIN statte ich meinen warmen Dank ab für seine niemals versagende Anteil-
nahme und Hilfe. Ebenso habe ich das Vergnügen, das angenehme Zusammenarbeiten
mit Dr. DIETRICH anzuerkennen. Nicht am wenigsten stehe ich in großer Dankesschuld
bei Oberingenieur E. WIESLER (Stockholm), durch dessen bereitwillige Hilfe ich instand
gesetzt worden bin, die zugängliche russische Literatur über dieses Gebiet zu benutzen.

Nach der Drucklegung dieser Veröffentlichung kam ich durch die Übersendung des Fossilmaterials (um es mit schon bekanntem asiatischen Material zu vergleichen) mit Prof. Dr. KURT LEUCHS in briefliche Verbindung; ich bin dadurch imstande, seine Auffassung der geologischen Stellung des Fossilmaterials mit anzuführen.

Geheimrat Professor Dr. FRANZ KOSSMAT in Leipzig hatte die Güte, die sprachliche Korrektur des deutsch geschriebenen Teiles dieser Abhandlung zu überwachen und auch die deutsche Übersetzung des schwedisch geschriebenen Teiles durchzusehen.

Es ist mir eine Ehre, den Herren Geheimrat KOSSMAT und Professor LEUCHS meine Dankbarkeit für ihr liebenswürdiges Interesse an meiner Arbeit auszusprechen.

Im Anschluß an die Untersuchung dieses Materials wurden von Dr. DIETRICH auch Studien an den fossilführenden Handstücken einer Gesteinssammlung gemacht, die aus 39 Nummern besteht und von Dr. HEDINS Reisen durch die Wüste Takla-Makan und das Tarimbecken im Jahre 1895 herrührt. Ein Teil der fossilfreien Handstücke ist früher von Professor HELGE BÄCKSTRÖM beschrieben worden im Anschluß an Dr. HEDINS vorläufige Schilderung seiner Reisen in diesen Gegenden.[1]

Stockholm, im Mai 1922.

BROR ASKLUND.

---

[1] Petermanns Mitteilungen, Ergänzungsband 28. 1900.

INHALT

17. IX.

I. KAPITEL.

KURZE ÜBERSICHT DER LITERATUR ÜBER DIE GEOLOGIE DES PAMIR.

Außer in dem »Handbuch der regionalen Geologie« findet sich eine ausgezeichnete Zusammenstellung der Ergebnisse der bis heute im Pamir und den angrenzenden Gebieten ausgeführten Forschungen in dem Werk »Landeskundliche Forschungen im Pamir« von ARVED SCHULTZ.[1]

Von früheren Forschungsreisenden folgten STOLICZKA[2], BOGDANOWITSCH[3] und zum Teil auch PRINZ[4] den gleichen Reisewegen wie HEDIN. STOLICZKA schlug während der »Second Yarkand Mission« in der ersten Zeit seiner Reise dieselbe Route ein, mit der HEDIN im Jahre 1894 seine Reise im östlichen Pamir einleitete. STOLICZKAS Weg geht also von Kashgar über Yangi-hisar, Igis-yar, Sasik-teke, Kashka-su, Chihil-gumbes, Pas-rabat, Tarbashi, Bargon, Tash-kurgan nach Keng-shevär, worauf die Routen sich trennten, also so weit westwärts, als das Gebiet des Sarikol-Gebirges reicht. BOGDANOWITSCHS Profile laufen zum Teil in unserem Gebiet, vom Mus-tagh-ata über Kara-tash-davan nach Igis-yar und Yangi-hisar.

Im Gegensatz zu STOLICZKAS mehr der Übersicht dienenden, rasch ausgeführten Reisen im Pamir (deren Ergebnis Stoliczka selbst nicht mehr veröffentlichen konnte, da er vor Abschluß seiner Reisen starb), hat BOGDANOWITSCH in seiner großen Beschreibung des Tien-shan und Kwen-lun die erste allgemeinere geologische Darstellung der Teile des Pamir gegeben, die diese Schrift angehen. Es mag jedoch hervorgehoben werden, daß BOGDANOWITSCH selbst betont, sein Ergebnis sei unvollständig und diene nur der Übersicht. Seiner großen vergleichenden Tabelle über die geologische Ausbildung des Kwen-lun und Tien-shan entnehmen wir umstehende Übersicht der Teile des westlichen Kwen-lun, die sich südöstlich und südlich von Kashgar ausbreiten (das Gebiet Kashgar-Yarkand-Tagarma-Kette und das Kashgar-Gebirge im Westen):

---

[1] Abh. des Hamburgischen Kolonialinstituts. Bd. XXXIII, Reihe C. Hamburg 1916.
[2] STOLICZKA-BLANFORD, Scientific results of the Second Yarkand Mission. Bd. 1. Calcutta 1878.
[3] BOGDANOWITSCH, Geologische Untersuchungen in Ost-Turkestan (russisch). Ergebnisse der Tibet-Expedition 1889—1890, 2. Teil. St. Petersburg 1892.
[4] »Kuen-lun es Pamir«. Referat von VOGEL, Geolog. Zentralblatt. 1913. Nr. 1092.

Formationen	Petrographische Ausbildung	Sarikol-Yangi-hisar	Tagarma-Yarkand
Vormitteldevon. Formationen	Gneise (a)	Gneise der Gruppe Mustagh-ata.	Gneise des Passes Kök-moynak (Mustagh-ata). Gneise am Flusse Tarbashi.
	Kristalline Schiefer (b)		Glimmer und Gabbroschiefer am Flusse Tarbashi. Glimmerschiefer am Flusse Tsharlung.
Devonische Ablagerungen (Gesteine der Kwen-lun-Transgress.)	Gesteine der Serie der Kwen-lun-Transgression (d). (Hauptsächlich Tonschiefer.)	Quarzhaltige oder tonig-knotige Schiefer am Flusse Kara-tash-su. Tonhaltige Schiefer am Tshat-su und Ridshek-su.	Tonschiefer des Flusses Tarbashi.
	Kristalline Kalksteine, Dolomite und Kalkschiefer der Kwen-lun-Transgression (d).		Tonschiefer mit Schichten kristallinen Kalksteins auf dem Passe Turut. Kristalliner Sandstein bei Baga am Flusse Tsharlung.
	Schiefer und Sandsteine der Kwen-lun-Transgression (e).	Sandhaltige Tonschiefer, nach oben in Quarzsandstein übergehend, am Flusse Keng-kol.	Tonschiefer, mit Quarzitschiefer u. Konglomeraten untermischt, auf dem Passe Kara-davan. / Quarzite und Tonschiefer von grünlicher Farbe und oolithische Kalksteine am Flusse Arpalik-su.
Karbonische und spätere Ablagerungen	Kalk- und Sandsteine des Steinkohlensystems (c₁).		Rote Sandsteine des Passes Kisil-davan und am Flusse Arpalik-su.
	Serie der tibetischen Transgression (c).		
Mesozoische Ablagerungen		Tonhaltige Mergel und Sandsteine mit Muscheln bei Yangi-hisar (der Kreide zugehörend).	Dünnblättriger Tonschiefer mit dünnen Quarzitschichten untermischt (bei Chihil-gumbes). Dünnschiefrige Tonschiefer mit Steinkohlen (bei Kuserab, gehören dem Jura an).
Tertiär	n	Mürbe rote und dunkelbraune Sandsteine und Konglomerate mit Gips und Steinsalz.	
	g₁	Tonhaltige Konglomeratablagerungen (wahrscheinlich Tertiär).	

Mit dem hervorragenden Überblick, den BOGDANOWITSCH über umfassende Teile von Zentralasien besaß, konnte er die paläozoische Geschichte des Kwen-lun und Tienshan in der Hauptsache folgendermaßen darstellen: Einen aus älteren Gneisen und kristallinen Schiefern aufgebauten Kontinent überflutete das Meer im Mitteldevon (die Kwen-lun-Transgression), dabei grobklastische Sedimente absetzend, die im oberen

Teile des Devon allmählich eine feinere Struktur annehmen. Während der folgenden Regression setzte sich wieder gröberes Sediment ab. — Eine neue Transgression trat im Karbon ein, wobei in den mittleren Teilen des Kwen-lun mächtige Lager von rötlichen, kalkhaltigen Sandsteinen sich bildeten, die in großen Gebieten des westlichen Kwen-lun fehlen. In den letztgenannten Gebieten kommen bedeutende Massen karbonischer Kalksteine (Foraminiferen- und Productus-Kalkstein) vor, welche die oberen Partien der Gesteine der Kwen-lun-Transgression konkordant überlagern. Dies zeigt, daß die neue Transgression jedenfalls nach der Ablagerung des Foraminiferen- und Productus-Kalks stattgefunden hat.

Zur Kenntnis der mesozoischen und tertiären Ablagerungen des östlichen Pamir hatte BOGDANOWITSCH wenig beizutragen. Von Interesse ist jedoch, daß er bei Yangi-hisar Kreideablagerungen gefunden hat, die HEDIN später in dem Talgang des Keng-kol weit hinauf verfolgt hat.

Über die tektonische Entwicklung und die Dislokationen, die den westlichen Kwen-lun kennzeichnen, stellt BOGDANOWITSCH folgende Tabelle auf:

Bis zum Eintritt der Kwen-lun-Transgression	WNW—OSO. Monoklinale Verbiegungen und Verwerfungen.
Bis zum Eintritt der Tibet-Transgression	WNW—OSO.
Vom Schluß der Tibet-Transgression bis zur Tertiärepoche	WNW—OSO. Intensive Faltung.
Zur Tertiär-Periode und später	NW—SO-Faltung.
	NO—SW. Monoklinale Verbiegungen und Verwerfungen.

Die Forschungen von PRINZ im östlichen Pamir kennt der Verfasser nur durch das Referat von VOGEL. Drei Profile werden mitgeteilt: eins vom Kara-tash (im westlichen Kwen-lun) bis zum Dorf Tash-malik, eins durch das Kashgar-Gebirge und das dritte durch dessen nördlichen Teil. Die Untersuchungen von PRINZ scheinen BOGDANOWITSCHS Ergebnisse zu bestätigen.

Die erwähnte Abhandlung von SCHULTZ enthält eine geologische Übersichtskarte von Pamir.

II. KAPITEL.

BESCHREIBUNG DER HANDSTÜCKE IN FORTLAUFENDEN NUMMERN.

Die Handstücke sind hier in Hinsicht auf die Karte nach fortlaufenden Nummern zusammengestellt. Ursprünglich sind sie in zwei Reihen geteilt, die eine das Jahr 1894, die andere das Jahr 1895 umfassend. Bei der letzteren ist die Ursprungsnummer an die Nummer der zusammengefügten Reihe angeknüpft, z. B. 230 (75).

Die von Dr. DIETRICH untersuchten fossilführenden Handstücke und Dünnschliffe sind im Anhang S. 175 ff. beschrieben (Das von Dr. HEDIN aus dem Tarimbecken und dem östlichen Pamir mitgebrachte fossilführende Gesteinsmaterial. Von Dr. W. O. DIETRICH).

Am Schluß eines großen Teils der Beschreibungen der Handstücke ist ein Zeichen hinzugesetzt (z. B. KT, PG, KS), das sich auf die chronologisch-petrographische Einteilung des Materials bezieht, die der Verfasser durchzuführen versucht hat (siehe Weiteres hierüber in Kapitel III).

(1894.)

1. Graugelber feldspathaltiger **Sandstein.**

   Klastischer Sandstein, hauptsächlich aus mehr oder weniger wohlgerundeten Quarzkörnern bestehend, mit Körnern von *Plagioklas, Mikroklin* oder *Mikroklinperthit.* Das Zement ist sehr feinkörnig, enthält ein wenig *Muscovit* und *Chlorit* und zeigt schwache Umkristallisation (Diagenese). Winzige Kristalle von *Turmalin* und *Zirkon* kommen vor. (KT)

   Am Flusse Tasgun, SO. des Dorfes Tatür. Das Fallen ist 66° NO.

2. Rotgrauer feldspatreicher **Quarzitschiefer.**

   Quarz ist das Hauptmineral, daneben ist ein saurer *Plagioklas* sehr gewöhnlich. *Chlorit* und *Epidot* zusammen mit *Muscovit* geben dem Gestein die parallelschiefrige Mikrotextur. *Calcit* ist nicht selten. — Wahrscheinlich

156

ist das Gestein ein dynamometamorpher feldspatreicher Sandstein mit ursprünglich kalkspatreichem Zement. (KT)

Bei Ak-bash-masar, mit dem Fallen 53° O.

3. Hellgrüner **Tonschiefer.**

In der beinahe amorphen Grundmasse sieht man unter dem Mikroskop sehr häufige Glaukonitkörner, wie auch spärliche Quarzkörner und limonitähnliche Klumpen. (KT)

Anstehend etwas südlich von (2). Das Fallen ist 72° WSW.

4. Graugelber plagioklashaltiger **Sandstein.**

Ähnelt Nr. (1). Die klastische Struktur ist deutlich, trotzdem das Gestein Spuren der Dynamometamorphose (beginnende Granulierung) zeigt. Das Bindemittel führt reichlich *Sericit.* (KT)

Bei Tasgun unweit des Sar-unkur. Das Fallen ist 22° WNW.

5. Schwarzer dichter **Tonschiefer.** (M)

Bei Tasgun südlich von Kefsh-kakti. Das Fallen ist 72° S.

6. Grauschwarzes **Sandsteinkonglomerat.** (Pl. I, Fig. 1.)

Ähnelt Nr. (1) und (4). Der *Plagioklas* ist ein saurer *Oligoklas-Albit,* oft sericitisiert. Gewöhnlich mit kleinen Tonschieferstücken wie auch Quarzitgeröllen in der Sandsteinmatrix. (KT)

Zusammen mit (7) bei Tasgun unweit von Arka-terek. Fallen nicht angegeben.

7. **Kalksteinkonglomerat.**

Die Gesteinsmatrix ist ein dichter, ein wenig silifizierter Kalkstein, mit Quarzkörnern wie auch kleinen zusammengekitteten Sandsteingeröllen. (KT)

8. Porphyrischer grauweißer **Gneisgranit.**

Unter dem Mikroskop wie auch makroskopisch erkennt man Einsprenglinge und Grundmasse. Als Einsprenglinge kommen *Quarz* und *Plagioklas* vor. Der *Quarz* zeigt teilweise dihexaedrische Ausbildung, löscht immer undulös aus, und seine Ränder sind granuliert. Die Plagioklaseinsprenglinge sind meist gut idiomorph, Zusammensetzung sauer, ungefähr der des Oligoklasbits entsprechend. Sericit-Zoisitbildung ist gewöhnlich.

Die Grundmasse ist granoblastisch und besteht aus einer Mischung von *Quarz* und in gleicher Menge auftretendem *Plagioklas, Mikroklin* und häufigem graugrünem *Chlorit.* — *Kalkspat* kommt nur spärlich vor. (PG)

Vom östlichen Ufer des Keng-kol, südlich von Arka-terek.

9. Grünweißer **Granit**. (Pl. I, Fig. 2.)

Von den Bestandteilen überwiegt ein saurer *Plagioklas*, beinahe reiner *Albit*. Der *Plagioklas* zeigt oft eine angedeutete Idiomorphie gegen die übrigen Mineralien, gegen *Mikroklin* zeigt er Myrmekitränder. — *Mikroklin* ist im Verhältnis zum *Plagioklas* relativ selten, er ist perthitisch, wie auch der *Plagioklas* oft antiperthitische Einschlüsse von *Mikroklin* enthält. *Quarz* kommt in großen allotriomorphen Individuen vor. — Grasgrüner *Chlorit* ist spärlich.

Das Gestein hat wohl ursprünglich eine typisch hypidiomorph-körnige Struktur gehabt, jetzt zeigt es aber eine Kataklase, die teilweise den Charakter einer beginnenden Mylonitisierung hat. Dieser Prozeß verläuft nach den dünnen Chlorit-Sericit- und quarzreichen Zonen, die als anastomosierende, hauptsächlich in einer Richtung verlaufende Bänder ausgebildet sind. Die Plagioklase sind oft gekrümmt und von undulös auslöschenden Zwillingslamellen durchwachsen. Bisweilen sind sie zerstückelt, und die einzelnen Stücke sind jetzt voneinander abgedrängt; daß sie aber ursprünglich ein Plagioklasindividuum ausgemacht haben, sieht man deutlich an den charakteristischen Albit- oder Periklinlamellen. — Der *Quarz* zeigt undulöse Auslöschung und ist oft kräftig granuliert. (PG) Südlich (8), bei Keng-kol.

10. Völlig saussuritisierter **Gneisgranit**. (PG)
    Südlich (9), N. von Sarik-goy.

11. Quarzreicher grauschwarzer **Tonschiefer**. (M) (Pl. II, Fig. 3.)
    Bei Tokai-bash. Das Fallen ist 50° SSW.

12. Ähnelt völlig (11). (M)
    Bei Keng-kol westlich von Korumdeh. Das Fallen ist 40° SSO.

13. Dichter schwarzer **Tonschiefer**. (M)
    Bei Sasik-teke. Das Fallen ist 82° O.

14. Gebänderter **Tonschiefer**.
    Zeigt eine schöne Schichtstruktur mit wechselnden quarzreichen und tonigen Lagen. (M)
    Bei Sasik-teke. Das Fallen ist 32° NNW.

15. **Tonschiefer**, ähnelt (13). (M)
    Bei Yeshil. Das Fallen ist sehr steil, nahezu vertikal, gegen O.

16. Feldspatreicher **Kalksandstein**.
    Schöne klastische Struktur mit überwiegenden Quarzkörnern. *Plagioklas* ist sehr häufig, ferner kommen auch Körner von *Mikroklin* vor. Kleine

Fragmente von *Quarzit* wie auch von *Hornstein* spärlich vertreten. Das Zement besteht meistens aus winzigen Calcitkörnern. (KT)

Ein wenig südlich von Yeshil, zusammen mit (17). Das Fallen ist 76° WSW.

17. **Kalksandstein.**

Von ungefähr demselben Typus wie (16). Enthält Fossilien und ist daher von DIETRICH näher beschrieben, S. 178. (KT)

18. **Kalksandstein.**

Ähnelt völlig (16). (KT)

Anstehend zwischen Kara-agil und Tuyuk-yar.

19 und 22. **Kalksandsteine.**

Enthalten Fossilien (s. DIETRICH, S. 177, 178). (KT)

20 und 21. Grauwackenartige **Sandsteine.**

(19),(20),(21) und (22) stehen an längs des Weges unweit (18). (22) fällt 54° WNW.

23. **Kalksandsteinkonglomerat.** (Pl. II, Fig. 4 und Pl. III, Fig. 5.)

Der *Quarz* ist das Hauptmineral. Er bildet rundliche und eckige Körner in der feinkristallinen Calcitmatrix. Kleine Gerölle von *Hornstein, Phyllit* und *Quarzit* sind gewöhnlich, ebenso auch kleine Splitter von *Plagioklas* und *Mikroklin.* Der *Plagioklas* hat die Zusammensetzung eines *Oligoklasalbits.* (KT)

Steht bei Ak-tö an.

24. Dichter **Tonschiefer** mit **Calcitadern.** (M)

Bei Keng-kol-aul.

25. **Kalksandstein.**

Ähnelt (23) und anderen beschriebenen Gesteinen desselben Typus. Das Gestein zeigt eine schwache Schieferung, auch ist die klastische Struktur durch die Quetschung ein wenig verwischt. (KT)

Südlich von Keng-kol-aul. Das Fallen ist 65° NO.

26. Dichter **Tonschiefer.**

Zeigt eine von der Schichtung sehr deutlich abweichende Transversalschieferung. (M)

Südlich von Keng-kol-aul.

27. **Kalksteinkonglomerat** vom gewöhnlichen Typus.

Die zusammengeschwemmten Quarz- und Plagioklaskörner zeigen oft eine vor der Gesteinsbildung empfangene Quetschung. Geröllchen von *Quarzit* und *Phyllit* finden sich häufig darin. (KT)

Zwischen dem Passe Kara-su (3972 m) und Chihil-gumbes-karaul. Das Fallen ist 40° SW.

18. IX.

28. **Kalksandstein.** (KT)

Südlich von Chihil-gumbes-karaul. Das Fallen ist 28° S.

29. **Kalksandsteinschiefer.** (Pl. III, Fig. 6.)

Zeigt deutliche Spuren von Dynamometamorphose, z. B. sind die Quarzkörner in elliptische Körper ausgewalzt. Das Zement ist in eine feinkristalline Calcitmatrix verwandelt.

30. Marmorisierter **Kalkstein.** (KK)

Macht ein Lager in (29) aus.

Vom Passe Terart.

31. **Marmor,** den Kalksandstein überlagernd. (KK)

Südlich vom Terart-Passe.

32. **Kalksandsteinschiefer.**

Dynamometamorpher Kalksandstein mit auch makroskopisch sehr wohlentwickelter Parallelstruktur. Der *Calcit* hat die Ausbildung von dünnen Linsen, die in der Schieferungsrichtung gestreckt sind. Von der Dynamometamorphose sehr deutlich abhängig ist die nicht unbedeutende Ausbildung von *Biotit* und *Muscovit*.

Wenig unterhalb Teke-sekerik.

33. Unreiner marmorisierter **Kalkstein** mit Schichten von Tonschiefer.

Macht Schichten in (32) aus.

34. Weißer **Granit.**

Panidiomorph-körniges Gestein von intermediärer Zusammensetzung. Unter den Feldspaten herrscht ein oft gut idiomorpher *Andesinplagioklas* vor. Er ist älter als der *Mikroklin*, von welchem er bisweilen eingeschlossen oder korrodiert wird. Der *Mikroklin* enthält öfters kleine Quarzeinschlüsse, die besonders gern eine dihexaedrische Ausbildung annehmen. — Quarzkörner mit allotriomorpher Ausbildung sind gewöhnlich.

Von dunklen Mineralien kommen *Biotit*, *Granat* und *Hornblende* vor. Der *Biotit* zeigt kräftigen Pleochroismus von olivgelb bis beinahe rein schwarz. Er ist früh auskristallisiert und scheint teilweise älter als die saureren Ränder des *Plagioklases*. — *Granat* trifft man spärlich, am meisten mit der *Hornblende* assoziiert. Er bildet bisweilen eigentümliche myrmekitähnliche Verwachsungen mit dem *Plagioklas*. — Die *Hornblende* zeigt schönen Pleochroismus in gelbgrünen und lebhaft dunkelblaugrünen Tönen. Ihr Achsenwinkel ist auffallend klein, überdies zeigt sie eine kräftige Bisektricendispersion. Der hastingsitische Charakter der Hornblende ist deutlich markiert. (PG)

Steht in der Talschlucht des Pas-rabat an. Das Fallen ist 48° NO.

160

35. Grauweißer **Glimmerschiefer** und
36. **Sericit-Knotenschiefer.**

   Lose Blöcke bei der Mündung des Borumsal-jilga. (KS)

37. Kräftig geschieferter kalkhaltiger **Quarzit.** (M)

   Bei Chong-oljeke. Das Fallen ist 60° NO.

38. Weißer **Granit**, ähnelt (39). (PG)

   Bei Ak-taldu.

39. Weißer **Granit.** (Pl. IV, Fig. 7.)

   Mikroskopisch zeigt das Gestein eine porphyrgranitische Struktur zusammen mit einer ziemlich deutlichen Fluidaltextur, welche besonders durch die parallelgerichteten Biotitschuppen angedeutet wird.

   Mikroklin kommt teilweise als diffuser Einsprengling oder in Form von Augen vor; teilweise allotriomorph gegenüber den Plagioklaskörnern der »Grundmasse». Die Mikroklinaugen schließen oft kleine relativ basische Plagioklaskörner ein. Sowohl die Einsprenglinge als der *Mikroklin* der »Grundmasse» zeigen perthitische Verwachsung. — Der *Plagioklas* macht einen wesentlichen Teil der granitischen »Grundmasse» aus. Er ist ganz deutlich zonar gebaut, die anorthitreicheren Kerne desselben zeigen nämlich auf Schnitten senkrecht gegen P und M eine symmetrische Auslöschung von ungefähr $+ 7°$ (Ab_{73} An_{27}), während die saureren Ränder eine Auslöschung von $- 9°$ (Ab_{90} An_{10}) geben. Die *Plagioklase* enthalten auffallend zahlreiche antiperthitische Einschlüsse von *Mikroklin,* der öfters ein Gitter mitten in den *Plagioklasen* bildet. Der *Quarz* erscheint in allotriomorphen, oft gestreckten Körnern.

   Von dunklen Mineralien sind *Biotit* und *Hornblende* ungefähr im Gleichgewicht vorhanden. Der *Biotit* hat einen ausgeprägten Pleochroismus in olivgelben und dunkelrotbraunen Tönen. Er scheint sowohl früher als später als der *Plagioklas* auskristallisiert zu sein. Die *Hornblende* ist hauptsächlich jünger als der *Biotit* (enthält Einschlüsse von *Biotit*). Letzterer ist jedoch älter als der *Quarz* und der *Mikroklin* der »Grundmasse». Die *Hornblende* hat einen ausgeprägten hastingsitischen Charakter. — Von Accessorien sind *Titanit, Apatit* und spärlicher *Orthit* zu nennen. *Granat* von hellroter Farbe, wahrscheinlich *Almandin,* ist nicht selten. Er bildet Einschlüsse sowohl in den Feldspatkörnern als auch in dem *Quarz.* (PG)

   Steht an im Flusse Tengi-tar südlich des Yangi-davan.

40. Weißer granatführender **Gneisgranit.** (Pl. IV, Fig. 8.)

   Ähnelt (39), ist aber reicher an *Orthit; Myrmekit* ist auch sehr gewöhnlich darin. Die Mikroklinaugen zeigen eine kräftige Auswalzung, sie haben die Ausbildung von Linsen oder ausgestreckten Bändern. Kataklaserscheinungen fehlen jedoch völlig. (PG)

In Tengi-tar W von (39). Die Schichten stehen fast vertikal, die Fallrichtung ist bald NW, bald SO.

41. Graugesprenkelter granatführender **Gneisgranit**.
Ähnelt (40), hat aber noch kräftigere Parallelstruktur. Der *Quarz* ist relativ spärlich vorhanden. (PG)
Steht an südlich des Tugu-boyun-davan.

42. Weißer **Albitpegmatit**. (PG)

43. Graugesprenkelter granatführender **Gneisgranit**. (PG)
(42) bildet Bänke in (43). Das Fallen ist 87° W.
Steht an unweit östlich vom Passe (3722).

44. Weißer quarzreicher **Gneisgranit** mit *Biotit, Hornblende* und *Granat*. (PG)
Nahe dem Passe (3722).

45. Gesprenkelter muscovitreicher **Gneisgranit**. (PG)
Westlich vom Passe (3722).

46. Grauweißer gesprenkelter **Gneis** mit *Granat* und *Biotit*. (PG)
Bei Chil-öttök.

47. **Augengneis**.
Ähnelt (46), führt aber große Mikroklinaugen, die ihn (34) ähnlich machen. (PG)
Vermutlich vom Chicheklik-davan.

48. **Augengneis**. (PG)
Ähnelt völlig (47).
Vom Kata-kök-moynak.

49. Dunkelgesprenkelter **Amphibolit**. (KS)
Bildet einen einige Meter breiten Gang in (48)

50. **Augengneis**.
Ähnelt (47) und (48), führt aber nur spärlich *Granat*. (PG)
Am Flusse Därshet unweit dem Kata-kök-moynak.

51. **Amphibolit** mit wenig *Kalkspat*. (KS)
Gang in (50).

52. **Amphibolit**. (KS)
Sehr reich an *Biotit*. Handstück aus dem Kontakt von (51) gegen (50).

53. Flasriger **Augengneis.**

Ähnelt (47), enthält aber ein wenig *Hornblende.* (PG)

Am Flusse Därshet.

54. **Kalksteinschiefer.**

Loses Handstück aus dem vom Hangenden des (53) herabgefallenen Material.

55. **Amphibolit.** (Pl. V, Fig. 9.)

Pflasterkörniges Gestein mit hauptsächlich *Plagioklas* und *Hornblende.* Der *Plagioklas* ist sehr basisch ($Ab_{55} An_{45}$); er zeigt deutliche inverse Zonarstruktur. — Die *Hornblende* zeigt die gewöhnliche Ausbildung, sie enthält zahlreiche eingeschlossene Magnetitkörner. — *Biotit* und *Quarz* kommen spärlich vor, wie auch die Accessorien: *Magnetit, Apatit* und etwas *Titanit.* (KS)

Das Gestein bildet einen mächtigen Gang in (53).

56. **Amphibolit.** (KS)

Zusammen mit (55).

57. **Gneis.**

Parallelschiefriger, schwach mylonitisierter, *Biotit* und *Hornblende* führender *Plagioklasgneisgranit.* (PG)

Am Flusse Därshet.

58. Weißer **Albitpegmatit** mit *Granat* und *Chlorit.* (PG)

Bildet zahlreiche Adern in (57).

49. Weißer **Mylonitgneis.** (Pl. V, Fig. 10.)

Das Gestein zeigt schon makroskopisch eine ausgeprägte Parallelstruktur. Es führt ungefähr gleiche Mengen von *Plagioklas (Oligoklas-Andesin), Mikroklin* und *Quarz.* Spärlich kommt auch ein grünlich-brauner *Biotit* vor, der hauptsächlich nach den sehr deutlichen Quetschflächen angeordnet ist. In diesen zonenweise auftretenden Quetschflächen zeigt sich eine kräftige Granulierung der Mineralien, besonders ist der *Quarz* angegriffen. Zwischen den Quetschflächen zeigt das Gestein ein gewöhnliches Gneisgranit-Aussehen, wobei jedoch der *Quarz* eine deutlich scheibenförmige Ausbildung hat. (PG)

Steht am südlichen Abhang des Mus-tagh-ata an, S. von dem Gletscher Sar-agil.

60. Biotitreicher **Gneismylonit.** (PG)

Westlich von dem Chum-kar-kashka-Gletscher. Das Fallen ist 18° NW.

61. **Amphibolit.** (KS)

Ähnelt (55), ist aber reicher an *Titanit.* Die *Hornblende* enthält vereinzelte Körner von frischem grünlichem *Augit.*

Mächtige Lagerintrusion im Hangenden von (60).

62. **Sericitschiefer.** (Pl. VI, Fig. 11.)

Sowohl makroskopisch als mikroskopisch zeigt das Gestein eine ausgeprägte Kräuselung infolge lebhafter Faltung. Die Quetschung ist sehr kräftig. Hie und da sieht man als Überbleibsel kleine Linsen, hauptsächlich aus *Quarz* und *Plagioklas* bestehend. Die Quetschflächen sind von *Sericit* überkleidet. (PG) Bei Gumbes nahe dem Flusse Su-bashi. Das Fallen ist 30° NNO.

63. Schöner, weißer **Marmor.** (KK)

Nördlich (62).

64. Kräftig geschieferter **Kalksandstein.**

Quarz und *Plagioklas* sind die gewöhnlichen Bestandteile. Die Matrix besteht aus gestreckten Calcitkristallen. *Sericit* ist gewöhnlich. Er schmiegt sich gern dem Quarz oder den Feldspatkörnern an. (KS)

65. Geschieferter **Kalksandstein.**

Ähnelt völlig (64), aber die Quarzkörner zeigen eine typische Mörtelstruktur als Resultat der Mylonitisierung. (KS)

66. Geschieferter **Kalksandstein** mit Quarzadern.

67. Harter glimmerarmer **Schiefer.** (KS)

Liegendes von (66).

68. Grauschwarzer dolomitischer **Kalkstein.**

Zeigt unter dem Mikroskop eine dichtkristalline Struktur. Etwas brecciös, mit dolomitgefüllten Äderchen. (KK)

Die Stücke (62)—(68) machen eine Suite aus, die das von HEDIN untersuchte Profil von Gumbes nach dem Lager vom 24. Juli 1894 illustriert.

69. **Granat-Hornblende-Gneisgranit.** (Pl. VI, Fig. 12.)

Das Gestein ist schwach granuliert, was eine ausgeprägte Parallelorientierung der Mineralien ergibt.

Von den Feldspaten ist *Plagioklas* (Ab$_{75}$ An$_{25}$) sehr gewöhnlich, der *Mikroklin* aber relativ selten. — Der *Quarz* ist kräftig granuliert. — Von dunklen Mineralien kommen hastingsitartige *Hornblende*, nußbrauner *Biotit* und große poikiloblastische Granatindividuen vor. Sowohl die *Hornblende* als der *Biotit* sind teilweise chloritisiert. (PG)

Stammt wie (70) aus großen Gneisblöcken der Ike-bel-su-Moräne am östlichen Ufer des Kleinen Kara-kul.

70. Weißer feinschiefriger **Gneis.**
Hat eine gewöhnliche granoblastische Struktur mit parallelgeordneten Biotit-schuppen.
Von den Feldspaten kommt nur *Plagioklas* (Ab_{80} An_{20}) vor; er ist das Haupt-mineral des Gesteins. *Quarz* ist gewöhnlich, seltener ist ein schwarzbrauner *Biotit.* Winzige Körner von einem blauvioletten *Turmalin* sind ebenfalls häufig. (PG)

71. Grauweißer **Sericitschiefer** und **Quarzitschiefer.**
Bei der Mündung des Kuntöi-jilga in den Kleinen Kara-kul. (PG)
Das Fallen ist 32° NNO.

72. **Gneismylonit** mit Feldspatadern.
Bei Keng-shevär (Lager vom 25. Juli). Das Fallen ist 32° NNO.

73. Graugrüner **Schiefer.**
Die Handstücke (73)—(81) sind alle von dem westlichen Ufer des Kleinen Kara-kul. — Das Fallen ist 63° NO.

74. **Mylonit.** (KS)
Ähnelt völlig (78). Bildet ein Lager in (73).

75 und 76. Schwarzer **Graphitschiefer.** (KS)
Das Fallen ist 64° NO.

77. **Quarzadern** in (75) und (76).

78. **Granitmylonit.** (Pl. VII, Fig. 13.)
Der Schliff besteht hauptsächlich aus ziemlich großen Quarzfeldern, die eine helycitische Struktur aufweisen. Die Verteilung des Materials ist sehr auf-fallend, der *Quarz* bildet wie der *Mikroklin* deutliche parallele Bänder. Der *Feldspat* (Mikroklin völlig überwiegend) ist nicht so kräftig gequetscht als der Quarz. — Von Glimmern kommt nur *Muscovit* in dünnen Bändern vor. (PG)
Das Fallen ist 40° NO.

79. Kräftig mylonitisierter **Porphyr.** (Pl. VII, Fig. 14.)
Die Einsprenglinge haben deutliche Linsenform. Sie bestehen aus wenig granulierten Albitaugen, kräftig granulierten Mikroklinkörnern und öfters völlig zerquetschten Quarzaugen.
Die stark mylonitisierte Grundmasse besteht aus demselben Material wie die Einsprenglinge, dazu kommen aber lange, undulös auslöschende Bänder von grauweißem *Sericit* und feingraupige Massen von *Epidot.* (PG)

80. **Gneismylonit.**

Kräftig gequetschtes Gestein mit makroskopisch sehr deutlicher Planschieferung. Alle Verschieferungsplänchen sind von *Sericit* ausgekleidet. Gerundete Augen von *Albit* wie auch kräftig zerquetschte Quarzaugen sind spärlich in der Grundmasse vorhanden. (PG)

81. **Grünschiefer.**

Unter dem Mikroskop tritt eine deutliche kleinkräuselige Parallelschieferung hervor, die durch den häufigen *Chlorit* oder *Biotit* zum Ausdruck gebracht wird. Zwischen den Bändern dieser Mineralien tritt eine feinstreifige Grundmasse von *Albit* und *Quarz*-Individuen hervor, die reichlich mit feingraupigem hellgrünem *Epidot* durchmischt ist. (PG)

82. Kräftig geschieferter **Kalksandstein.**

Kalkspat macht den Hauptbestandteil des Gesteins aus. Er hat eine ausgeprägte Parallelorientierung. In dieser Grundmasse liegen abgeplattete *Quarz-* und *Plagioklas-*Körner. *Graphit* bildet dünne Streifen, der Schieferungsrichtung folgend.

Von der Nordostseite des Berges Jenyi. Das Fallen ist 50° NO.

83. Weißer **Marmor.** (KK)

Südlich des Basik-kul.

84. Dichtkristalliner, siderithaltiger **Kalkstein.** (KK)

Nördlich des Basik-kul. Das Fallen ist 30° NNO.

85. Grobkristalliner **Kalkstein.** (KK)

Zeigt ein wenig mit *Quarz* und *Chlorit* bekleidete Verschieferungsplänchen, was dem Gestein einen hellgrünen Farbton gibt.

Nördlich des Basik-kul.

86. Kräftig geschieferter grobkristalliner **Kalkstein** mit muscovit- und graphithaltigen Bändern. (KK)

Nördlich des Basik-kul.

87. **Quarzklümpchen** in (86).

88. Mylonitisierter **Porphyr,** (79) völlig ähnlich. (PG)

Nahe dem nördlichen Ufer des Basik-kul. Das Fallen ist 32° NNO.

89. Mylonitisierter **Porphyr,** (88) völlig ähnlich. (PG)

Landspitze an der östlichen Seite des Basik-kul. Das Fallen ist 26° NNW.

90. **Grünschiefer.** (PG)

Das Gestein besteht aus einer feingraupigen, völlig strukturlosen Masse von *Quarz, Epidot* und *Albit.*

91. **Quarzadern** in einem Sericitschiefer.

Nahe (90), am nordwestlichen Ufer des Basik-kul.

92. **Amphibolgneis.**

Basischer *Plagioklas* (Ab_{65} An_{35}) mit antiperthitischen Einschlüssen von *Mikroklin,* der übrigens für sich nicht vorkommt. — *Quarz* tritt reichlich auf, öfters kräftig granuliert. — Von dunklen Mineralien sind *Hornblende* (gemeine) und nußbrauner *Biotit* gewöhnlich. Sie sind immer parallel orientiert. Accessorisch kommen *Apatit* und *Titanit* vor. (PG)

Von der Westseite des Korumdeh-Gletschers am nördlichen Abhang des Mus-tagh-ata. Das Fallen ist 38° N.

93. **Amphibolit.**

Ähnelt (92), ist aber reicher an *Hornblende* und ärmer an *Quarz.* — Nördlich des Passes Sarimek, mit dem Fallen 38° N.

94 und 95. **Granat-Andalusit-Gneis.** (Pl. VIII, Fig. 15.)

Sehr quarzreich mit Helycitstruktur und sericitbekleideten Verschieferungsflächen. Zwischen den letzteren sieht man Körner von *Andalusit* und *Granat.* — *Graphit* kommt spärlich vor. (KS)

Von der Westseite des Yam-bulak-Gletschers.

96. Flasriger grauweißer **Gneisgranit.** (PG)

Blöcke aus der Moräne des Yam-bulak-Gletschers.

97. Sillimannit-granatreicher **Biotitgneis.** (KS)

Aus der Moräne des Kamper-kishlak-Gletschers.

98. Flasriger, porphyrischer grauweißer **Gneisgranit.**

Die Augen bestehen aus abgeplattetem *Mikroklin* und *Plagioklas.* — Die Grundmasse ist eine Mischung von *Feldspat,* linsenförmigem granuliertem *Quarz* und etwas *Biotit. Chlorit* und *Epidot* reichlich vorhanden. (PG)

Block aus der nördlichen Seitenmoräne des Kamper-kishlak-Gletschers.

99. **Plagioklas-Sericitgneis.**

Parallelstruiertes, nach schmalen Zonen gequetschtes Gestein. Saurer *Plagioklas* (Ab_{93} An_{7}) ist das Hauptmineral, *Mikroklin* und *Quarz* kommen nur spärlich vor. Rotbrauner *Biotit, Sericit* und *Epidot,* etwas *Graphit* und *Granat* machen ein Netzwerk zwischen den übrigen Mineralien aus. (PG)

Steht an an der südlichen Seite des Yam-bulak-Gletschers (5200 m).

19. IX.

100. **Plagioklas-Sericitgneis.** (PG)
      Ähnelt (99). Steht an auf 5600 m Höhe unweit des Yanı-bulak-Gletschers.

101. **Granat-Glimmerschiefer.** (KS)
      Block aus der südlichen Seitenmoräne des Yam-bulak-Gletschers.

102. Mylonitisierter **Plagioklasgneis.** (PG)
      Von der nördlichen Seite des Chal-tumak-Gletschers. Das Fallen ist 21° NNW.

103. Flasriger antiperthitischer **Plagioklasgneis** mit nußbraunem Biotit (PG)
      Oberhalb von (102). Das Fallen ist 20° NNW.

104. Weißer **Marmor.** (KK)
      Bildet eine 100 m dicke Bank in 4750 m Höhe.

105. Unreiner grobkristalliner **Marmor.**
      Enthält reichlichen *Aktinolit*, etwas *Diopsid, Muscovit*, rotbraunen *Biotit*
      und etwas *Titanit.* (KK)
      Loses Handstück oberhalb von (104).

106. Chloritreicher **Plagioklasgneis.** (PG)

107. Biotit-Muscovit reicher **Plagioklasgneis.** (PG)
      (106) und (107) lose Handstücke oberhalb von (104).

108. Kräftig gequetschter antiperthitischer **Plagioklasgneis.** (PG)
      Steht an an der südlichen Seite des südlich vom Chal-tumak-Gletscher
      liegenden Gletschers.

109. **Plagioklasgneis.**
      Mikroklin wie auch *Granat* sind selten. Das Hauptmaterial ist wie ge-
      wöhnlich *Plagioklas* (Ab$_{75}$ An$_{25}$). — Das Gestein ist grobgranuliert mit deut-
      lichen Quetschflächen.. (PG)
      Macht eine Bank in (108) aus.

110. **Plagioklasgneis.** (PG)
      Ähnelt (108). Zusammen mit (108), (109), (111) und (112). Die Lagerung
      ist horizontal.

111 und 112. **Augengneise.** (Pl. VIII, Fig. 16).
      Das Gestein hat eine grobflasrige Ausbildung mit deutlichen Augen von
      Mikroklinperthit, der mit kleinen Quarzkörnern vollgespickt ist. Die Augen
      sind gewöhnlich umkränzt von kleinen *Biotit-* und *Muscovit*-Schuppen, die
      oft kleine Einschlüsse von *Granat* enthalten. — *Plagioklas* ist relativ selten,
      er liegt in Form kleiner, nicht gequetschter Individuen in kräftig zerquetschten
      Quarzpartien. — Der *Biotit* ist teilweise chloritisiert. (PG)

113. **Plagioklasgneis.** (PG)

Ähnelt (108). Zusammen mit (114), lose Handstücke aus der Seitenmoräne des Chum-kar-kashka-Gletschers.

114. **Plagioklasgneis.**

Das Gestein besteht hauptsächlich aus ungestreiftem oder wenig gestreiftem (saurem) *Plagioklas*, der in größeren gestreckten Individuen zwischen Quarzmaterial in der Schieferungsrichtung liegt. Den Schieferungsflächen folgen Bänder von grünlichem *Biotit* und *Epidot*. Schmale Quetschzonen durchziehen das Gestein. (PG)

Blöcke aus der Seitenmoräne des Chum-kar-kashka-Gletschers.

115. **Granatglimmerschiefer** mit Plagioklasaugen.

Das Gestein hat eine Grundmatrix von *Quarz* und grünlichbraunem *Biotit*. In dieser Matrix liegen Porphyroblasten von *Granat* und ausgezogene *Cordierit*-Individuen. Daneben kommen scharfbegrenzte Augen von ziemlich idiomorphen antiperthitischen *Plagioklas*-Individuen mit wenig *Quarz* vergesellschaftet vor. Ein teilweise fibrolitähnlicher *Sillimannit* ist spärlich. Sehr gewöhnlich sind aber winzige Körner von einem olivgrünen *Turmalin*.

Wahrscheinlich ist das Gestein ein feldspatisierter Glimmerschiefer. Das Fallen ist 18° N 40° O. Steht an bei dem Chum-kar-kashka-Gletscher.

116. Weißer **Albitpegmatit.** (PG)

Steht an unmittelbar unter (115).

117. Grauweißer gesprenkelter **Plagioklasgneisgranit.**

Mittelkörniges Gestein. *Plagioklas* (Ab$_{75}$ An$_{25}$) herrscht vor; *Mikroklin* dagegen ist nur spärlich vorhanden. — *Quarz* ist gewöhnlich. — Von dunklen Mineralien ist *Hornblende* am häufigsten. Sie zeigt kräftigen Pleochroismus in dunkelolivgrünen und schwärzlich blaugrünen Tönen, die Doppelbrechung ist auffallend niedrig und der Achsenwinkel sehr klein (das Mineral erscheint beinahe einachsig). Die *Hornblende* kommt in kleinen, miteinander assoziierten Körnern vor, die schon makroskopisch sehr deutlich sind. — Der *Biotit* ist frisch und schön, zeigt kräftigen Pleochroismus in gelben und dunkelbraunen Farben. Er kommt aber ebenso wie ein rötlicher *Granat* nur spärlich vor. Hellgrüner *Epidot* mit hoher Doppelbrechung (wahrscheinlich *Pistazit*) und *Calcit* kommen selten vor. — Von Accessorien sind *Turmalin* und *Apatit* zu nennen. (PG)

Die Handstücke (117)—(123) sind Lesesteine aus der südlichen Seitenmoräne des Tergen-bulak-Gletschers.

118. Grauweißer **Plagioklasgneisgranit** mit Hornblendestriemen. (PG)
Ähnelt (117).

119. Weißer, hornblendegesprenkelter **Plagioklasgneis.**
Petrographisch ähnelt er völlig (117), hat aber eine beinahe granulitische Struktur. (PG)

120. Hornblende führender, weißer **Granit** von frischem Aussehen. (PG)

121. Granatführender, granulitischer **Plagioklasgneis.** (Pl. IX, Fig. 17 und 18).
Ähnelt (117) und (119). Hie und da kommen Verwachsungen zwischen hastingsitischer *Hornblende* und *Granat*, wie auch *Granat* mit *Calcit* oder *Magnetit* vor. (PG)

122. Grobflasriger, weißer **Gneisgranit** mit großen abgeplatteten Mikroklinaugen und Chloritstriemen. (PG)

123. Durch sekundäre Färbung rotgefärbter **Plagioklasgneis.**
Plagioklas (Ab$_{90}$ An$_{10}$) überwiegt völlig. *Mikroklin* ist spärlich vorhanden, dazu rotbrauner *Biotit*. — Die Struktur ist granulitisch mit undulös auslöschendem *Quarz*. (PG)

124. **Plagioklasgneismylonit.** (Pl. X, Fig. 19 und 20).
Feingequetschte Grundmasse von *Plagioklas* und *Quarz*. *Chlorit* und *Epidot* sind häufig. — Quarzadern durchziehen das Gestein nach kleinen Querspalten. (PG)
Vom Wege nach dem Gipfel des Mus-tagh-ata in einer Höhe von 5950 m.

125. **Sandstein.**
Ein hornfelsartiges Aggregat, in dem sienafarbiger *Biotit* um die Quarzkörner auskristallisiert ist. Die klastische Struktur sieht man sehr deutlich an den gerundeten größeren Quarzkörnern.
Die Handstücke (125)—(144) stammen von einem Ausflug Dr. HEDINS nach Pamirski Post und westlich davon.
(125) steht in dem Quellgebiet des Kosh-agil, eines Nebenflusses des Murghab (Ak-su), an.

126. Quarzhaltiger, etwas Kalkspat führender **Tonschiefer.**
Unweit südlich (127).

127. Grauer, oolithischer fossilführender **Kalkstein.** (KT)
(Siehe die Beschreibung von DIETRICH S. 177.)
Steht bei der südlichen Biegung des Murghab, östlich von Pamirski Post an.

128. Oolithischer **Kalkstein**. (KT)
(Von DIETRICH beschrieben, S. 177.) Unweit nördlich (127).

129. **Sandsteinschiefer** mit kalkspatgefüllten Spalten.

130. Dichter gelbgrauer **Kalkstein** mit beginnender Umkristallisierung.
Enthält kleine Hornsteingeröllchen.

131. Schwarzer **Tonschiefer**.

132. Gelbgrauer dichter **Kalkstein**.

133. Quarzreicher **Mylonit**.
In der feingequetschten Grundmasse liegen kleine eckige *Quarz*-Fragmente.
Plagioklas-Trümmer sind gewöhnlich. (PG)

134. **Kalksandstein**.
Dichtes Zement, in welchem wohlgerundete Körner von *Quarz* und wenig
Plagioklas sichtbar sind. (KT)

135. Schwarzer **Tonschiefer** mit quarzreichen Schichten. (M)

136. Schwarzer **Tonschiefer**. (M)

137. Schwarzer **Tonschiefer** mit quarzreichen Schichten. (M)
Die Handstücke (129)—(135) sind am Wege vom Murghab nach dem
Passe Agalshar gesammelt, die Handstücke (136) und (137) zwischen Pass
Agalshar und Chatir-tash.

138. **Plagioklasgneismylonit**. (PG)
Wenig westlich von Chatir-tash.

139. Dichtkristalliner **Kalkstein**.
Unweit westlich von (138).

140. Chlorit-Epidot reicher **Plagioklasgneis**. (PG)
Von Alichur unweit des Yeshil-kul.

141. **Plagioklasgneismylonit**.
Vom Kleinen Mardschania unweit des Yeshil-kul.

142. Quarzreicher **Biotit-Plagioklasgneisgranit**.
Von Gunt nahe dem Yeshil-kul.

143. Oolithischer **Kalkstein**.
Von DIETRICH beschrieben, S. 177. Steht bei Naisa-tash an.
Nach brieflicher Mitteilung von Prof. K. LEUCHS, München, gehört das
Gestein der permisch-triassischen Reihe an, welche STOLICZKA dort nachwies.

144. **Mylonit.**
Etwas östlich von Mus-kuruk.

145. **Biotit-Hornblende-Plagioklasgneisgranit.** (PG)
Block aus der Moräne von Kara-korum.

146. **Sericitschiefer** mit groben Quarzadern.
Zusammen mit (145).

147. Hornblendereicher **Plagioklasgneisgranit.** (PG)
(147) und (148) sind Handstücke aus riesigen Blöcken von dem Schutt-kegel des Kara-korum.

148. Feinschiefriger basischer amphibolreicher **Plagioklasgneis.** (PG)

149. Gewöhnlicher **Biotit-Hornblende-Plagioklasgneisgranit.** (PG)
Steht an bei dem Lager vom 23. September 1894, mit dem Fallen 75° SW.

150. **Plagioklasgneismylonit.** (PG)
Steht an bei Teressössö, mit dem Fallen 58° O.

151. Harter **Biotitschiefer** mit Quarzadern (KS)
Steht an bei Merke am Kusen-darya, mit dem Fallen 7° WNW.

152. Gesprenkelter **Biotit-Gneisgranit.** (PG)
Steht am Kusen-darya an.

153. Kräftig geschieferter kristalliner **Kalkstein.** (KK)
Steht bei Tamde-jilga an.

154 und 155. Kräftig gepreßter kalkhaltiger **Schiefer.** (KS)
Nahe dem Suget-jilga.

(1895.)

156. (1). **Plagioklasgneis** mit beginnender Mylonitisierung.
Der *Plagioklas* ist stark umgewandelt, mit reichlichem feinstaubigen *Epidot* in albitischer Substanz. — *Mikroklin* kommt nicht vor, auch der immer gequetschte *Quarz* ist spärlich. *Calcit* ist auffallend reichlich, wie auch grasgrüner *Chlorit* und kleine *Pyritkörner.* (PG)
Von Kirk-sheit. Das Fallen ist 28° N 10° O.

157. (2). Kristalliner **Kalkstein**.

Das Gestein zeigt deutliche Spuren der Dynamometamorphose, die Calcitkriställchen sind nämlich öfters gebogen und zeigen kräftige undulöse Auslöschung. Reste von unbestimmbaren Fossilien sind sichtbar. (KK) Etwas westlich von (156). Das Fallen ist 28° N 10° O.

158. (3). **Grünschiefer**.

Chlorit und *Epidot* bilden den Hauptteil des Gesteins. Spärliche Relikte von *Hornblende* und ein wenig *Albit* kommen vor. (PG) Steht bei Uruguma an. Das Fallen ist 23° S 60° O.

159. (4). **Plagioklasgneismylonit**. (PG)

Sehr kräftig gequetscht und saussuritisiert. Wenig westlich von (158). Das Fallen ist 30° O 40° S.

160. (5). Dichtkristalliner **Kalkstein** mit kalkspaterfüllten Spalten. (KT) Steht ein wenig westlich von (159) an. Das Fallen ist 13° S 60° W.

161. (6). **Kalksandstein**. (KT)

Das Zement besteht aus feinkristallinem *Kalkspat*, in welchem Körner und Splitter von *Quarz, Plagioklas* und wenig *Mikroklin* liegen. Oberhalb des Lagers 14.—16. Juli 1895. Das Fallen ist 10° N 60° O.

162. (7). **Plagioklasgneismylonit**. (PG)

Nahe dem Ulug-art-davan. Das Fallen ist 35° O.

163. (8). Grober **Sericitschiefer**. (PG)

An dem Abhang unterhalb des Passes Ulug-art-davan. Das Fallen ist 21° NNO.

164. (9). **Kalkschiefer**.

Steht westlich von (163) an. Das Fallen ist 10° SSO.

165. (10). Feldspathaltiger **Sandstein**.

Deutlich klastische Struktur mit Körnern von *Quarz* und *Plagioklas*. Das Zement zeigt eine schwache diagenetische Umkristallisation. (KT) Bei der Mündung des Tuyuk-dur. Das Fallen ist 39° S 23° W.

166. (11). **Biotitschiefer**.

Vielleicht ist das Gestein ein umkristallisierter *Phyllit*. Enthält zahlreiche Pegmatitäderchen. (KS) Steht in der Gegend von Muchi an (3440). Das Fallen ist 15° S 22° W.

167. (12). Quarzreicher **Biotitschiefer**. (KS)

Ähnelt (166), führt aber reichlicher *Muscovit*.
Anstehend bei Kün-times. Das Fallen ist $72°$ S $22°$ W.

168. (13). **Plagioklasgranit**.

Hauptmineralien sind *Plagioklas* (Ab_{90} An_{10}) und *Quarz*. *Mikroklin* fehlt ganz. Rotbrauner *Biotit* und heller *Muscovit*. Das Gestein zeigt eine schwache Granulierung. (PG)

Steht bei Kum-jilga an. Das Fallen ist $29°$ S $24°$ O.

169. (14). Quarzreicher **Biotitschiefer** mit wenig Muscovit und Fibrolith. (KS)

Nahe Tash-kiya. Das Fallen ist $26°$ W.

170. (15). **Plagioklasgneis** mit beginnender Mylonitisierung. (PG)

Mikroklin fehlt ganz. Der *Plagioklas* ist öfters gebogen, der *Quarz* aber völlig zerquetscht.

Steht am Chaker-agil-kul an.

171. (16). **Hornblende-Gneisgranit** des gewöhnlichen Typus. (PG)

Steht am nördlichen Ufer des Chaker-agil-kul an. Das Fallen ist $40°$ S $24°$ W.

172. (17). Feinkörniger, graugrüner, epidotreicher **Gneisgranit**. (PG)

Anstehend bei Bulung-kul. Das Fallen ist $49°$ S $21°$ W.

173. (18). Weiße **Albitpegmatitäderchen** aus Gneisgranit. (PG)

Anstehend bei Bulung-kul. Das Fallen ist $66°$ S.

174. (19). **Gneisgranit** mit beginnender Mylonitisierung. (PG)

Am Tengi anstehend. Das Fallen ist $25°$ O $10°$ S.

175. (20). **Saussuritamphibolit**. (PG)

Steht am Hunserab, südlich von Masar. Das Fallen ist $14°$ S $21°$ W.

176. (21). **Hornblende-Gneisgranit**. (PG)

Vom Passe (4849) nördlich von Ulu-tör.

177. (22). Salischer **Plagioklasgneisgranit**. (PG)

Wenig nördlich vom Uprang-davan. Das Fallen ist $24°$ N $30°$ O.

178. (23). **Plagioklasgneisgranit**. (PG)

Das Gestein zeigt eine granitische Struktur, jedoch sieht man deutliche Spuren der Kataklase: der *Quarz* ist granuliert und zeigt immer undulöse Auslöschung, die *Plagioklas*-Individuen sind öfters gebogen oder zerbrochen. — Der *Plagioklas* hat die Zusammensetzung eines *Andesins*.

Er ist bisweilen antiperthitisch, mit kleinen Einschlüssen von *Mikroklin*. Die *Plagioklas*-Individuen haben öfters idiomorphe Ausbildung. Rotbrauner *Biotit* mit kleinen Einschlüssen von einem hellroten *Granat* ist spärlich. *Mikroklin* für sich allein fehlt dagegen ganz. Zusammen mit (177).

179. (24). **Marmor.** (KT)

Von DIETRICH beschrieben, S. 177. Das Fallen ist 53° O 14° S. Zusammen mit (180) und (181) vom Uprang-davan.

180. (25). **Kalkstein.** (KT)

Von DIETRICH beschrieben, S. 177. Loses Handstück zusammen mit (26).

181. (26). Plagioklashaltiger **Sandstein.** (KT)

Loses Handstück zusammen mit (25).

182. (27). Schwarzer **Phyllit.** (M)

Nördlich von dem Passe Uprang-davan. Das Fallen ist 12° WSW.

183. (28). Fehlt in der Sammlung.

184. (29). Kristalliner **Kalkstein** mit zahlreichen Pyritkörnern. (KK)

Am Kara-su. Das Fallen ist 73° S.

185. (30). Schwarzer **Phyllit.** (M)

Nordöstlich von dem Passe Ilik-su. Das Fallen is 87° N 30° O.

186. (31). Oolithischer **Kalkstein.** (KT)

Von DIETRICH beschrieben, S. 177. Das Fallen ist 68° N 46° O. Bei Ilik-su.

187. (32) **Phyllit.** (M)

Nahe Sarik-jilga am Tagdumbash. Das Fallen ist 64° S 60° W.

188. (33). **Plagioklas-Muscovitgranit.**

Das Gestein hat eine gewöhnliche granitische Struktur. Hauptmineralien sind *Plagioklas* und *Quarz*. — Der *Plagioklas* hat die Zusammensetzung des *Albits*, er stammt aber deutlich von einem anorthitreichen *Plagioklas* ab, denn der *Albit* ist mit kleinen Zoisitkörnern vollgespickt. — Der *Albit* zeigt gegenüber dem *Quarz* deutliche Idiomorphie, der letztere besitzt undulöse Auslöschung, ist aber nicht granuliert.

Anhäufungen von kleinen *Epidot-Chlorit*-Individuen sind häufig. Sie sind deutliche Zersetzungsprodukte der *Hornblende*. — *Muscovit* ist

20. IX.

sehr reichlich vertreten, teils in Form größerer Tafeln, teils als winzige Schuppen. (PG)

Steht bei Kamar-utuk an.

189. (34). Weißer **Granitporphyr** mit Quarzeinsprenglingen. (PG)

Steht bei dem Vakjir-Paß an.

190. (35). Brecciöser **Granit**. (PG)

Zusammen mit (191) bei Tash-kupriuk. Das Fallen ist 87° W.

191. (36.) **Tonschiefer.** (M)

Anstehend bei Bozai-Gumbaz. Das Fallen ist 86° NW.

192. (37). Quarzreicher kalkhaltiger **Schiefer.**

Steht nördlich an dem Chakmaktin-kul an.

193. (38). Fehlt in der Sammlung.

194. (39). Zwei Handstücke, das erste ein **Grünschiefer**, das zweite ein **Zwei-glimmergranit.** (PG)

Am Shinde westlich von Lakshak-bel. Das Fallen ist 27° O 17° S.

195. (40). Fossilreicher **Kalkstein.** (KT)

Von DIETRICH beschrieben, S. 177.

Unweit von Kuse-jilga. Das Fallen ist 51° S 19° W.

196. (41). Fossilhaltiger **Kalkstein.** (KT)

Von DIETRICH beschrieben, S. 177.

Nahe dem Lakshak-bel. Das Fallen ist 81° N 60° O.

197. (42). **Olivinbasalt.**

Zeigt Intersertalstruktur; in einer Grundmasse von kleinen Plagioklas-leisten, kleinen Körnern von serpentinisiertem *Pyroxen* und einem geringen Rest von gelbbraunem Glas liegen spärliche Einsprenglinge von *Olivin* und *Plagioklas;* der letztere ist saussuritisiert.

Steht östlich von Lakshak-bel an.

198. (43). Kristalliner **Sandstein.**

Steht ein wenig westlich von Keng-shevär an.

199. (44). Dichter grauer **Kalkstein.** (KT)

Zusammen mit (43). Das Fallen ist 78° N 20° O.

200. (45). Grober **Porphyrgranit** mit bis 5 cm großen Mikroklinaugen. (PG).

Nahe dem Kara-korum. Das Fallen ist 40° N 30° O.

201. (46). **Syenit.** (PG).

Mittelkörnige Granitstruktur. Das Hauptmineral ist ein *Mikroklin* mit spärlichen Perthitschnüren. *Quarz* kommt sehr spärlich vor. — Von dunklen Mineralien kommt nur ein pleochroitischer *Pyroxen* vor. Er zeigt *a* und *b* in gelbgrünen Tönen, *c* ist grasgrün. Wahrscheinlich ist er ein *Ägirinaugit*, der öfters zonar gebaut ist und helle oder farblose, *Augit*-reiche Kerne aufweist. Accessorisch kommt *Apatit* und *Titanit* vor.

Am Shinde nahe Yangelik. Das Fallen ist sehr steil (fast vertikal) gegen O 35° N.

202. (47). Mittelkörniger **Plagioklasgranit.** (PG)

Steht bei Shinde westlich von Tash-kurgan an.

203. (48). **Glimmerschiefer** mit Pegmatitäderchen. (KS)

Bei Toglan-shah. Das Fallen ist 77° N 10° O.

204. (49). **Quarz-Granat-Biotitschiefer.** (KS)

Bei Särghak (4032 m). Das Fallen ist 69° S 10° W.

205. (50.) Biotitführender **Gneisgranit.** (PG)

Mikroklin und *Plagioklas* kommen in gleichen Mengen vor. Der *Quarz* ist kräftig granuliert.

Steht bei Bäldir an. Das Fallen ist 41° S 20° W.

206. (51). **Plagioklasgneis.** (PG)

Enthält wenig *Graphit*.

Steht bei Bäldir-khan-kelide an. Das Fallen ist 59° S 19° W.

207. (52). **Chloritschiefer.**

Bei Ütshe nördlich von Masar. Das Fallen ist 37° S 20° W.

208. (53). Hellgrauer **Quarzit.**

An dem Passe Kandahar. Das Fallen ist 70° N 50° O.

209. (54). Chloritführender hellgrauer **Gneisgranit.** (PG)

Bei Lab-dilush anstehend. Das Fallen ist sehr steil (fast 90°) gegen N 20° O.

210. (55). **Grünschiefer.** (PG).

Saussuritisierter *Amphibolit* mit Adern von *Sphalerit* und *Schwefelkies.* Nahe Chirakunch (3037). Das Fallen ist 35° O 14° S.

211. (56). **Quarzsyenit.**

Granitische Struktur. Sowohl *Plagioklas* als auch *Mikroklin* kommen vor. Die *Plagioklase* sind öfters als lange idiomorphe Prismen ausgebildet. Ihre Zusammensetzung ist ungefähr Ab_{74} An_{26}. Selten in *Zoisit-* und *Sericit-*Massen umgewandelt. — Der *Mikroklin* ist perthitisch und enthält öfters kleine Einschlüsse eines basischen *Plagioklases*, die von *Myrmekit* umkränzt sind. *Quarz* kommt spärlich vor. — Eine gemeine *Hornblende* ist das einzige dunkle Mineral. Von Accessorien sind *Apatit, Titanit* und *Magnetit* zu nennen. (PG)

Steht ein wenig nördlich von dem Lager vom 30. September 1895 an.

212. (57). **Quarzsyenit.**

Ähnelt völlig (211), mitten in den *Hornblende-*Individuen sieht man jedoch Relikte von einem grünlichen *Augit*. (PG)

Steht bei Achema an.

213. (58). Granulierter **Quarzsyenit.**

Ähnelt (212) und (213), zeigt aber eine kräftige Granulierung. Die *Hornblende* ist in *Chlorit* und der *Plagioklas* in *Epidot-Sericit-*Massen umgewandelt. (PG)

Steht bei Tichman an.

214. (59). Granulierter **Quarzsyenit.** (PG)

Ähnelt völlig (213).

Nahe Lenger. Das Fallen ist 40° N 60° O.

215. (60). Granulitischer **Gneis.** (PG)

Steht bei Shäravian an. Das Fallen ist etwa 90° S 20° W.

216. (61). **Biotitschiefer.** (KS)

Am Tong nahe Kengerabun. Das Fallen ist 55° S 23° W.

217. (62). Chloritisierter und saussuritisierter **Gneisgranit.** (PG)

Steht bei Kuruk-lenger an.

218. (63). Weißer **Pegmatit.** (PG)

Anstehend bei Ghar-masar. Das Fallen ist 74° S 28° W.

219. (64). **Quarzit.**

Steht bei Panje-baskan an. Das Fallen ist 51° S 21° W

220. (65). **Chloritschiefer.**

Bei Topusghan. Das Fallen ist 26° S 48° W.

221. (69). **Amphibolit** mit Schwefelkieskörnern.
Bei Sugetlik anstehend. Das Fallen ist 21° S 63° W.

222. (67). Chlorithaltiger heller **Gneisgranit.** (PG)
Von dem Passe Arpa-talak. Das Fallen ist 76° S 21° W.

223. (68). Chlorithaltiger grüner **Syenit.** (PG)
Steht bei Igis-arik-karaul an.

224. (69). Grauer **Kalkstein.** (KT)
Wie (70) von DIETRICH beschrieben, S. 177.
Nahe Kisil-kor. Das Fallen ist 14° O 56° S.

225. (70). Oolithischer **Kalkstein.** (KT)
Von DIETRICH beschrieben, S. 177.
Bei Unkurluk anstehend. Das Fallen ist 68° O 14° S.

226. (71). Saussuritisierter **Amphibolit** (Grünschiefer).
Steht bei Kush-utek an. Das Fallen ist 53° S 25° W.

227. (72). Hellgrauer feinkristalliner **Kalkstein.** (KT)
Zwischen Tokus und Baku anstehend. Das Fallen ist 47° S 26° W.

228. (73). **Foraminiferenkalkstein.** (KT)
Von DIETRICH beschrieben, S. 177.
Steht bei Ütsh-bäldir an. Das Fallen ist 34° S.

229. (74). Hellgrauer **Kalkstein.** (KT)
Nahe Kelik. Das Fallen ist 90° S 26° W.

230. (75). Rötlicher, rostiger, feldspatreicher **Sandstein.** (KT)
Unter (76) von Kisil-kiya. Das Fallen ist 47° N 80° O.

231. (76). **Kalkstein,** (75) überlagernd. (KT)
Das Fallen ist 40° N.

232. (77). **Foraminiferen-Korallenkalk.** (KT)
Von DIETRICH beschrieben, S. 177.
Wie (78) ein wenig östlich von Kisil-kiya anstehend. Das Fallen ist 63° N 80° O.

233. (78). Kalkiger **Glaukonitsandstein.**
Von DIETRICH beschrieben, S. 176.

179

III. KAPITEL.

PETROGRAPHISCHE ÜBERSICHT DES HANDSTÜCKMATERIALS.

Bei einem Versuch, eine übersichtliche Darstellung des Materials zu geben, erweist es sich als vorteilhaft, von der üblichen Klasseneinteilung, wie sie z. B. ROSENBUSCH vorgenommen hat, beträchtlich abzuweichen. So wäre es z. B. des Zusammenhanges wegen sehr unzweckmäßig, die petrographisch sehr charakteristischen, weit verbreiteten Granite und ihre metamorphen Derivate, Gneisgranite und Mylonite, zu teilen. In der Gruppe »Kristalline Schiefer« sind unter anderem die aus Grünsteinen entstandenen Schiefer untergebracht, ebenso wie Schiefer von vermutetem Paratypus und die von den Graniten deutlich beeinflußten Sedimentgesteine, die durch Kontakt- und Regionalmetamorphose eine meist grobkristalline Ausbildung erfahren haben.

Eine ganze Reihe zum Teil fossilführender, wahrscheinlich alttertiärer oder spätkretazeischer Ablagerungen von feldspatreichen Sandsteinen, Kalksteinen, dichten feinkristallinen Kalksteinen und Oolithkalksteinen zeigt einen so deutlichen Feldzusammenhang, daß sie zweckmäßig zusammen beschrieben werden müssen.

Die Übersicht erhält folgendes Aussehen:

I. Die Zentralgranite und ihre metamorphen Derivate (PG = Pamirgneise).
    A. Syenitische Glieder der Zentralgranite.
    B. Granitporphyrische Glieder der Zentralgranite.
    C. Granite.
    D. Metamorphe Derivate der Granite.

II. Kristalline Schiefer. (KS)
    A. Amphibolite.
    B. Grünschiefer.
    C. Glimmerreiche Schiefer.

III. Kristalline Kalksteine. (KK)

IV. Sedimentgesteine, schwächere Metamorphose aufweisend (M = mesozoische Ablagerungen).

V. Sedimentgesteine, meistenteils nicht metamorphosiert oder schwache Metamorphose zeigend (KT = Kreide-Tertiär-Ablagerungen).

I. DIE ZENTRALGRANITE UND IHRE METAMORPHEN DERIVATE.

Von allen Forschern, welche die in dieser Schrift behandelten Gegenden bereist haben, wird das Vorkommen granitischer Gesteine in den Zentralgebieten der Gebirgsketten bestätigt. Im Tien-shan ist im großen gesehen das Gleiche der Fall.[1] Der Ausdruck »Zentralgranite» scheint daher besonders geeignet zu sein, das Vorkommen dieser Eruptivgesteine in den Gebirgsketten wiederzugeben und ihre tektonische Lage als betont syntektonische oder orogenetische Intrusionen zu kennzeichnen.

In ihrem petrographisch-chemischen Charakter zeigen die Zentralgranite und ihre gneisigen Formen Ähnlichkeiten mit den tonalitischen Gesteinen der österreichischen Alpen sowie mit den westamerikanischen Granodioriten. Ebenso liegt eine Annäherung an die aus den schwedisch-norwegischen Hochgebirgen bekannten Trondhjemite vor. Auf Grund des durchgehend hohen Quarzgehalts der Pamirgesteine hat der Verfasser jedoch die Bezeichnung Granit beibehalten.

Mit Ausnahme einer Reihe untergeordneter syenitischer und saurer granit-porphyrischer oder porphyrgranitischer Glieder sind die Zentralgranite und ihre Gneise ausgesprochene Plagioklasgesteine mit hervortretendem Biotitgehalt oder Biotit-hornblendegehalt. Dazu kommt oft auch Muscovit- oder primärer Chloritgehalt, sowie auch zum Teil Granat und Kalkspat, welch letztere in einigen vereinzelten Fällen den Charakter wesentlicher Gesteinsmineralien annehmen. Im Anschluß an die ganze Granitreihe kommen augenscheinlich sehr oft Pegmatitbildungen vor. Sie treten teils in größeren gangartigen Partien auf, teils bilden sie, und zwar augenscheinlich in weit größerer Ausdehnung, kleinere Adern, welche die Gesteine entsprechend vorhandenen Verschieferungsebenen durchziehen. Die pegmatitischen Adern scheinen auch in ganz großem Umfang in die diese Granite umgebenden kristallinen Schiefer einzudringen, indem sie mutmaßlich nicht unwesentliche metasomatische Veränderungen derselben verursachen (z. B. Feldspatisierung, wie in einigen Fällen beobachtet wurde).

Vom petrographisch-chemischen Standpunkt aus weist die ganze Granitgruppe große Eigentümlichkeiten auf, die ihre Übereinstimmung mit den schwedisch-norwegischen Hochgebirgsgraniten deutlich betonen.[2] Außer dem Granat- und Kalkspatgehalt deutet das Vorkommen von primärem Muscovit- und Chloritgehalt, ebenso wie der Pegmatitreichtum und das durch BOGDANOWITSCH bekannte häufige Vorkommen von *Nephrit* darauf hin, daß das Granitmagma im ganzen auffällig wasserreich war und daß sich in ihm und in seinem Kontaktgebiet hydrochemische Prozesse abgespielt haben.

---

[1] Vgl. z. B. BOGDANOWITSCH, sowie H. KEIDEL und ST. RICHARZ, Ein Profil durch den nördlichen Teil des zentralen Tian-schan. Abh. math.-phys. Kl. d. Akad. d. Wiss. München 23, 1906. Auch LEUCHS, Geologische Untersuchungen in Chalyktau, Temurlyktau, Dsungarischen Alatau (Tienschan). Abh. math.-phys. Kl. d. Akad. d. Wiss. München 25, 1912.

[2] V. M. GOLDSCHMIDT, Geologisch-petrographische Studien im Hochgebirge des südlichen Norwegen, V. Die Injektionsmetamorphose im Stavanger-Gebiete. Kristiania 1921.

A. SYENITISCHE GLIEDER DER ZENTRALGRANITE.

Über das quantitative Vorkommen der Syenite im Pamir ist ganz wenig bekannt. Sie werden von BOGDANOWITSCH erwähnt und beschrieben; HEDIN hat einige Handstücke davon gesammelt. Strukturell haben sie gewöhnlichen Granithabitus mit hypidiomorphkörniger Ausbildung. Von Feldspaten kommt spärlich *Plagioklas* mit der Zusammensetzung des *Andesin* und in reichlicher Menge stark perthitischer *Mikroklin* vor. Die *Plagioklase* haben oft gute Idiomorphie und prismatische Ausbildung. Der *Mikroklin* hat bisweilen angedeutete Augenbildung und schließt oft (ebenso wie in den Porphyrgraniten) kleine basische Plagioklaskerne ein, die gewöhnlich einen schönen Myrmekitkranz haben. Von dunklen Mineralien kommen *Hornblende* und *Augit* vor. Den letzteren sieht man meistens als Reliktpartien in gemeiner *Hornblende*, die sich wohl auf Kosten des *Augits* bildete. *Glimmer* scheinen in den Syeniten zu fehlen mit Ausnahme von *Chlorit*, der aus der *Hornblende* gleichzeitig mit der Saussuritisierung des *Plagioklases* sekundär entstand.

B. GRANITPORPHYRISCHE GLIEDER DER ZENTRALGRANITE.

Von solchen sind nur ein paar Handstücke in der Serie vorhanden. Sie enthalten Einsprenglinge von *Plagioklas, Mikroklin* und *Quarz*. Die Grundmasse hat ungefähr dieselbe Zusammensetzung wie die Einsprenglinge. Von Glimmern sieht man nur *Muscovit*.

C. GRANITE.

Echte Granite mit vorwiegend mittelkörniger granitischer Ausbildung nehmen oft große Teile der inneren Partien des Granitmassivs ein. Sie haben oft typisch granitische, d. h. unter ruhigen Verhältnissen entstandene hypidiomorphkörnige Struktur.

Trotzdem diese typisch granitische Ausbildung vorzuherrschen scheint, kann man doch im einzelnen eine ganze Reihe von Strukturvariationen unterscheiden. So kommen untergeordnet Typen von feinkörnigen Granitporphyren angefangen (siehe oben) bis zu ganz groben Porphyrgraniten vor. Die ersteren erscheinen meistens in den Randgebieten des Granitmassivs oder in kleineren, augenscheinlich von diesem auslaufenden Lagerintrusionen. Meistens sind sie deutlich metamorphosiert. — Die Verbreitung der porphyrgranitischen Gesteine im Verhältnis zu den mittelkörnigen ist bei den wenigen geognostischen Beobachtungen, die es bisher gibt, schwer näher zu präzisieren. Offenbar kommen sie beinah überall vor, oft in Wechsellagerung mit mittelkörnigen Typen. Ihre Strukturbildung scheint nahe verbunden zu sein mit ihrem chemischen Charakter als intermediäre Granite mit ungefähr gleichviel Kali- und Natrongehalt oder mit etwas betontem Kaligehalt. Quantitativ spielen diese Granittypen entschieden eine untergeordnete Rolle im Verhältnis zu den mittelkörnigen.

Die mittelkörnigen Granite bilden in petrographischer Hinsicht eine in engen Grenzen variierende Serie. Ihr hauptsächlichster Charakterzug ist der Reichtum an *Plagioklas* von der Zusammensetzung des *Oligoklasandesins* oder *Andesins*. Der *Kalifeldspat* (immer *Mikroklin*) kommt in dieser Gruppe nur ganz untergeordnet als freier Bestandteil, häufiger in Form antiperthitischer Einschlüsse vor. Sehr oft (vielleicht meistens) fehlt er vollständig, wobei der vorhandene Kaligehalt offenbar von den Glimmern vollständig absorbiert wird. Der Quarzgehalt ist in der ganzen Gesteinsserie auffallend hoch, trotz des relativ hohen Anorthitgehalts des *Plagioklases*. Von dunklen Mineralien kommen *Hornblende* und *Biotit* gewöhnlich vereinigt vor, der letztere tritt jedoch oft allein auf, wobei der Anorthitgehalt des *Plagioklases* sinkt. Der *Biotit* ist oft mit *Muscovit* und sogar mit *Chlorit*[1] vereinigt. Ein oft beobachtetes, im allgemeinen wenig bekanntes Mineral der Granite ist ein almandinartiger *Granat*, der meist accessorisch vorkommt, aber bisweilen den Charakter eines wesentlichen Gesteinsminerals annimmt.

Von accessorischen Mineralien treten *Titanit* und *Apatit* mehr in den Vordergrund, außerdem kommt *Magnetit* vor, und in einigen Fällen ist auch *Orthit* beobachtet worden. In einer Reihe von Gesteinen kann auch *Kalkspat* ganz häufig sein, ebenso wie *Epidot* (gewöhnlich auf Kosten des *Plagioklases* ausgebildet) oft in den chloritführenden Graniten vorkommt.

Die *Hornblende* und der *Biotit* haben durchgehends einen ganz besonderen Charakter. Die erstere zeichnet sich optisch durch ihre blaugrünen oder dunkelblaugrünen Interferenzfarben aus, während gleichzeitig der Achsenwinkel auffällig klein ist. Mineralogisch scheint sie sich also derjenigen eisenoxydulreichen Abart der gemeinen *Hornblende* zu nähern, die unter dem Namen *Hastingsit* bekannt ist. — Der *Biotit* zeigt optisch sehr kräftig hervortretende rotbraune oder schwarzbraune Interferenzfarben und hat also starke Annäherung an lepidomelanartigen *Biotit*.

Mit Hinsicht auf die Erstarrungsfolge der Mineralien zeigen die mittelkörnigen Granite eine ausgeprägte Kontinuität. Außer den Nebenmineralien *Apatit*, *Titanit* und *Magnetit* bildet sich *Plagioklas* in einem frühen Stadium aus. Wahrscheinlich hat der am frühsten ausgebildete *Plagioklas* eine größere Basizität gehabt, als man jetzt in den Gesteinen konstatieren kann. Dies ergibt sich deutlich aus den kleinen Plagioklaseinschlüssen, die man in den Mikroklinaugen des Porphyrgranits sieht. Im Verlaufe der Erstarrung ist der früher einmal mehr ausgeprägte Kalkgehalt offenbar ausgeglichen worden, was aus dem meistenteils recht wenig hervortretenden Zonenaufbau hervorgeht. Gegenüber den sonstigen Gesteinsmineralien weist der *Plagioklas* die am besten entwickelte idiomorphe Ausbildung auf. Der *Biotit* hat ebenfalls in einem frühen Stadium zu kristallisieren begonnen, möglicherweise zum Teil eher als der

---

[1] Außer Chlorit kommen auch grünliche Biotite (durch die gewöhnliche Doppelbrechung der Biotite gekennzeichnet) vor.

11. IX.

Plagioklas, obgleich sein Kristallisationsintervall länger als das des ersteren gewesen zu sein scheint. Die *Hornblende* ist entschieden jünger als der *Biotit*, was deutlich daraus zu schließen ist, daß sie bisweilen kleine Biotitschuppen enthält. — Der *Mikroklin* hat sich, wo er selbständig beobachtet worden ist, deutlich als einem bedeutend späteren Kristallisationsintervall zugehörig gezeigt, das von dem des Quarzes nicht weit abliegt. Vor dem letzteren hat sich *Muscovit* gebildet, oft den *Feldspat* verzehrend. Der *Quarz* hat seinen gewöhnlichen allotriomorphen Charakter.

Die porphyrgranitischen Typen variieren offenbar auch innerhalb sehr enger chemisch-petrographischer Grenzen. Sie werden durch eingestreute Mikroklinperthitaugen charakterisiert, die angefangen von mehr diffusen Einsprenglingen mit einer vom *Plagioklas* wenig abweichenden Größe bis zu Durchmessern von 3—4 cm anwachsen können. Petrographisch auffällig ist auch ein bedeutender Mikroklingehalt in der aplitisch struierten Grundmasse, ebenso wie der Mangel an *Hornblende*. *Muscovit* dürfte in diesen Typen allgemeiner sein. Dagegen scheint der Quarzgehalt nicht anders zu sein als in den mittelkörnigen Typen.

Zu den bedeutenden chemischen und strukturellen Unterschieden, die zwischen den mittelkörnigen und porphyrgranitischen Typen herrschen, kommen auch wesentliche Verschiedenheiten des Kristallisationsverlaufs. In den letzteren Gesteinen treten deutlich zwei verschiedenartige *Plagioklase* auf, nämlich kleinere, in die Mikroklinaugen eingeschlossene basische Plagioklaskörner und in der »Grundmasse« auftretende, mehr saure *Plagioklase* (Oligoklas), die ebenso wie die *Plagioklase* der mittelkörnigen Granite oft gute Idiomorphie gegenüber den anderen Bestandteilen aufweisen. Der *Biotit* und der *Muscovit* zeigen die gleichen Eigenschaften wie oben erwähnt. — Der im Verhältnis zur vorhergehenden Gruppe andersartige Kristallisationsverlauf der Feldspatkomponenten scheint ungefähr folgendermaßen skizziert werden zu können: Wie schon oben erwähnt, kristallisierten früh kleine basische Plagioklaskerne, die später teils zu den *Plagioklasen* der »Grundmasse« auswuchsen, teils aber auch in kristallisierenden Mikroklinperthitkristallen eingeschlossen wurden, deren im Verhältnis zum *Plagioklas* schnelles Anwachsen zu größeren Individuen ein Umschließen kleinerer Plagioklaskörner ermöglichte. Die Mikroklinperthitaugen schließen auffällig oft kleine Biotitschuppen ein, die manchmal zonenartig in den Randgebieten des Einsprenglings angeordnet sein können.

Der *Granat* tritt in den primär-struierten Graniten meistens in Gestalt kleiner Einschlüsse im *Biotit* auf, selten selbständig in der Quarzmasse. Als Einschluß im *Feldspat* ist er nicht beobachtet worden; daher wird es schwer, sich bestimmte Begriffe von den Ausbildungsverhältnissen zu machen. In Zusammenhang mit den metamorphen Gliedern der Granitreihe können möglicherweise einige weitere Daten angegeben werden. Auch das Auftreten des *Kalkspats* scheint leichter in diesen zu beurteilen zu sein.

Die chemisch-petrographische Charakteristik, wie sie hier dargestellt worden ist, gilt auch für die metamorphen Derivate der Granite und wird so zum Teil zum Einteilungsgrund auch für diese Gesteinsgruppen.

D. DIE METAMORPHEN DERIVATE DER GRANITE.

Von diesen kann man im großen zwei Gruppen unterscheiden: Gneisgranite und Mylonitgneise.[1] Übergänge zwischen den beiden Typen sind vorhanden, und hierdurch wird man geneigt gemacht, sich diese als Resultat einer einheitlichen Dynamometamorphose zu denken, die sich in einem früheren Stadium als Umkristallisationsgranulierung und in einem späteren Stadium durch Quetschung oder Mylonitisierung auslösen kann.

Die Gneisgranite weisen eine recht reichliche Typenschwankung auf. Meistens kommen unter ihnen auch mittelkörniger *Hornblende-Biotit* oder nur *Biotit* führende stark plagioklasbetonte Gesteine vor, also der gleiche Haupttypus wie unter den Graniten. Die Gneisbildung wird durch die Parallelorientierung der dunklen Mineralien betont, die bisweilen sehr hervortretend ist. Gleichzeitig werden die Quarzkörner abgeplattet und zu Massen von kleineren Bruchstücken granuliert, die eine starke Undulosität aufweisen. Von den *Feldspaten* zeigt der *Plagioklas* starke Widerstandskraft gegen die Granulierung und behält seine Idiomorphie bei, obgleich er gewöhnlich seine Längenausdehnung in der Richtung der Gneisstreckung einordnet. Der *Mikroklin* zeigt nicht denselben Widerstand gegen die Granulierung, obgleich er nicht im selben Umfang wie der Quarz zerstückelt wird. In den augenführenden Gneisgranittypen behalten die großen Mikroklinaugen ihre Idiomorphie und Ausbildung bei, obgleich sie sich oft in die Gneisstruktur einordnen. Wenn kleinere Mikroklinaugen ausgebildet sind, werden sie gern zu Linsen abgeplattet.

Von ziemlich anderer Art als Vergneisung im Zusammenhang mit Umkristallisationsgranulierung ist eine oft auftretende Gneisbildung mit sehr hervortretender Parallelorientierung sämtlicher Gesteinsmineralien, ohne daß irgendeine Granulierung vor sich zu gehen scheint. Das vielleicht auffallendste mikroskopische Charakteristikum, das diese Gneise geben, ist die in die Länge gezogene Linsenform der vollkommen frischen Quarzkörner (»Quarz-feuilleté«-Struktur). Diese eigentümliche Struktur scheinen die Gesteine in Zusammenhang mit der Erstarrung erhalten zu haben. Dafür spricht unter anderem auch noch der Umstand, daß die Quarzscheiben oft ältere aneinandergrenzende Mineralien gleichsam trennen und zwischen den alten Körnerfugen heraus kristallisieren, deren oft implizierter Verlauf sehr charakteristisch ist. In diesen Gneisen mit dünnplattiger Ausbildung des Quarzes kommt fast immer *Granat* vor. In ein paar

---

[1] Diese Bezeichnung wird in ungefähr derselben Bedeutung gebraucht wie in der Arbeit von P. QUENSEL, Zur Kenntnis der Mylonitbildung. Bull. of the Geol. Inst. of Upsala. Vol. XV. Upsala 1916. S. 99.

Fällen ist das Zusammenwachsen von *Granat* und *Hornblende* beobachtet worden (Pl. IX, Fig. 17 und 18), wie auch von *Granat* und *Magnetit*. *Kalkspat* ist auch ziemlich häufig.

Die mylonitische Ausbildung bei den Gneisen und Graniten weist in der Hauptsache zwei Typen auf, die mit der ursprünglichen Struktur der Granite zusammenhängen. In den Augengneisen oder Porphyrgraniten wird der Quarz zerquetscht, wobei gleichzeitig die Randpartien der Augen schöne und typische Mörtelstruktur aufweisen. In allen mittelkörnigen Gneisen und Gneisgraniten läuft dagegen die Quetschung sehr deutlich in einer bestimmten Richtung, der Verschieferungsrichtung folgend. Die Quetschung verläuft entsprechend schmalen, mehr oder weniger zahlreichen Zonen oder Ebenen, nach denen eine Zermalmung sowohl von Feldspaten, wie von Quarz stattfindet. Die Glimmer scheinen nicht direkt von der Quetschung beeinflußt, sie werden aber gleichzeitig in großem Umfang chloritisiert. — Der *Plagioklas* hat sich im allgemeinen am besten erhalten, er wird oft gebogen und erhält gleichzeitig eine starke Undulosität. Oft sieht man, daß sich kleine Differenzialbewegungen entsprechend der Mylonitisierungsebene ausgelöst haben; das geht aus den Plagioklasprismen hervor, durch welche Quetschungsebenen rechtwinklig zur Zwillingsstruktur verlaufen. Mit Hilfe von charakteristischen Zwillingen kann man dann direkt ablesen, wie weit die vorher zusammengehörigen Stücke eines Kristalls im Verhältnis zueinander verschoben worden sind (Pl. I, Fig. 2). — Der *Quarz* erweist sich bei Quetschung als wenig widerstandsfähig: entweder wird er zu einer wirren Ansammlung kleiner Bruchstücke zerquetscht oder, was seltener geschieht, es nimmt eine vorher ganze Quarzoberfläche eine rutenartige Struktur mit stark gezähnten Fugen zwischen den kleinen Quarzkörnern an. — Der *Mikroklin* zeigt oft starke Zerquetschung mit gleichzeitiger kräftiger Serizitisierung.

Die petrochemischen Veränderungen, von denen die Gesteine bei der Mylonitisierung betroffen werden, sind vor allem starke Zerlegung der Plagioklase in Albit- und Epidotsubstanz, Serizitisierung des Mikroklins und gewöhnlich vollständige Chloritisierung der Glimmer und der Hornblende.

Die Mylonitisierung hat im allgemeinen nur eine mäßige oder geringe Stärke erreicht. Man kann also kaum von echten Myloniten sprechen; sondern der Ausdruck »Mylonitgneis« ist eine besonders zweckmäßige Benennung für die kataklastischen Gneisgranite des östlichen Pamir. Bisweilen hat die Kataklase mit dem Charakter einer Breccienbildung deutlich granitstruierte Typen betroffen, die entsprechend der schwedischen Terminologie am ehesten als *Kakirite* bezeichnet werden sollten.[1]

Unter dem Material kommen einige vereinzelte Handstücke stark feldspathaltiger Glimmerschiefer vor, die durch starke Kataklase und hervortretenden Serizitgehalt charakterisiert werden. Wahrscheinlich sind sie stark mylonitisierte Glieder der Zentralgranitserie, obgleich man kaum wagen darf, sie mit Bestimmtheit zu klassifizieren.

---

[1] Siehe QUENSEL, a. a. O.

II. KRISTALLINE GNEISE UND SCHIEFER.

In diese Gruppe sind Gesteine sowohl des Orthotypus wie des Paratypus aufgenommen. An die ersteren schließen sich einige Amphibolite an, die in älteren Gneisen als Gänge aufzutreten scheinen, und ebenso eine Reihe stark saussuritisierter und chloritisierter Grünschiefer, hervorgegangen aus Grünsteinen, die vermutlich der Zentralgranitgruppe nahegestanden haben.

Zu den glimmerreichen Schiefern sind alle Schiefer des Paratypus gerechnet. Sie scheinen an die Kontaktzonen der Zentralgranite angeschlossen und somit wahrscheinlich sowohl von dynamischer Metamorphose wie von Kontaktmetamorphose betroffen zu sein.

A. AMPHIBOLITE.

Gesteine mit Pflasterstruktur, meistenteils aus *Hornblende* und basischem *Plagioklas* (Andesin-Labrador oder Labrador) bestehend. *Quarz* und *Biotit* kommen sparsam vor. In *Hornblende* eingeschlossen ist in einem Fall *Pyroxen* (hellgrüner Augit) beobachtet worden.

B. GRÜNSCHIEFER.

Kräftig parallelstruierte, weiche Schiefer mit gewöhnlich chloritbekleideter Verschieferungsebene. Unter dem Mikroskop tritt oft deutlich eine durch die Chloritbekleidung bedingte Kräuselung hervor. Von *Feldspat* werden nur kleine stark granulierte Albitkörner bemerkt. *Epidot-Serizit* ist sehr gewöhnlich, ebenso ist *Quarz* ziemlich häufig.

C. GLIMMERREICHE SCHIEFER.

Im Zusammenhang mit den Mylonitgneisen wurde eine Anzahl feldspathaltiger mylonitischer Glimmerschiefer erwähnt. Wahrscheinlich gehört in diese Gruppe, wie oben erwähnt wurde, hauptsächlich Granitmaterial von kleineren granitischen Lagerintrusionen. Indessen kommen auch zusammen mit diesen Myloniten Schiefer des Paratypus vor, die z. B. durch Feldspatisierung einen beinah eruptiven Charakter erhalten haben. Ein Versuch, diese Frage zu erklären, möge der Zukunft vorbehalten sein. Der Verfasser hat jedoch auf diese eigentümlichen Verhältnisse hinweisen wollen.

Die glimmerreichen Schiefer scheinen keiner bestimmten Metamorphosezone im Sinne von GRUBENMANN [1] anzugehören; sollten sie einer solchen beigezählt werden, so wäre es begreiflicherweise die obere. Der Versuch einer Gruppeneinteilung auf Grund der geringen Anzahl der Handstücke ist überflüssig. Am häufigsten scheinen biotitquarzreiche, oft granathaltige Schiefer zu sein. Im übrigen kommt in diesen Gesteinen

---

[1] Vgl. GRUBENMANN, Die kristallinen Schiefer. 2. Aufl. Berlin 1910.

selten *Feldspat* vor, oft *Chlorit* und *Serizit*, sowie häufig *Epidot.* Der *Granat* hat gewöhnlich eine braunrote Farbe und ist zuweilen in eine bräunliche, epidotähnliche Substanz verwandelt, gleichzeitig wie *Chlorit* und *Epidot* in das Gestein hineinkommen (Diaphtorese?). Graphitgehalt ist oft zu beobachten; in einem chloritreichen Schiefer (76) macht der *Graphit* einen bedeutenden Bestandteil aus. — Wahrscheinlich sind diese gewöhnlich biotitreichen Schiefer aus einigen tonreichen Sedimenten (Phylliten oder quarzigen Phylliten) hervorgegangen.

Eine andere Art dieser Gruppe sind stark verschieferte, kalkhaltige, serizitreiche, grauwackeähnliche Schiefer, deren klastischen Ursprungscharakter man bisweilen feststellen kann.

Die kristallinen Schiefer zeigen durchgehend Spuren stark dynamischer Metamorphose: Quetschung und Streßerscheinungen. Diese Metamorphose scheint sich zu mildern, je weiter man sich von dem Granitmassiv der Bergketten entfernt, weshalb man allen Grund hat, sich einen engen Zusammenhang der Metamorphose mit der Eruptivgeschichte dieser Bergketten zu denken.

III. KRISTALLINE KALKSTEINE.

Mangels stratigraphischer Anhaltspunkte für zahlreiche Handstücke kristalliner Kalksteine schien es dem Verfasser am zweckmäßigsten, diese in eine besondere Gruppe einzuordnen. Meistens sind die kristallinen Kalksteine weiße oder helle Marmorarten, obgleich es auch Typen gibt, die starke kataklastische Spuren aufweisen.

Kristalline Kalksteine sind besonders bezeichnend für die älteren, in größerer Nähe der Zentralgranite auftretenden kristallinen Schiefer oder Schiefer überhaupt. Sogar hoch oben auf der Südwestseite des Mus-tagh-ata traf HEDIN mächtige Marmorlager an, die sich wahrscheinlich nicht weit von den Kontakten der Granite befinden. Nur ein paar Kalksteinhandstücke zeigen doch deutliche Spuren von Kontaktmetamorphose mit Neubildung einiger Mineralien, wie *Diopsid* und tremolitischer *Amphibole.*

IV. SEDIMENTGESTEINE, SCHWÄCHERE METAMORPHOSE AUFWEISEND.

Zu dieser Gruppe zählt eine Reihe dunkler *Tonschiefer*, oft mit quarzitischen oder sandsteinartigen Einlagerungen. Vom stratigraphisch-geologischen Gesichtspunkt aus bilden sie wahrscheinlich eine einheitliche Formation (Angaraschichten). Mikroskopisch kann man die dichte Grundmasse der *Schiefer*, in welche oft kleine gerundete Quarzkörner eingelagert sind, nicht zerlegen. Die quarzigen Schichten haben gewöhnlich quarzitischen Charakter, bisweilen kann man jedoch eine primär klastische Struktur unterscheiden.

V. SEDIMENTGESTEINE, NICHT METAMORPHOSIERT ODER SCHWACHE METAMORPHOSE ZEIGEND.

Diese bilden sowohl geologisch wie petrographisch eine sehr gut abgegrenzte Gruppe, die durch frische klastische Strukturen und schwache, wahrscheinlich diagenetische Umkristallisierung der vorkommenden Kalksteine charakterisiert wird. Da diese Gesteine sich oft als fossilführend erwiesen haben, ist es gelungen, eine einigermaßen sichere stratigraphische Bestimmung der Gruppe zu erhalten. (Vgl. Dr. DIETRICHS Untersuchung, S. 175 ff.)

Die ganze Reihe zeichnet sich durchgehend durch Kalkgehalt aus. Sie scheint einen deutlich unteren konglomeratisch grauwackeähnlichen Sandstein- oder Kalksandsteinhorizont und einen oberen Kalkstein- oder Oolithkalksteinhorizont zu umfassen. Untergeordnet sind auch grüne glaukonitführende Schiefertone beobachtet worden.

Der stark klastische Charakter des unteren Horizonts tritt sehr hervor, und man könnte geneigt sein, einen Vergleich mit der Flyschformation zu wagen, doch muß dabei der feinkonglomeratische Charakter betont werden. Die Konglomeratknollen bestehen aus kleinen gerundeten Bruchstücken darunterliegender schwarzer *Tonschiefer* und wahrscheinlich von diesem herstammenden Quarzitknollen, ebenso werden bisweilen kleine Gneisgranitfragmente vom Typus der Zentralgranite beobachtet. Kleine Hornsteingerölle sind auch allgemein. Am hervortretendsten ist jedoch der Reichtum an gerundeten Quarzkörnern, ebenso der oft wesentliche Gehalt an Feldspatkörnern. Unter diesen überwiegt ein Oligoklas-Andesin-ähnlicher *Plagioklas,* dessen Abstammung von den Zentralgraniten über alle Zweifel erhaben scheint. Das Gesteinszement hat meist ein grünlich-schwarzes, undurchsichtiges Aussehen und enthält zahlreiche, äußerst kleine Quarzkörner. Wenn das Bindemittel kalkhaltig ist, zeigt sich eine feinkristalline Ausbildung.

Der obere Horizont besteht meistens aus dunklen oder graugelben Kalksteinen, die zum Teil eine feinkristalline oder dichte Ausbildung haben, mit Andeutung von Umkristallisierung oder oolithischer Struktur. Die Oolithe haben meist einen konzentrisch-schaligen Bau, granosphärische sind auch beobachtet worden.

Die fossilführenden Gesteine dieser Reihe ergeben folgende Fossilienliste: *Foraminiferen:* agglutinierende Foraminiferen? Textulariden, Globigeriniden *(Globigerina?),* Rotaliden, Nummuliniden. — *Korallen:* Hexakorallen? (Gewebefetzen). — *Echinodermen:* Stacheln und andere Echinodermentrümmer. — *Serpula? — Bryozoen:* Fragmente *(Cyclostomota).* — cf. *Gryphæa vesicularis* Lam.

Die ganze Reihe zeigt nur selten Spuren metamorpher (dynamometamorpher) Ausbildung, trotzdem sie im allgemeinen ziemlich stark gefaltet scheint.

Bezüglich des Alters der fossilführenden Gesteine deutet die Untersuchung Dr. DIETRICHS an, daß sie wahrscheinlich geologisch junge (alttertiäre?) Ablagerungen darstellen. Das Gestein Nr. 233 gehört wahrscheinlich der oberen Kreide an. Um eine Vergleichung mit schon bekanntem Material dieser Gegenden zu erhalten, wurden die Stücke Herrn Prof. Dr. KURT LEUCHS in München übersandt. Nach der von ihm vorgenommenen Durchsicht gehört der »Kalkstein vom Naisa-tash (Nr. 143, S. 149) zu der permisch-triassischen Reihe, welche STOLICZKA dort nachwies». Die übrigen sind zur sog. »Ferghanastufe» zu rechnen und schließen sich an das Tertiär am Rande des Tarimbeckens an. Prof. LEUCHS hat liebenswürdigst dem Verfasser folgende Besprechung der Stellung und des Alters der jüngeren fossilführenden Gesteine überlassen:

»Im südlichen Turkistan sind seit dem Beginn der geologischen Erforschung dieses Landes marine Ablagerungen bekannt, welche zum Teil der oberen Kreide, zum Teil dem Eozän angehören. Das Hauptverbreitungsgebiet dieser Schichten liegt im Westen (Ferghanabecken, Ostbuchara), aber an manchen Stellen greifen diese Schichten, und zwar hauptsächlich die eozänen, nach Osten bis in das Tarimbecken über, wo sie am West- und Südwestrande aufgeschlossen sind.

»Das Wichtigste über diese Schichten ist in meinen Arbeiten: *Ergebnisse neuer geologischer Forschung im Tianschan* (Geolog. Rundschau, 1913) und *Zentralasien* (Handbuch der regionalen Geologie, 1916) kurz angeführt. Es handelt sich bei diesen Schichten um Ablagerungen des Meeres, welches in der Oberkreide transgredierend über das Land vordrang und wenigstens teilweise, bis zum Alttertiär, bestehen blieb.

»Bei der Größe des Gebietes und der bis jetzt nur spärlichen Durchforschung sind neue Funde natürlich von größter Bedeutung. Das gilt auch für die hier vorliegenden, von Dr. HEDIN gesammelten Gesteine. Sie machen wahrscheinlich, daß das alttertiäre Meer viel größere Ausdehnung hatte, als bisher angenommen werden durfte, und ermöglichen zugleich, die Art dieses Meeres und seine Abhängigkeit von dem angrenzenden Lande genauer zu erkennen.»

IV. KAPITEL.

DIE GEOLOGISCHEN BEOBACHTUNGEN IM ANSCHLUSS AN DEN REISEWEG.

AUF GRUND DER TAGEBÜCHER Dr. HEDINS UND DER HANDSTÜCKE.

IGIS-YAR—PAS-RABAT.

Von Igis-yar geht der Weg über flaches Gelände in den Talgang des Tasgun hinein, in dem stark gefaltete kretazisch-tertiäre Gesteine [(4)—(7)] bis in die Gegend von Arka-terek verfolgt werden. Hier werden sie möglicherweise direkt unterlagert von Gneisgranit [(8)—(10)] des Zentralgranittypus, welcher die Fortsetzung der westlich am Keng-kol sich ausbreitenden Gebirgskette darstellt. Der Fluß bildet hier ein ziemlich langes Durchbruchstal. Südlich vom Gneisgranit und diesen überlagernd folgen von der Gegend von Sarik-goy an Angaraschichten, gewöhnlich als Tonschiefer ausgebildet, mit einer quarzitischen Schichteinlagerung [(11)—(15)]. Unterhalb Yeshil liegt die Grenze zwischen der Tonschieferreihe und den vorher genannten kretazisch-tertiären Gesteinen. Diese bestehen aus Kalksandsteinen, die gegen das Liegende hin ausgeprägteren Konglomeratcharakter haben [(16)—(23)]. Nach Pas-rabat zu kommen abwechselnd ältere Tonschiefer und darüberlagernde Kalksandsteine vor, die offenbar nur kleine, nach allen Richtungen hin auslaufende Vertiefungen in alten Flußtälern zum Ausdruck bringen [(24)—(28)]. (Vgl. STOLICZKA und BOGDANOWITSCH.)

PAS-RABAT—SÜDFUSS DES MUS-TAGH-ATA.

Etwas westlich vom Terart-Paß beginnen Gesteine von bedeutend älterem Aussehen als die vorher genannten. Sie bestehen aus kalkhaltigen Sandsteinschiefern mit oft bedeutenden Einlagerungen von kristallinem Kalkstein und Marmor [(29)—(33)]. Westlich von Pas-rabat wird die kalksteinführende Reihe von Graniten und Gneisgraniten [(34)—(58)] unterlagert, die mit geringen Unterbrechungen [(37), (49), (51), (52), (55)] bis an den Südabhang des Mus-tagh-ata anhalten. Im Flußtal des Därshet werden die Granite von dynamometamorphem Kalkstein (54) überlagert.

MUS-TAGH-ATA.

Der Mus-tagh-ata bildet eine große Antiklinale, die nach Süden zu mit der Tagarma-Kette zusammenhängt und nach Norden zu, wie der Gesteinszusammenhang

22. IX.

191

zeigt, Verbindung mit dem Sara-tumshuk und dem Kashgar-Gebirge gehabt hat. Topographisch ist der Anschluß durch das Durchbruchstal des Ike-bel-su zerstört worden.

HEDINS Beobachtungen zeigen, daß die auf dem Zentralgranitmassiv des Mus-tagh-ata ruhenden, im Untergrund der Bergabhänge sich ausbreitenden kristallinen Schiefer und Kalksteine stets von den zentralen Teilen der Bergkette steil abfallen. Auf der Nordnordwestseite hat der Granit offenbar eine recht mächtige Grünsteinzone am Kontakt mit den Schiefern ausgebildet. — Die Granite stellen eine ziemlich veränderliche Reihe dar. Die Kataklase scheint nach oben hin an Stärke zuzunehmen.

Vom Mus-tagh-ata und seinen Abhängen stammen die Handstücke (59)—(124).

MUS-TAGH-ATA—PAMIRSKI POST UND YESHIL-KUL.

Auf diesem Ausflug wurden die Handstücke (125)—(144) genommen.

MUS-TAGH-ATA—KASHGAR.

Auf dem Rückweg vom Mus-tagh-ata nach Kashgar im Jahre 1894 wurden wenige Handstücke genommen (150)—(155).

KASHGAR—BULUNG-KUL (1895).

Der Weg steigt von Upal hinauf zum Paß Ulug-art. Granite und ihre metamorphen Derivate [(156), (159), (162), (163), (170), (171)—(174)] treten hier in den Kernpartien der Bergkette und deren kleinerer Ausläufer auf. An beiden Flanken des Kashgar-Gebirges breiten sich Gesteine aus, die zu der kretazisch-tertiären Reihe [(161), (165)] gehören; im übrigen kommen kristalline Schiefer mit Kalksteinen und außerdem einige Grünschiefer vor.

HUNSERAB—UPRANG-PASS.

Innerhalb dieses Gebietes scheinen die Granite in großer Ausdehnung von kretazisch-tertiären Gesteinen überlagert zu sein, die oft die höchsten Paßhöhen (Uprang-davan 5013 m) einnehmen. Von hier stammt die Reihe (175)—(186).

HUNSERAB—BOZAI-GUMBAZ—TASH-KURGAN.

Aus diesen Gebieten, nämlich den das Mus-tagh-Gebirge umgebenden Talgängen, und den Gegenden des Sarikol-Gebirges stammt die Reihe (187)—(202). Der Reiseweg fällt teilweise mit dem STOLICZKAS zusammen (Ak-tash—Tash-kurgan).

TASH-KURGAN—TONG—YARKAND-DARYA.

Bis an das Tal des Ütsh-bäldir breiten sich meistens Gneisgranite und kristalline Schiefer aus [(203)—(223)]. Von der Gegend des Kisil-kor an sind ihnen fossilführende Gesteine aufgelagert, die der kretazisch-tertiären Reihe angehören [(224)—(232)]. Nach dem Yarkand-darya zu breiten sich hauptsächlich rötliche, rostige, feldspathaltige Sandsteine derselben Reihe aus, oft in Wechsellagerung mit Konglomeratbänken.

V. KAPITEL.

GEOLOGISCHE ENTWICKLUNG UND BAU DES ÖSTLICHEN PAMIR.

ZUSAMMENFASSENDE ÜBERSICHT.

Die Arbeiten aller früheren Forscher in unserem Gebiet haben die großen Schwierigkeiten ergeben, die sich den Versuchen entgegenstellen, einen historisch-geologischen Umriß der Formationen dieses Gebietes zu zeichnen. Hierbei erweisen sich der Mangel an Fossilien und die durchgreifende Metamorphose, die alle älteren Sedimentkomplexe betroffen hat, als die größten Hindernisse. — Die Untersuchung kann, was diese älteren Komplexe anlangt, leider keinerlei stratigraphische Anhaltspunkte geben. Die Ergebnisse knüpfen sich hauptsächlich an die Ausbildung und das Alter der Zentralgneise, sowie an die spätmesozoische (oberkretazische) Transgression und ihre Ausdehnung.

Auf Grund der bisher ausgeführten Arbeiten im östlichen Pamir liegen keine Beweise dafür vor, daß das Gebiet einen kontinentalen Kern archäischen Ursprungs gehabt hätte. Die Gesteine, die z. B. von BOGDANOWITSCH und STOLICZKA als älteste Glieder aufgefaßt wurden, nämlich die unter den kristallinen Schiefern in großer Ausdehnung zutage tretenden Gneise, erweisen sich, wie auch LEUCHS[1] hervorhob, unzweifelhaft als metamorphe Derivate großer Granitmassen, mit deren Intrusion die Umwandlung benachbarter älterer Sedimentformationen zu kristallinen Schiefern in engem Zusammenhang steht.

Auf Grund von BOGDANOWITSCHS und STOLICZKAS Ergebnissen könnte man geneigt sein, anzunehmen, daß das Gebiet ursprünglich einen altpaläozoischen (silurischen) Kern besessen hat, den das Meer im Mitteldevon überflutete (die Kwen-lun-Transgression). Die in großen Teilen des Kwen-lun in der Zeit des Spätdevon erfolgte Regression scheint den westlichen Kwen-lun nicht durchgreifend betroffen zu haben und somit auch nicht den östlichen Pamir. Demnach dürfte hier wenigstens teilweise die Sedimentation bis in das unterste Karbon hinein fortgedauert haben. —

---

[1] Handbuch der regionalen Geologie. Bd. V, 7.

193

Der ganze bisher erwähnte Schichtenkomplex dürfte, was den östlichen Pamir betrifft, in dem Grenzbereich der großen Zentralgranitgebiete zu suchen sein. Es ist ferner zu bemerken, daß für verschiedene Gegenden des östlichen Pamir ein gewisser Parallelismus innerhalb dieser Gesteinsgruppen besteht. Den Graniten zunächst kommt ein offenbar sehr bedeutender Komplex grober Glimmer- oder Granatglimmerschiefer, die wahrscheinlich von einem primär aus Tonschiefern zusammengesetzten Komplex herstammen. Zusammen mit diesen in inniger Wechsellagerung, aber oft bedeutend anschwellend, kommen grobkristalline Kalksteine vor. Dieser ganze, sicher aus umfangreichen stratigraphischen Gruppen zusammengesetzte Komplex ist in großer Ausdehnung reich an (porphyrischen und pegmatitischen) Injektionen aus den wahrscheinlich die Metamorphose verursachenden Zentralgraniten, mit denen er gemeinsam durch die Faltung betroffen wurde. Die Metamorphose nimmt wahrscheinlich in den höheren Teilen der Serie ab, so daß man in diesen Gesteine mit deutlich primären klastischen Strukturzügen finden kann [z. B. Nr. (82)].

Die dynamischen und hydrochemischen Nachwirkungen (Pegmatitinjektion), welche die Intrusion der Zentralgranite kennzeichnen, sind BOGDANOWITSCH zufolge jünger als die Gesteine der Kwen-lun-Transgression. Aber wenigstens ein Teil der syenitischen Intrusionen wird nach BOGDANOWITSCH von Oberdevon überlagert. Trotz dieser letzteren Behauptung ist der Verfasser geneigt, die Intrusionszeit der Granite als spätkarbonisch oder postkarbonisch aufzufassen. Hierfür spricht unter anderem die vollständige Übereinstimmung zwischen den Pamirgraniten und den nachkarbonischen Graniten, die von KEIDEL und RICHARZ aus dem nördlichen Teil des Zentral-Tienshan beschrieben worden sind.

Es muß hervorgehoben werden, daß diese Auffassung der Gebirgsbildung des östlichen Pamir sich von mehreren früher ausgesprochenen Betrachtungsweisen unterscheidet, weshalb es nötig scheint, sie ein wenig näher zu begründen. Das Material läßt deutlich erkennen, daß es nur in drei große Altersgruppen geteilt werden kann. Die eine von diesen, nämlich die kretazisch-tertiäre Gruppe (s. unten), hebt sich mit einer deutlichen Diskordanz ab. Die Tonschieferreihe (mit quarzitischen Einlagerungen) macht auch eine besondere Gruppe aus (s. unten), die man mit guten Gründen den sogenannten Angaraschichten zuweisen kann. Die übrigen Gesteine, sowohl die Granite und ihre metamorphosierten Derivate als die kristallinen Schiefer und die ihnen eingelagerten kristallinischen Kalksteine oder Kalksteinschiefer, machen (trotzdem vereinzelte, wenig metamorphosierte Gesteine sporadisch in den höheren Teilen dieser Schichtserie vorkommen können) einen fast zusammengelöteten Komplex aus, dessen Ausbildung deutlich einer einheitlichen Intrusions- und Faltungsepoche zuzuschreiben ist. Es ist dem Verfasser sehr wahrscheinlich, daß wir in diesem Komplex die ganzen paläozoischen Ablagerungen von Ostpamir zu suchen haben. Ebenso ist zu betonen, daß die Zentralgranite eine sehr ausgeprägte Gruppe bilden, die wir nicht in mehrere ungleichaltrige Komplexe zerlegen können. Der ausgesprochene petrographisch-chemische Verwandtschaftscharakter der Eruptiva wird in diesem Zusammenhang nochmals betont; wahrscheinlich wird dieses Merkmal zur größten Hilfe bei der Trennung oder Verknüpfung zentralasiatischer Eruptivgesteine werden.

Auf Grund der angeführten Tatsachen scheint dem Verfasser die Annahme begründet, daß sich der östliche Pamir hinsichtlich der paläozoischen tektonischen Vorgänge ganz eng an den Westpamir und Tien-shan anschließt.

Manche Gründe liegen also vor, die ganze Faltung, die dem Pamir seinen Charakter gegeben hat, als herzynisch zu betrachten. Wie viele herzynische Faltungsgebiete hat auch der Pamir einen sehr ausgeprägt einfachen diklinalen Faltenbau. Die Bergketten bilden einfache Antiklinalzüge mit wenig hervortretender Faltung der Längsachsen. Auch die Querachsen sind nur sanft geneigt. — Ein prägnant herzynischer Charakterzug ist auch das syntektonische Auftreten der Eruptivgesteine. Somit bilden die Granitmassive langgestreckte Antiklinalrücken in den hochgelegenen Zentralgebieten der Bergketten. Wie in der Beschreibung der Granite und ihrer metamorphen Derivate betont wurde, spricht eine Anzahl von Gründen dafür, daß Intrusions- und Faltungsverlauf einen engen Zusammenhang haben, und daß die kataklastische Metamorphose, welche die Randgebiete der Granite und die Schiefer längs deren Grenze betroffen hat, als Nachwirkung der großen, die Faltung kennzeichnenden Dynamometamorphose aufzufassen ist. Betont wurde auch der z. T. tonalitische Charakter der Granitreihe und die Mannigfaltigkeit ihrer Differentiationsderivate (Grünsteine, Porphyre, tonalitische Granite, Porphyrgranite und Pegmatite). Es mag nur noch hinzugefügt werden, daß wir in diesen Gesteinen ein neues Beispiel des belangreichen Rätsels zu sehen haben, welches der Zusammenhang zwischen diesem weitverbreiteten Magmatyp und seiner Intrusionsweise darbietet.

Nach der gebirgsbildenden Faltungsperiode und wahrscheinlich in Zusammenhang mit ihr tritt eine allgemeine Regression ein, und vermutlich eine bedeutende Denudationsperiode, während der die Granitkerne der Gebirgsketten teilweise bloßgelegt wurden. Die späteren Ablagerungen, deren stratigraphische Verhältnisse deutlich aus den Beobachtungen entlang der Strecke Igis-yar—Chihil-gumbes hervorgehen, ruhen nämlich teils direkt auf den Gneisgraniten, teils auch auf kristallinen Schiefern (westlich von Chihil-gumbes). Diese späteren Ablagerungen bestehen überwiegend aus Tonschiefern und ihnen oft eingelagerten Quarziten. Kalksteineinlagerungen dürften selten sein. Diskordante Schichtung scheint häufig vorzukommen. Die ganze Reihe gehört zu den sogenannten Angaraschichten, deren limnischer, beziehungsweise terrestrischer Charakter von LEUCHS hervorgehoben wurde. In unseren Gegenden des Pamir scheint ihre Mächtigkeit nicht besonders groß zu sein, weshalb die Bildungszeit wahrscheinlich eng begrenzt ist (Trias?, Jura?). Sie sind mäßig metamorphosiert. zeigen jedoch ein entschieden deutlicheres metamorphes Gepräge, als die jüngere fossilführende Reihe. Man ist daher zu der Schlußfolgerung gezwungen, daß tektonische Bewegungen auch im Mesozoikum (Jura?) stattgefunden haben.

Eine neue umfassende Transgression trat wahrscheinlich erst in der oberen Kreide ein, deren stark klastische Sedimente sich auf den Angaraschichten absetzten. Der klastische Charakter der jüngeren fossilführenden Sedimente weist gleichzeitig auf starke Denudation des Gebirges hin, durch welche ihre älteren Glieder ziemlich große Ähnlichkeit mit Flysch erhalten. Die Zentralgranite wie die Angaraschichten scheinen viel Material beigetragen zu haben.

Wahrscheinlich ist diese junge Transgression, Tälern und größeren Senkungen folgend, weit in den Zentral-Pamir hineingelangt; vielleicht ist sie teilweise durch den ganzen Pamir gedrungen, so daß sie in Verbindung mit den gleichzeitig vom Meere bedeckten Teilen Westasiens trat. Jedenfalls hat der östliche Pamir während der Transgression, die der Tertiärepoche voranging, Inselcharakter gehabt. In den südlichen Teilen unseres Gebietes (Uprang-Pass, 5013 m) scheinen die Kreide-Tertiär-Ablagerungen eine bedeutende Höhe über dem Meere zu erreichen, weshalb diese Gegenden möglicherweise engere Beziehungen zu den großen tektonischen Bewegungen zeigen, die in Zusammenhang mit der alpinen Faltung stattgefunden haben. Zu dieser gehören wahrscheinlich die nicht unwesentlichen Lagerungsstörungen und Faltungen, welche die kretazisch-tertiären Ablagerungen des östlichen Pamir betroffen haben. Vorgänge einer stärkeren Dynamometamorphose scheinen sich während dieser Faltung nicht abgespielt zu haben.

Von quartären Ablagerungen sind keine Proben mitgebracht worden.

ANHANG.

DAS VON Dr. HEDIN AUS DEM TARIMBECKEN UND DEM ÖSTLICHEN PAMIR MITGEBRACHTE FOSSILFÜHRENDE GESTEINSMATERIAL.

Von Dr. W. O. DIETRICH.

TARIMBECKEN.

Von Dr. HEDINS Reise durch die Wüste Takla-makan und das Tarimbecken liegen 39 Handstücke vor. Sie sind teils auf dem Wege zwischen Merket und dem südlichen Masar-tag, teils auf der Route zwischen Uch-turfan und Kashgar gesammelt. Die fossilfreien Gesteine sind schon in Petermanns Mitteilungen, Ergänzungsband 28 (Heft 131), beschrieben. Von den fossilführenden Gesteinen sind aber bisher keine Untersuchungen veröffentlicht worden, weshalb es zweckmäßig erscheint, die Beschreibung mit dieser Schrift zu vereinigen.

Die Fundorte der Gesteine sind:

13. Lager V, 14. 4. 1895.
14. Kleiner Berg nördlich von den Seen NW. vom südlichen Masar-tag.
18. Lager X, 22. 4. 1895.
25. Uch-turfan, 9. 6. 1895.
26. Uch-turfan, 9. 6. 1895.
29. Taushkan-Tal, 5 km nördlich von Uch-turfan.
31. Bei dem kleinen Paß Kok-beles zwischen Uch und Kisil-eshme.
32. Kisil-eshme.
35. Zwischen Kisil-eshme und Pchan.
38. Zwischen Pchan und Kashgar.
39. Zwischen Pchan und Kashgar.

SANDSTEINE:

38 und 14. Unfrische, feinkörnige, plattige bis schiefrige, rote Sandsteine, die fossileer sind. Mit Kalk- und Tongehalt. Etwas *Plagioklas* und *Glaukonit*, viel *Hämatit* bzw. *Limonit*. Die glimmerigen Komponenten sind zersetzt. Keine Mineralneubildungen.

KALKSTEINE:

13, 18, 32, 35 und 39. Graue und braune, (durch Dynamometamorphose?) marmorisierte, zuckerkörnige Foraminiferenkalke. Sie haben zum Teil ein pseudo-oolithisches Aussehen (39), zum Teil enthalten sie makroskopische Fossilien, z. B. Nr. 32, ein etwas bituminöser Kalk, der die offene Steinkerndublette eines kleinen Zweischalers enthält. Dieses Fossil ist vielleicht ein primitiver Pectinide *Streblopteria sp.* Zur sichern Identifikation dieser Gattung fehlt der Nachweis des hinteren Ohres. Die Foraminiferen sind vielleicht Textulariden, lassen sich aber nicht näher bestimmen. Echinodermentrümmer kommen auch vor.

Ferner liegen vor:

29 und 31. Harte dunkle Kalke mit *Pyrit*. Sie sind stellenweise verkieselt und liegen in metamorphem Zustand vor; ursprünglich dürften es Kalkschlamm-bildungen, Sumpfkalke, zum Teil organogener Entstehung (Kalkalgen, Characeen?, viele Foraminiferen, Molluskenschalentrümmer) gewesen sein. An Mineralien ent-halten sie u. a. *Pyrit* und anderes Erz; *Dolomit* findet sich in den verkieselten Partien in kleinen Rhomboederchen, eine weltweit verbreitete Erscheinung.

KALKSANDSTEINE:

25 und 26. Braune, zum Teil fossilführende Kalksteine (Mollusken, Foramini-feren, nicht näher bestimmbar).

PAMIR.

SANDSTEINE:

233. Fossilreicher, konglomeratischer, kalkiger Glaukonitsandstein. Das Hand-stück enthält Austernschalen und deren Trümmer. Sie lassen sich mit *Gryphæa vesicularis* Lam. aus dem Senon vergleichen, doch fehlt der Nachweis der Anal-furche, bzw. des Analsinus (VADÁSZ, Paläontologische Studien aus Centralasien. Mitt. a. d. Jahrb. kgl. ungar. geol. Reichsanstalt 19, 1911, gibt diese Art nebst *Ostrea* und *Exogyra* aus dem Ferganabecken an). Ferner wurde ein Bryozoen-fragment *(Cyclostomata)* beobachtet. U. d. M. Foraminiferen und Hornstein-geröllchen.

KALKSTEINE:

127. Dunkle, dichte oder versteckt oolithische Foraminiferenkalksteine (Textulariden, Nummuliniden?).

128. Calcitoolith. Die Ooide gelegentlich mit einer Foraminifere als Kern *(Globigerina?)*, im übrigen rein anorganogen.

143. Granosphärischer Calcitoolith. Das Gestein ist stark umkristallisiert, keine Fossilien beobachtet.

KALKE OHNE HANDSTÜCKE, NUR MIKROSKOPISCH CHARAKTERISIERT:

179. Ziemlich reiner Calcitmarmor, stylolithisch, ungleichkörnig, mit organischen Komponenten. Der Schliff ist zu dünn, um mehr aussagen zu können.

180. Metamorpher Kalk. Viele Calcitneubildungen und Umkristallisationen. Einschlüsse eines dichten Kalkes. Möglich, daß organische Reste vorhanden. Schliff für paläontologische Untersuchungen viel zu dünn.

186. Oolithischer bzw. pisolithischer Kalk mit zahlreichen Foraminiferen (Rotaliden, Textulariden), Knäuel agglutinierender Foraminiferen? und anderen organischen Komponenten, z. B. Echinodermenstacheln.

195. Fossilreicher Kalkstein. Organische Komponenten im Dünnschliff unbestimmbar.

196. Dynamometamorpher Kalkstein, daher flasriger Kalk. Organische Komponenten zurücktretend, bzw. zerstört.

224. Kalkschlammoolith anorganischer Entstehung. Mehrere Generationen von Ooiden. Ooide konzentrisch schalig oder radialfasrig. Ihr Kern besteht aus dichtem Kalkschlamm oder einem Fremdkörper, z. B. einem Quarzkorn. Das Zement ist ziemlich grobkristallin-calcitisch. Organismen zurücktretend, wenigstens im Schliff.

225. Oolithischer Foraminiferenkalk. Ooide und Foraminiferen voneinander abhängig, die Foraminiferen oft dick und umkrustet. Einige gute Durchschnitte: Nummuliniden? Rotaliden? Schliff für paläontologische Bestimmungen zu dünn, alles kristallin-calcitisches Mosaik.

228. Foraminiferenkalkstein, reich an organischer Substanz. Fetzen zerrissener Foraminiferen.

232. Foraminiferen-Korallenkalk. Gewebefetzen von ?Hexakorallen, Schalenfragmente großer und kleiner Foraminiferen.

GESTEINSPROBEN UND SCHLIFFE:

19. Schwarzer, dynamometamorpher Korallenkalk. Korallen unbestimmbar. Foraminiferenreste. — Dieser Kalk steht im Verband oder Übergang mit

23. IX.

17. dunklen, grobkörnigen Kalksandsteinen, die auch konglomeratisch werden. In ihrer calcitischen Grundmasse zahlreiche Rotaliden oder Nummuliniden, ferner dickwandige, kurze, zum Teil verbogene, an *Serpula* erinnernde Röhrchen. Echinodermentrümmer. Bemerkenswert sind auch Lydit-, Hornstein- und Quarzitgeröllchen;

22. mit dunklen, kalkigen, feinkonglomeratischen Grauwacken. Gepreßte Quarzit- und Hornsteinmikrogerölle (der Hornstein mit den bezeichnenden Carbonatrhomboederchen, vgl. Tarim Nr. 29, S. 176). Größere, zerstörte Foraminiferen sind auch vorhanden. Diese bieten so wenige strukturelle und morphologische Merkmale, daß es nicht möglich ist zu entscheiden, ob Nummuliniden vorliegen. Ein Durchschnitt in (17) hat randlich schuppenförmige Zellen, äquatorial zieht ein nach der Mitte anschwellendes Band aus Calcit hindurch; das erinnert an *Lepidocyclina*-Vertikalschnitte, aber der Nachweis äquatorialer Kammern fehlt, so daß es bei der bloßen Vermutung bleiben muß. Echinodermentrümmer kommen auch vor.

ZUSAMMENFASSUNG DER ERGEBNISSE.

Der paläontologische Befund der übergebenen Suite erlaubt eine stratigraphische Auswertung leider nur in sehr beschränktem Maße.

Über das Alter der Sandsteine aus dem Tarimbecken läßt sich mangels Fossilien nichts aussagen. Die vorliegenden Kalksteine aus dem Tarimbecken gehören vielleicht dem Carbon an, doch ist dieses Resultat nicht ganz sicher. Noch schwieriger ist es, über das Alter der Oolithe, Foraminiferenkalke und Kalksandsteine aus dem Pamirgebiet etwas Sicheres auszusagen, denn die zwar zahlreich vorhandenen Foraminiferen sind wenig charakteristische Formen; weder Fusulinen, noch Alveolinen, noch Nummuliten u. dgl. ließen sich nachweisen. Sicher ist nur, daß es marine, küstennahe und vielfach mit terrigenem Material durchsetzte Gesteine sind. Der allgemeine Eindruck ist, daß es sich eher um geologisch junge (alttertiäre?) als um geologisch alte Gesteine handelt.

Was das Gestein Nr. 233 betrifft, so gehört es wahrscheinlich der oberen Kreide an.

Fig. 1. Sandsteinkonglomerat mit Geröllchen von Tonschiefer und Quarzit. Plagioklaskörner sind zahlreich. Vergr. 16:1. (6)

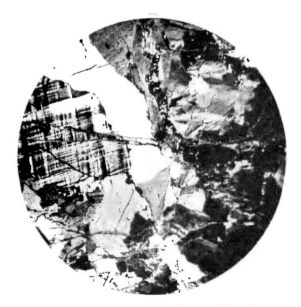

Fig. 2. Granit mit Brecciénstruktur (beginnende Mylonitisierung). Vergr. 16:1. + Nicols. (9)

Fig. 3. Tonschiefer mit quarzitischen Schichten (gehört den sogenannten Angaraschichten an).
Vergr. 16 : 1. (11)

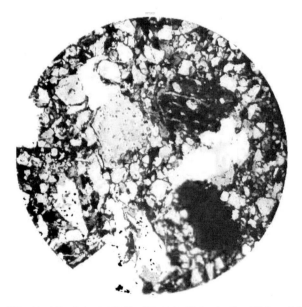

Fig. 4. Kalksandsteinkonglomerat mit Geröllchen von Hornstein, Tonschiefer und Quarzit.
Splitter von Plagioklas und Mikroklin sind zahlreich. Vergr. 16 : 1. (25)

Fig. 5. (23) bei Vergr. 35 : 1.
Die Mikrophotographie zeigt gequetschte Feldspatkörner wie auch Fragmente eines Granitmylonits.
+ Nicols.

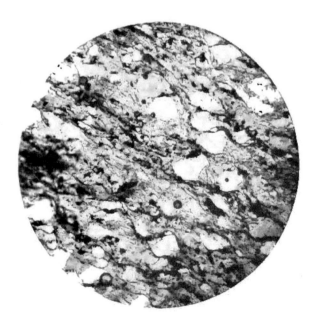

Fig. 7. Granit mit mikroskopisch deutlichen Mikroklinaugen.
Vergr. 16 : 1. + Nicols. (39)

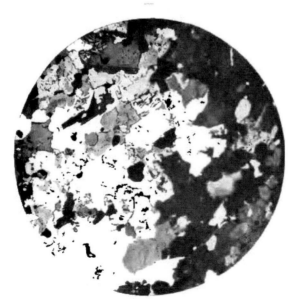

Fig. 8. Granatführender Gneisgranit. Vergr. 16 : 1. + Nicols. (40)

Fig. 9. Amphibolit. + Nicols. (55)

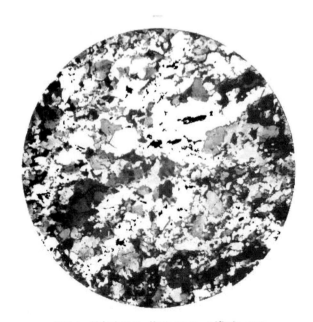

Fig. 10. Mylonitgneis. Vergr. 16:1. + Nicols. (59)

Fig. 11. Sericitschiefer.
Vermutlich ist das Gestein ein kräftig mylonitisierter Plagioklasgneis. Vergr. 35:1. + Nicols. (62)

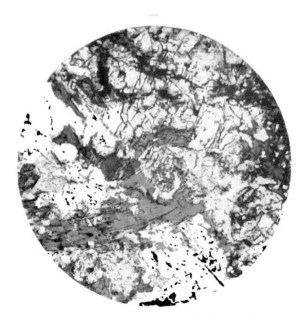

Fig. 12. Granatreicher Gneisgranit mit Biotit und Hornblende. Vergr. 35:1. (69)

Fig. 13. Granitmylonit. Vergr. 16:1. + Nicols. (78)

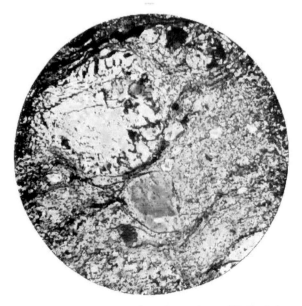

Fig. 14. Mylonitisierter Porphyr. Vergr. 16:1. + Nicols. (79)

Fig. 15. Granat-Andalusit-Gneis. Vergr. 16 : 1. (94)

Fig. 16. Granulierter Augengneis. Vergr. 16 : 1. + Nicols. (111)

215

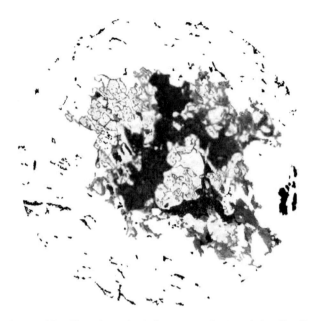

Fig. 17. Granulitischer Plagioklasgneis (121) mit Zusammenwachsung zwischen Hornblende und Granat. Vergr. 35:1.

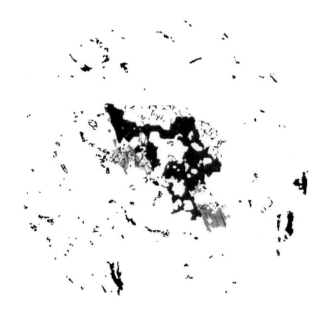

Fig. 19 und 20. Plagioklasgneismylonit. Vergr. 16:1. (124) Fig. 20. + Nicols.

KARTE
von
OSTPAMIR
mit eingezeichneten Fundorten
der verschiedenen geologischen Formationen
Maßstab 1:1.500.000

Kilometer

ABBILDUNGEN.

Pl. I. Fig. 1. Sandsteinkonglomerat mit Geröllchen von Tonschiefer und Quarzit. Plagioklaskörner sind zahlreich. Vergr. 16 : 1. (6)

Fig. 2. Granit mit Breccienstruktur (beginnende Mylonitisierung). Vergr. 16 : 1. + Nicols. (9)

Pl. II. Fig. 3. Tonschiefer mit quarzitischen Schichten (gehört den sogenannten Angaraschichten an). Vergr. 16 : 1. (11)

Fig. 4. Kalksandsteinkonglomerat mit Geröllchen von Hornstein, Tonschiefer und Quarzit. Splitter von Plagioklas und Mikroklin sind zahlreich. Vergr. 16 : 1. (23)

Pl. III. Fig. 5. (23) bei Vergr. 35 : 1. Die Mikrophotographie zeigt gequetschte Feldspatkörner wie auch Fragmente eines Granitmylonits. + Nicols.

Fig. 6. Kalksandsteinschiefer mit deutlichen Spuren der Dynamometamorphose. Vergr. 35 : 1. (29)

Pl. IV. Fig. 7. Granit mit mikroskopisch deutlichen Mikroklinaugen. Vergr. 16 : 1. + Nicols. (39)

Fig. 8. Granatführender Gneisgranit. Vergr. 16 : 1. + Nicols. (40)

Pl. V. Fig. 9. Amphibolit. + Nicols. (55)

Fig. 10. Mylonitgneis. Vergr. 16 : 1. + Nicols. (59)

Pl. VI. Fig. 11. Sericitschiefer. Vermutlich ist das Gestein ein kräftig mylonitisierter Plagioklasgneis. Vergr. 35 : 1. + Nicols. (62)

Fig. 12. Granatreicher Gneisgranit mit Biotit und Hornblende. Vergr. 35 : 1. (69)

EINE
CHINESISCHE BESCHREIBUNG
VON TIBET

VERMUTLICH VON JULIUS KLAPROTH
NACH AMIOT'S ÜBERSETZUNG BEARBEITET,

HERAUSGEGEBEN VON ERICH HÄNISCH

In den Sammlungen der Königlichen Bibliothek in Berlin findet sich eine französische Handschrift[1] mit dem Titel »*Description historique et géographique du Thibet appellé par les Chinois Si-thsang. Traduite du Chinois* 1822«.[2]

Der Verfasser der Übersetzung ist nicht genannt, ebensowenig der Titel der Vorlage, nach der übersetzt wurde. Doch deuten alle Anzeichen darauf hin, daß wir es mit einer Arbeit Klaproths zu tun haben, vielleicht einer Übersetzung des chinesischen Werkes *Hsi-Tsang chi* 西 藏 記 »*Aufzeichnungen über Tibet*«. Zwar ist die Hand nicht die des großen Sinologen, wie die Vergleichung mit einigen in der Bibliothek aufbewahrten eigenhändigen Briefen des Forschers ergibt. Vielmehr handelt es sich um eine von einem Schreiber, nicht nach Diktat, sondern nach Konzept[3] angefertigte Abschrift. Folgende Punkte jedoch sprechen hinreichend für die Urheberschaft Klaproths: Die Handschrift stammt aus dem Nachlasse Klaproths und ist, unter Nr. 3912, zugleich mit einer Sammlung von Karten accessioniert[4], die von Klaproth gezeichnet und signiert sind.[5] Weiter hat Klaproth sich nachweislich gerade in den zwanziger Jahren des vorigen Jahrhunderts eingehend mit der Geographie Tibets beschäftigt. Schließlich ist außer ihm niemand aus der europäischen Gelehrtenwelt der damaligen Zeit bekannt, der eine solche Vertrautheit mit den einschlägigen Sprachen besessen hätte, wie sie die Übersetzung verrät. Der Rückschluß auf die chinesische Vorlage ist nicht so unbedingt sicher: Die Übersetzung ist mit keinem der aus der chinesischen Tibet-Literatur bekannten Werke identisch. Nur mit dem Tibet-Abschnitt der großen »Reichsgeographie«[6] 大清一統志 deckt sie sich auf weite Strecken, aber nicht vollständig. So deutet sie entweder auf Auszüge aus verschiedenen Literaturwerken hin oder aber auf eine einzelne Vorlage, die der Reichsgeographie verwandt ist. Nun erwähnt Klaproth im Vorwort zu seiner französischen Bearbeitung des vom Pater Hyakinth ins Russische übersetzten *Wei-Tsang Fu-chih* 衛藏圖識, daß er von einem andern einschlägigen Buche, eben dem *Hsi-Tsang chi*, eine Übersetzung unternommen, sie aber bei Erscheinen der

---

[1] Signatur Ms gall. 179, Folio, 290 Seiten stark.

[2] Der Fund ist den Herren Dr. A. Herrmann und Dr. F. Schillmann, Berlin, zu danken. Die jetzt um 100 Jahre zurückliegende Arbeit Klaproths kam durch einen glücklichen Zufall bei der Durchsicht der französischen Handschriften zutage, unter die sie eingereiht war. — Die Generalverwaltung der K. B. hat in dankenswerter Weise die Erlaubnis zur Benutzung und Herausgabe der Handschrift erteilt.

[3] Das ergibt sich aus einigen wiederkehrenden Fehlern, die nur einer falschen Lesung entsprungen sein können.

[4] Im Jahre 1854 als Geschenk des Königs von Preußen.

[5] Veröffentlicht von Sven Hedin in Vol. III.

[6] *Ta Ch'ing I-t'ung chih*, zitiert T. I.

[7] Im *Nouveau Journal Asiatique*, t. IV, 1829.

Hyakinthschen Arbeit zurückgestellt habe. Da er gleich hinzufügt, daß er nach Durchsicht der russischen Übersetzung enttäuscht sei und bedauere, seine eigene nicht durchgeführt zu haben, so liegt der Schluß nahe, daß er sie später doch noch fertiggestellt hat. Kommen wir dazu, die vorliegende Handschrift als eben jene Klaprothsche Übersetzungsarbeit anzusehen, so wäre ihr Beginn nach der Datierung in das Jahr 1822, ihre Vollendung in die Zeit nach 1829 zu setzen.

Das Nächstliegende wäre, die Übersetzung mit dem chinesischen Texte zu vergleichen. Haben wir es wirklich mit dem *Hsi-Tsang chi* zu tun, so liegt auch die Urheberschaft Klaproths als Übersetzers damit fest. Aber das *Hsi-Tsang chi* ist ein, wenigstens in Europa, seltenes Buch und der deutschen Wissenschaft nicht zugänglich.[1] Da Klaproth in den fraglichen Jahren in Paris lebte, ist anzunehmen, daß es in den dortigen Büchersammlungen zu finden wäre.

Wir müssen uns also hinsichtlich der Vorlage und des Übersetzers mit unsern Anhaltspunkten bescheiden und zur Sache selbst fragen: Welche Stelle nimmt der Text an sich innerhalb der chinesischen Tibet-Literatur ein? Sodann: bringt er uns Neues bei zur Kenntnis von Tibet, das ihn der Veröffentlichung wert machte? — Zur chinesischen Tibet-Literatur führt W. Woodville Rockhill, der das obenerwähnte *Wei-Tsang t'u-chih* in englischer Sprache herausgegeben hat[2], noch 13 Quellen an, aus den Jahren 1759 bis 1886. Die Liste soll hier nicht wiederholt, auch kein Urteil über ihre Genauigkeit abgegeben werden. Dazu ist uns die chinesische Literatur immer noch zu wenig bekannt. Nur das mag bemerkt sein, daß ein Werk, wohl die ausführlichste Darstellung von Tibet, darin noch fehlt: das *Wei-Tsang t'ung-chih*, 衞藏通志, das »Handbuch von Tibet«, dem weiter unten eine eingehende Besprechung gewidmet sei. Ebensowenig ist das *Hsi-Tsang chi* erwähnt. Den Wert dieses Buches gegenüber den andern Werken der Liste abzuschätzen, dürfte ohne eine genauere Vergleichung mit ihnen nicht möglich sein.[3] Aber so viel läßt sich doch sagen, daß es unter ihnen eine bedeutende Stellung einnimmt. Von dem erwähnten *Wei-Tsang t'ung-chih* wird es angeführt, während es selbst sich auf keines der andern Tibetwerke stützt, mit Ausnahme des Tibet-Abschnittes aus der Reichsgeographie. Das deutet auf ein höheres Alter hin. Sein Erscheinungsjahr wird also voraussichtlich nur wenig später fallen als das der Reichsgeographie (1764). Von den 16 Literaturwerken (den bei Rockhill angegebenen 14, dazu den beiden dort ausgelassenen) ist nun, bis auf den mehr geschichtlichen Tibet-Abschnitt des *Sheng-wu chi* 聖武記, einem Auszuge aus dem die Tibet-Expedition enthaltenden »Dsungarenkrieg«[5] 平定準噶爾方略 und einigen Stellen aus der Reichsgeographie[6] bisher nur das *Wei-Tsang t'u-chih* übersetzt worden, in drei Sprachen, in das Russische, Französische und Englische.

---

[1] Im Kaiserlichen Katalog aufgeführt, Buch 52, ebenso bei Wylie, *Notes on Chinese literature*, new ed., Shanghai 1901, S. 64.

[2] Illustrierte Beschreibung von Tibet, *Journal of the Royal Asiatic Society*, 1891, zitiert R.

[3] Dafür wissen wir zu wenig vom *Hsi-Tsang chi* selbst. In der vorliegenden Übersetzung ist weder der Verfasser noch das Jahr der Ausgabe genannt. Klaproth macht bei seiner Anführung im *Nouveau Journal Asiatique* auch keine Angaben. Sie fehlen auch bei Wylie, der sich mit der dürftigen Bemerkung begnügt: a record of the country and customs of Tibet, with an itinerary at the end.

[4] Das Kriegsbuch der Mandschudynastie, Abschnitt V, ins Französische übersetzt von I. Iwanoffsky, *De la conquête du Tibet par les Chinois*, *Muséon* III, S. 165 ff.

[5] *P'ing-ting Jun-gar fang-lio*, die militärischen Operationen bei der Niederwerfung der Dsungaren, 1736, 171 Bücher, daraus die auf Tibet bezüglichen Schriftstücke ausgezogen und übersetzt von E. Hänisch, *T'oung Pao*, Vol. XII.

[6] Z. B. Klaproth über den Lauf des Yarou-Tsangbo-Flusses, *Magasin Asiatique*, Paris 1825.

Dazu gibt es aber noch eine ältere bedeutende Arbeit, die weder bei ROCKHILL, noch auch in der *Bibliotheca Sinica* unter Tibet aufgeführt ist: die *Mémoires concernant les Chinois* der Jesuiten bringen im Bd. XIV, Paris 1789 unter dem Titel *Introduction à la connoissance des peuples Chinois* 17 Kapitel (10—26), die sich als eine gekürzte Übersetzung des Tibet-Abschnittes der Reichsgeographie erweisen. Mit dieser Übersetzung des P. Amiot zeigt nun unsere Handschrift eine Übereinstimmung, die unmöglich auf Zufall beruhen kann. Nur ordnet sie die Teile bisweilen anders ein, weicht auch in den Kürzungen etwas ab und hängt schließlich noch einen großen Abschnitt der Itinerare an. Halten wir am *Hsi-Tsang-chi* als Vorlage der Handschrift fest, so ist diese nicht als selbständige Übersetzung einzuschätzen. Dagegen behält sie bei der völligen Durcharbeitung der Ortsnamen, die bei Amiot nur im chinesischen Gewande erscheinen, doch ihren besonderen Wert. Es dürfte sich daher ihre kommentierte Herausgabe sehr wohl rechtfertigen, zumal die *Mémoires* schwer zugänglich sind.

Eine große Schwierigkeit bei den Übersetzungen aus dem Chinesischen bietet die Wiedergabe der mit chinesischen Zeichen geschriebenen fremdländischen, nichtchinesischen Namen. Nur in seltenen Fällen wird der Sinn und damit der Lautwert der Namen klar erkennbar oder mit diesen oder jenen Hilfsmitteln festzustellen sein. Fehlen feste Anhaltspunkte, so ist der Leser, gerade wenn er gewisse sprachliche Kenntnisse besitzt, leicht geneigt, mit Hilfe der Wörterbücher die chinesisch geschriebenen Fremdnamen in eine einheimische Form zu pressen: solche Lösungen gelingen nur selten. Besonders gefährlich ist diese Behandlungsart bei tibetischen Namen mit ihren vielen stummen Buchstaben und mancherlei mundartlichen Sonderheiten. Von grundlegender Bedeutung wird hier die nur selten sicher zu beantwortende Frage sein, ob die Namen nach einer Aufzeichnung in tibetischer Schrift, etwa nach einer tibetischen Landkarte, ins Chinesische umschrieben wurden, oder ob die chinesische Umschreibung auf eine mündliche Überlieferung zurückgeht. Im ersten Falle muß man sich dessen bewußt sein, daß viele tibetische Ortsnamen (die noch oft mit fremdsprachlichen Bestandteilen gebildet sind, durch den Buddhismus eingedrungenen indischen Sprachelementen und durch Nomaden- und Kriegszüge hereingekommenen mongolischen Wörtern) erst ihr chinesisches Gewand angenommen haben, nachdem sie auf den alten Karten durch mandschurische Schreibung gegangen sind.[1] Im Falle der mündlichen Überlieferung kommt es auf zwei Punkte an: In welcher tibetischen Mundart ist der Ortsname dem chinesischen Gewährsmann vorgesprochen worden, und welchen chinesischen Dialektwert legt dieser der chinesischen Schrift zugrunde? Denn es gibt kein amtliches einheitliches Umschreibungssystem, und nur für die gebräuchlichsten Ortsnamen haben sich bestimmte Schreibungen durchgesetzt. Sonst mag man denselben Namen bei dem einen Schriftsteller so, bei dem nächsten anders geschrieben finden. Und diese Verschiedenheiten der Schreibung gehen selbstverständlich zum Teil auf die mundartliche Eigenheit des Schreibers zurück.[2] Das heißt also, man dürfte bei der Lesung der

---

[1] Dies drückt sich im Falle der palatalen Zischlaute aus: tsa und dsa werden im Mongolischen noch entsprechend wiedergegeben, im Mandschurischen aber durch die Palatalen tscha und dscha und erscheinen dann im Chinesischen nach der Umschreibung von den mandschurischen Karten ebenfalls in den palatalen Lauten 紮 und 扎.

[2] Hierzu ein Beispiel: die chinesischen Umschreibungen der Karte Turkistans, auf der sogen. Wutschang-Karte, tragen zum Teil unverkennbar das Gepräge einer mittelchinesischen Mundart, d. h. sie lassen sich nicht auf die einheimischen Formen zurückführen, wenn man bei den Zeichen die nordchinesische Aussprache zugrunde legt. Diese Erscheinung hat ihre Ursache jedenfalls darin, daß die Siedler und dem Herkommen nach auch die dortigen chinesischen Beamten, besonders seit der Neueroberung des Landes durch Tso Tsung-t'ang, sich lange Zeit aus der Provinz Hunan ergänzten. Auf deren Angaben geht die Karte zurück.

Ortsnamen nicht ohne weiteres den Lautwert der nord-chinesischen Aussprache, des sogenannten *Kuan-hua*, voraussetzen und sich dann etwa bei der Umschrift in lateinische
Schrift einfach einer modernen Transkription bedienen. Diese ist natürlich besonders un-
angebracht bei den Fremdwörtern, die zu einer Zeit ins Chinesische umschrieben wurden,
als die der betr. Romanisation zugrunde gelegten heutigen Lautwerte auch für das Nordchinesische noch nicht zutrafen. Aber auch bei den Umschreibungen der Neuzeit sieht
man nicht ein, warum ein Wort wie »die Pagode«, das im Tibetischen *K'yung* geschrieben
und ebenso gesprochen wird, nun bei der Wiederherstellung aus dem Chinesischen in der
Form *ch'iung* erscheinen soll, nur aus dem Grunde, weil das chinesische Transkriptions-
zeichen heute in Peking so und nicht *k'iung* gesprochen wird wie in andern chinesischen
Mundarten. Es erhellt, daß die Zugrundelegung einer so verwischten und abgeschliffenen
Mundart wie des Pekinesischen, in dem die Laute ki und tsi in dji zusammenfallen, und
einer Transkription, die in diesem Falle z. B., mit *chi*, noch dazu weder die deutsche noch
die englische Aussprache, vielmehr einen besonderen technischen Wert darstellt, die Ableitung der Namen aus der Ursprache stark erschweren muß. Wenn Rockhill in seiner
erwähnten, höchst verdienstvollen Arbeit selbst die Wadesche Umschreibung anwendet,
mit der Begründung, die Peking-Mundart sei die einzige ihm vertraute[1], so wird dieser
Mangel dadurch wettgemacht, daß er die tibetischen Namen unmittelbar erklärt mit Hilfe
seiner Sprachkenntnisse und eines ihm zur Verfügung stehenden geographischen Wörter-
buches[2] 西域同文志. Nicht ohne Grund wird an dieser Stelle auf die Frage der Namen-
schreibung in der tibetischen Geographie eingegangen. Verworrene und uneinheitliche
Schreibung der Ortsnamen hatte uns die Karte von Tibet recht unleserlich und unverständlich
gemacht.[3] Das ist nicht verwunderlich, denn die Namengebung geht auf drei verschiedene
Quellen zurück: auf die alten europäischen Karten, auf die einheimischen tibetischen und chinesischen Karten und Geographiewerke und schließlich auf die Aufzeichnungen neuzeitlicher
Reisender. Die ersteren sind hinsichtlich ihrer Schreibung oft schwer nachzuprüfen. Von der
zweiten Art sind die tibetischen Karten in ihrer Originalschrift nicht immer geeignet, wegen
der vielen vorkommenden Konsonantenhäufungen, die heute nicht mehr gesprochen werden.
Bei den chinesischen Karten müßte man den Quellen nachgehen und dann im Einzelfalle der
Frage nach der Mundart des chinesischen Gewährsmannes, die bei der Bewertung der chinesischen Zeichen berücksichtigt werden muß. Zur richtigen Beurteilung der Namenangaben bei

---

[1] Übrigens bemerkt er ausdrücklich, daß er den Laut einiger Zeichen nach südlicher Aussprache gegeben habe.

[2] Hsi- yü t'ung-wen chih. Auch E. v. Zach hat in seinen *Lexikographischen Beiträgen* I und III. Peking 1902 und
1905 (zitiert Z.), dies Werk bearbeitet, durch Auszug der tibetischen Ortsnamen, und sich bei der Umschreibung sicherlich des besten Verfahrens bedient. Er bringt zunächst die den Lautwert des Ortsnamens darstellende mandschurische
Schreibung in lateinischer Umschrift, sodann die danach genommene chinesische Transkription in Zeichen, also
die Namen, die wir auf den chinesischen Karten und in der Literatur finden, und schließlich die tibetischen Grund-
werte, voll ausgeschrieben in lateinischer Umschrift. Wenn der Herausgeber des großen Sammelwerkes sich zur
Anwendung dieser gangbarsten Umschreibungsmethode von *Wade* entschlossen hat, so geschah das trotz der
Bedenken aus reinen Zweckmäßigkeitsgründen zur Erzielung einer Einheitlichkeit. Aus diesem selben Grunde ist
auch in den Noten der vorliegenden Einzelarbeit überall da, wo die Namen nach der chinesischen Schreibung,
d. h. in Silben abgeteilt und mit Strichen verbunden, gegeben werden, die *Wade*'sche Methode angewandt worden.
Der Übersetzungstext selbst legt französischen Lautwert unter.

[3] Die Verwirrung ist auf manchen innerasiatischen Karten noch so stark, daß man fast allein aus der
Schreibung der Ortsnamen die Wege der einzelnen Reisenden verfolgen, womöglich herauslesen kann, an welcher
Stelle der Reiseweg eines Engländers von einem Russen gekreuzt wird. Die Möglichkeit zu verschiedenartigen
Schreibungen der Ortsnamen ist gerade in den chinesischen Kolonialgebieten so groß, daß wir sie hier garnicht
erschöpfend betrachten können.

den neuzeitlichen Reisenden wäre zunächst zu fragen, in welcher Weise die Namen festgestellt wurden, ob unmittelbar durch Erfragung bei den Eingeborenen oder durch Vermittlung der Führer, deren Sprachzugehörigkeit dann ins Gewicht fiele, ebenso wie die
der Reisenden selbst. — Das richtige Verfahren auf der Reise ist selbstverständlich, sich
neben der phonetischen Festlegung der Ortsnamen nach der Aussprache der Eingesessenen
die Namen auch in der Landesschrift aufschreiben und möglichst auch die Bedeutung
geben zu lassen. — Je nach der zugrundeliegenden Quelle kann ein und derselbe Ortsname auf mehreren Karten in ganz verschiedenen Formen erscheinen. Als Beispiel wählen
wir die Klosterstadt des Pantschen Lama's, die uns unter dem Namen *Taschilunpo* bekannt
ist, d. h. nach der gebräuchlichsten tibetischen Aussprache. Geschrieben wird sie im
Tibetischen »*bkraschis-lhunpo*», was soviel bedeutet wie »Berg der Seligkeit». Unter dieser
Aussprache kommt sie nirgends mehr vor, wohl aber neben der erstgenannten noch in
verschiedenen andern. Rockhill gibt die Form *Trashilunpo*, die vom Norden und Nordosten eingewanderten Mongolen hören und umschreiben *Raschilumbo*, was wieder in manche
chinesische Karten und Bücher als *Laschilunpo* übergegangen ist, während im allgemeinen
die Chinesen nach der Schreibung der mandschurischen Expeditionskarten *Jašilumbo* nun
auch die Zeichen *Tschaschilunpo* schreiben, oder nach dem Wade'schen System romanisiert
Chashilunpo, nach französischem *Tchachiliunpo*. Wir könnten also diesem einen Ort in
acht verschiedenen Schreibungen begegnen. Und so ähnlich liegt es sonst überall. Um
die erstrebenswerte Einheitlichkeit in die Karte zu bringen, müßte man eigentlich auf die
tibetische Originalschreibung zurückgreifen. Nun ist aber das zur Verfügung stehende
tibetische Kartenmaterial noch sehr gering. Man sollte suchen, es in jeder Weise zu ergänzen, durch Auszüge aus der tibetischen Literatur[1] und tibetischen Inschriften[2], schließlich durch Nutzbarmachung der chinesischen Hilfsbücher, wie es im Falle des *Hsi-yü t'ung-
wen chih* Rockhill und Zach getan haben.[3] Mangels tibetischer Schreibungen könnte
man aber auch mongolische und mandschurische benutzen, die als Lautschriften immer
noch einen besseren Anhalt geben als die chinesischen Verstümmelungen. Die mongolischen sind deswegen besonders geeignet, weil sie sich bemühen, das Tibetische in der
Schriftform, also mit den stummen Buchstaben, wiederzugeben. Die mandschurischen, die
nach der Aussprache transkribieren, sind wieder besonders reich vertreten, denn sie bilden
einmal für viele Kolonialkarten der Mandschuzeit überhaupt die Grundsprache und sind
außerdem in den sehr stoffreichen großen Generalstabswerken über die Kolonialkriege der
Mandschuzeit enthalten, in den mandschurischen Parallelausgaben. Würde man die sehr
umfangreichen Werke alle ausziehen und ein Ortsnamenverzeichnis nach der mandschurischen
Lautschrift von ihnen anfertigen, so bekäme man einen höchst wertvollen Stoff zusammen.[4]
Da dorthin zielende Vorarbeiten aber noch nicht oder noch nicht in genügendem Maße
geleistet worden sind, so stützt man sich heute auf die tatsächlich verfügbaren, reichhal-
tigsten und zuverlässigsten Quellen, die chinesische geographische Literatur. Entschließt
man sich, diese bei einer Durchkorrigierung der tibetischen Karte zu Grunde zu legen, so

---

[1] Das ist bisher kaum noch geschehen. Die tibetische Literatur ist bisher ja leider fast ausschließlich
als Hilfssprache zu buddhistischen Studien verwandt worden.

[2] Diese sind bearbeitet worden von Maurice Jametel, *L'épigraphie chinoise au Tibet*, Péking-Paris 1880.

[3] Auch die viersprachige Ausgabe des Mandschu-Wörterbuches 御製四體清文鑑 Yu-chih sze-t'i
Ch'ing-wen chien (Berlin K. B., S. M. I) gibt in den geographischen Abschnitten manche Anhaltspunkte für die
Etymologie der tibetischen Ortsnamen.

[4] Für die ostibetische Landschaft Chin-ch'uan ist diese Arbeit durch den Herausgeber des vorliegenden
Aufsatzes geleistet worden und soll an einer anderen Stelle des Sammelwerkes erscheinen.

läßt sich das mit Rücksicht auf die Vereinheitlichung der Ortsbezeichnungen durchaus rechtfertigen. Für die sich dann erhebende Frage der Romanisation der chinesischen Zeichen bleiben die obenangeführten Gesichtspunkte in Geltung. Jedenfalls sollte man die Transkription einheitlich mit der der entsprechenden Chinakarte gestalten. Besser ist immer noch die einfache Umschreibung der chinesischen Form eines tibetischen Ortsnamens, auch nach dem unbrauchbarsten System, als der Versuch einer eigenmächtigen Rekonstruktion der tibetischen Wörter, ohne gründliche Kenntnis der beiden Sprachen oder ohne literarische Hilfsmittel. Die Ergebnisse davon sind fast immer falsch. Falsch ist es z. B. deswegen, weil das Chinesische ein »r« nicht kennt und diesen Laut bei Umschreibungen von Fremdwörtern mit »l« wiedergibt, nun umgekehrt bei einer Rekonstruktion ins Tibetische für jedes »l« wieder ein »r« einzusetzen.[1] Es scheint, daß auch Klaproth, der eine für seine Zeit ungewöhnliche Sprachkenntnis besaß, in dieser Beziehung im vorliegenden Manuskript oft zu eigenmächtig verfahren ist: Rockhill macht ihm hinsichtlich seiner Ausgabe des *Wei-Tsang t'u-chih* den Vorwurf, daß er das Tibetische falsch konstruiert habe. Klaproth hat, wie wir sehen werden, versucht, auch in der vorliegenden Arbeit, jedem Fremdnamen aus der chinesischen Schreibung heraus gleich seine richtige Form zu geben. Es ist dies ein sehr heikles Unterfangen, das ihm sicherlich nicht stets geglückt ist. In allen zweifelhaften Fällen ist hier eine Bemerkung in die Fußnote eingesetzt worden, gegebenenfalls mit der richtigen Form, wo sie mit Hilfe der chinesischen Literatur festgestellt werden konnte. Als Literatur wurde vor allen Dingen die *»Reichsgeographie«* herangezogen, denn diese ist, wie schon bemerkt, unserm Texte verwandt, hat entweder seine Vorlage gebildet oder aber hat mit ihm die gleiche Vorlage gehabt.

Die Einteilung des Abschnittes Tibet in der Reichsgeographie ist folgende: 1. Verwaltungsgeschichtlicher Überblick mit einem Verzeichnisse der Städte und einem Anhange über die Stämme. 2. Ethnologie. 3. Topographie. 4. Altertumskunde: Das Reich T'u-fan[2] 土蕃. Die T'ang-Inschrift. 5. Furten und Brücken. 6. Tempel. 7. Erzeugnisse.

Die Klaprothsche Übersetzung ist eingeteilt: 1. Geschichtliche und geographische Beschreibung. 2. Gebirge. 3. Flüsse. 4. Furten. 5. Brücken. 6. Wichtigste Tempel. 7. Allgemeine Erzeugnisse. 8. Gebräuche. 9. Über das Reich T'u-fan. 10. Alte und neue Reisewege. Abschnitte 2—5 entsprechen fast wörtlich den Nummern 3 und 5 der Reichsgeographie. Sie sind weit reichhaltiger als die entsprechenden Teile des von Rockhill übersetzten *Wei-Tsang t'u-chih*. Dafür sind wieder die Klaprothschen Teile 6—10 bei Rockhill fast völlig enthalten, sollen daher in vorliegender Ausgabe fortgelassen werden. So bleibt in der Hauptsache nur die eigentliche Geographie übrig, die aber auch den wichtigsten Abschnitt bilden dürfte. Als Ausgleich für die fortgefallenen Teile der Handschrift soll eine Ergänzung der Literatur versucht werden durch eine genaue Inhaltsangabe des bisher unbekannten Tibetwerkes *Wei-Tsang t'ung-chih*. Bei diesem *»Handbuch von Tibet«* haben wir es mit einem der bedeutendsten einschlägigen Werke zu tun. Sein Alter steht nicht genau fest. Doch dürfte es nur wenig jünger sein als das von ihm zitierte *Wei-Tsang t'u-chih*. Jedenfalls sind die letzten Erlasse, die es in seinem Text erwähnt, vom Jahre 1791. Das Buch ist mit Verbesserungen und Zusätzen im Jahre 1896 auf Grund einer Handschrift erstmalig herausgegeben worden. Es konnte daher in der 1891 erschienenen

---

[1] In den chinesischen Umschreibungen unbekannter fremder Namen kann man also für »l« auch »r« lesen.
[2] Nach alter Aussprache t'u-ban, die Umschreibung für tö-bö (stod-bod), Obertibet. So bei Rockhill l. c., S. 5.

Rockhillschen Arbeit noch nicht berücksichtigt werden. Der Verfasser wird nicht genannt, ebensowenig wie der Herausgeber. Auch wird die Geschichte der Handschrift nicht gegeben. Das Inhaltsregister zeigt ein dem Originaltexte neu hinzugefügtes Sonderbuch (Kapitel), sodann den Abdruck der Handschrift in 16 Büchern: 1. Tibet in der alten Literatur. 2. Gebietseinteilung. 3. Topographie. 4. Verbindungswege. 5. Lamaismus. 6. Tempel. 7. Eingeborenenhäuptlinge. 8. Heerwesen. 9. Verwaltung. 10. Geldwesen. 11. Handel. 12. Bestimmungen. 13. Geschichtsabriß. 14. Volksfürsorge (neu eingefügt). 15. Stämme. 16. Buddhistische Literatur.

Diesem Text ist nun ein reichhaltiger einleitender Abschnitt mit Ergänzungen aller Art vorausgeschickt, der in zwei Teile zerfällt: chüan-shou 卷首, »Einleitungsband« mit dem Beisatz »neu zugefügt«, und t'i-yao 提要, »Angezogene wichtige Angaben« (aus der Literatur). Der erste Teil enthält 11 Nummern:

1. Die Steininschrift an der Brücke Lu-ting ch'iao[1] 瀘定橋 von 1691.
2. Die Steininschrift von der Unterwerfung Tibets aus der Zeit Kanghi.[2]
3. Die Steininschrift vom Tempel Hui-yüan-miao[3] 惠遠廟 aus der Zeit Yungtscheng.
4. Allgemeine Abhandlung über die »buddhistischen Traktate« vom Jahre 1733.
5. Spätere Vorrede zu den »buddhistischen Traktaten« vom Jahre 1733.
6. Vorrede zum Leng-yen Sutra[4] vom Jahre 1763.
7. Vom Kaiser verfaßte Vorrede zu der Mandschu-Übersetzung des großen buddhistischen Kanons, vom Jahre 1790.[5]
8. Abhandlung des Kaisers Kienlung über die Lamas.
9. Vom Kaiser verfaßte »zehn vollständige Aufzeichnungen« 十全記.[6]
10. Vom Kaiser verfaßte Gedichte vom Jahre 1793.[7]
11. Kaiserliche Bestallung für den Herzog Rabtan Namjal vom Jahre 1792.

Noch sehr viel reichhaltiger ist der Abschnitt der ergänzenden Literaturangaben, der 40 Nummern zählt. Ihre Titel seien hier untergebracht, da sie einen Begriff von dem großen Stoffe geben, der für die Tibetstudien vorhanden ist:

---

[1] Die große eiserne Hängebrücke über den T'ung-Fluß östlich von Tatsienlu.

[2] Vom Jahre 1720, vgl. Hänisch l. c.

[3] hui-yüan bedeutet Gnade und Mitgefühl (des Kaisers) für die fernen Gebiete.

[4] Śuraṅgama Sūtra.

[5] Das Vorhandensein dieser Übersetzung war bezweifelt worden. Vgl. Laufer, *Skizze der manjurischen Literatur*, S. 48.

[6] Die Verbindung shih-ch'üan stammt aus dem Ritenbuch der Chou-Zeit. Die große literarische Konkordanz P'ei-wen yün-fu führt als erstes Beispiel folgende Stelle auf: »Am Ende der Ernte sammelte er die Erträgnisse, um die Verpflegung zu regeln. Waren die Zehn voll, so galt das als Nummer 1, fehlte eins von Zehn, so galt das als Nummer 2 . . ., fehlten vier von Zehn, so galt das als schlecht«, d. h. eine Zehnzehntelernte galt als erstklassig, eine Sechs-zehntelernte als minderwertig. Der Ausdruck bezeichnet die Vollständigkeit, Vollendung. Hier ist er durch die beiden Zeichen 武 功 wu-kung »Kriegstaten« zu erweitern, also die shih-ch'üan wu-kung chi-Aufzeichnungen über die »vollkommenen« Kriegstaten. Es handelt sich um einen Kaiserlichen Erlaß über die zehn siegreichen Kriege aus der Regierung Kienlung, die als »shih-ch'üan« unübertreffbare militärische Leistung hingestellt werden. Sie werden aufgezählt: zwei siegreiche Kriege gegen die Dsungaren, einer gegen die Mohammedaner, zwei im Goldstromlande, einer auf Formosa, einer in Birma, einer in Annam und zwei gegen die Gorkhas.

[7] Die Beischriften zu den Kupferstichen, den sogen. chan-t'u 戰 圖 Kriegsbildern, mit Darstellungen aus den Feldzügen der Regierung K'ienlung. Es werden hier acht auf Tibet bezügliche angeführt: die Siege bei Tscham, bei Ma-ka-r-hsia-r-chia, bei Chi-lung, bei der Seilbrücke Jo, bei Hsich-pu-lu, am Berge Tung-chio und bei P'a-lang-ku, dazu ein Bild von der Ankunft der Gorkha-Lehnsfürsten in Peking.

2. IX, 4.

1. Shih-chien lei-han 史鑑類函, Tsa-shu' 雜 書, alte Berichte seit der Han- und T'ang-Zeit.
2. Das alte Tibet-Handbuch 舊藏志, nach einer im Jahre 1788 in Ch'eng-tu gefundenen Handschrift, und zwar daraus die Abschnitte: Ethnologisches und Geographie.
3. Die Topographische Beschreibung von Tibet, und zwar die Abschnitte: Gebiet, Sehenswürdigkeiten, Wege und Dörfer, Tempel, Ethnologisches und Erzeugnisse.
4. Die Chroniken von Potala, Tschaschilunpo und andern großen Tempeln, aus tibetischen Büchern (kartschag's) übersetzt, dazu Erhebungen über neugebaute Tempel.
5. Ein Abschnitt aus den Lebensbeschreibungen der Dalai Lama, Pantschen Erdeni und aller Hutuktu und Hubilgane.[2]
6. Alte Akten vom Gorkha-Aufstand 1788.
7. Expedition gegen die Gorkhas und ihre Unterwerfung 1791.
8. Berichte des Großfeldherrn Fukangga[3], des Statthalters Horin, des Großsekretärs Sun-Shih-i 孫 士 毅 über Reorganisationen vom Jahre 1791.
9. Kaiserliche Edikte vom Jahre 1791.
10. Eingabe Fukanggas und Horins über die Errichtung eines Obo[4] an der Grenze.
11. Liste der persönlichen und erblichen Herzog- und Taidji-Titel.
12. Bestimmungen über Gradverleihungen und Gehälter, sowie Beförderung und Kommandierung der Offiziere vom ka-pu-lun (bka'-blun)[5] abwärts.
13. Inschriften: Die T'ang-Inschrift, die Kanghi-Inschrift, die vom Kaiser (Kienlung) selbst verfaßte Inschrift: Shih-ch'üan chi[6], die Inschriften in den chinesischen Kriegsgott-Tempeln (kuan-ti-miao) in der Stadt Tschaschi[7] und auf dem Berge Mopan, die Tafel mit der Aufzeichnung der Kriegstaten im Tempel Ta Chao[8], die Inschrift in Hinter-Tibet, die Inschrift mit der Ermahnung zum Kampf gegen die Pocken, die Bekanntmachung des Verbotes der alten Bestattungssitten.
14. Listen der Namen der im Kampfe Gefallenen in der Halle Ching-chung-tse 旌 忠 祠.
15. Die Errichtung von Schulen zum Unterricht in der Gorkha-, Chinesischen, Tanggutischen und Mandschurischen Sprache.
16. Exerziervorschriften für die Eingeborenen- und chinesischen Truppen.
17. Dankschreiben des Gorkha-Königs (für seine Begnadigung) und Liste der Tributgeschenke.
18. Dankschreiben des Dalai Lama und des Pantschen Erdeni.
19. Geschichtliche Übersicht über die an der Grenze wohnenden Stämme.
20. Namen aller Stämme auf der Strecke von Tatsienlu bis Lhasa.
21. Übersetzung der tibetischen Wörter aus den Ortsnamen, Personennamen und Beamtentiteln.

---

[1] Der erste Büchertitel deutet auf eine nach Gegenständen geordnete Sammlung aus den Geschichtswerken, bei Wylie nicht erwähnt, tsa-shu sind Bücher gemischten Inhalts.

[2] Die Titel der Kirchenfürsten. Man beachte die darin enthaltenen mongolischen Wörter Dalai, Erdeni, Hutuktu und Hubilgan, die einen Schluß auf die vielen mongolischen Elemente in der kirchlichen und amtlichen Terminologie ermöglichen.

[3] Ein besonders verdienter mandschurischer General aus der Zeit der Kolonialkriege, in der chinesischen Umschreibung Fu-k'ang-an, vgl. Giles, *Chinese biographical dictionary*, Nr. 590.

[4] Eine Pyramide aus angehäuften Steinen.

[5] bka'-blun, Zivilbeamter, mit dem dritten chinesischen Beamtenrang.

[6] Vgl. oben.

[7] = Tschaschilunpo.

[8] Tschao ist das tibetische jo aus Jo-wo K'ang, Tempel des Buddha Tathâgata in Lhasa.

22. Ort und Zahl der auf die Türme und Sperren verteilten Unteroffiziere und Mannschaften des Grünen Banners.
23. Zahl der Wachmannschaften und Pferde auf den Relaisstationen.
24. Beamte und Vorsteher der Proviantspeicher.
25. Amtsobliegenheiten der in Tibet beamteten Kommissare, Sekretäre und Proviantbeamten.
26. Angelegenheiten der Münze und der Schatzkammer.
27. Die an die Angehörigen der Eingeborenenstämme zum Dienstverkehr und Handel amtlich ausgegebenen Passierscheine.
28. Satzungen für den an den Stationen (Proviantstationen?) von den Eingeborenen zu leistenden Posthilfsdienst (Ula).[1]
29. Amtsobliegenheiten der tanggutischen Häuptlinge.
30. Aufzählung der Tauschwaren bei den einzelnen Stämmen und in Tibet.
31. Der auf Kaiserlichen Erlaß eingesetzte Bumba P'ing-ch'ien-ch'ê[2] Hubilgan.
32. Der von den Mongolen-Taidjis nördlich des Himmelsgebirges mit den Karawanen nach Lhasa geschickte geröstete Tee.
33. Die jährliche Abordnung eines Kampo seitens des Dalai Lama und Pantschen Erdeni zur Audienz und Tributüberreichung (in Peking).
34. Die aus Szetschuan zu beschaffenden jährlichen Erfordernisse.
35. Die nach den Festsetzungen über Szetschuan zu befördernden Soldgelder, Schriftstücke und andere Sachen.
36. Abschnitt gemischten Inhalts: Sitten der Tangguten: Ackerbau der männlichen und weiblichen Arbeiter, die ansässigen Angehörigen der Stämme, Buddhakult der Lamas, Satzungen für die im Statthalteryamen und in den Zivil- und Militäryamen angewandten Maße.
37. Satzungen für den Amtsverkehr der Statthalterei mit dem Kolonial- und Finanzministerium.
38. Die an die tibetischen Mönche aus Yünnan und die Eingeborenenfürsten von Kuku Noor, der Mongolei und Szetschuan auszustellenden Pässe für ihre Botensendungen nach Lhasa zum Teetransport und Lesen der heiligen Bücher.
39. Zahl der Kaiserlichen Truppen von den Dam-Mongolen.
40. Die auf der Strecke von Lhasa nach Turkistan und Pei-lu errichteten Sperren.

Auf diese Literaturangaben folgt noch die Einteilung des Textes in der alten Form, danach eine Liste *Errata* und schließlich das »nachträgliche Begleitwort« zur Druckausgabe des Werkes. Bei dem Abschnitt mit den ergänzenden Literaturangaben handelt es sich leider zum größeren Teile um unveröffentlichte und unzugängliche Akten und Satzungen. Doch zeigt auch der alte Text des *Wei-Tsang t'ung-chih* selbst manche Teile, die mehr enthalten als die bisher übersetzten Bücher aus der Tibet-Literatur und daher eine Veröffentlichung verdienten.

Zu den Quellwerken, die das *Wei-Tsang t'ung-chih* anzieht, gehört auch das *Hsi-Tsang chi*, das wir in unserer vorliegenden Handschrift zu erblicken vermeinen. Der französische Text der Handschrift folgt hierunter mit Fortlassung derjenigen Teile, deren Inhalt uns schon anderorts bekannt geworden ist.

---

[1] Der von den Eingeborenen zu leistende Post- und Beförderungsdienst. Diese Einrichtung besteht noch heute, tibetisch 'ulag, mongolisch ulaga genannt, nach dem türkischen Worte ulag für Lasttier.

[2] Die tibetische Form ist nicht mit Sicherheit festzustellen.

DESCRIPTION
HISTORIQUE ET GÉOGRAPHIQUE DU THIBET
APPELLÉ PAR LES CHINOIS SI-THSANG.[1]

TRADUITE DU CHINOIS. 1822.

TABLE DES MATIÈRES:

I. DESCRIPTION HISTORIQUE ET GÉOGRAPHIQUE.

On donnait anciennement les noms de *Khiang* 羌 et de *Joung* 戎 à toute cette vaste étendue de pays qui est au Sud-ouest de la Chine, qui sont plutôt ceux des peuples qui en étaient les habitans. Tout le pays situé a l'Occident portait le nom de *Thou-fan* ou *Thou-po*, qui semble d'être une altération de celui de *Thibet*.[2] Après les *Tcheou* et les *Han* (on vint parler apparemment, dans cet endroit, des deux petites dynasties qui ont précédé les *Soung*), *Thou-fan* fut le nom distinctif d'un royaume particulier, dont le fondateur s'appellait *Hou-ty-phou-tsou-ye* 鶻 提 勃 窣 野, qui se soumit tous les tribus des *Khiang* et

---

[1] Die Umschreibungen chinesischer und tibetischer Wörter im Text sind französisch zu lesen. Die Handschrift enthält keinerlei chinesische Zeichen. Diese mußten vom Herausgeber aus der Literatur ergänzt werden. Sie stammen großenteils aus der chinesischen Reichsgeographie. Die chinesischen Ortsnamen sind der Zeichenersparnis wegen durch Nummern bestimmt worden, welche sich auf Playfair, *Cities and towns of China* (zitiert Pl.) beziehen, und zwar Auflage II. Shanghai 1910.
Der erste Abschnitt deckt sich in längeren Teilen mit der Reichsgeographie.
[2] Vgl. Rockhill, S. 5.

faisait son séjour au-delà de la rivière *Sy-tchy-chouy*[1], d'où il donnait les loix à toutes ces vastes régions vers lesquelles le soleil se couche.

Depuis les *Tcheou* jusqu'aux *Soui*[2], les Thibétains ne vinrent point à la Chine, et on n'y entendit point parler d'eux, dit un texte Chinois: ce qui paraît supposer qu'ils y étaient venus sous les *Tcheou*. La huitième année de *Tching-kouan* (en 634), sous *Thay-tsoung*, second Empereur de la Dynastie des *Thang*, le Roi de *Thou-fan*, appellé *Loung-tsan-tché*[3], est le premier qui ait envoyé des Ambassadeurs à la Chine pour payer le tribut en qualité de vassal de l'Empire, dont il voulait bien se donner le titre. La quinzième année du même Empereur (en 641), Sa Majesté lui donna une princesse de sang en mariage, qui s'appellait *Ouen-tchhing*. Le Roi de *Thou-fan* fit de jour en jour de nouvelles conquêtes, détruisit *Thou-kou-houn*[4] 吐谷渾 et toutes les tribus des *Khiang*, de *Tsin-tchin*[5] *Yang-thoung* 羊 同, *Thanghiang*[6] 党项 etc., et se rendit maître de plus de dix mille lys de pays. La prospérité des Thibétains dura environ trois-cens ans; mais leur puissance s'affaiblit beaucoup sur la fin des *Thang*. Au commencement de la Dynastie des *Soung*, c'est-à-dire vers l'an de Jésus-Christ 977, ils vinrent apporter leur tribut; et on leur donna toujours le nom de *Thou-fan*. Depuis ce tems, ils sont venus constamment rendre leurs hommages dans les tems qu'on leur avait préscrits pour cela.

Sous le règne de *Hian-tsoung* ou *Mengo*, Empereur de la Dynastie Mongole des *Yuen*, on fit un grand nombre de départemens, sous lesquels on rangea les différentes petites hordes qui composaient alors la nation Thibétaine. On bâtit des villes et des forteresses, on créa des Tribunaux et des Magistrats, on nomma des Lieutenans-Généraux et des Gouverneurs et tout prit une forme nouvelle. D'un côté, on assigna *Ho-tcheou*[7] pour ville principale; et de l'autre, au-delà des limites du *Szu-tchhouan*, on bâtit une nouvelle ville, pour être le séjour des Magistrats et des Officiers qui devaient avoir soin de tout ce qui concernait les affaires des lieux voisins, comme *Tiao-men*[8] 弔門, *Yu-thoung* 魚通, *Ly-ya* 雅䉤, *Tchhang-ho* 長河, *Si-ning*[9], etc. Plus tard *Chy-tsou* ou *Koublai-khan* voulut faire un petit Royaume qui fut l'apanage des Religieux de l'ouest, qui étaient dispersés çà et là dans le Thibet, appellé alors *Ou-szu-thsang*.[10] Le chef de ces Religieux s'appellait *Pasba*.[11] L'Empereur fit bâtir des villes et des villages, dont il donna la souveraineté à *Pasba*, qu'il décora du nouveau titre de *Ta-pao-fa-ouang*; ce qui, rendu en Français, signifie le Roi de la grande et précieuse doctrine. Il faut remarquer ici, que la souveraineté des Lamas, et leur établissement en ordre hiérarchique, dans la forme qui est observée aujourd'hui parmi eux, ne datent que du regne de cet Empereur *Chi-tsou* ou *Koublai-khan*, petit-fils de *Tchingkis-khan*, et premier Empereur de la Dynastie des *Yuen*, dont le regne, comme Empereur de la Chine, n'a été que de quinze ans, ayant commencé l'an 1280 et ayant fini

---

[1] Tibetisch k'yi-tsch'u, vgl. R. S.
[2] d. h. bis zum 7. Jahrhundert.
[3] Die letzte Silbe ist hier ein grammatisches Zeichen der Hervorhebung und gehört nicht zum Namen, der auf den König Srong-btsan (sgampo) weist.
[4] Volkstamm am Kuku Noor.
[5] Die beiden Zeichen Tsin-tchin 鑫 臣 sind zu übersetzen: »er machte sie sich insgesamt botmäßig».
[6] Eine alte Bezeichnung für die Tangguten am oberen Huangho.
[7] Pl. 2062.
[8] Wörtlich ein Tor mit einem Kampfturm.
[9] Nach den Ming-Annalen, Buch 331, ist zu lesen Tchhang-ho-si und Ning-Youan.
[10] dbus-gtsang, Mittel- und Westtibet.
[11] 'Pags-pa bla-ma. Das erste Wort entspricht dem buddhistischen Prädikat Ārya.

237

l'an 1295. Cette époque, comme l'on voit, n'est pas bien ancienne. Il est très probable néanmoins que les Lamas, qui étaient établis depuis longtems dans la *Tartarie*, ne firent qu'ajouter à l'ancienne forme de leur Gouvernement domestique, la pompe extérieure, les titres et tout l'appareil des honneurs dont ils furent comblés par les Princes Mongols, et après eux par les Empereurs Chinois, comme on pourra le conclure par ce qui suit. Les disciples du *Ta-pao-fa-ouang* reçurent le titre de *Szu-koung*, c'est-à-dire un comte des Temples. (*Szu* signifie Cour, Temple; et *Koung* est un titre qui répond à-peu-près à celui de Comte[1]): Le Comte des Temples eut inspection sur tout ce qui avait rapport aux cérémonies qui s'observent dans les Temples. D'autres furent nommés *Szu-thou* [2] pour les affaires temporelles et civiles, et *Koue-koung* 國公 pour les affaires de la guerre. On donna aux uns et aux autres des sceaux de pierre de *Yu* [3] ou d'or, conformément à leurs dignités.

Sous la Dynastie *Ming*, la sixième année de *Houng-ou* (en 1373) l'Empereur nomma *Nié-ty-chy-nian-kia-pa-thsang-bou* [4] à la dignité de *Tchhy-ching-foe-pao-koue-szu*, ou, maître qui allume et élève le précieux Royaume de Foe ou Bouddha. Il lui fit présent d'un sceau fait de pierre précieuse, érigea dans le pays les deux départemens, dont l'un fut appellé *Ou-szu-thsang-tchy-hoey-szu* et l'autre *Tho-kan-tchy-hoey-szu* [5]; établit des préfectures sous le titre de *Siuan-ouey-szu* 宣慰司 et *Tchao-thao-szu* 招討司; des *Fou* ou villes du premier ordre de 10000 et des bourgs de 1000 familles, et en donna la souveraineté au *Koue-koung*, établi par les Mongols, dont le nom était *Nangosdanba* 南哥思丹八. en laissant subsister les autres dignités antérieures.

On divisa leur pays en deux départemens généraux qui eurent l'un et l'autre le nom *Tou-tchi-hoey-chi-szu*, comme qui dirait Chambre générale qui indique, sans exception, tout ce qu'il faut faire, parce qu'on les soumit à des Tribunaux qui sont ainsi appellés et dont l'un fut placé à *Thokan*, et l'autre à *Ou-szu-thsang*.

Il me paraît que les *Tou-tchi-hoey-chi-szu* ont une jurisdiction à peu près semblable à celle de nos intendans, et que les simples *Tchi-hoey-szu*, ou une subdélégation, à *Loung-tha* [6] On érigea trois autres Tribunaux du titre de *Siuan-ouei-szu*, c'est-à-dire, qui préconise, qui fait valoir les miséricordes, qui tâche d'exciter la commisération, etc.: l'un fut placé à *Thokan*, l'autre à *Doungboukhankhou*, et le troisième à *Thoung-ning-yuan*. [7] On érigea aussi six Tribunaux du titre de *Tchao-t'ao-chy-szu* (c'est-à-dire, qui cherche, qui appelle, qui fait signe de venir, qui s'informe, qui est attentif à saisir les occasions de rappeler etc.). On plaça le premier à *Tho-kan-szu*, le second à *Tho-kan-loung-tha*, le troisième à *Tho-kan-tan*, le quatrième à *Tho-kan-thsang-thang*, le cinquième à *Tho-kan-tchhouan* et le sixième à *Mo-euth-kan*. On créa quatre dignités du titre de *Ouan-hou-fou* (c'est-à-dire Chef de dix mille

---

[1] Im T. I. stehen hier die Zeichen 司空 szé-k'ung, d. h. der die Beschauung überwacht. Die Handschrift hat nach den fast gleichlautenden Zeichen 寺公 szé-kung übersetzt, die wohl jedenfalls nicht in dem chinesischen Text gestanden haben. Es dürfte ein Versehen des Übersetzers vorliegen.

[2] Im T. I. 司徒, d. h. der der Aufsicht über die Anhänger (der buddhistischen Lehre) ausübt. Die Erklärung im französischen Text ist unverständlich.

[3] Nephrit.

[4] Auch hier liegt ein Irrtum des Übersetzers vor. Bei T. I. sind die ersten drei Silben geschrieben 攝帝師 und gehören nicht zum Namen, sondern sind zu übersetzen: Der Priester (oder Beamte), der für den Kaiser die Regierung führt. Das erste Zeichen ist eben offenbar mit dem Zeichen 慕 nieh verwechselt worden. Der Name selbst lautet dann im T. I. Nam-kia pa tsang-pu, bei R. S. 198 in die tibetische Form Nam-jya-pa tsan-po.

[5] d. h. zwei Distriktsbeamte für dBus-Tsang und To-kan 朵甘.

[6] Dieser Satz ist lückenhaft, daher unverständlich.

[7] Die Ortsnamen waren, da dieser Abschnitt bei T. I. fehlt, nicht festzustellen.

familles). Le premier fut mis à *Cha-culh-ko*, le second à *Nai-tchou*, le troisième à *Lo-szu-touan*, et le quatrième à *Pie-szu-ma*.[1] On créa dix-sept autres dignités ou chambres du titre de *Thsian-hou-fouo* etc. (c'est-à-dire, qui gouverne mille familles). Ceux qui furent nommés pour Chefs de ces mille familles, furent placés, le premier à *Tho-kan-szu*, le second à *Latsoung*, le troisième à *Po-ly-kia*, le quatrième à *Tchhang-ho-si-la*, le cinquième à *Tho-pa-tsan-soun*, le sixième à *Kia-pa*, le septième à *Tchao-yé*, le huitième à *Na-tchou*, le neuvième à *Loun-ta*, le dixième à *Kouo-yeou*, le onzième à *Cha-ly-ko-ha-szu*, le douzième à *Po-szu-kia-szu-thoung*, le treizième à *Sa-ly-lou-culh-kan*, le quatorzième à *Thsan-pou-lang*, le quinzième à *La-tsou-ya-la*, le seizième à *Y-ly-pa*, le dix-septième à *Kouo-tsé-lou-soun*.[2] On fit outre cela des réglemens, suivant lesquels les trois Princes *Tchhan-houa-ouang*, *Tsan-kiao-ouang* et *Fou-kiao-ouang*, pouvaient envoyer leur tribut par le *Szu-tchhouan* ou par le *Chen-sy*. Le nombre des hommes qui pouvaient entrer à la Chine, chaque fois que ces princes envoyaient le tribut, était ou de cent, ou seulement de cinquante, à leur volonté. Le *Ta-pao-fa-ouang* et le *Ta-cheng-fa-ouang* envoyaient chacun dix Lamas pour chaque Ambassade. Tous les autres Princes ou chefs de horde qui voulaient envoyer, devaient se pourvoir, dans le Temple dit *Tsé u-ngen-szu* 慈 恩 寺, de deux Lamas pour être à la tête de chacune de leurs Ambassades. Ils pouvaient entrer dans la Chine par *Ly-tcheou*[3] ou par *Thian-tsiuan*[4] du *Szu-tchhouan* ou bien par *Thao-tcheou*[5] du *Chen-si*. De *Tchhang-ho*, *Si-yu* et *Thoung-ning-yuen*[6] on envoyait chaque année une Ambassade, et chacune n'était composée que de cinquante ou toute-au-plus de soixante personnes. Elles entraient à la Chine par *Ya-tcheou*[7] du *Szu-tchhouan*. De *Tho-kan-szu* et de *Toung-bou-khankhou*, on envoyait aussi une fois chaque année. Les Envoyés entraient en Chine par *Ya-tcheou*. Ceux de *Ouei-mao*[8], de *Soung-phan*[9], du *Kiu-tchouan* 金 川, de *Tsa-kou*[10], de *Ta-szu-man* et d'autres peuples d'au-delà des frontières du *Szu-tchhouan*, pouvaient envoyer une fois de trois ans en trois ans. Des temples situés dans le pays de *Thao-tcheou* et de *Min-tcheou*[11] on envoyait une fois chaque année. Des différentes hordes voisines en envoyait une fois de deux en deux ans. On ne permettait pas que ces Ambassades fussent composées de plus de cent personnes, et de moins de dix; mais qu'il y en eût cent ou seulement dix, il n'y en avait jamais que dix qui venaient à la Cour, les autres étaient obligées d'attendre sur les frontières que leurs Compagnons fussent de retour, pour se rendre ensuite tous ensemble dans les lieux d'où ils avaient été envoyés.

La quatrième année de *Houng-ou* (en 1371) on établit à *Thao-tcheou-ouei* un Tribunal qui eut le nom du *Kiun-min-tchi-hoei-chy-szu*, et auquel on attribua une jurisdiction très étendue, tant pour ce qui avait rapport au militaire, que pour les autres affaires, qui concernaient le gouvernement des peuples qui sont sur les frontières.

La onzième année de *Houng-ou* (en 1378), on établit à *Min-tcheou-ouei* un autre Tribunal général du titre de *Tou-tchi-hoei-chy-szu*. Outre cela, on en établit un particulier

---

1 u. 2 Die Ortsnamen waren, da dieser Abschnitt bei T. I. fehlt, nicht festzustellen.
3 Pl. 3717?
4 Pl. 6414.
5 Pl. 6293, heute zu der Provinz Kansu gehörend.
6 Falsch abgeteilt: zu lesen Tchhang-ho-si, Yu-thoung und Ning-yuen.
7 Pl. 7213.
8 Nicht feststellbar.
9 Pl. 5977.
10 Pl. 6302 = der Bezirk Li-fan 理 番.
11 Pl. 4457.

du titre de *Tchha-ma-szu* 茶 馬 司, pour présider aux échanges qui se faisaient sur les frontières, du thé des Chinois contre les chevaux des Tartares. Des frontières de *Si-ning*, on présentait trois mille cinq cens chevaux. Le *Tchha-ma-szu* les examinait et les partageait en trois classes, en bons, en médiocres, et en communs. Pour chaque cheval de la première classe on donnait cent vingt livres de thé; on en donnait soixante-dix pour chaque cheval médiocre, et cinquante seulement pour chaque cheval commun ou de la dernière classe. Les cinq Chefs de horde, décorés du titre de *Ouang*, pouvaient envoyer faire des échanges de leurs marchandises contre celles des Chinois. Tous les Chefs des Lamas eurent la même permission.

La neuvième année de *Young-Lo* (en 1411) on établit un autre *Tchha-ma-szu* à *Thao-tcheou-ouei*. Le Chef de la horde de *Ho-pa-tsang*[1] s'engagea a présenter chaque année trois mille cinquante chevaux: les commissaires députés par les Tribunaux *Tou-tchi-hoei-chy-szu* et *Tchha-ma-szu* de *Ho-tcheou-ouei* en pouvaient choisir tel nombre qu'ils jugeaient à propos pour servir de tribut. Ceux de *Pili*, de *Eulh-tcheou*, de *Tsi-tchan*[2] et autres, dont le nombre était de vingt-neuf Chefs de horde, s'offrirent à présenter chaque année sept mille sept cens cinq chevaux, parmi lesquels on prendrait pour le tribut ceux qu'on jugerait à propos.

Vers le milieu du regne de *Young-Lo*, c'est-à-dire vers l'an 1414, l'Empereur donna de nouveau titres aux principaux d'entre les Lamas. Il y en eut huit qui eurent le nom de *Ouang* ou de Roi. Le premier et le principal, ainsi qu'il a été dit plus haut, s'appellait *Ta-pao-fa-ouang*. Le second fut appellé *Ta-ching-fa-ouang*[3], c'est-à-dire, Roi de la loi grande et élevée. Le troisième eut le titre de *Ta-thzu-fa-ouang* ou de Grand et Miséricordieux Roi de la loi. Le quatrième fut nommé *Tchhan-kiao-ouang* ou Roi qui manifeste la doctrine. La cinquième eut le nom de *Tchhan-hoa-ouang* ou de Roi qui manifeste les changemens. Le titre du sixième fut celui de *Fou-kiao-ouang* ou de Roi aide et soutien de la doctrine. Le septième fut appellé *Tsan-chen-ouang* ou Roi qui préconise le bien; et le huitième eut le titre de *Hou-kiao-ouang* ou Roi protecteur et gardien de la doctrine.

L'Empereur fit donner à chacun de ces nouveaux Rois des patentes qui constataient leurs dignités et un sceau particulier pour être apposé à tout ce qui émanerait de leurs jurisdictions respectives. Dans les années *Siuan-te* (1426—1435) et celles appellées *Tchhing-hoa* (1465—1487) on décora l'ordre des Lamas de nouvelles dignités et établit postérieurement les dignités de *Dalai-Lama* et de *Bantchan-Lama*, qui sont au-dessus de tous les *Ouang* ou Rois du *Thibet*. *Dalai-Lama* signifie le *Lama* qui voit clairement tout ce qui se passe, et *Bantchan-Lama* veut dire le *Lama* qui préside aux méditations du *Dalai-Lama*.[4]

La dix-neuvième année de *Tchhing-hoa* (en 1483) un Chef de horde nommé *Man-soung*[5] leva l'étendard de la révolte, entra à main armée dans les terres de l'Empire, et y fit des ravages qui eussent eu des suites très-funestes, si le Vice-Roi *Ma-ouen-ching* 馬 文 升, ne fût accouru promptement à la tête de toutes les troupes qui se trouvaient alors dans la province qu'il commandait. Le brave Officier combattit les Barbares avec un plein

---

[1] Nicht feststellbar.

[2] Diese Ortsnamen sind nicht festzustellen.

[3] Die beiden ersten Zeichen dieses Namens 大 乘 »großes Gefährt», sind ein buddhistischer Terminus »mahayana», die Lehre von der großen Überfahrt. Der ganze Titel lautet also »Gesetzeskönig von der Mahāyana-Lehre».

[4] Eigentlich sind es chinesische Umschreibungen eines mongolischen und eines tibetischen Wortes, mit den Bedeutungen »Meer», d. h. die meeresweite Religion und »Großer Lehrer» vom indischen paṇḍita.

[5] Nach den Ming-Annalen Man-sze.

succès et les poursuivit même jusque sur les frontières de leur pays, d'où ils n'osèrent sortir de longtems. Ils étaient venus par le *Chen-si*.[1]

La neuvième année de *Kia-thsing* (en 1530), ceux du *Si-fan* se révoltèrent et vinrent faire du dégat sur les frontières du *Chen-si*. L'Empereur donna ordre à *Tching-sing*, Lieutenant-Général de cette province, d'aller à la tête de ses troupes pour faire rentrer les Barbares dans leur devoir. *Tching-tsing* obéit, c'est-à-dire, qu'il alla contre les révoltés; mais il fut battu et sa petite armée fut taillée en pièces.[2] Depuis cette époque les frontières du *Chen-si* ne furent jamais tranquilles. Les Barbares venaient lorsqu'on s'y attendit le moins, pillaient et massacraient et se retiraient ensuite chargés de butin, lorsqu'on se mettait en devoir de les aller combattre. L'Empereur pensa sérieusement à les exterminer. Il mit l'affaire en délibération, et ordonna à tous ceux qui composaient son conseil de dire librement leur avis. *Ouang-kioung*[3] 王 瑃 dit que la voie des armes était la seule qu'on pût employer pour mettre en sûreté les frontières et même l'Empire, et qu'ainsi il jugeait, qu'il fallait mettre sur pied une puissante armée, et l'envoyer pour combattre les Barbares partout où l'on pourrait les rencontrer. *Ly-tching-ki* ne fut pas du même avis; il représenta que l'expérience du passé était un indice certain du peu de succès qu'on avait lieu d'attendre, si l'on s'en tenait à la voie des armes; qu'on pourrait bien vaincre ces peuples, mais qu'on ne saurait les exterminer; et qu'à moins qu'on n'eût toujours les armes à la main, on ne pourrait jamais se flatter de les contenir dans le devoir. Cela étant, ajouta-t-il, il me paraît que l'unique moyen d'assurer la tranquillité de nos frontières, serait d'envoyer un homme intègre, prudent, et qui eût de l'expérience, afin que par ses paroles et plus encore par sa conduite il fit entendre à ces peuples que leur plus grand intérêt dépendait de leur bonne intelligence avec la Chine et que l'intention de l'Empereur était de leur faire tout le bien qui dépendrait de lui. *Ouang-kioung* répliqua que cet expédient ne lui paraissait bon, qu'autant qu'on aurait déjà dompté ces Barbares par la voie des armes; qu'avant toutes choses, il fallait les combattre, afin de les convaincre qu'on ne les craignait pas, et qu'ensuite on leur rendrait la paix, et on les traiterait avec autant de bonté et de douceur qu'on en avait pour les propres sujets de l'Empire. On s'en tint au sentiment de *Ouang-kioung*. L'Empereur lui ordonna de se rendre sur les frontières, avec un plein pouvoir de faire tout ce qu'il jugerait à propos, et de la manière dont il le jugerait à propos. Il lui donna deux bons Généraux pour commander les troupes: le premier s'appellait *Pong-kian* 彭 械. et le second *Licou-ouen* 劉 文. L'un et l'autre entendaient fort bien les affaires de la guerre. On mit promptement une armée sur pied, et on lui assigna *Kou-yuen*[4] du *Chen-si* pour le lieu de rendez-vous général. Quand tout fut en état, et que les troupes qui s'étaient rendues à *Kou-yuen*, eurent reçu leurs derniers ordres, les deux Généraux *Pong-kien* et *Licou-ouen* se mirent à leur tête et marchèrent ensemble jusque dans le pays de *Thao-tcheou* et de *Min-tcheou*. Là ils partagèrent leur armée, et allèrent par différens côtés porter la terreur des armées Chinoises chez toutes les hordes des Tartares rebelles. Ils combattirent tous ceux qui se mirent en devoir de leur résister, et firent grace à tous ceux qui se soumirent volontairement. Soixante Chefs de horde vinrent se présenter d'eux mêmes et demander la paix. On la leur accorda et on les laissa tranquilles. Seize Chefs de horde, plus opiniâtres que les autres, voulurent combattre. Ils furent vaincus et on ne leur rendit la paix qu'après avoir fait mourir publiquement trois-cens-soixante-dix, tant officiers que

---

1.2 Über diese Ereignisse ist in den Pen-chi 本 記 der Ming-Annalen nichts zu finden, ebensowenig im Provinzialhandbuch von Shensi.

3 Name im Provinzialhandbuch von Shensi Buch 82. 杞 求.

4 Pl. 3288.

3. IX, 4.

soldats, qu'on choisit parmi eux. Après cet acte de justice, *Ouang-ktoung* intima à tous ces Tartares les réglemens auxquels ils devaient se conformer; et par sa bonne conduite, il vint à bout de rendre les frontières aussi tranquilles qu'elles l'avaient jamais été dans les plus beaux jours de l'Empire.

En 1643, les Lamas voyant que c'en était fait de la Dynastie des *Ming*, envoyèrent des Ambassadeurs à l'Empereur des *Mandchoux*, pour le féliciter de son heureux avénement au trône, se déclarer leurs vassaux, et demander en conséquence les mêmes honneurs et la même protection dont ils avaient joui ci-devant. On leur accorda tout ce qu'ils demandèrent et on les combla de nouveaux honneurs.[1] La neuvième année de *Chun-tchi* (en 1652) le *Grand-Lama* envoya avec beaucoup d'appareil une Ambassade à *Péking*, tant pour payer le tribut, que pour rendre en son nom un hommage solemnel au grand Prince qui réunissait sous une domination, la plus glorieuse qui fut jamais, les deux Empires de la *Tartarie* et de la Chine. L'Empereur fut infiniment flatté de la conduite que le *Foe* vivant tenait à son égard: et pour lui en témoigner sa reconnaissance, outres les riches présens qu'il lui envoya, outre les honneurs dont il combla ceux qui étaient venus de sa part, il ajouta les titres les plus honorables à ceux dont ce Chef de la Religion des Tartares occidentaux jouissait déjà. Il l'appella *Si-thian-ta-chen-thsu-tsai-fo*, c'est-à-dire *Foe* du Ciel occidental, qui existe par lui-même dans la plus grande bonté; il l'appella encore *Ling-thian-hia-chi-kiao-Poutoung-Watchira-Dara-Dalai-Lama*: les premiers mots de ce titre, *Ling-thian-hia-chi-kiao* signifient celui qui gouverne le monde par la Religion de Bouddha: les autres sont des mots Thibétains transcrits en Chinois.[2] Sa Majesté lui fit présent d'un magnifique sceau d'or à la marque de la nouvelle Dynastie des *Mandchoux*. Depuis ce tems-là, la commerce entre la Chine et le Thibet a toujours été très intime, à l'exception de quelques petites brouilleries qu'il y eut vers le milieu du regne de *Khang-hi*.

Le Royaume qui est proprement l'apanage des Lamas, s'appelle *Thibet*: on l'appelle aussi le Royaume du *Banchan-Lama*. Outre celui qui gouverne les affaires temporelles de ce Royaume et qu'on appelle aujourd'hui du nom de *Diba*[3], il y a encore un Prince *Monggou*, auquel on donne le titre de *Khan* ou de Souverain. Le fondateur des Lamas, ou, pour me servir des expressions Chinoises, le premier qui professa la Religion des bonnets jaunes, est un nommé *Dsoungkaba*.[4] Il faisait son séjour à *Lassa* et de là il gouvernait les Lamas ses inférieurs, et donnait ses ordres à tous ceux de sa Religion. Voilà le premier des Lamas que l'histoire Chinoise reconnaît pour Pontife souverain de la Religion de Foe. On voit donc que la hiérarchie Lamaïque n'a commencé que du tems des *Yuan*, entre 1280 et 1300. On en va voir la preuve dans la succession des Grands Lamas.

Le second qui ait eu le titre de *Grand Lama*, s'appellait *Ghendun-Ghiamdso*.[5] C'est lui qui se déchargea du soin des affaires temporelles, et qui régla que ce serait desormais le *Diba* qui les gouvernerait. Le troisième *Grand Lama* est un nommé *Sonom-Ghiamdso*.[6] Il a été le premier qui ait porté le titre de *Dalai Lama*. Le quatrième s'appellait *Yundan-*

[1] Uber diese Gesandtschaft vergleiche Tung-hua lu, Die Sammlung der politischen Akten der Mandschu-Dynastie.

[2] Watchira Dara ist das indische Wadschradhara, der Scepterhalter.

[3] S. Rockhill, l. c. S. 220 (sde-ba).

[4] Btsong-k'a-pa. Wie der eingeschobene Satz und auch manche andere Stelle zeigt, liegt hier in diesem Abschnitt nicht eine wörtliche Textübersetzung vor.

[5] Vgl. Dge-'dun rgya-mts'o. Die tibetischen Namen der Kirchenfürsten sind gegeben nach R. l. c., S. 285 ff.

[6] Bsod-nams rgya-mts'o.

Ghiamdso.[1] Le cinquième a été *Mou-Lobbsang-Ghiamdso.*[2] Il y eut de grandes troubles sous son pontificat. *Tsangba-Khan*[3], Roi de *Thsang*, qui gouverna de tribus nomades se mit en tête de détruire tous les Lamas et leur religion avec. Le *Diba* eut recours à *Gouchi-Khan*[4] qui était alors Roi des *Eleuths*. *Gouchi-Khan* prit les Lamas sous sa protection, leva des troupes, alla contre le *Tsangba-khan*, le vainquit et le dépouilla de ses Etats qu'il vendit ensuite au fils ainé de ce Prince, à condition, qu'il n'entreprendrait jamais rien contre les Lamas. Le nouveau Roi s'appellait *Dayan*. Il ne fut pas long-tems sur le Trône et eut pour successeur *Latsang*, petit-fils de *Gouchi-khan*. Je ne trouve point si *Latsang* était fils de *Dayan* ou de quelqu'un de ses frères, ni la raison pourquoi *Dayan* régna si peu de tems. Quoiqu'il en soit, la tranquillité fut rendu au *Thibet*, du moins pour quelques années.[5]

La trente-deuxième année de *Khang-hi* (en 1694) l'Empereur voulant gratifier le *Diba*, lui envoya des patentes par lesquelles il le constituait Roi du *Thibet*. Il lui fit présent en même tems d'un magnifique sceau d'or, convenable à la dignité dont il le décorait. Sa Majesté comblait ainsi d'honneur et de bienfaits un fourbe qui ne tarda pas à donner des preuves de son ingratitude et de son mauvais cœur comme on s'en convaincra par le qui suit.

Le *Grand-Lama* ayant cessé de vivre, le *Diba* ne donna avis de sa mort qu'au seul *Galdan*[6], Roi des *Eleuths*. Il la cacha avec grand soin à tous ceux qui auraient pu en instruire l'Empereur; et après bien des intrigues entre lui et le Roi des *Eleuths*, il fut déterminé qu'ils publieraient la mort du *Grand-Lama* et que tout de suite ils lui nommeraient un successeur à l'insu de l'Empereur de la *Chine* et des Lamas eux-mêmes. Leur complot ne fut pas si secret qu'il n'en transpirât quelque chose au-dehors. L'Empereur fut informé de la liaison intime qui s'était formée depuis quelques tems entre le *Galdan* et le *Diba*; il en soupçonna la raison, mais il dissimula. Il envoya secrètement sur les lieux pour sonder le Lama *Banchan-Koutouktou* et savoir de lui quel était l'objet des intrigues du *Diba*. Le Lama *Banchan-Koutouktou* fit dire à Sa Majesté qu'il n'entrait pour rien dans tout ce qui se tramait, et que quoi qu'il pût arriver, il serait toujours inviolablement attaché à son devoir et au service de l'Empire. Sur cette réponse, l'Empereur le manda pour qu'il eût à venir a *Pé-king*. Le *Banchan-Koutouktou* se disposait à obéir, lorsque le *Diba* usa de toute son autorité, et des forces qu'il avait en main, pour rompre ce voyage. Il continua a cacher la mort du *Grand-Lama* et sous divers prétextes, il empêcha pendant près de dix ans, que l'Empereur ne fut instruit juridiquement de ce qui se passait au *Thibet*.

La quarante-quatrième année de *Khang-hi* (en 1705), le *Dalai-khan Latsang*, indigné de la conduite du *Diba*, vint à bout de se saisir de sa personne, et le fit mettre à mort, en punition, disait-il, de ses crimes, et en particulier de son ambition. Il en donna avis à l'Empereur qui en fut bien aise, et qui donna mille éloges à cet acte de justice qui le

---

[1] Yon-tan rgya-mts'o.

[2] Ngag-dbang blo-bzang rgya-mts'o. Die Handschrift weicht hier ab von R.'s Quelle, deckt sich aber mit T. I.

[3] Vgl. Huth, *Jigs-med nam-mk'a*, II, 252.

[4] Guyuschi Khaghan.

[5] Zu den geschichtlichen Begebenheiten dieser Zeit, vergl. M. Courant, *L'Asie centrale aux XVIIe et XVIII siècles*, Lyon-Paris 1912, zu der hierauf folgenden Schilderung der Vorgeschichte zum chinesischen Kriege vgl. Hänisch l. c.

[6] Der chinesische Kaiser hatte gegen ihn einen langwierigen Krieg zu führen von 1685—1705, der in einem besonderen Kriegswerk beschrieben ist »Feldzug in der nördlichen Gobi«, abgekürzter Titel 朔漠方略 *Shuo-mo fang-lio*, in 48 Büchern. Vgl. auch Courant l. c.

délivrait d'un brouillon qui par ses ruses et son manège avec le *Galdan*, serait peut-être venu à bout de lui aliéner le corps des Lamas, et conséquemment la plupart des hordes Tartares qui ne se conduisent que par la direction de ces Ministres de *Foe*. Sa Majesté fit présent au *Dalaï-khan* d'un sceau d'or et lui donna le titre de *Fou-kiao-koung-chun-khan*, ce qui signifie Khan très respectable, le soutien et le pacificateur de la religion. Outre cela elle envoya *Hechou* 林 寿, Président d'un des premiers Tribunaux de Péking, avec quelques autres officiers, pour soutenir *Latsang* contre les mal-intentionnés et pour achever de mettre le bon ordre parmi les Lamas partisans du *Diba*. *He-chou* et ses collègues réussirent dans leur commission, et de concert avec *Latsang* et les principaux d'entre les Lamas, ils conclurent que l'Empereur serait supplié de vouloir bien permettre qu'on élût *Kwang-Yssi* pour sixième *Dalaï-Lama*, sans avoir égard aux oppositions de quelques partisans secrets ou créatures du Roi des *Eleuths*: ce que l'Empereur accorda avec plaisir.

La cinquante-troisième année de *Khang-hi* (en 1714), le Roi des *Dsoungares*, qui était alors *Tse-ouang-raptan*, voulut, sous prétexte de venger la mort du *Diba*, se venger de *Latsang-khan* et de tous les Lamas, qu'il regardait comme des ennemis, depuis que pour l'élection du nouveau Grand-Lama, ils avaient pris les ordres de l'Empereur préférablement aux siens. Il leva des troupes, mit sur pied une nombreuse armée, alla contre *Latsang*, qu'il défit aisément et qu'il fit mettre à mort, brûla tous les temples et les monastères des Lamas partout où il en trouva, et serait allé se saisir de la personne du *Grand-Lama* même, si l'Empereur instruit de sa rébellion et de tous les désordres qu'il commettait, ne se fût mis en devoir de le châtier. Il employa d'abord toutes les voies de douceur et d'insinuation pour le faire rentrer dans son devoir; mais voyant que tout cela était inutile, il prit à témoin le Ciel et ses ancêtres, de la violance, qu'il était obligé de faire à son bon cœur, en se déterminant à entreprendre une guerre qu'il ne terminerait qu'après avoir détruit toute la race de *Tseouang-raptan*, et le royaume des *Dsoungares*.[1] En effet, il fit partir plusieurs corps d'armée, à la tête d'un desquels il se mit lui-même. Peu s'en fallut que ce grand Prince, qui n'avait avec lui que dix mille hommes lorsqu'il se trouva tout-à-coup vis-à-vis de l'armée ennemie, ne fût enveloppé et enlevé avec tous ceux de sa suite qui n'était composée que de dix mille hommes, tandis que ses ennemis étaient au nombre de plus de quarante mille. Son courage et plus encore sa prudence le tirèrent d'embarras. Il fit bonne contenance et ne voulut jamais changer de porte quelques instances qu'on lui fit pour l'y engager. *Tse-ouang-raptan* ne put se persuader que l'Empereur de la Chine fût avec si peu de monde. Il soupçonna quelque stratagème de sa part, et n'osa s'avancer pour attaquer, jusqu'à ce qu'il pût être mieux instruit. Ce délai fut cause de sa perte. Les autres corps d'armée qui devaient joindre celui que commandait l'Empereur, arrivèrent enfin, et donnèrent avec tant d'impétuosité et de bravoure sur l'armée ennemie, qu'ils la rompirent et la taillèrent en pièces. Après la déroute de son armée le Roi des *Eleuths*, qui s'était sauvé, erra quelque tems de montagne en montagne et de désert en désert, mais voyant bien qu'il lui serait impossible de ne pas tomber tôt ou tard entre les mains de ses ennemis, il mit fin lui-même à ses jours. L'empereur ne voulut plus qu'il y eût un Prince qui eût le titre de Roi des *Eleuths*. Il nomma *Kangdsinai* pour gouverner tout ce qui formait autre-fois ce Royaume et lui donna le titre de *Beitse* ou du Régulo du quatrième ordre.

---

[1] Diesen Krieg behandelt des Eingangs erwähnte große Werk »Der Dsungarenfeldzug«. Vgl. auch Courant l. c. und Mailla, *Histoire générale de la Chine*, Paris 1817, Bd. IX, S. 538 ff.

L'histoire de cette guerre que *Khang-hi* termina si glorieusement, est un des plus beaux morceaux de l'histoire de ce Prince; mais comme elle n'est pas de mon sujet, je n'en dirai pas davantage.

La cinquième année d'*Young-tching* (en 1727) il y eut de grands troubles parmis les *Eleuths*; la plupart des Chefs de hordes que *Khang-hi* avait soumis a *Khangtsynai*, se révoltèrent et firent mourir *Khangtsynai*[1] lui-même. Un *Taïdsi* du *Djasak*[2] nommé *Polonai*, en donna promptement avis à l'Empereur et le pria de lui donner quelques troupes pour l'aider à faire rentrer les rebelles dans leur devoir. En attendant les secours de la Chine, *Polonai* se mit à la tête des *Djasaks*, livra plusieurs batailles aux rebelles, les vainquit, les défit entièrement, et alla jusqu'au *Si-thsang*, où il fit descendre du trône *Arbouba*, qui l'avait usurpé, et fit main-basse sur tous ceux qui l'avaient aidé dans sa téméraire entreprise. Quand les troupes de l'Empire furent arrivées, elles achevèrent de mettre le bon ordre; et toutes les factions furent dissipées. L'Empereur voulant recompenser la fidélité, la prudence et la valeur de *Polonai*, changea son titre de *Taïdsi*[3], qui signifie Seigneur, Chef, etc. en celui de *Beitse*, que portent les Princes du quatrième ordre, et il le nomma *Gousan-Beitse*.[4] La neuvième année d'*Young-tching* (en 1730), l'Empereur satisfait des services de *Polonai*, le décora du titre de *Beile* ou de Prince du troisième ordre, et lui donna l'inspection générale sur toutes les forteresses du pays des *Tangouts*. Sous l'Empereur regnant la quatrième année de *Khian-loung* (l'an 1739) *Polonai* obtint enfin les honneurs de *Doroi-Giun-ouang* ou du Prince du second ordre avec des patentes et des sceaux conformes à la dignité, et une autorité comme Royale sur toutes les hordes dépendantes du *Si-thsang*.

Quand on parle ici d'autorité, à l'occasion des petits Princes ou Chefs des hordes, il faut toujours entendre une autorité subordonnée à celle de la cour de *Péking* et du Grand-Lama.

Les vastes pays de la *Tartarie*, qui reconnaissent le Grand-Lama pour leur souverain Pontife sont divisés en quatre grandes provinces, qui ont chacune un nom particulier qui la désigne. La première espèce est celle des *Ouei*, la seconde celle des *Thsang*, la troisième celle des *Kamou* et la quatrième celle des *Ngari*.

I. La province d'*Ouei*.[5]

Elle est située au Nord-ouest de *Ta-tsian-lou*[6] 打前爐, à la distance de plus de trois mille lys. Elle portait autrefois le nom de *Ou-szu-thsang*, et de *Tchoung-thsang*, parce qu'elle se trouvait dans le centre du pays de *Thsang*. Aujourd'hui l'*Ouei* est borné a l'Est

---

1 Hier wechselt die Umschreibung. Es ist derselbe Name wie oben Kangdsinai. Vgl. hierzu die *Kriegsgeschichte der Mandschuzeit*, Sheng-wu-chi IX b.

2 Djasak ist eine mongolische Stammeseinteilung.

3 Eine mongolische Form des chinesischen 太 子 *t'ai-tse*, Kronprinz.

4 d. h. Banner-Prinz, vom mandschurischen *gūsa*.

5 Die Beschreibung der Provinzen stimmt mit dem entsprechenden Abschnitt der Reichsgeographie überein. Die Namen der Städte, die bis auf einige Abweichungen sich bei R. finden, werden hier fortgelassen.

6 Die chinesische Schreibung dieses Ortsnamen bedeutet eine Schmiede, in der Pfeile geschmiedet werden. Dort soll der General Chu-ko Liang in der Han-Zeit (185—234), der damals an den Grenzen Kriege mit den Eingeborenen führte, ein Waffenwerk angelegt haben. Es ist aber eigentlich eine Umschreibung der tibetischen Bezeichnung Tar-dje-mdo = Zusammenfluß des Tar und Dje. Vgl. R., S. 34.

par le bord occidental de la rivière *Mourous¹-oussou*, qui le sépare des tribus Mongols du *Khoukhou-noor*, et à l'Ouest par la montagne *Gambala*, qui fait la frontière du *Thsang*; son étendue de l'Est à l'Ouest est de quinze cens trente-trois lys. Il est borné au midi par la montagne *Omragandjoung²*, et au Nord par la rivière *Yarghia-tsangbou³*. Leur longueur du Nord au Sud-est est de deux mille deux cens lys.³ Les villes principales de cette province sont: *Lassa* à l'Ouest, um peu au Nord de *Ta-tsian-lou* du *Szu-tchouan*, à la distance de trois mille quatre cens quatre-vingt lys. Elle n'est point fortifiée et n'est pas même entourée de muraille.

Ce qu'il y a de plus remarquable est le Temple, aux environs duquel le *Dalai-Lama* fait sa résidence. Ce temple a été par les soins et la libéralité de la princesse *Ouen-tchhing*, fille du second Empereur de la Dynastie des *Thang*. C'est ainsi que l'assurent les gens du pays. Il est bâti sur une montagne et domine sur tous les autres édifices qui forment ce qu'on appelle la ville de *Lassa*, dans laquelle, outre le grand nombre de Lamas qui y font leur séjour, il peut y avoir environ cinq mille familles. Les maisons, tant celles du peuple que celles des Magistrats et des Officiers, sont sur le penchant de la montagne; et au pied de la montagne, il y a de petits fossés et des murailles fort basses, dans la forme et le goût de celles qu'on met autour des villes. C'est pour cela qu'on donne le nom de ville à cet amas de maisons qui couvrent une partie de cette montagne. Les maisons sont assez bien bâties, et ont jusqu'à deux et trois étages. Toutes les affaires des hordes soumises au Grand-Lama, se traitent à *Lassa*...⁵

Ces trente villes, qui forment la province *d'Ouei* ont chacune un ou deux gouverneurs particuliers, dont les grades sont plus ou moins élevés, selon le nombre des habitans et la grandeur des lieux. Le nom général de ces Magistrats est *Dsoungboum*.⁶ Ils sont uniquement chargés de gouverner le peuple et de maintenir le bonordre.

Les habitans de ces villes ont soin de l'entretien de la milice. Ils lèvent eux-mêmes les troupes de la manière suivante. De cinq en cinq familles, on tire un homme de guerre; de l'assemblage de ces hommes de guerre, on forme le corps des Officiers, celui de la cavalerie et celui des fantassins, suivant le rang qu'ils occupent parmi les citoyens. Les Officiers sont de simples *Dingboum⁷*, qui sont chacun à la tête de cinquante hommes, dont vingt-cinq sont des cavaliers, et les vingt-cinq autres des fantassins. Si la ville est con-sidérable, et les habitans en grand nombre, on tire jusqu'à dix de ces *Dingboum*, lesquels sont obligés de marcher à la tête de leur compagnie, toutes les fois, qu'ils en sont requis pour les besoins de l'Etat. Tous les guerriers, comme je l'ai dit plus haut, sont entretenus aux dépens des villes d'où ils ont été tirés; ils ne paient que de leurs personnes, les armes, les habits, la nourriture, tant pour eux que pour leurs chevaux, leur étant fournis par leurs concitoyens. La guerre finie, chacun s'en retourne chez soi, et y vit en simple particulier, comme il faisait ci-devant.

---

¹ T. 1. schreibt ohne s. ebenso R. und auch die Mandschurische Wiedergabe. Es ist der mongolische Name für den Chin-sha chiang »Goldsandfluß«, murui (mouron) heißt »krumm» und usu (oussou) entspricht dem tibetischen tschu ('tchou) »Wasser«, »Fluß«. Vgl. R. l. c., S. 250, Anm. 1.

² Omla?

³ Yal?

⁴ Bis hier übereinstimmend T. 1.

⁵ Es folgt eine Liste von 30 Städten, die alle bei R., S. 118—119, zu finden sind, wenn auch oft in ab-weichenden Schreibungen. Nur ein in der Handschrift aufgeführter Name fehlt bei R.: die Stadt Senghé-dsoung, seng-ge rdsongs, Löwenstadt, 430 Meilen s. w. von Lhasa.

⁶ Lies Dzong-pon (rdzongs-dpon) »Bürgermeister« R. 220, die Silbe dsoung bei Städtenamen ist stets das tibetische rdsongs »Burg«.

⁷ Lies Ding-pon (lding-dpon) R. 241.

Près des tribus Mongols du *Khoukhou-noor* et sur les bords de la rivière *Khara-oussou*, il réside un *Kanbou-Lama*[1] qui gouverne le pays, et les Mongols de la rivière *Mourous-oussou* sont sous le commandement de *Dsaisang's*.[2] Les chefs doivent fournir de chevaux aux envoyés et aux employés du gouvernement qui voyagent pour les cours de *Pé-king* et du *Thibet*. Ils n'ont pas de demeure fixe et changent leurs campemens.

II. La province de *Thsang*.

Elle est bornée à l'Est par le mont *Gambala*, qui est censé d'appartenir à celle *d'Ouei*: à l'Ouest par la montagne *Maryam*[3] qui la sépare du *Ngari*; et sa longueur de l'Est à l'Ouest est de mille huit cens quatre-vingt-deux lys. À midi elle a la montagne *Bimra*[4], qui se trouve près de la ville de *Paridsoung*, et au Nord par le lac *Tarouk-yomdso*[5] qui se trouve au Nord des nomades de *Djéba*; et sa longeur du Nord au Sud est de mille trois cens lys.

La ville *Jikadsé*[6] est la capitale de la province de *Thsang*; et c'est là que le *Dsangba-khan* tenait autrefois sa Cour. Cette ville est au Sud-ouest de *Lassa*, à la distance de cinq cens trente-trois lys.

Actuellement le *Banchan-Lama*[7] qui est le premier en dignité après le Dalai-Lama, a fait sa résidence. Le nombre des habitans est à-peu-près de vingt-trois à vingt-quatre mille familles, et la garnison, ou, pour mieux dire, la milice ordinaire, est de cinq à six mille hommes...

Ce qui fait en tout dix-sept villes, dont les principales sont *Jikadsé* et *Ghiyandsé*.[8] Les coutumes et le gouvernement de *Tsang*, ne diffèrent point des coutumes et du gouvernement *d'Ouei*.

III. La province de *Kamou*.[9]

Elle est au Nord de *Ly-kiang-fou*[10] du *Yun-nan*. Elle est bornée à l'Est par la rivière *Ya-loung-kiang*[11], et à l'Ouest par la montagne *Noubou-goungra*.[12] Son étendue de l'Est à l'Ouest est de quatorze cens lys. Elle est bornée au midi par la montagne *Gakra-Gangri*[13],

---

[1] Tib. mk'an-po eigentlich Abt eines großen Klosters.

[2] Titel der mongolischen Stammesfürsten.

[3] Nach T. I. Maryom.

[4] Bimla?

[5] Dalouk? Das Wort yomdso, bei T. I. 兩木樹 yü-mu-ts'o ist jedenfalls der bei Seen oft vorkommende Name gyu-mts'o »türkisenblauschimmernder See«.

[6] Tib. gži-ka-rtze; ka-rtse bedeutet Säulenspitze, als pars pro toto ein häufiger Name bei Tempeln und Palästen, gži ist wahrscheinlich eine Verkürzung von ε'os-gži »Kloster«. Danach das Ganze »Säulenspitze des Klosters«. Der Name dieser Stadt wird in unserer Handschrift stets Tikadse geschrieben, ein Schreibfehler, aus dem zu ersehen ist, daß, wie in der Einleitung gesagt, die Handschrift nicht nach Diktat, sondern nach einer Vorlage angefertigt worden ist.

[7] Lies Bantschan (Pantsch'en).

[8] Bei R., S. 119, Gyantsé, bei Zach I, S. 87, rgyal-rtse »Königspalast«.

[9] Tib. K'ams, chinesische Schreibung 喀木 k'a-mu oder 康 k'ang.

[10] Pl. 3737.

[11] Tib. yar-klung »großer Strom«, so Zach, S. 134. Jäschke, *A tibetan-english dictionary*, London 1881, gibt auf S. 508 den Namen als Jar-lung. Die Schreibung ohne r geht auf die chinesische Wiedergabe zurück 牙龍江 ya-lung chiang. Auf diese Abweichung wird noch im Abschnitt der Flüsse eingegangen werden.

[12] T. I. Nu-p'u kung-la (= Nou-pou goung-la), die letzte Silbe ist *la* zu lesen. Das Wort bedeutet einen Bergpaß oder einen mit einem Paß versehenen Bergzug, entsprechend dem chinesischen 嶺 ling.

[13] Tib. 'gag-la gangs-ri; Zach: 'gag ist eine Sperre, 'gag-la also ein Paß mit einer Sperre; gangri ist »Schneeberg«.

et au Nord par le bord méridional de la rivière de *Mourous-oussou*: du Nord au Sud elle comprend dix-sept cens lys de pays; du Sud-est au Nord-ouest, c'est-à-dire depuis la partie qui confine a *Tha-tchhing-kouan* 塔城關[1], du *Yun-nan* jusqu'à la ville de *Sok-dsung*[2] et les nomades du *Khoukhou-noor*, elle comprend dix-huit cens lys; du Nord-est au Sud-ouest, c'est-à-dire, depuis le lac *Khoukhou-noor* et la montagne *Akdamra*[3] jusqu'à la montagne *Sairemagangry*[4], son étendue est de mille cinq cens lys.

La province de *Kamou* comprenait autrefois treize villes, dont la capitale est *Balang*. Aujourd'hui elle n'en comprend plus que dix.

La cinquantième année de *Kanghi* (1711), l'Empereur ordonna que les villes de *Balang* et de *Lytang*, seraient désormais du district de la province du *Szu-tchhouan*, et sous les ordres du Gouverneur général de ladite province; et que la ville de *Tchoung-tian-Sangatchoungdsoung*[5], serait du district de *Yun-nan*. En conséquence on mit une garnison Chinoise dans chacune de ces trois villes.

IV. La province *Ngari*.

Elle est bornée à l'Est par la montagne *Maryom*, et à l'Ouest par *Badykhombou*; ce qui fait une étendue de deux mille cent lys. Au midi, elle est bornée par le mont *Dsamsara*, et au Nord par celui appelé *Oubara*.[6] Sa longueur Nord et Sud est de treize cens lys.

Le gouvernement des *Ngary* est un peu différent de celui des autres provinces. Il n'y a dans chaque ville qu'un seul magistrat, dont l'autorité s'étend également sur le Militaire et sur le Civil. Chaque famille fournit un homme de guerre.

TRIBUS NOMADES DU THIBET.

1. La tribu de *Gakbou*, au Sud-est de *Lassa*, à la distance de huit cens quarante lys, au de là des frontières d'*Ouei* et de *Kamou*. *Gakbou* est au voisinage du royaume de *Lokboudja*. Les nomades de *Goungbou*[7] sont voisins et mêlés avec les *Gakbou*. Les deux peuplades ensemble peuvent avoir environs trois-mille familles qui paient tribut au *Dalai-Lama*. Ce tribut est de deux chevaux par an.

2. La horde de *Saga*, au Sud-ouest de *Jikadsé*, à la distance de huit cens trois lys.

3. La horde de *Djochout*, aux frontières Occidentales du *Tsang* et Orientales du *Ngari*.

4. La horde *Djiba*, à l'Ouest de *Jikadsé*, à la distance de quatre cens vingt lys. Ces trois dernières ont chacune un Lama et un Gouverneur particulier.

5. La horde de *Lo*, au Sud-ouest de *Jikadsé*, à la distance de onze cens dix lys.

---

[1] Chin. ein Paß mit einer Mauer, an der eine Pagode steht.

[2] Tib. sok-rdsongs, Z., S. 92.

[3] Z., S. 119, führt einen Berg an 'ag'-dam-ri; T. I. hat Akdomla.

[4] T. I. Sai-lo-ma gang-ri.

[5] Hier ist dem Übersetzer ein Fehler unterlaufen: eine Stadt dieses Namens gibt es nicht. Die beiden letzten Silben sind zu streichen. Bei der Aufzählung der Städte heißt es bei T. L: »Die Stadt Dsièdam (weder bei R. noch bei Z. aufgeführt) liegt 580 Meilen s. ö. von Batang.« Dann fährt der Text des T. I. fort 其地舊 名中甸桑阿, »dieser Ort hieß früher Chung-tien sanga«. Der Übersetzer hat hier entweder einen verderbten Text gehabt oder falsch gelesen, nämlich statt der beiden ersten Zeichen *ch'i-ti*, dieser Ort, die Zeichen 其也 ch'i-yeh und diese als neuen Ortsnamen aufgefaßt: »Kiyé, qui s'appelait anciennement Tchoung tian-sanga tchoung-dsoung«. Die beiden letzten Zeichen 充宗 Ch'ung-tsung (tchoung-dsoung) gehören zum nächsten Satze und bilden den Namen einer andern Stadt, die sich auch bei R. findet.

[6] Die letzte Silbe der beiden Namen lies *la*.

[7] Vgl. R., S. 200, Kung-po.

Le camp de *Gardao* est à deux mille cinq cens lys au Nord-ouest de *Lassa*. Toutes les villes qui dépendent de *Dakla* et de *Goughé*, de même que la horde des *Djéba*, y envoient chacune cent hommes qui sont sous un Chef Mongol et Thibétain. Ils se tiennent dans le camp pour protéger la frontière Septentrionale de la province de *Ngari*. Dans le pays situé au Nord de la province *Kamou* il y a les hordes *Lato*, *Choubouloumba*, *Gherdsi*, *Sairdsanargarou* et *Wachou*, qui dépendent des *Taidsi* Mongols du lac *Khoukhou-noor* et du *Dalaï-Lama*.[1]

---

[1] Dieser kleine Abschnitt steht wörtlich bei T. I. Bei R. fehlen die Stammesnamen. Dagegen bringt das *Wei-Tsang T'ung-chih*, Buch XV, eine große, und wie es scheint, erschöpfende Liste, die zur Ergänzung hierunter gegeben sei. Von den näheren Angaben über die Stärke der einzelnen Stämme sowie ihre Wohnplätze, mußte hier abgesehen werden.

1. Die Tanggut.

2. Die Dam-Mongolen (alte Einwanderer n. von Lhasa).

3. Die 79 Geschlechter: Als im 9. Jahre der Regierung Yungtscheng der Süden neu unterworfen wurde, bezeichnete man die Eingeborenen aus der Gegend von Bayan als die 79 Geschlechter und ihr Land als *T'ufan*. Es liegt zwischen Sze-ch'uan, Tibet und Hsi-ning. Im Altertum war es den Kuku-Noor-Mongolen untertan. Nach dem Aufstande Lobzang Danjin's kamen die Stämme allmählich alle unter chinesische Oberhoheit ...

a) Die 40 Geschlechter, die unter Hsi-ning stehen: Alak, Mongoltschin, Yung-hsi, Yü-shu, Gorbu, Suruk, Niamtso, Gutscha, Ch'eng-to, Dungba, Dolon nitok antu, Asak, Ko-leh-yü, Ke ayung, Ke yertsi, Ke lardsi, Ke dienba, Lungbu, obere Lungba, Cha-wu, obere und untere, Cha-wu pan-yo, obere Abakscho, obere Lungba, untere Lungba, Surniang, Baili, Harscheu, die bergaufwärtswohnenden Gorgi, die unteren Gorgi, die Gorgi, Bayan-Nantscheng, Nantscheng-Sangbar, Nantscheng-Lungdung, Nantscheng-Dschodar, Tschoireng-Dora, die bei den Bayant-Nantscheng nomadisierenden Lama's, die in Lobkuk nomadisierenden Lama's.

b) Die 39 Geschlechter, die unter Tibet stehen: Naschuk gungba, Biru, Bengpen, Dagolu, Lak, Serdscha, Dschamar, Adschak, untere Adschak, Hor tschuan musang, Hor dscham sutar, Hor dscham sutar dschido, — Wala, Hor, Malu, Ningta, Nidschar, San mabma, Niamdscha, Lisung maba, Lodak, Domaba, Yangba, Hor, die in I-jung nomadisierenden Hor, Hor, Pengtama, Horlasai, obere Ganggalu, untere Ganggalu, Kiungbu laklu, Galu, Serdscha, obere Dorschu, untere Dorschu, San dscha, San Nalaba Pudsu.

4. Die «umwickelten Köpfe» — Turbanträger, mit anderem Namen Kaschimir.

5. Die K'atsi, noch ein anderer Name für die ebenaufgeführten.

6. Burugba, von Lhasa s. w. etwa einen Monat Reise, Brug-pa = Butan, R., S. 128.

7. Balbu, s. w. von Lhasa, zwei Monate Reise, Balpo = Nepal. R., S. 129.

8. Gorka.	12. Kuni.	16. Gungbu giangda.	20. Schobando.
9. Dschemen-hiung.	13. Pai-mu-jung.	17. Bomi, obere und untere.	21. Lorung dsung.
10. Dsomulang.	14. Dili batscha.	18. Lali.	22. Lo-wu-ch'i.
11. Lomintang.	15. Bardi sadsar.	19. Bienba.	23. Tschamdo.

Die eingemeindeten Stämme von Tschamdo (die sich unter chinesische Botmäßigkeit gestellt haben) **und ihre Plätze.**

Muru badun mit den schwarzen Zelten ö. von Tschamdo.	Tschulin dutu genau ö.	Lieh-yü n. w.	
Ch'ang-ch'uan chung 常川 中 n. v. T.	Bula-u	Dangwo	
Ts'ang-chu-hei-pa-shang-chia (上 卡) n.	Lungbu ⎫ n. o.	Tschiba n. ö. dicht bei	
Baschu n. w.	Gudsa n. ö.	Siku ⎬	Ladsi Lungbu.
Dsadschu ⎱ n. ö.	Ya-chieh n. w.	Tschengdo ⎭	Banschi
Dschulaschi ⎰	Dschuba n. ö.	Natsu n. w.	

(Fortsetzung dieser Fußnote auf der nächsten Seite.)

4. IX, 4.

Untergeordnete Bezirke von Batang.

11 Kolonialpräfekten 安 撫 司 an-fu-sze:

Batang	Hor Dschuwo	Die Maschu	von Hor gantze	Hordsa
Wu-shu hsieh-k'o	Hor Dschangu	Die Kungsa		Derge
	Tschunko, Liu tsung, Schang nado (obere Nado?)			

7 Unterpräfekten 長 官 司 chang-kuan-sze:

Seta, Waschu-Gengping, Hor-Baili, Hor-Dungko, Tschunko-Gaoji (ži), Tschandui-Ju (žu), Monggo-Kič.

Untergeordnete Bezirke von Litang.

Jung-li-ma, Shao-ku-chung, An-chio-chung, Ts'a-ma-chung (der Ort, wo der Dalai-Lama sich verkörpert hat), La-tsung-chung, Ts'a-ch'u-ch'i, West-Olo, Ma-kai-chung, Ho-k'ou, chines. »Flußmündung« (Grenze nach Tatsienlu), Ober-Olo, Unter-Olo, Yaba, Leidsa, Ober-Muna, Unter-Muna, Kia-chung, Tschung-pa, Ts'ang-mu, Sha-pu-lu, Mu-lo (Grenze nach Ning-yüan-fu, Pl. 4714), Larbu, Gungga-ri(li?), Daoba (Dooba), Hsiang-ch'eng 鄕 城 (heute der bedeutendste Handelsplatz der Gegend). Shuo-ch'u, Lama-ya, Örh-langwan, Li-teng samba (zam-pa Brücke, Grenze nach Batang). Yaba, P'u-en, Dschungga der Eingeborenenbeamte von Gagi (schwarze Zelte), Tschereng der Eingeborenenbeamte von Mao-jung-ya (schwarze Zelte), Sonom Lob der Eingeborenenbeamte von Mao-ya (schwarze Zelte), Kangdschu der Eingeborenenbeamte von Tien-teng (schwarze Zelte), Duna-Taidji der Eingeborenenbeamte vom Bunla-Berge (d. h. die Zeltlager dieser Fürsten).

Untergeordnete Bezirke von Tatsienlu.

Kolonialoberpräfekt 宣 慰 使 司 hsüan-wei shih-sze von Ming-cheng 明 正 (Stammesname).

6 Kolonialpräfekten:

Tschoskyab, Gebschitsa von Dandung, Badi, Lagun 喇 滚, Ragun? 拉 滚, Tschandui.

1 Eingeborenen-Ch'ien-hu (Beamter über 1000 Familien):

Tsa-li.

18 Eingeborenen-Po-hu (Beamte über 100 Familien):

Mu-ch'u, Pa (八) Wu-Jung, Yo-nang, Chi-ts'eng, Mu-ka, Tso-su-ts'č, Ko-wa-kia, Pa-li-lung, La-li, Sha-kia, Wa-ch'i, Ka-na-kung-lung, Pai-sang, O-lo, P'a-sang, O-jo, So-wo-lung-pa, T'a-hai, O-la, Ka-la-ch'u-so an der oberen Furt 上 渡, Ch'u-pa, Mu-ts'ang-shih in Unter-Cha-pa, Jo-ts'o in Mittel-Cha-pa, Ye-wa-shih in Mittel-Cha-pa, T'o in Mittel-Cha-pa, Ya-ch'u-kia an der mittleren Furt, O-tieh in Ober-Cha-pa, Ch'o-ni in Ober-Cha-pa, Obere Pa-i, Pai-yü, Unter Pa-i, Sha-wu-shih, So-pu, Sung-kuei in Ch'ang-kie, Tschangla, Chien-tscheng, Tsu-pu, Dunggu in Lu-mi (Rumi-dschanggu', Ch'u-chien in Ch'ang-kie, Ta-ma, Ko-sang, Kuo-tsung, Pén-kun, Cho-lung, Ta-kie-ts'ang in Lu-mi (Rumi), Mu-lu.

DES MONTAGNES DU THIBET.[1]

La plus considérable de toutes les montagnes du *Thibet* est sans contredit *Gangdis*.[2] C'est la même montagne qui est appellée *Kantel* par les uns, *Kenley* par les autres et *Ken-toui-see* dans la carte du *Thibet*, qu'on trouve dans l'ouvrage du *P. Duhalde*.[3] Elle est au Nord-est de *Dakla*[4], du département des *Ngari*, à la distance de trois cens dix lys. Elle s'étend jusqu'à *Si-ning-fou* du *Chensi*, ce qui fait une longueur de cinq mille cinq cens quatre-vingt-dix lys, c'est-à-dire près de cinq cens soixante lieues. Sa circonférence, dans les endroits isolés, est de cent quarante lys ou de quatorze lieues; et sa hauteur, en la prenant depuis le pied jusqu'à l'extrémité du pic, est de cinq mille cinq cens pieds chinois. C'est la plus haute de toutes les montagnes qu'on connaisse. Elle domine sur toutes celles du *Thibet*, et les surpasse en hauteur d'environ mille pieds. Son sommet est toujours couvert de neige, et il en coule sans cesse une centaine de ruisseaux qui vont se perdre dans la terre lorsqu'ils sont arrivés au pied de la montagne. On a observé que depuis les frontières de la *Chine* du côté du Sud-ouest, on va toujours en montant, pour arriver au pied de la montagne *Gangdis*.

Cette montagne se partage en plusieurs branches et ces branches en plusieurs rameaux. Ses principales branches sont, du côté du Nord-ouest, *Senghe kabab* et *Gangri-moussoun*.[5] Elles terminent la partie Nord du département des *Ngari* et s'étendent jusqu'au Royaume de *Katsi*[6], ce qui fait une longueur de plus de deux mille cinq cens lys. Du côté du Nord-est sont *Daprisirke*, 札布列斜爾克, *Ghio-urke*, 角烏爾克, *Niantsiantangra*,

---

[1] Bei R. finden wir die Berge und Flüsse unter den einzelnen Landschaften zusammengestellt und mit ganz knappen Angaben versehen, die nur in einigen Fällen durch Heranziehung der Reichsgeographie ergänzt werden. Dagegen bringt der geographische Teil unserer Handschrift den vollständigen Wortlaut der betreffenden Abschnitte der Reichsgeographie selbst. Die Übersetzung ist bis auf einige Irrtümer zuverlässig, die in den Fußnoten berichtigt sind. Die Feststellung der tibetischen Formen bei den Ortsnamen beruht, wo nicht anders bemerkt, durchweg auf den Angaben des *Hsi-yü l'ung wen-chih* nach den vorerwähnten Auszügen von Zach, sie wäre ohne dies Hilfsmittel überhaupt unmöglich. Leider gibt die chinesische Quelle, abgesehen von der Anführung der Provinzen, keine nähere Bestimmung über die Lage der Orte, so daß die Identität in manchen Fällen noch zweifelhaft bleiben mag.

Die Silbe *li*, wiedergegeben durch die chinesischen Zeichen 里, 立 oder 礰, bedeutet am Ende des Namens in der Regel das tibetische Wort *ri* »Berg« = chinesisch shan 山. Die Silbe *la*, wiedergegeben durch die chinesischen Zeichen 拉 oder 喇, steht für das tibetische *la* »Gebirgszug mit Paßweg« = chinesisch *ling* 領. In der vorliegenden Handschrift wird diese Silbe in vielen Fällen fälschlich mit *ra* umschrieben.

Auf eigentlich geographische Fragen ist der Herausgeber der Handschrift im allgemeinen nicht eingegangen.

[2] gangs ti-se, Gletscher Tise.

[3] Description de l'Empire de la Chine, à la Haye 1736.

[4] Vielleicht identisch mit der Stadt stag-ral-t'ang, »Tigermähnen-Ebene«.

[5] gangs-ri, Gletscherberg, moussoun = mo. müsün, Eis?

[6] Vgl. o. S. 25 Anm. 1, 5.

Samtan-gondsa. *Nomkhon-oubachi*, *Baïan-khara*[1] et autres. Ces montagnes bornent la province d'*Ouei*, qu'elles entourent jusqu'au lac *Khoukhou-noor*[2], et forment une chaîne de la longueur de six mille lys: elles s'étendent ensuite du côté de *Si-ning* et autres lieux du *Chen-si*. La branche qui s'étend du côté du Sud-ouest, forme les montagnes *Menaknir*, *Samtaigang*[3] et autres, qui entourent les *Ngari*, du côté du midi, l'espace de deux mille lys, jusqu'au royaume d'*Enetke*[4], ou l'*Hindoustan*. Enfin la dernière branche, c'est-à-dire celle qui s'étend du côté du Sud-est, forme les montagnes *Damtchonk-kabab*, *Garchami*, *Noughingangkhoua*[5] et autres, qui entourent la province de *Tsang* et une partie de celle d'*Ouei*, jusqu'à *Dakam*[6], c'est-à-dire l'espace de plus de sept mille lys, et vont ensuite jusqu'au *Yun-nan* et au *Szutchhouan*.

Telle est la division principale des montagnes du *Thibet*, dont les noms n'ont pas beaucoup de rapport avec ceux qu'on trouve dans les cartes qu'on en a données en Europe, mais que le lecteur Géographe reconnaîtra cependant, s'il veut se donner la peine de les comparer avec la position qui est indiquée.[7]

La cinquante-sixième année de *Kang-hi* (1717) l'Empereur voulant se procurer des connaissances sur le *Thibet* plus exactes que celles qu'on avait eues jusqu'alors, envoya de *Péking* des Géographes de sa nation à la tête desquels il mit un nommé *Ching-tchou* 勝住, Mandarin dans le Tribunal des affaires étrangères, pour leur procurer sur la route tous les secours dont ils pourraient avoir besoin; et nomma les deux Lama *Tchourtsin-tsangbou* et *Ranmoudjanba*[8], pour leur assurer la tranquillité et la liberté de faire leurs opérations dans des pays où l'on est plein de respect pour ces Prêtres de Bouddha. Ces Géographes eurent ordre de mesurer la hauteur des montagnes et de déterminer la véritable position du *Thibet*, des côtés du *Si-hai* et de tout ce qu'on appelle le *Si-tsang*. Ils s'acquittèrent de leur commission; et en remettant au Tribunal qui est chargé du dépôt des cartes, celles qu'ils avaient dressées des lieux que je viens de nommer, ils en donnèrent par écrit une explication fort ample, dont on trouve un abrégé, corrigé depuis sur les observations des Lama, dans le nouvel *Y-thoungtche*.[9]

On y trouve l'article suivant: »Ces lieux, y est-il dit, sont le dos de la terre, et les montagnes, qu'on y voit, sont les artères auxquelles tiennent toutes les autres montagnes.« On lit dans le *Choui-king* 水經:[10]

[1] Für die beiden ersten Namen, denen die Schreibung der Reichsgeographie beigefügt ist, ließen sich die tibetischen Formen nicht ermitteln. Für die übrigen Namen finden sich die Formen mnyan-ts'an t'ang-lha (Bedeutung?); samdan gangdsa (so nach der Schreibung der Reichsgeographie) = bsam-gtan, in Beschauung versunken, die letzte Silbe vielleicht rtsa, Fuß, Wurzel, also gangdsa, Fuß des Gletschers. Bei Z. findet sich samdan gangri, Gletscherberg der Beschauung. Die beiden letzten Namen sind mongolisch, nemhon ubasi »Der fromme Laienbruder« (upàsaka) und bayan kara »Der reiche schwarze«.

[2] mo. kükü nagor, blauer See, chinesisch ch'ing-hai 青海, auch hsi-hai 西海. Westmeer.

[3] rman nag nyil, die erste Silbe ist unklar, nag ist schwarz, nyil ein Bergrutsch. Der andere Name ist nicht feststellbar.

[4] Enetek, mongolischer Name für Indien.

[5] Der erste Name eingangs besprochen, die beiden andern nicht feststellbar.

[6] Falsche Übersetzung. Die Stelle lautet bei T. 1. (Reichsgeographie): 藏衛連喀木, li Tsang-Wei ta k'a-mu (der Gebirgszug) »erstreckt sich durch die Landschaften Tsang und Wei hindurch bis nach K'am hin«. Ein Ort des Namens Dakam ist nicht bekannt.

[7] Hier erkennen wir einen Zusatz des Übersetzers.

[8] Nach dem eingangs erwähnten »Dsungarenfeldzug«, mandschurische Ausgabe, Teil I, Buch VIII, Bl. 35, handelt es sich um nur zwei Beauftragte, den Sekretär aus dem Kolonialministerium, Sheng Chu, und den Lama Čulčim Zangbu Ramjamba (mandschurische Schreibung).

[9] D. i. das Ta Ch'ing I-t'ung chih, »die Reichsgeographie«.

[10] Der »Wasserklassiker«, eins der ältesten Geographiebücher aus dem 3. Jahrhundert.

»Au Sud-ouest de la montagne *O-neou-ta-chan*[1] il y a un ruisseau qui porte le nom de *Yao-nou:* à quelque distance de là, en tournant un peu vers l'Est, il y a le ruisseau appellé *Sahan;* et plus à l'Est encore, un autre ruisseau qu'on appelle *Heukia* 黑 俱. Ces trois ruisseaux, continue le même livre, sortent de la même montagne et vont se jeter dans la rivière *Heng-chou*.»

Pour savoir ce que c'est que cette rivière *Heng-choui* il faut consulter le *Khang-thay-fou-nan-tchouan* 康 泰 扶 南 傳.[2] L'auteur de ce livre dit que: »du côté de l'Occident il coule une grande rivière, qui sort de la montagne *Kun-lun-chan*. De cette montagne, ajoute-t-il, il coule cinq ruisseaux qui, se réunissant, forment la grande rivière de *Tché-hou-ly*, laquelle coule du Nord-ouest de la montagne vers le Sud-est, et va se perdre dans la mer. Or, ce *Tché-hou-ly*, n'est autre que *Heng-choui*. Le *Ngari* est la partie la plus Occidentale[3] du *Thibet* qui confine du côté du midi ou l'*Hindoustan*, que les Chinois appellèrent anciennement *Thian-tchou-koue*. Du côté de l'Ouest des montagnes de *Ngari*, il sort trois ruisseaux, dont le premier s'appelle *Lang-tchou*, le second *Latchou* et le troisième *Matchou*.[4] Ces trois ruisseaux vont se réunir pour former le *Ganga* et se jettent dans la mer *Australe*. Peut-être que cette montagne est la même que l'*O-neou-ta-chan*.»

»En comparant ce que les Chinois disent de la montagne *Kun-lun* avec ce que nous savons de l'*O-neou-ta-chan*, dit une description des pays de l'Occident, composée par un prêtre *Thibétain*, il parait que c'est une même montagne, à laquelle nous avons donné un nom et les Chinois un autre. Cependant, comme cela n'est pas entièrement sûr, quand nous aurons occasion de parler de la montagne que les Chinois appellent *Kun-lun-chan*, nous lui donnerons aussi le nom *Kun-lun-chan;* de même que nous l'appellerons simplement *O-neou-ta*, lorsque ce que nous en rapporterons lui aura été attribué sous cette dénomination etc.»

De la montagne *Senghe-Kabab*.[5]

Cette montagne est au Nord-est de la ville de *Goughé-Djachiloumbou*, à la distance de trois cens soixante lys. Elle confine au Nord de la montagne *Gangdis*.[7] Les gens du pays lui ont donné le nom de *Senghe-kabab*, qui signifie montagne du lion, parcequ'ils croient la voir représentant la figure de cet animal. La rivière de *Latchou* prend sa source au midi de cette montagne.

De la montagne *Djidabri*.[8]

Elle est au Nord-est de *Goughé-Djachiloumbou*, à la distance de deux cens quarante lys. Elle forme une même chaine avec la précédente. Les *Ngari* lui donnent le nom de la grande montagne de neige.

---

[1] Anavatapta.

[2] Ein unbekanntes Werk »Berichte über den Süden» von einem Verfasser K'ang T'ai-fu?

[3] Bei T. I. heißt es: Das südwestlichste Land.

[4] T. I. schiebt hier ein: Sie fließen alle in westlicher Richtung und biegen dann nach Südosten um. Über die Flüsse selbst vergleiche den nächsten Abschnitt.

[5] seng-ge, Löwe; k'a, Maul; 'babs, herausströmen, also eine Quelle, die aus einem Löwenmaul hervorströmt.

[6] Name eines alten Reiches in Tibet.

[7] T. I. hat hier einen Satz: man nennt ihn einen von den »sich benachbarten» vier großen Bergen des Gangdis. Zu diesen vier Bergen vergleiche auch das erwähnte geographische Edikt des chinesischen Kaisers bei Hänisch l. c., Kap. 34.

[8] Nach T. I. Djedabri, Bedeutung nicht feststelbar.

Gangri-moussoun.

se trouve à 380 Lys au Nord-ouest de la ville de *Roudok*.[1] Elle tire de la montagne *Djidabri* vers le Nord, et fait la frontière Septentrionale du pays de *Ngari*. A l'Occident du *Gangri-moussoun* est le Royaume de *Katchi*.

Langtsian[2]-kabab.

Cette montagne est au Nord-est de la ville de *Dakla*, à la distance de deux cens cinquante lys. Elle est un des rameaux di *Gangdis*. Les gens du pays croient la voir sous la figure d'un éléphant: c'est pourquoi ils lui ont donné le nom de *Langtsian-kabab*, qui signifie montagne de l'éléphant. C'est de là que la rivière de *Langtchou*[3] tire sa source.

Menak-nir.

Elle forme une même chaîne avec la montagne de l'éléphant. Elle est aussi haute et se trouve à l'Ouest du lac *Mapinmon-dalai*, et Nord-est de *Dakla*, dont elle n'est éloignée que de deux cens cinquante lys.

Maboughia-kabab.[4]

Elle est à l'Ouest de *Dakla*, à la distance de cent quarante lys. Elle est contiguë à la précédente. Son nom signifie montagne du paon, parcequ'en la voyant, les gens du pays croient voir la figure de cet oiseau. Elle est liée à la montagne *Menaknir* et est une des quatre grandes montagnes dans la chaîne *Gangdis*. C'est à la partie méridionale de cette montagne que la rivière *Matchou* prend sa source: d'où elle coule à l'Ouest pour aller se jetter dans la rivière de *Langtchou*. déjà réunie à la rivière de *Latchou*.

Samtaigang.

Elle est au Sud-ouest de la ville de *Bidi*[5], à la distance de deux cens vingt lys. Cette montagne est une branche du *Menaknir*. Elle s'étend depuis le Nord-est jusqu'au Sud-ouest, l'espace de plus de deux mille lys. et sert de limite, de ce côté-là, du département des *Ngari*.

Toutes les montagnes dont nous venons de parler appartiennent au pays de *Ngari*.

Damtchouk-Kabab.[6]

Elle est au Sud-ouest des nomades de *Djochout*. dont elle est éloignée de trois cens quarante lys. Elle est contiguë, du côté du Sud-est, à la montagne *Menaknir*. Elle est une des quatre grandes montagnes de la chaîne de *Gangdis*. Son nom signifie dans la langue du pays montagne du cheval. parcequ'elle ressemble à la figure de cet animal. Le fleuve *Yarou-tsangbou* prend sa source à l'Est de la montagne, et elle borne la province de *Tsang* au Sud-ouest.

Kouben-Gangtsian.[7]

Elle est au Sud-ouest des nomades de *Djochout*. dont elle est éloignée de deux cens cinquante lys. Elle est contiguë à la *montagne du cheval*. Elle est très haute et comme elle a plusieurs pics inégaux qui sont toujours couverts de neige, elle a un air majestueux.

---

[1] lo-tog = lotog nik'ar, »Fort im Ernteland«.
[2] glang-č'en, Elefant.
[3] glang-č'u, Elefantenfluß.
[4] Lies Mabghia, tib. rma-bya.
[5] Bedeutung nicht feststellbar.
[6] rta mč'og, Wunderpferd.
[7] gangs-č'en, großer Gletscher.

Bardjoung-Gangtsian.

Elle est au Sud-ouest des nomades de *Djochout*, à la distance de deux cens trente lys: c'est une branche de la montagne *Konben-Gangtsian*, au Nord-ouest de laquelle elle est contiguë. Elle a un pied[1] fort élevé, qui est couvert de neige.

Fanmousoumgangoum.[2]

Elle est au Sud des nomades *Djochout*, à la distance de deux cens vingt lys. Elle a deux pointes peu éloignées l'un de l'autre et à-peu-près d'égale hauteur.

Djabri-Garbou-Dakna.[3]

Elle est au Nord-est de *Gangdis* et de la même hauteur que celui.[4]

Changou-yara-kmarak.

Elle est au Nord-ouest des nomades de *Djochout*, à la distance de deux cens quatre-vingt lys. Elle est contiguë à la précédente montagne. Elle a au Sud-est *Chaghia-rnighiar*, au Sud-est de laquelle encore il y a *Lounghia-rlounngmar*. Elles forment une même chaine de hautes montagnes de neige.

Ghiemra-chourmou.

Elle est au Nord-ouest des *Saga* à la distance de cent quatre-vingt-dix lys.

Sü'rdjoung.

Elle est au Nord-ouest des *Saga* à la distance de cent dix lys. Elle a un pic très élevé, qu'on voit encore à la distance de plus de cent lys, et dont la pointe entre dans les nues.

Kioourdjoung.

Elle est au Nord-ouest des *Saga*, dont elle est éloignée de trente-huit lys. Elle est très haute et très escarpée.

Tsaosouo-Kho.[5]

Elle est au Nord-ouest de la ville de *Changnamourin*, dont elle est éloignée de quatre-vingt-dix lys.

Langbou.[6]

Elle borne la province de *Tsang* du côté du Nord et se trouve près du bord Septentrional du lac de *Langbou*.

Dargou.

Elle est au Nord de la province de *Tsang* et à l'Est de la montagne *Langbou*. Elle a plus de cent lys de hauteur et sept pieds de différente hauteur.

Gangar-Chami.

Elle est au Sud-est de la ville de *Dsonng*[7], du département des *Nga-li*[8] à la distance de soixante-dix lys. Elle est fort élevée et toujours couverte de neige. Elle est d'une espèce de pierre qui est blanche: la terre qui s'y trouve est blanche aussi.

---

[1] Lies *pic*. T. I.: er hat einen großen Schneegipfel, der wie ein Pavillondach alleinstehend aufragt 亭然獨立.

[2] Jedenfalls ein nicht tibetischer Name.

[3] T. I. hat: Che-pu-lieh et kia-rh-pu to-k'o-na.

[4] T. I.: an Höhe und Größe folgt er gleich nach dem Gangdis.

[5] Nach T. I.: Ts'ao sok-po. Die vorhergehenden Namen waren nicht feststellbar.

[6] glang-po ri, Elefantenberg.

[7] rtsongs, »befestigte Stadt«.

[8] Ari, tib. mnga-ris.

Tseringhina.

Elle est au Sud-ouest de la ville de *Losigar*, à la distance de cent quatre-vingt-dix lys. Sur son sommet il y a cinq pointes qui s'élèvent fort haut.

Chourmou-tsangra.[1]

Elle est au Sud-est des *Saga*, à la distance de deux cens cinquante lys. C'est une branche des montagnes *Gangar-Chami*. Elle entoure le fleuve *Yarou-tsangbou* du côté du midi. Elle est très élevée. La rivière *Phephoungtchou*[2]*-tsangbou* prend sa source dans cette montagne.

Tchoum-ouma.

Elle est au Nord-ouest de *Losigar*, à la distance de cent-quatre-vingt lys.

Noughin-gangtsang.

Elle est au Midi de la ville de *Nagardsé*[3], dont elle est éloignée de deux cens lys. Elle est très haute et toujours couverte de neige. Elle vient de la montagne de *Damtchouk-kabab*. Toutes ces montagnes sont du pays de *Tsang*.

Tchououly.

Elle est à l'Ouest de la ville *Jikar-goungkar*[4], à la distance de trente lys seulement.

Goungla-Gangri.[5]

Elle est au Sud-est de la ville *Ouyouk-lingka*[6], à la distance de quatre-vingt-dix lys. Elle est auprès du lac *Yamrouk*. Elle est contiguë à la partie Nord-ouest de la montagne *Noughin-gangtsang*. Elle est très haute et toujours couverte de neige.

Yara-changbou.[7]

A Sud-est de la ville de *Tchoui-ghiaprang*[8], à la distance de trente lys. Elle a un grand et un petit pic qui tous les deux sont couverts de neige et très escarpés.

Dsaly.[9]

Elle est au Sud-ouest de la ville de *Doungchoun*, dont elle est éloignée de quatre-vingt-dix lys. Elle borne la province d'*Ouei* au midi. Son sommet est très uni; et il y a plus de cent lacs, tant grands que petits.

Dakbou-Sira-gangtsian.[10]

Elle est au Sud-ouest de la ville de *Na*, à la distance de cent quatre-vingt lys. Elle est contiguë à la partie Nord-ouest de la montagne *Dsaly*.

Loumtsian-Garwa-garbou.[11]

Elle est au Sud-est de la ville de *Ghini*, à la distance de cent trente lys. Elle borne la province d'*Ouei* au Sud-est, et de là elle entre dans le pays des *Kamou*.

---

[1] žol-mo gtsangla.
[2] Bei T. I. fehlt die erste Silbe: Pʻeng-chʻu tsang-pu.
[3] = Nagardsung? sna-dkar-rdsongs »Weißnasen-Stadt«, dse = rtse, eigentlich Spitze (eines Gebäudes) als pars pro toto.
[4] gžig-god-dkar, hohes, weißes Fort.
[5] gong-la gangs-ri.
[6] u-yug ling-ka, Kloster in den Bergwolken.
[7] Vgl. yar-la šam-bhoi.
[8] čʻos-rgyal pʻo-brang, Palast des Gesetzeskönigs.
[9] Lies Dsari.
[10] T. I. hat hsi-li 悉立 = Sanskrit śrī, gang-tsian ist wieder gangs-čʻen, großer Gletscher.
[11] Vgl. den Berg in Wei: glo-mčʻin la.

Touroung-Gangri.[1]

Elle est au Nord-ouest de la ville de *Doungor*, à la distance de cinquante lys.

Niantsien-Tangra.[2]

Elle est au Nord-ouest de la ville de *Phoungdo*[3], dont elle est éloignée de cent trente lys. Elle touche au bord Oriental du lac *Tengri-noor*.[4] Elle est très haute et toujours couverte de neige.

Samtan-Gangdja.[5]

Elle est au Nord-est de la ville de *Phoungdo*, à la distance de cent quatre-vingt lys.

Gounga-Bakama.[6]

Elle est au Midi de la source de la rivière de *Khara-oussou*.

Nykouri.[7]

Elle est au Sud-ouest de la précédente. Elle borne la province d'*Ouei* du côté de l'Est, et les *Kamou* du côté de l'Ouest.

Doukla.[8]

Elle est au Sud-ouest de la ville de *Dschragang*, à la distance de deux cens quarante lys. Elle regarde le Sud-est de la montagne *Nykouri*, environne la rivière *Yarou-tsangbou* jusqu'à ses bords orientaux, et s'étend ensuite du côté de l'Est. Elle est très escarpé et paraît plutôt un amas de gros quartiers de rochers entassés confusément les uns sur les autres, qu'une véritable montagne. Il n'y a ni chemin ni sentier, et il est impossible d'y grimper. La rivière de *Yarou-tsangbou* se précipite à travers tous les rochers; on n'en voit pas les eaux, mais on en entend le bruit.

Bouka.

Elle est sur les bords Septentrionaux de la rivière *Kharaoussou*. Elle tire son nom de la figure sous laquelle on la voit, qui est celle d'un taureau. *Bouka*, en langue *Mongole*, signifie taureau ou bœuf sauvage. Elle est très haute.

Bassa-toungram.

Elle est au Nord de la ville de *Lassa*, à la distance de huit cent lys. C'est de-là que le *Kin-cha-kiang* 金 沙 江 tire sa source. Cette montagne est très haute et a la figure d'une vache: c'est la signification du nom *Bassa-toungram*, qu'on lui a donné.[9] La rivière *Mourous-oussou* coule de la partie Orientale de cette montagne jusqu'au *Yun-nan*, où elle prend le nom de *Kin-cha-Kiang*, comme qui dirait rivière du sable d'or. La rivière *Yarghia-tsangbou* coule de la partie Occidentale de cette même montagne. On lit dans l'*Y-thoung-tchi* des *Ming*: »la source du *Kin-cha-kiang* est dans une montagne qui est sur les frontières des *Thou-fan*. Cette montagne s'appelle *Ly-chi-chan* 犛 石 山 (*ly* signifie bœuf, dont la peau est marquée de différentes couleurs, et *chi* signifie pierre. Ainsi *Ly-chi-chan* signifie montagne du bœuf marqueté). La rivière qui coule de cette montagne est appellée *Lychoui*, comme qui dirait *eau de bœuf*.

---

[1] Vgl. den Berg in kam dug-rong-la, »l'aß der schwarzen Schlucht«. T. l. hat dulong 阿 龍.

[2] Lies tangla, vgl. oben.

[3] = p'u-ndo, Straßenknotenpunkt?

[4] mo., Göttersee.

[5] Die letzte Silbe ist unklar, zu samtan vgl. oben.

[6] gungs K'a-pa ga-ma, die Berge K'a-pa und Gama im alten Lande Gung.

[7] Vgl. den Berg in Kam snye-gu-ri.

[8] gdugs-la, Baldachinberg; T. l. hat dukri 都 克 立 (statt la 拉).

[9] ba, tib. Rind.

5. IX. 4.

Nomkhoun-oubachi.[1]

Elle est au Nord-est de la ville de *Lassa*, à la distance de huit cens quatre-vingt-dix lys. Elle touche le côté de l'Est de la montagne *Bouka*. Au Sud-ouest du *Nomkhoun-oubachi* est la source de la rivière *Nou-kiang* 怒 江. Cette montagne et la précédente ne forment qu'une même chaîne, et la rivière *Nou-kiang* coule par le Sud-est, ainsi que la rivière *Kin-cha-kiang*, jusqu'au *Yun-nan*.

Gherghi-dsagana.[2]

Elle est au Nord-est de *Nomkhoun-oubachi*, à la distance d'environ trois cens lys. Elle sert de borne à l'Est de la province d'*Ouei* et au Nord-ouest des *Kamou*. Elle est très haute, et c'est d'elle que la rivière *Lan-thsang-kiang* tire sa source. »*Lan-thsang-kiang*«, dit le *Yun-nan-tché* (c'est une description historique et géographique et statistique de la province de *Yun-nan*) »prend sa source dans la montagne *Lou-chi-chan* 鹿 石 山« (c'est-à-dire dans la montagne du cerf).

Saïn-koubakhoun ou *Saïn-kouboukhoun*.[3]

Elle est au Nord de la précédente.

Doungbouroun.

À Nord de la précédente.

Soukbou-Soukmou.

Elle est à l'Est de la source du *Lan-thsang-kiang* et au bord méridional du *Kin-cha-kiang*. Elle est composée de sept montagnes, desquelles sortent les sept rivières qui portent le nom de *Tsilsirkhana* et de *Koukou-oussou*.

Gouodjangrou-kougarya.

Elle est au Midi de la précédente, au Sud-est de la province d'*Ouei* et au Nord des *Kamou*.

Lesir-oulan-dapsou-oola.[4]

Elle est au Nord-ouest de la montagne *Bassa-toung-ram*, à la distance de quatre cens lys. Elle est très haute. Les roches, dont elle est formée, sont rouges. Elle produit du sel qui est rouge, et qui ne diffère du sel ordinaire que par sa couleur. La rivière *Katsi-oulan-mouren*[5] prend sa source dans cette montagne.

Sighin-oulan-tolokhai.[6]

Elle est à l'Est du *Lesir-oulan-dapson*. Elle s'étend de l'Est à l'Ouest, en passant par le Nord, jusqu'au lac *Khoukhou-noor*, ce qui forme une très-longue chaîne, qu'on appelle du nom général de *Baya-khara-oola* ou la montagne riche et noire. De l'Est au Nord elle environne la rivière *Mourous-oussou*, du côté du midi elle borne les tribus nomades du lac *Khou-khou-noor*, et atteint la source du *Houang-ho*; et depuis cette montagne jusqu'à *Tchououry*, c'est la province d'*Ouei*.

Doungra-Gangri.[7]

Elle est au Midi de la ville de *Choubando*, à la distance de quatre-vingt-dix-sept lys.

---

[1] Vgl. oben, S. 28.

[2] Jedenfalls mo. gergei, Gattin.

[3] mo. saïn kübegün, guter Sohn.

[4] oulan dapsou ist mo. ulagan dabsun, rotes Salz, oola ist mo. agula, Berg.

[5] oulan mouren, mo. roter Fluß.

[6] mo. tolugai, Kopf.

[7] dung-la, muschel(farbener) Berg, also Schneeberg mit einem muschelfarbenen Passe.

Moutoung.

Elle est au Nord-est de la ville de *Chou-pan-touo*[1], dont elle est éloignée de cent lys.

Bilakra-Dansouk.

Elle est au Sud-ouest de la ville de *Sok-dsoung*, à la distance de quatre-vingt-dix lys.

Ragang-moukma.

Elle est au Sud-est de la ville de *Sok-dsoung*, à la distance de cent quarante lys.

Nakosot.[2]

Elle est au Sud-est de la ville de *Sok-dsoung*, à la distance de cent soixante-cinq lys.

Sok.[3]

Elle est au Nord-est de la ville de *Sok-dsoung*, à la distance de dix-neuf lys.

Tsinbou-mardja-boumasoum.

Elle est au Nord-est de la ville de *Sok-dsoung*, à la distance de quatre-vingt-dix lys.

Dsanak.[4]

Elle est au Nord de la ville de *Sok-dsoung*, dont elle est éloignée de cent quarante lys.

Bou-mrly?[5] 布稳禮

Elle est à l'Est de la ville de *Lo-roung-dsoung*[6], à la distance de soixante lys.

Mamghiam-Gangri.

Elle est au Sud-ouest de la ville de *Lo-roung-dsoung*, à la distance de cinquante lys.

Ghiamaroungri.[7]

Elle est au Nord-ouest de la ville de *Podsoung*, à la distance de cent cinquante lys.

Dayary.

Elle est au Nord-ouest de la ville de *Podsoung*, à la distance de deux cens lys.

Sairam[8]*-Gangri.*

Elle est au Sud-ouest de *Podsoung*, à la distance de cent vingt lys.

Nimbou-tchounmoubri-Gangri.

Elle est au Sud-est de la ville de *Podsoung*, à soixante-dix lys de distance.

Tsara[9]*-Gangri* 察喇岡里.

Elle est au Sud de la ville de *Sangatchoungdsoung*, à la distance de quatre-vingt-trois lys.

Garbou-Gangri.

Elle est au Sud-est de la ville de *Sangatchoungdsoung*, à la distance de deux cens trente lys.

---

[1] Der gleiche Name wie die letzterwähnte Stadt, šo-pa-mdo, vgl. oben.

[2] nags-gśod-la (nakśot), Bergrücken, an dessen Fuß sich ein großer Wald befindet.

[3] sog-la, Grasberg, sog-rdsongs, Grasstadt.

[4] rdza-nag, schwarzes Gestein.

[5] Nach der vom Herausgeber beigefügten Lesart bei T. I. ist der in der Handschrift unzweifelhaft verschriebene Name Bou-mou-ly zu lesen: d. h. Bumu-ri oder Bum-ri, vielleicht von 'bum, also Berg der 100000 (Spitzen) oder von 'bum-pa, Berg der Gräber.

[6] lho-rong rdsongs, Stadt nördlich der Schlucht.

[7] Vgl. rgyal-mo rongri, Berg der Buddha-Schlucht in Kam.

[8] Oder Sailam.

[9] z'a-la, warmer Paß. Die Schreibung bei T. I. lautet ch'a-la (tscha-la), vgl. p'ra-la, kleiner Schneeberg.

Goungra-Gangri.[1]

Elle est au Sud-ouest de la ville de *Sangutchoungdsoung*, à la distance de deux cens trente-cinq lys.

Tamouyoungroung 達木永隆.[2]

Elle est au Sud-est de *Tsa-tsono-ly-kang-tcheng*, à la distance de soixante lys.

Dordsi-yourdyoum.

Elle est au Nord-est de la ville de *Dsatsorgaug*, à la distance de cent soixante-cinq lys.

Djomo.[3]

Elle est au Nord-ouest de la ville de *Goundjokdsoung*, dont elle est éloignée de quarante-cinq lys.

Badma-gotchou.[4]

Elle est à l'Est du pays de *Dsidam* et au Nord-est de *Gardsoung*, à la distance de trente lys.

Bardan-gouidjou.

Elle est au Sud-est du pays de *Dsidam*, à la distance de cent soixante lys.

Ramly-Gangri.

Elle est au Sud-ouest de la ville de *Lythang*, à la distance de cent quatre-vingt lys.

Gambonnai.

Elle est au Sud-ouest de la ville de *Lythang*, à la distance de cent soixante lys.

Gouoradsiang-garting.

Elle est au Nord-est de la ville de *Lythang*, à la distance de quatre-vingt-quinze lys.

Amonni-Gansam.

Elle est au Nord-ouest de la ville de *Sourman*, à la distance de trente lys. Les *Kamou* s'étendent depuis la montagne de *Doungra-gangri*, jusqu'à celle-ci.

---

[1] g'ong-la.

[2] Vgl. den Berg in Kam Damma Jungjung gangri, geschrieben brtan-ma gyung-drung (die letzte Silbe konnte mundartlich vielleicht auch *rung* gesprochen werden). Bedeutung: mächtiger Schneeberg mit dem Svastika-Zeichen. Die Schreibung bei T. 1. lautet Damu (Dam) yung lung (rung), dam yung rung).

[3] = jomo ri, Gottinnenberg.

[4] badma = padma, sanskrit. Lotusblume.

DES MONTAGNES,
TRAVERSÉES PAR UN CHEMIN PRATICABLE,
APPELLÉES *LING* 嶺 EN CHINOIS.

Ho-thsin-ling.

Elle est sur les bords Méridionaux de la rivière *Mourous-oussou*, qu'elle côtoie en remontant du côté de sa source.[1] Elle s'étend jusqu'à *Si-ning-fou* et autres lieux du *Chen-si*. C'est en suivant cette montagne, qu'on va de la Chine aux pays de *Tsang* et d'*Ouei*. Près de cette montagne il y en a une autre qui porte le nom de *Kou-kou-sair-dabahn*[2], qui se joint le long des rives du *Mourous-oussou* aux montagnes *Djerin*, *Banmoubra* et *Doung-broun*.[3] Ce dernier s'avance vers le Sud.

Jke-nomkhoun-oubachi-dabahn.

Elle est au Midi de *Doungbroun*. Elle s'étend vers le Nord-est jusqu'à *Sining-fou* du *Chen-si*; ce qui fait une longueur de deux mille quatre cens lys. Elle a à son Midi la montagne *Bakhan-nomkhoun-oubachi*.[4]

Baidou-dabahn.

Elle est au Midi de la rivière *Mourous-oussou*. Elle touche, par sa partie Occidentale, à la montagne *Gardjan-goutcha*. Celle-ci est près de la source de *Mourous-oussou*. Au Midi du *Baidou-dabahn* sont les montagnes *Abra-gangsoun*[5] et *Boumdsa-siri*.[6] Après avoir passé la rivière *Khara-oussou*, en allant au Sud-est, il y a la montagne *Sirctou-dabahn*.[7]

Yanggara.[8]

Elle est au Nord-ouest de la ville de *Phoungdo*[9], à la distance de cinquante-cinq lys. Elle a au Nord, à la distance de cent quarante lys, la montagne *Larghin*, et au Sud-ouest,

---

[1] Bei T.I. heißt es: Das Gebirge liegt am Südufer des Oberlaufes des Muru-usu = Flusses.

[2] sair = mo. dsair ist der Eisgang auf einem Flusse, dabahn = mo. dabagan entspricht dem chinesischen ling Bergpaß, tibetisch la.

[3] T.I. schreibt djélin, banmubula, dungbulun.

[4] mo. yeke und bagan nomhoun ubasi großer und kleiner frommer Laienbruder, vgl. oben S. 28.

[5] T.I. schreibt als letztes Zeichen 穆 mu, also einen m-Auslaut. Z. bringt aus dem Hsi-yü t'ung-wen chih unter der Landschaft Kam einen Gebirgspaß 'ara sgang-gsum la, dessen erstes Wort die chinesische Glosse erklärt als »graue Ratten«, also der Paß der grauen Ratten, mit drei Erhebungen.

[6] Der zweite Bestandteil des Namens entspricht der mongolischen Wiedergabe des Sanskritwortes śrī »Schönheit«. Da das Mongolische im Silbenanfang keine Konsonantenhäufung duldet, muß es bei den Fremdwörtern, die es sich einbürgert, zwischen die Konsonanten einen Vokal einschieben, z. B. brahmana = biraman der Brahmane.

[7] mo. siregetü dabagan. Der Paß mit dem Thronsitz.

[8] Z. bringt unter der Landschaft Wei einen Paß gyang-ra-la »Paß der vereinigten Glückseligkeiten«.

[9] p'u-mdo, Knotenpunkt der Straßen.

à la distance de vingt-sept lys, les montagnes *Djakra*[1] et *Yatsu*, qui s'étendent jusqu'à la ville de *Loundjoub-dsoung*.[2]

Ladjoungkatsian.[3]

Elle est au Sud-ouest de la ville de *Doungor*, à la distance de vingt-deux lys, sur les bords de la rivière *Gardjao-mouren*.[4]

Gambala.

Elle est au Sud-ouest de la ville de *Tchouchours*[5], à la distance de trente cinq lys. Toutes les montagnes dont on vient de parler, bordent la province d'*Ouei* à l'Ouest et celle de *Tsang* à l'Est.

Gouireng.[6]

Cette montagne est au Sud-ouest de *Lassa*, à la distance de deux cens dix lys.

Gogara.

Elle est au Sud-est de la ville de *Detsin*[7], à la distance de quatre-vingt-huit lys.

Gangara.[8]

Elle est au Nord-est de la ville de *Merou-koungga*, à la distance de cent vingt lys.

Berghenla.

Elle est au Nord-est du temple appelé *La-ly*, à cent vingt lys de distance. Au Sud-ouest du même temple, à la distance de cent soixante-douze lys, il y a le mont *Pingdara*; et à l'Est, à la distance de soixante-douze lys, il y a la montagne *Noubou-goungra*.[9] Toutes ces montagnes depuis celle de *Gouireng*, bornent l'*Ouei* à l'Est et les *Kamou* à l'Ouest.

Bara.[10]

Elle est au Nord-est de la ville de *Dakdsa*, à la distance de quatre-vingt-quinze lys.

Tchoura.[11]

Elle est au Nord de *Tcha-mou-to-tcheng*[12], à la distance de cent six lys.

Semloungra.

Elle est à l'Est de la ville de *Djoumdsoung*, à la distance de cent quatre-vingt lys. Au Sud-ouest de celle de *Doungchoun*, à la distance de soixante lys, il y a la montagne *Mingbira*; au Sud-ouest de *Mandsouona*[13], il y a *Mamoura-Gangdjoung*[14], à la distance

---

[1] T. I. schreibt clf a-k'o-la, also »der Pass Tschak« (Tchak); vielleicht lcags-la »Eisenpaß«.

[2] Hier liegt ein Übersetzungsfehler vor. T. I. schreibt 入 … 此 道 ju yü tz'e ling, was zu verstehen ist »wenn man dann diesen Paß übersteigt« (und an die Südwestseite der Stadt L. gelangt, dann ist da der Paß G'ola 郭 拉). Die Übersetzung hat aus den beiden mittleren Zeichen einen Namen gemacht. Die tibetische Form des Stadtnamens wäre lhun-grub rtsongs, Stadt der guten Ernte. Der letztgenannte Paß ist in der Handschrift garnicht erwähnt.

[3] T. I. schreibt la-chung-la-ch'ien (Ladjoung-latsian), latsian vielleicht = tib. la-č'en großer Paß.

[4] In der ersten Silbe g a r ist vielleicht das tib. Wort rgal »Furt« zu erblicken; mouren ist mo. müren Strom.

[5] Tib. č'u-šul rdsongs Stadt am kleinen Wasserlauf.

[6] Z. bringt in der Landschaft Wei einen Paß 'gul-ring-la »Paß, der einem langen Halse ähnelt«.

[7] Tib. bde-č'en rdsongs, Stadt des Glückes.

[8] Jedenfalls Paß (la statt ra) des Ganges.

[9] T. I. hat nu-p'u (Noupou) = tib. nub, Westen.

[10] Vielleicht = tib. ba-la, Kuhpaß. Z. gibt 'ba-la.

[11] Vielleicht = tib. č'u-la, Wasserpaß oder č'u-lha, Wassergeist.

[12] Nach T. I. Cha-nou-ta (Dja-mou-da) = čamda. Die letzte Silbe tcheng ist das chinesische Zeichen für »ummauerte Stadt« = tib. rdsongs, gesprochen dsong, in der Handschrift dsoung, also »die ville de Dja-mou-da«.

[13] Tib. mon mtš'o-sna rdsongs, Stadt am Ufer des Sees im alten Lande.

[14] Nach der Schreibung bei T. I. wäre zu lesen Mamla (Mamra)-Mon-Gang-tchoung.

de cent cinquante lys; et à la distance de soixante lys, au Sud de *Dedsoung*[1], il y a la montagne *Djoumra*.[2] Tous ces monts bordent l'*Ouei* au Midi jusqu'à *Ho-thsing-ling*. Tout ce pays du côté du Midi est de la province d'*Ouei*.

Loungtsian.[3]

Elle est au Nord-ouest de la ville de *Losigar*, à la distance de deux cens soixante-six lys.

Bangra.[4]

Elle est à l'Ouest de la ville de *Djang-abrins*, à la distance de cent soixante lys.

Langra.[6]

Elle est au Nord-ouest de la ville de *Pansoukling*[7], à la distance de soixante lys.

Djarak-Langwan.[8]

Elle est au Nord de la province de *Tsang*, qu'elle borde jusques près du lac salé.

Djimara.

Elle est au Sud-ouest de la ville de *Paridsoung*, à vingt lys de distance. Au Sud-ouest de la ville de *Dsiroung*, à la distance de cent quarante lys, il y a la montagne *Boura-masoum*.[9] Au Sud-ouest d'*Aridsoung*[10], à la distance de vingt lys, il y a le mont *Chapan*: et au Sud-ouest des nomades *Djochout*, à la distance de deux cens vingt lys, il y a la montagne *Angdsa*. Ces quatre montagnes bordent le *Tsang*, du côté du Midi.

Maryom.[11]

Elle est à l'Ouest du tribu nomade de *Djochout*, dont elle est éloignée de deux cens quatre-vingt neuf lys. C'est une branche du *Gangdis* qui s'étend vers le Midi. Sa partie méridionale borne le *Tsang* à l'Ouest, et la partie Nord borne le *Ngara (Ngari?)* à l'Est. Le *Tsang* s'étend depuis cette montagne jusqu'à celle de *Loungtsian*.

Noubou-Gioungra.[12]

Elle est au Sud-ouest de la ville de *Dardsoung*[13], à la distance de trois cens lys. Elle sépare les *Kamou* d'*Ouei*.

Charoura.[14]

Elle est à l'Est de la ville de *Sokdsoung*[15], à la distance de soixante lys.

Gak-Gangri.[16]

Elle est au Nord-est de *Sangatchoungdsoung*[17], à la distance de trois cens lys.

---

[1] rdo-rdsongs, Steinstadt.

[2] junila, geschrieben grum-la, Dachspaß.

[3] Vielleicht = tib. glo-më'in la, Leberpaß.

[4] sbang-la, Graspaß.

[5] Vgl. die Stadt byañ (gesprochen dsiang) d'm-ring.

[6] Lies Langla.

[7] p'un-ts'ogs-gling, Ort der Fülle der Vollkommenheit (Name eines Klosters).

[8] Nach T. I. lies Tcharak oder Tchalak.

[9] Vielleicht blamasum = tib. blama gsum, die drei Lamas.

[10] Hauptstadt der Landschaft Ari (Ngari)?

[11] Z. nennt in der Landschaft Ari einen mar-yong la »glänzender Paß«. Vgl. oben S. 23, Note 3.

[12] S. oben S. 23 u. 24.

[13] dar-rdsongs, Stadt des Aufschwungs.

[14] Vielleicht zum »Südost Berge«, šar-lho-ri in Kam gehörig?

[15] sog-rdsongs, Grasstadt, d. h. Stadt im Graslande, wie ein Teil der Landschaft Kam bezeichnet zu werden pflegt. Die Chinesen sagen 草地 ts'ao-ti.

[16] Vgl. 'gag-la gangs-ri.

[17] Vgl. die Stadt gsang-sngags č'us rdsongs, gesprochen sang-ak tschui dsung, »Stadt der religiösen Hymnen«, in der Landschaft Kam gelegen.

Kianggoura.

Elle est au Sud de la ville de *Choubando*[1], à cent cinquante lys de distance. De-là jusqu'au mont *Noubou-gonngra*, ce sont les *Kamou*.

Langra.[2]

On a déjà parlé d'une montagne du même nom, qu'on ne doit pas confondre avec celle-ci: le caractère Chinois *lang* de la première 狼 signifie loup et diffère de celui de la seconde 郎.[3] Cette montagne est la branche du *Gangdis*, qui s'étend vers le Nord. Elle est au Nord-est de *Dakla*, à la distance d'environ trois cens quarante lys. Au Midi de la même ville de *Takla (Dakla)*[4], à la distance de cent quarante lys, il y a la montagne *Giara*.[5]

Tsatsa 察察.[6]

Elle est au Nord-est de la ville de *Roudok*[7], à la distance de quatre cens cinquante lys. Non loin d'elle il y en a une autre, qu'on appelle *Kerié*.[8] Au Nord-ouest de *Roudok*, à la distance de trois cens lys, on trouve le mont *Labtsi;* à Sud-est de la ville de *Ladak*, à la distance de trois cens quatre-vingt lys, il y a la montagne *Noupra*.[9] Toutes ces montagnes bornent le pays de *Ngari* du côté du Nord, et forment une immense chaîne de montagnes de neige.

Badikhombou.

Elle est au Sud-ouest de *Ladak*, à la distance de trois cens lys. Elle borne le pays de *Ngari* du côté de l'Ouest.

Dsamsara.[10]

Elle est au Sud-ouest de la ville de *Djachi-loumbodsé*, à la distance d'environ sept cens lys. Toutes les montagnes, depuis celle de Langra jusqu'à *Dsamsara* sont dans le terrain de *Ngari*. C'est par les chemins qui traversent les montagnes de la seconde classe, appelées *ling*, que passent les grands chemins du *Thibet* ou *Si-tsang:* chemins très mauvais, puisqu'ils ne sont unis nulle part et qu'il faut toujours monter ou descendre. Outre les dangers que l'on court à travers tant de précipices, il y en a d'une autre espèce, qui ne sont pas moins à redouter. Sur les hauteurs, il croît une plante qui ressemble à peu-près à l'oignon; si par malheur les voyageurs ou les bêtes même viennent à mettre le pied dessus, ils tombent sur le champ et risquent de se casser le cou. On appelle cette plante *Tarthcoutsaodun*. Dans les lieux bas, il règne un air pestilentiel et des vapeurs nuisibles, qui infectent les passans mêmes, s'ils ne font diligence pour s'en tirer promptement.

Le rocher escarpé *Dsagari-manitou*.[11]

Il est au Nord-ouest de la ville de *Lythang*, à la distance de quarante lys. Sur son sommet il y a un temple dans lequel est une représentation de *Bouddha*. On pourrait donner à ce rocher le nom de rocher noir, parceque tous les rochers dont il est composé sont de cette couleur.

---

[1] Tib. šo-pa mdo rdsongs, Stadt bei der viereckigen Ebene?

[2] Lies Langla, vielleicht — tib. glang-la, Rinderpaß.

[3] In der Bedeutung »Herr« als Höflichkeitsanrede. Leider liegt es nicht so, daß die chinesische Umschreibung etwa das eine Zeichen für den Laut lang, das andere für rang gebrauchte. Beide stehen für lang wie für rang.

[4] Lies Dakla.

[5] Tib. brgya-la, Paß der 100 (Berge).

[6] T. I. schreibt ch'a-ch'a (Tchatcha), nicht 察察 ts'a-ts'a (Tsatsa).

[7] Lies Loudok — tib. lo-tog, Ernte?

[8] Die bekannte Stadt an dem von Khotan in Turkistan nach Tibet herüberführenden Passe.

[9] nub-la, Westpaß?

[10] dsamsa-la.

[11] manitu mo., wo sich ein Mani befindet, ein Wall aus Steinen, auf denen die Gebetsformel »om mani padme hum« eingemeißelt ist.

DES RIVIÈRES DU THIBET.

Les Chinois distinguent plusieurs sortes de rivières qu'ils désignent par des noms généraux, sous lesquels ils rangent chaque espèce. Les rivières de la première espèce sont les *Kiang* 江, celles de la seconde sont les *Ho* 河, et celles de la dernière sont les *Choui* 水. C'est à peu-près comme si l'on disait les *fleuves*, les *rivières* et les *ruisseaux*.[1]

DES GRANDES RIVIÈRES,
APPELLÉES EN THIBÉTAIN *GTSANGPO*[2] ET *KIANG* EN CHINOIS.

Le *Ganga* ou *Setledy*.[3]

La source primitive du *Ganga* est, comme on l'a dit plus haut, dans la montagne *Gangdis*, d'où se forment les lacs *Mapinmou*[4]-*dalai* et *Langa*. Les eaux qui sortent de ces deux lacs, forment une rivière qui coule vers l'Ouest, sous le nom de *Langtchou*.[5] Après avoir coulé vers l'Ouest l'espace d'environ deux cens lys, la rivière de *Langtchou*[6] fait un coude du côté du Nord, reprend son cours du côté de l'Ouest, où elle coule près de la ville de *Goughé-djachiloumboudsé*, descend au Midi, et de là va à l'Ouest, jusqu'aux frontières du *Ngari*, dans le pays de *Sangna-soumdo*, où elle se joint à la rivière de *Latchou*[7], ce qui fait un cours de quinze cens lys. La rivière de *Latchou* prend sa source dans la montagne *Senghé-kabab*, à la distance de trois cens soixante lys de la ville de *Goughé-djachiloumboudsé*, du côté du Nord-est. Elle coule vers l'Ouest l'espace d'environ mille six cens lys, fait un coude vers le Midi d'environ trois cens cinquante lys, après lesquels elle se joint à la rivière de *Langtchou*. Ces deux rivières, dont les eaux sont confondues, coulent vers le Midi l'espace d'environ deux cens lys, passent à l'Ouest de la ville de *Bidi*, à près de deux cens lys de distance, tournent vers l'Est, où elles coulent l'espace d'environ

---

[1] Eine solche genaue Unterscheidung gibt es weder im chinesischen Schrifttum noch im Sprachgebrauch.

[2] Unter der Bedeutung »Strom« ist dies Wort bei Jäschke aufgeführt, Z. übersetzt es »Strom der Reinheit« nach dem Wortstamme gtsang, »rein«. Ob es, der Bedeutung des chinesischen Zeichens 清 ch'ing entsprechend, als Beiname für die klares Wasser führenden Flüsse zu gelten hat? Vgl. dazu hei-shui, schwarzes Wasser, mo. kara usu, tib. č'u-nag, als generelle Bezeichnung für Flüsse mit trübem Wasser. Die gebräuchlichsten Bezeichnungen für Gewässer sind: Wasser: tib. č'u (tchou), mo. usun (oussou); Fluß: tib. klung (loung), gžung (choung), mo. mören (mouren), gool; See: tib. mts'o, mo. nagor (noor), dalai.

[3] = Setledj.

[4] Nach Hsi-yü t'ung-wen chih = ma-pam in der Bedeutung »riesig«.

[5] Bei T. i. steht: Er entspringt aus den südlich des Gangdis-Gebirges gelegenen Seen Ma-p'in-mu dalai und Langa. Von dem Westausfluß aus dem (diesem letztgenannten) See an heißt er Lang-ch'u.

[6] = glang-č'u, Ochsenfluß.

[7] lha-č'u, Götterfluß.

6. IX, 4.

mille lys, jusqu'au Nord du pays *Nakra-soumdo*, et reçoivent les eaux du *Matchou*, dont la source est à cent quarante lys au Nord-ouest de *Dakla*. Elle sort de la partie méridionale de la montagne *Mabonghia-kabab*, et après un cours d'environ quatre cens lys, elle se jette dans le *Langtchou*. Ces trois rivières, *Langtchou*, *Latchou* et *Matchou* [1], après avoir reçu les eaux de quantité de ruisseaux qui coulent des différentes montagnes dont on a parlé, se réunissent pour former un seul fleuve qui se jette dans la mer méridionale.

Yarou-tsangbou. [2]

Cette rivière prend sa source à l'Ouest de la province de *Tsang*, au Nord-ouest des nomades *Djochout*, à la distance d'environ trois cens quarante lys de la montagne *Damou-tchouk-kabab*. Elle reçoit plusieurs ruisseaux, avec lesquels elle coule l'espace d'environ deux mille cinq cens lys, après quoi elle passe au Nord de la montagne *Gambala*, entre dans la province d'*Ouei*, va au Nord-est de la ville de *Jikargoungkar* [3], où elle se réunit à la rivière de *Gardjao-mouren*. Ces deux rivières coulent dans un même lit, l'espace de mille deux cens lys vers le Sud-est, passent au Midi au pays d'*Ouei* dans le Royaume de *Loha-boudjan*, tournent ensuite vers le Sud-ouest, entrent dans le Royaume d'*Enetke* ou de l'*Hindoustan*, d'où elles vont se jeter dans la mer du Sud. [4]

Gardjao-mouren. [5]

Cette rivière est dans le district de *Lassa*, au Nord-est de la ville de *Phoungdo*. Elle prend sa source dans un endroit appellé *Djariktou* [6], et s'appelle alors fleuve de *Dam*. [7] Elle se joint à plusieurs ruisseaux et coule au Sud-ouest l'espace d'environ cent quarante lys, après lesquelles elle coule vers le Sud-est l'espace de cent lys, range la ville de *Phoungdo* et se joint à la rivière *Midik-tsangbou*. Celle-ci prend sa source du lac *Midik* [8], qui est au Nord-est de la ville de *Merou-Gounga*, à la distance de deux cens soixante-dix lys. Depuis ce lac jusqu'au Midi de la ville de *Phoungdo*, où elle se joint à la rivière de *Dam*, son cours est d'environ trois cens vingt lys. Ces deux rivières, depuis leur confluent, prennent le nom de *Gardjao-mouren*, qui coule droit au Midi l'espace d'environ trente lys; tourne ensuite du côté de l'Est, où elle coule l'espace de cent quarante lys; après lesquels elle prend son cours par le Sud-ouest, range les villes *Diba-dakdsa* [9], *Detsin*, jusqu'au Midi de *Lassa*, passe à *Doungar*, à *Jiganiou* [10], à *Tchousoura* [11], à *Jigargoungar* etc.; et se réunit au *Yarou-tsangbou*, dans lequel elle perd son nom.

---

[1] rma-č'u, Name des oberen Huangho.

[2] gyas ru gtsang-po č'u (yairu), vgl. Kl.'s Aufsatz, Magas. Asiat., 1826. S. 302 ff.

[3] gžik-god-dkar, hohes weißes Fort.

[4] T. I. bringt hier, wie auch bei den meisten der folgenden Flüsse, einen kritischen Anhang über die Nachrichten der älteren geographischen Literatur, vor allem des Yü-kung 禹貢. Insonderheit wird eine Festlegung des dort angeführten »Schwarzen Flusses« versucht.

[5] = Galdjao?

[6] Hier haben wir einen mongolischen Ortsnamen in Innertibet, der auf die dort vorhandene mongolische Besiedelung deutet. Das Wort djarik ist allerdings nicht belegt, vielleicht sollte man lesen: djari-tou, wo es Schnepfen gibt, oder djaram-tou, wo es Antilopen gibt.

[7] Die von den Mongolen besiedelte Landschaft nördlich von Lhasa.

[8] Nach T. I. zu lesen moudik.

[9] sde-pa stag-rtse rdsongs, auf dem Tigerpik gelegene Residenz des Deba.

[10] Vgl. gži-ka nub-rdsongs.

[11] č'u-šul rdsongs, Stadt am kleinen Wasserlauf, cf. o.

Lou-kiang 路汇 ou *Khara-oussou.*[1]

Cette rivière est au Nord-est de la ville de *Loroungdsoung*, à la distance de soixante lys. Son nom *Mongol* est *Khara-oussou* et les *Thibétains* l'appellent *Oïrtchou*. Elle prend sa source à deux cens quatre-vingt lys au Nord de *Lassa*, d'un lac appellé *Bouka*[2], dont la largeur est d'environ quatre cens cinquante lys. Depuis sa source elle coule vers le Nord-ouest l'espace d'environ cent lys, entre dans le lac *Erghighen*[3], dont la grandeur est d'environ cent trente lys, sort de ce lac, coule vers le Sud-est l'espace de cent cinquante lys, entre dans un autre lac, qu'on appelle *Khara-noor*, dont la grandeur est à peu-près de cent vingt lys; au sortir de ce lac, elle coule quelque tems vers le Midi et prend le nom de *Khara-oussou*; elle remonte vers le Nord-est, vient passer à cent lys de distance de la ville de *Sokdsoung*, après un cours de quatre cens cinquante lys, sort ensuite du terrain d'*Ouei* et entre chez les *Kamou*, où elle perd son nom pour prendre celui de *Oïrtchou*. Sous ce nom elle coule vers le Sud-est pendant l'espace d'environ deux cens lys, passe au Nord-est de *Loroungdsoung*, et après un cours de trois cens lys, elle coule droit au Midi, pendant l'espace de huit cens lys, après lesquels elle entre dans le pays de *Mira-loung*, arrose près de deux cens lys et se rend chez les *Nou-y* 怒夷.[4] C'est là qu'elle prend le nom de *Nou-kiang*[5]; de ces *Nou-y* jusqu'au *Yun-nan*, son cours est d'environ trois cens lys. Arrivée au *Yun-nan*, près de *Ly-kiang-fou*[6], elle perd son nom pour prendre celui de *Lou-kiang*, passe sur les frontières des peuples sauvages qui sont au Midi de cette province, va dans le *Mien-tian*[7] ou *Pegou*, d'où elle se jette dans la mer du Sud. »Dans l'application des anciennes cartes Chinoises, dit l'*Y-thoung-tchi*, il est dit qu'à l'Ouest du *Si-fan*, et au Midi de *Ta-lieou-cha* 大流沙 (grand désert de sables mouvantes) il y a un lac qu'on appelle *Ti-kia-hou*[8], et que l'eau qui coule de ce lac vers le Midi, forme la rivière de *Lou-kiang*. Par l'inspection des cartes d'aujourd'hui, continue l'*Y-thoung-tchi*, on juge que *Ti-kia-hou* est le même que *Khara-noor*.« Le nom *Mongol* de cette rivière signifie eau noire, car *khara* est noir et *oussou* est eau. (Cette rivière est très grande à *Lan-thsang* et à *Ye-yu*.[9] Ses eaux sont noires, et c'est pour celà, qu'on lui a donné le nom de la rivière noire.) Sa véritable source est dans la province d'*Ouei* et vient du lac *Bouka*, dont les eaux sont noires et profondes. C'est apparemment cette rivière que le grand *Yu* appella du nom de *Hé-choui*, qui veut dire *eaux noires*. Quelques auteurs prétendent que la rivière que le grand *Yu* appella *Hé-choui*, est le *Lan-thsang-kiang* d'aujourd'hui; mais il est plus probable que c'est le *Khara-oussou* des *Mongoux*, qui est le vrai *Hé-choui*.

---

[1] mo. Schwarzes Wasser.

[2] mo. Stier.

[3] Vielleicht mo. eljigen, Esel?

[4] D. h. das Wildvolk Nu.

[5] Die Silbe Lu (Lou) in Lukiang ist vielleicht eine mundartliche Aussprache des Stammesnamens Nu.

[6] Pl. 3737.

[7] Birma.

[8] T. I. hat kia-hu 嘉湖.

[9] Hier ist sicher der Text falsch aufgefaßt. T. I. hat 此水大於閜沧葉榆. Lantsang ist der Name des Flusses, nicht etwa ein Ortsname. Die beiden letzten Zeichen yeh-yü »Blätter-Ulme« bezeichnen nach der großen Konkordanz P'ei-wen yün-fu einen See in der Präfektur Yung-ch'ang (Pl. 7836), welche der Lantsang-Fluß durchströmt. Eine Stadt ist nach dem See benannt. Das Wort yeh-yü selbst entstammt jedenfalls einer Eingeborenensprache. Der chinesische Satz wäre zu übersetzen: Dies Gewässer (der Khara-noor) ist größer als der Yeh-yü = See des Lantsang-Flusses (oder -Gebietes).

Loung-tchouan[1]-kiang.

Loung-tchouan-kiang ou la rivière du *Dragon*, dont le nom *Thibétain* est *Po-tsang-bou;* elle coule au Midi de la ville de *Podsoung*, à deux lys de distance. Elle a deux sources: la première est dans la montagne *Tchoundo*, à trois cens lys au Nord-est de la ville de *Podsoung*. La rivière qui sort de cette montagne, reçoit les eaux de six ruisseaux, coule vers le Sud-ouest, et porte le nom de *Va-loung-ho*. La seconde vient de la montagne *Doungra*, à cinq lys au Nord-ouest de la ville de *Podsoung*, reçoit les eaux d'une dixaine de ruisseaux, et prend le nom d'*Etchou*[2], coule vers le Sud-est jusques près de la ville de *Podsoung*, où elle se joint à *Va-loung-ho*. Depuis leur confluent, ces deux rivières n'en font plus qu'une, qui porte le nom de *Potsang-bou*, et qui prend son cours vers le Sud-ouest, tourne ensuite vers le pays des nomades *Gakbou;* de là elle va passer chez ceux appellés *Menbou*, dans le pays de *Lokboudja*, entre dans le *Yun-nan*, va jusqu'à la ville de *Teng-Yue-tchou*[3], où elle prend le nom de *Loung-tchhouan-kiang*. D'après la géographie des *Ming*, le *Loung-tchhonan-kiang*, prend sa source dans le pays des *Barbares* appellés *Otchang*, coule au Nord de la chaîne des hautes montagnes appellées *Ly-koung-chan*, qui confinent aux sept districts des *Tsang* ou *Thibétains*. En sortant de la *Chine* par un défilé on passe cette rivière par un vieux pont de cordes. De-là elle coule jusqu'à la ville de *Thay-konng-tchhing* 太 公 城, et se joint au fleuve *Thay-yng-kiang* 大 盈 江. D'après la description géographique de la province de *Yun-na*, le *Loung-tchhouan-kiang* a trois sources. L'une sort de la montagne *Ming-konang-chan* 明 光 山, l'autre de celle d'*A-hing-chan* 阿 幸 山 et la troisième du mont *Nan-hiang-tianchan* 南 乔 甸 山. Ces trois rivières forment le *Loung-tchhouan-kiang*, qui coule en Chine jusqu'au fort de *Hou-kiu-kouan* 虎 踞 關, où il entre dans le Royaume de *Mian* ou *Pegou*.

Lan-thsang-kiang[4]; en *Thibétain Latchou.*

Cette rivière a deux sources: la première vient de la montagne *Gerghi-dsagana*, à mille lys au Nord-ouest de la ville de *Dsatsorgang*. Au sortir de cette montagne, elle s'appelle *Dsatchou*. La seconde source vient de la montagne *Burak-ladan*[5]*-sunk* et porte le nom d'*Omtchou*. Les rivières *Dsatchou* et *Omtchou*[6] prennent d'abord leur cours vers le Sud-est; elles dérivent ensuite vers le Sud, passent au Nord-est de la ville de *Dsatsorgang*, à trois cens lys de distance, près du temple appellé *Tchamdo;* là elles se joignent, et prennent le nom de *Latchou*. La rivière de *Latchou* coule droit au Midi, l'espace d'environ neuf cens lys, après lesquels elle entre dans la partie Occidentale du *Yun-nan*, et va à *Ly-kiang-fou*, où elle perd son nom pour prendre celui de *Lan-thsang-kiang*. De *Ly-kiang-fou* elle va à *Young-tchhang-fou*, à *Chun-ning-fou*[7], à *Mong-houa-fou*[8] et *King-toung-fou*[9], passe sur les terres des Royaumes d'*Ava* et de *Lao-tchoua*, se rend au *Kiao-tchy* 交 阯 ou *Toungking*, où elle se jette dans la mer du Sud.

---

1 Lies tchhouan.
2 T. I. 危 墅 wei-ch'u = dbui-č'u, mittlerer Lauf?
3 Pl. 6344.
4 Dieser Name ist sicher auch tibetisch.
5 brag-la = Felsenpaß.
6 'om-č'u = großer Fluß.
7 Pl. 5819.
8 Pl. 4375.
9 Pl. 1138.

Kin-cha-kiang 金沙江[1]; en *Mongol Mourous-oussou*.[2]

Cette rivière est connue sous plusieurs noms. On l'appelait anciennement *Ly-choui*, *Chin-tchhouan* 神川 et *Ly-nieou-tchhouan* 犛牛川. Ce dernier nom signifie rivière du *Yak* ou Bœuf Thibétain. Les *Thibétains* la connaissent sous les noms de *Boulaïtchou* et de *Batchou*.[3] Elle prend sa source dans la montagne *Bassa-doungram*, c'est-à-dire: dans la montagne de la vache. Cette source sort du pied même de la montagne, dans le département des *Ouei*, au Nord-ouest de *Lassa*, dont elle est éloignée de huit cens lys. Depuis sa source, elle coule vers le Nord-est l'espace d'environ neuf cens lys et porte le nom de *Mourous-oussou*. Elle passe au Nord de la montagne *Namtangroung* et dirige son cours vers le Sud-est pendant l'espace de huit cens lys; après lesquels elle entre chez les *Kamou*, où elle prend le nom de *Boulaïtchou*; de là elle coule au Midi, en prenant un peu vers l'Ouest, pendant l'espace de huit cens lys, jusqu'à la distance de soixante lys à l'Ouest de la ville de *Batang*. C'est là qu'elle prend le nom de *Batchou*. Elle descend vers le Sud-est, où elle coule l'espace d'environ six cens lys jusqu'aux frontières du *Yun-nan*, dans le district de *Ly-kiang-fou*, où elle prend le nom de *Kin-cha-kiang*. Elle passe au Nord de la grande montagne de neige qui est au Nord de *Ly-kiang-fou*, coule pendant quelque tems vers le Sud, passe par les districts de *Young-pei-fou*[4] et de *Ou-ting-fou*[5] et entre sur les frontières du *Szu-tchhouan* dans le voisinage du fort *Hoey-tchhouan-ouey* 会川衛. Alors elle se joint à la rivière *Ta-tchhoung-ho* 打冲河[6], va passer à l'Ouest de *Toung-tchhouan-fou*[7], au Midi de *Ma-hou-fou*[8], et se joint au *Tchhouan-kiang*[9], près de *Sin-tscheou-fou*.[10]

Le cours de cette rivière, en la prenant depuis sa source jusqu'à l'endroit où elle touche la Chine, est de plus de quatre mille lys. Elle reçoit, en chemin faisant, les eaux de quelques dixaines de rivières et d'un plus grand nombre de ruisseaux. Elle est très rapide, et presque partout très profonde. Elle exhale des vapeurs qui rendent ses bords mal-sains. Elle abonde en paillettes d'or; c'est ce qui lui a fait donner le nom de rivière au sable d'or »*Kin-cha-kiang*«.

Il est dit dans l'histoire des *Tsang*[11], dans le chapitre qui traite des Barbares du Sud, que le Général des *Nan-tchao*, appelé *Y-meou-hiun* 異牟尋, remporta (en 1175 après J. C.) une célèbre victoire sur les *Thou-fan* ou *Thibétains*, près de la rivière de *Chin-tchhoun*; et que pour empêcher les vaincus de retourner dans leur pays, il fit rompre le pont de fer, ce qui fut cause que plus de dix mille hommes d'eux trouvèrent la mort dans les eaux.

On trouve dans le même livre, dans le chapitre qui traite des pays Occidentaux, que dans le pays de *Domimou*, soumis aux *Sy-khiang* ou *Thibétains* Orientaux, pays appelé *Nan-mo* par les *Thou-fan*, il y ait une rivière qui porte le nom de *Ly-nieou-ho*, dans laquelle il se trouve beaucoup d'or. Dans l'ancienne Géographie *Tyly-tchy* 地理志 on lit, qu'après avoir passé la rivière de *Si-yuě-ho* 西月河, à deux cens dix lys de distance, en allant à

---

[1] Chines. = Goldsandfluß.
[2] Vgl. oben S. 22.
[3] Tib. = Rinderfluß.
[4] Pl. 7964.
[5] Pl. 7097.
[6] Lies Ta-tchhoung-ho.
[7] Pl. 6713.
[8] Pl. 4283.
[9] Szetschuan-Fluß = Jangtse.
[10] Pl. 2895.
[11] Lies Thang.

l'Ouest, on arrive sur les frontières du Royaume *Domi*, que là on longe la rivière *Ly-nieou-ho*, qu'on passe après sur un pont qu'on appelle *Teng-khiao* 藤橋 (pont de joncs) et que cent lys plus loin on trouve la station de *Lic-y* 列驛.[1]

Dans la géographie des *Ming*, il est dit que l'ancien nom de *Kin-cha-kiang* est *Ly-choui*; que sa source est dans le pays des *Thou-fan* ou *Thibétains*, au pied du rocher *Ly-chy*, dont le nom veut dire pierre du Yak ou Bœuf Thibétain: c'est pourquoi, ajoute-t-il, il ne faut point écrire *Ly-choui* par *Ly* 麗, qui signifie *brillant, beau*, comme on le trouve dans bien des auteurs, mais par *Ly* 犁, qui signifie le *Yak*.

Ya-Loung-Kiang.[2]

Son nom signifie *Rivière du corbeau* et du *dragon*. Elle coule à l'Est de la ville de *Lytang*, à la distance de deux cens quarante lys. Sa source est dans la montagne *Bayan-*

---

[1] Der Satz ist zu übersetzen: »nach weiteren 100 Meilen trifft man auf die Postlinie«.

[2] Bemerkung zur Frage *Yalung — Yarlung* und Berichtigung eines Irrtums in der Überlieferung von der tibetischen Urheimat.

Hinsichtlich dieses Flußnamens herrscht, wie schon oben auf S. 23 angedeutet wurde, in der Literatur und auf den Karten eine Unstimmigkeit, auf die bisher noch nicht eingegangen worden ist. Wir finden die beiden Formen *Yalung* und *Yarlung*. Die erste ist die allgemein gebräuchliche, die außer unserer Handschrift auch Wei-Tsang t'ung-chih, Wei-Tsang t'u-chih sowie die Reichsgeographie T. I. zeigen und danach die chinesischen Karten, z. B. die Szetschuan-Karte im Atlas der Commercial Press und wohl auch durchweg die neueren europäischen Karten. Die chinesische Schreibung ist 雅龍 oder 牙烏龍 = Krähe und Drache. Eine Übersetzung nur des ersten Zeichens aus dem Chinesischen = »Krähenfluß« ist nicht angängig. Der ganze Name ist tibetisch, und zwar geht er nach R. 249, Anm. 2, auf *Nya-lung* é'u oder *Nya-é'u* zurück, also »Fischfluß«. Ein anderer, kleinerer Fluß gleichlautenden Namens, bei T. I. 鴨龍 »Ente und Drache« geschrieben, ist oben S. 44 als Quellfluß des Lung-ch'uan erwähnt worden, der unter dem Namen Po-tsang-po durch das Land des G'ak-po-Stammes fließt. Er ist jedenfalls identisch mit dem Flusse *Yarong* 雅隆, tib. = obere Schlucht, den das Hsi-yü t'ung-wen chih als Quellfluß des G'akpo tsangbo é'u verzeichnet, s. Z. 132.

Dies viersprachige geographische Wörterbuch gibt nun (Z. 134, Provinz Kam) dem Namen des vorerwähnten großen Flusses die Form *Yarlung* 雅爾隆 = tib. yar-klung = großer Fluß (oberer Fluß?). Zach weist dazu auf Jäschkes Wörterbuch (*A Tibetan-English dictionary*, London 1881). Dies schreibt auf S. 508: »Yar-lung, a large tributary of the Yangtsekiang coming from the North, in western China, east of the town of Bathang«. Eine Übersetzung ist nicht gegeben. Sie würde heißen »oberes Tal«. Auch Kowalewskis *Mongolisch-Russisch-Französisches Wörterbuch*, Kasan 1844—49, hat, auf S. 2308, den Namen *Yarlung* vermerkt, mit der tibetischen Grundform yar-klung, also übereinstimmend mit dem geographischen Wörterbuch, und gibt dazu im russischen Teil die Erklärung »Fluß in Tibet, östlich von Litang«.

Auch der Name *Yarlung* kommt noch bei andern Flüssen vor: Stielers Handatlas Nr. 64 bringt ihn als kleines Nebenflüßchen des Ho-shui, eines Quellflusses des Min. Er wird in der Reichsgeographie, Buch 292, und auch im Wei Tsang t'ung-chih, Buch 3, nicht erwähnt. Dafür ist auf der Wutschang-Karte angeführt als 雅爾隆. Von dieser Karte ist der Name ebensowohl auf die neueren chinesischen Karten, wie die erwähnten Atlas der Commercial Press, als auch auf dem Wege über den Richthofenschen China-Atlas, II. Abtlg., Tafel 27, auf europäische Karten, wie eben die Stielersche, übergegangen. — Hinsichtlich des Min-Flusses sei bei dieser Gelegenheit erwähnt, daß nach dem geographischen Edikt des 59. Jahres Kanghi, vgl. oben S. 28/29, seine Quelle aus einem Bache Tsitsirhana vom Bayan-kara-Gebirge kommen soll, während die Reichsgeographie denselben Namen Tsitsirhana als Quellfluß des ebenfalls vom Bayan-kara-Gebirge hergeleiteten *Yalung* bezeichnet. Also auch hier eine Verwirrung. — Albert Tafel schreibt in seinem Werke »*Meine Tibetreisen*«, Stuttgart 1914, Bd. II, S. 179, Anm. 1, von einem kleinen Nebenflusse *Yarlung* des Brahmaputra (Yaru tsangpo), der aber weder in der Reichsgeographie noch im Wei-Tsang t'ung-chih zu finden ist. Schließlich nennt Richthofen, *China*, Bd. III, S. 381, denselben Namen für den Mekong (Lan-ts'ang).

In die Frage *Yalung — Yarlung* spielt nun der Umstand hinein, daß man in dem Flusse dieses Namens den Ort erblicken will, an dem nach der alten Überlieferung die ersten tibetischen Könige sich angesiedelt hätten, also den Ursitz der tibetischen Kultur. Tatsächlich geben uns, wie vorausgeschickt sei, die Quellen kein Recht, den Namen *Yarlung* in diesem Zusammenhange überhaupt als Fluß anzusprechen. In der chinesischen geographischen

khara-oola, au Nord-ouest de *Ly-thang*, dont elle est éloignée de huit cens lys. Elle porte
le nom *Mongol* de *Tsitsirkhana*. Elle coule l'espace de cinq cens lys vers le Sud-est,

---

Literatur findet sich bei den erwähnten Flüssen keine auf die Sage hinweisende Bemerkung. Das geographische Wörterbuch enthält sich jedes Zusatzes. Der Bearbeiter v. Zach weist, wie erwähnt, auf Jäschke, der seinerseits auf die alten
tibetischen Legenden deutet und eine Stelle aus Köppen, *Buddha*, Berlin 1859, Bd. II, S. 50, angibt. Diese bezieht
sich wieder auf den mongolischen Geschichtsschreiber Sanang Setsen, *Geschichte der Ostmongolen*, Text mit Uber-
setzung hrsg. von I. J. Schmidt, Petersburg 1829. Es ist möglich, daß Jäschke von seiner tibetischen Quelle nur
die Form des Namens selbst genommen, die Erklärung »Nebenfluß des Yangtse« aber aus der mongolischen
Überlieferung Köppen-Schmidt-Sanang Setsen entlehnt und kombiniert hat. Jene tibetische Quelle rgyal-rabs, die
Geschichte der Königsfamilie, hat B. Laufer in einem Aufsatze, Toung-pao 1901, besprochen und dabei auch den
Namen *Yarlung* erwähnt. Er schreibt auf S. 28: »Der Schauplatz, wo der Affe (der sagenhafte Stammvater des
tibetischen Volkes) seine Meditationen verrichtet, wird auf einen Felsen des *Yarlung* verlegt, der auf den Karten
als *Yalung* bezeichneten bekannten Nebenflusses des Blauen Stromes (Chin-sha chiang = Yangtse), der nach einer
anderen im folgenden besprochenen Tradition als Stammsitz der tibetischen Dynastie gilt.« Er zitiert dann auf
S. 30 als Gewährsstellen dafür wieder Köppen (= Schmidt-Sanang Setsen) und das kalmükische Geschichtswerk
Bodhi mör, »Pfad der Weisheit«, dies letztere wahrscheinlich auch nach den bei Schmidt (im Anhang zu Sanang
Setsen) angeführten Übersetzungsauszügen.

   Emil Schlagintweit, der das rgyal-rabs unter dem Titel »*Die Könige von Tibet*« mit Übersetzung heraus-
gegeben hat (Abh. d. k. b. A. d. W., 1. Cl., X. Bd., III. Abt., München 1866), schreibt in seiner Einleitung S. 15 (807):
»Das Territorium, über welches Buddhaçri (der erste König, in der zweiten Hälfte des 1. Jahrh. v. Chr., nach der
Berechnung des Herausgebers) gebot, der als König von Tibet gNya'-khri btsan-po heißt, wird Yar-lung, ,Oberes
Tal', es umfaßte die Uferländer des Yarlung-Flusses und seiner Zuflüsse; gegenwärtig trennt dieser
Fluß Tibet von den chinesischen Provinzen.« Als Belegstellen führt der Herausgeber die Übersetzungen Amiots
aus der chinesischen Topographie (= Reichsgeographie T. 1.) an, in den »Mémoires concernant les Chinois« XIV, 184,
den Klaprothschen Aufsatz über den Irawaddi in Mém. rel. à l'Asie, II, 407. Von diesen hat die erste
die Schreibung *Ya-lung*, die zweite auf Grund des Geographischen Wörterbuchs die Konstruktion *Yarlung*.
Schlagintweit glaubt die Gleichung *Yarlung* = *Yalung*-Fluß erklären zu müssen, um die Lage der tibetischen
Urheimat, die Einwanderung des aus Indien stammenden Königsgeschlechts in Osttibet, glaubhaft zu machen:
»Die Pässe, die dorthin (nach Osttibet) aus dem östlichen Himalaya führten, sind weniger hoch und beschwerlich
als in Nepal«. Tatsächlich ist dieser Zugang, also über Bhutan, Assam, wohl bedeutend schwieriger und an
Pässen reicher. Sind uns doch auch über die Geschichte kriegerische Einfälle aus den Himalayaländern nach
Osttibet nicht bekannt. Eine weitere Bemerkung Schlagintweits: »Yarlung entgegengesetzt ist Marlung, unteres
Tal, Maryul, unteres Land, ein Name, womit das westliche Tibet, besonders Ladak bezeichnet wird«, soll jeden-
falls auch dazu dienen, den Namen *Yarlung* auf Osttibet festzulegen. Es erscheint aber kaum angängig, die
Bezeichnungen *Maryul* in Ladak und *Yarlung*, also in Osttibet, zu einander in Beziehung zu bringen. Etwas anderes
ist es, wenn wir auf der Karte zum Ta-Ch'ing hui-tien 大清會典 an den Quellflüssen des Min die Namen
Yarlung und *Marlung*, »oberes und unteres Tal«, finden. Gehen wir nun aber auf den tibetischen Text des
rgyal-rabs zurück, so finden wir an den beiden Stellen fol. 13a und 14a den Namen mit dem Zusatz *yul* ver-
sehen = *yul yar-luṅ*, also Yarlung-Land. Von einem *Yarlung*-Fluß ist nicht die Rede. Dieser ist nichts als eine
Ableitung, die Kowalewski, Köppen, Schlagintweit, Jäschke, Laufer u. a. von einander oder im Grunde alle von
I. J. Schmidt übernommen haben, der in seinen Übersetzungen von Sanang Setsen und Bodhi mör als der alleinige
Gewährsmann für den »*Yarlung*-Fluß« als Stammsitz der tibetischen Kultur« anzusehen ist. In dem Index seines
Werkes finden wir die Angabe »Yarlung, ein Fluß in Tibet«. In dem mongolischen Texte kommt der Name
dreimal vor. Auf S. 23 übersetzt Schmidt: »er (der tibetische König) stieg herab in *die Talfläche des Yarlung . . .*«.
I. J. Schmidt, der Begründer der Mongolistik, ist sicher ein sehr gründlicher Kenner und zuverlässiger Arbeiter
gewesen. Aber hier hat er sich geirrt. Der mongolische Text »Yarlung-un erke-tü talan daki dürben hagalga-tu
suburga dergede kürün« kann nur bedeuten: »Er gelangte an eine Pagode mit vier Toren, die auf der *mächtigen
Ebene von Yarlung* gelegen war«. Talan ist die Ebene oder Steppe, *erke-tü* ist mächtig, gewaltig. Es mag sein,
daß Schmidt fälschlich *erkin* »das Ufer« gelesen hat. Aber auch die Verbindung *erkin-tü talan* »die Ebene, auf der
sich die Ufer (des Yarlung) befanden« wäre nicht recht verständlich. Ziehen wir die chinesische Übersetzung des
Textes heran, die »Mongolengeschichte« Meng-ku yüan-liu 蒙古源流, so finden wir die Stelle wiedergegeben: »er
gelangte nach der bei Yarlung-ťang befindlichen viertorigen Pagode«. Das Zeichen ťang 塘 bezeichnet — falls
wir es übersetzen wollen — eigentlich die beim Graben eines Teiches ausgehobene Erde, auch den Teich selbst

jusqu'auprès de la montagne *Mam-bayan-khara*, où elle se joint à une autre rivière qui sort de cette montagne et que les gens du pays appellent *Mam-tsitsirkhana*.[1] Elle coule vers le Sud-ouest et toutes les eaux du pays se joignent à elle. A l'Orient elle a la montagne de neige de *Nian*[2], d'où il sort la rivière de *Siétchou*. A l'Occident il y en a une autre montagne, appellée *Oïtchourgou*.[3] Ces deux rivières se joignent à la première, qui reçoit alors le nom de *Niaktchou*.[4] Elle coule l'espace de trois cens lys vers le Sud,

und als pars pro toto die am Dorfteich gelegene Ortschaft, eine Ansiedelung, aber nie einen Fluß oder das Ufer eines Flusses. Übrigens gehört es hier wahrscheinlich zum Namen und ist nichts anderes als das tibetische Wort für Ebene (mo. tala), das wir oben in den Städten Litang und Batang kennen gelernt haben. Eine weitere Stelle haben wir auf S. 39: Schmidt: »der Fürst von Yarlung«. Ohne weiteres klar ist die Stelle auf S. 20: Text: Tübet Yarlung obok-tan bolbai — »Sie wurden die Stammväter der tübetischen Yarlung (des Yarlung-*Stammes*)«. Auch die chinesische Übersetzung ist hier nicht mißverständlich: 為土伯特之雅國隆氏. »Sie bildeten den *Yarlung*-Klan der Tibeter«.

Hieraus geht klar hervor, daß es sich bei dem Worte Yarlung nicht um einen Fluß-, sondern um einen Landes- und Stammesnamen handelt. Auch die Stellen des Bodhi mör fügen sich diesem Sinne durchaus ein. Als Belegtext sei eine von Jülg verfertigte Abschrift des kalmükischen Geschichtswerkes herangezogen, aus den Sammlungen der Berliner K. B., Ms. orient., fol. 1359. Die Stelle, die Schmidt l. c. auf S. 318 übersetzt ». . . der seinen Sitz am Yarlung nahm«, kalmükisch: Yarlung-du sön, wäre wiederzugeben: »er ließ sich im Lande (der) Yarlung nieder«. Und der Satz der Schmidtschen Übersetzung S. 317: »er fand den schneebedeckten Yarlha Schambu hoch und das Tal des Yarlung schön« mutet schon an sich etwas unwahrscheinlich an. Im Kalmükischen steht: tsasutu Yarlha Šambu öndür kigēd oron Yarlunggi sain du ailadēi = »(als er von den Bergen herabgestiegen kam) erblickte er ganz deutlich (sain du) die schneebedeckte Yarlha-Schambu-Höhe sowie das Yarlung(-Land)« (vgl. die Verbindung oron aimak).

Der Hergang bei der weiten Verbreitung dieses Irrtums ist also jedenfalls der: Schmidt hat wohl unter dem Eindruck der falschen Lesung *erkin* statt *erke* in dem Namen *Yarlung* einen Fluß erblickt, diese Auslegung in den Index aufgenommen und auch seine Übersetzungen von Sanang Setsen und Bodhi mör angepaßt. Auf ihm fußend haben Kowalewski (dieser hat zweifellos auch die Sage im Auge) und Jäschke ihre Erklärungen in den Wörterbüchern entsprechend gestaltet. Das vielgelesene und mit Recht hochgeschätzte Köppensche Buch hat zur weiteren Verbreitung des Fehlers beigetragen, so daß wir heute immer wieder die müßige Frage erörtert sehen, welcher von den verschiedenen Flüssen des Namens *Yalung* als der *Yarlung* als der Stammsitz der Tibeter anzusprechen sei. Grünwedel allein setzt im Index zu seiner *Mythologie des Buddhismus in Tibet und der Mongolei*, Leipzig 1900, yar-luń als »alte Residenz der Könige von Tibet«, also Länder- oder Ortsname.

Wir hätten demnach für den großen Strom den Namen *Yalung* mit einer durch das geographische Wörterbuch belegten Variante *yar-kluń*, gesprochen yarlung, zwei Flußnamen, die in dieser Aussprache und vielleicht auch in der gleichen Schreibung, in Tibet jedenfalls auch sonst noch anzutreffen sind. Der Name *Yarlung* (yar-luń) ist eine generelle Bezeichnung, und zwar nicht für einen Fluß, sondern für ein Tal bzw. das anliegende Gebiet und mag gleichfalls häufiger zu finden sein.

Im Anschluß an obige Ausführungen sei darauf hingewiesen, daß es übrigens auffallen muß, wenn unsere Handschrift den Flußnamen (yaloung) anders schreibt als das geographische Wörterbuch (yarlung = yar-klung). Hat doch Klaproth am Schlusse seiner obenerwähnten Arbeit (vgl. S. 4, Note 6) über den Yaru-Tsang-po v. J. 1826 ausdrücklich betont, daß er für diese Arbeit das Hsi-yü t'ung-wen chih benutzt habe. Da man als wahrscheinlich annehmen könnte, daß Klaproth an der Hand dieses Wörterbuchs auch seine Arbeit von 1822 inbezug auf die Namensschreibung einer Durchsicht unterzogen hätte, so würde die noch vorhandenen mancherlei Abweichungen allenfalls geeignet, die Urheberschaft Klaproths an der vorliegenden Übersetzung in Zweifel zu stellen.

[1] tsitsirhana oder tsitsirgana = mo. Berberitze, s. Kowalewski, Mong. Wb., S. 2173. Das Beiwort Mam, chinesische Schreibung — ma-mu, findet sich auf der Karte der Commercial Press auch bei dem an der Quelle des Flusses eingezeichneten Gebirge Ma-mu pa-ven ha-la (= hayan kara). Kowalewski gibt auf S. 1996 ein Wort mamu als »böser Dämon« vom tibetischen ma-mo, vgl. Jäschke, S. 409.

[2] T. l. hat nien ni-mang-ch'i shan, was auf das mandschurische Wort nimanggi »Schnee« deutet.

[3] T. l. schreibt an dieser Stelle: Im Westen ist ein Fluß O-i-ch'u-rh-ku, der auf einem Berge Tsé-saikang entspringt.

[4] — tib. Strudelfluß.

jusqu'à l'Ouest de *Tchan-toui-ngan-fou-szu*[1], dépendant de *Ta-tsian-lou* du *Szu-tchhouan*, où elle perd son nom pour prendre celui de *Ja-loung-kiang*. Elle coule jusqu'à *Jan-tsing-ouei* 鹽井衛[2] du *Szu-tchhouan* l'espace de trois cens lys, et c'est là qu'elle prend de nom de *Ta-tchoung-ho*. Elle prend son cours du côté de l'Est pendant l'espace d'environ cent cinquante lys, après lesquels elle fait un coude vers le Sud d'environ deux cens lys, ensuite elle se joint au *Kin-cha-kiang*. Cette rivière sert aujourd'hui de limite: tout ce qui est à l'Est de ladite rivière est censé du district de *Ta-thsian-lou*, et tout le pays qui en est à l'Ouest est censé Thibétain.

Il paraît que dans la plus haute antiquité Chinoise cette rivière portait le nom de *Jo-chouy* et qu'elle fut considérée comme une des sources du grand fleuve *Kiang*. D'après la géographie des *Ming* les noms barbares de cette rivière etaient *He-houy* 黑惠 et *Na-y* 納夷.[3]

DES RIVIÈRES,

APPELLÉES EN THIBÉTAIN *TCHOUWO*[4] ET EN CHINOIS *HO*.

Menghé-djassou-altan.[5]

Elle tire sa source de la montagne *Gangdis*. Les eaux des neiges fondues se ramassent au pied de la montagne, et coulent du côté du Midi environ l'espace de vingt lys, après lesquels elles prennent leur cours vers le Sud-ouest pendant l'espace de quarante lys, et se perdent dans le lac *Langa*.

Koyoung.

Elle est au Sud-est des nomades de *Djochout* et est formée par quatre rivières. La première s'appelle *Loungri*[6]; elle prend sa source au pied de la montagne *Angdsé*, du côté du Nord; la seconde s'appelle *Kaïtchou* et tire sa source de la montagne *Kaïtchou-gangtsian*; la troisième s'appelle *Djouk*, et tire sa source de la montagne *Saïdan*; la quatrième s'appelle *Latchou*, et vient de la montagne *Larou-gangtsian*. Il ne faut pas confondre ce *Latchou* avec l'autre *Latchou*[7], dont-il est parlé plus haut à l'occasion du *Sétédjé*. Les caractères Chinois qui désignent les deux rivières ne sont pas les mêmes. Ces quatre petites rivières ont leur cours vers le Nord-est; elles coulent, chacune dans son lit particulier, l'espace d'environ deux ou trois cens lys, après lesquels elles ne font plus qu'une seule rivière, qui coule vers le Nord-est l'espace de soixante lys, après lesquels elle se jette dans *Yarou-tsangbou*.

Oungtchou.

Elle coule à deux cens lys de distance au Sud-ouest des nomades de *Saga*. Elle est, comme la précédente, formée par quatre autres petites rivières. La première vient de la source *Djamdoung-tala*[8]; la seconde de la source *Toukmar*[9]*-tala*; la troisième vient

---

[1] D. h. das Amtsgebiet des An-fu-sze (Kolonialpräfekten) für den Tschandu-Stamm, vgl. oben.

[2] = der Posten am Salzbrunnen.

[3] ein Wildvolk *Na*.

[4] = tchou, Wasser?

[5] Der mongolische Name ist bemerkenswert.

[6] T. I. hat lung-lieh, vielleicht = tib. lung lha'i-č'u, Götterfluß, der in einer Schlucht strömt.

[7] T. I. schreibt ihn dort 拉楚 und an dieser Stelle 拉出.

[8] Nach T. I. lies Tchamdoung, tala = mo. Steppe.

[9] Hierin steckt das tibetische Wort dmar »rot«.

7. IX. 4.

tout droit du Sud de la montagne *Namga*, et la quatrième du Sud-est de la source *Takla-tala*. Ces quatre petites rivières coulent dans leurs lits particuliers pendant l'espace de cent et quelques lys, en allant toujours vers le Nord, après lesquels elles se réunissent, et prennent le nom d'*Oungtchou*. Après un cours de dix lys vers le Nord la rivière *Oungtchou* se jette dans *Yarou-tsangbou*.

Chirdi.

Elle coule à cent lys environ au Sud-ouest des nomades de *Saga*; elle est formée par trois ruisseaux qui viennent de trois montagnes différentes; le premier vient du Sud-ouest de la montagne *Chapan*[1]; le second tout droit du Sud de la montagne *Choura*[2], et le troisième de la montagne *Gangra-watsian*. Ces trois ruisseaux coulent séparément vers le Nord environ cent lys depuis leurs sources, après lesquels ils se réunissent et prennent le nom de *Chirdi*. Cette rivière coule l'espace d'environ quatre-vingt-dix lys et se jette dans *Yarou-tsangbou*.

Sabtchou.

Elle est à quatre-vingt lys au Nord-ouest de la ville de *Jikadsé*. Elle est formée par les eaux qui sortent d'abord des montagnes *Djouranu*[3], *Khoungro* et *Djormo*, qui sont au Midi de *Jikadsé*. Ces eaux se réunissent presqu'au sortir de leur source, coulent vers le Nord l'espace d'environ cent lys et forment une rivière qui prend le nom de *Gatchou*. Cette rivière coule encore une centaine de lys vers le Nord, après lesquels elle reçoit deux autres ruisseaux, dont l'un vient du Sud-ouest et s'appelle *Ghié*, et l'autre vient du Sud-est, et s'appelle *Tangtchou*.[4] Elle prend alors le nom de *Sabtchou*, coule l'espace d'environ cent vingt lys au Nord et se jette dans *Yarou-tsangbou*.[5]

Niantchou.[5]

Elle est à dix lys au Nord de la ville de *Jikadsé*. Elle est formée par les eaux qui viennent des montagnes *Djoumram* et *Chunra*[6], qui sont au Sud de *Jikadsé*. Ces eaux coulent séparément environ deux cens lys vers le Nord-ouest, après lesquels elle se réunissent et font la rivière *Djanglou*[7], dont le cours, jusqu'à l'Est du temple dédié à la déesse *Niang-niang* 娘娘[8], n'est que de quatre-vingt lys. Là elle reçoit les eaux de huit petites rivières ou ruisseaux, prend son cours du côté du Nord-est, passe à une centaine de lys à l'Ouest des villes *Dsiang-dsé* et *Péman*, reçoit les eaux de deux autres rivières qui viennent du Sud-ouest et prend le nom de *Niantchou*. Elle tourne à l'Est, passe au Nord de *Jikadsé*, et après un cours de quarante lys, elle se jette dans *Yarou-tsangbou*.

Loungtsian.

Elle coule au Nord de la ville de *Rinbun*, à deux lys de distance. Elle tire sa source de la montagne *Djoum-khara*, qui est à l'Est de *Rinbun*.[9] Au sortir de la source elle coule vers l'Ouest l'espace d'environ cent lys, reçoit les eaux de plusieurs ruisseaux qui viennent de la montagne *Noughin-gangtsang*[10], qui est au Sud-ouest de la ville et va se jeter dans *Yarou-tsangbou*.

---

[1] Nach T. I. lies Chaban.

[2] = Choula.

[3] Nach T. I. lies Tchoula, die Abtrennung der drei Namen ist unsicher.

[4] = dvangs-č'u, Fluß des durchsichtigen Wassers.

[5] = gnyan-č'u, der Fluß des Schreckens.

[6] Lies Chunla.

[7] = lcang-lo č'u, Weidenfluß?

[8] Die Göttin Kwanyin des chinesischen Buddhismus.

[9] = rin-spungs rdsongs, Stadt der aufgehäuften Schätze.

[10] = gnod-sbyin gangs-bzang la, Schneeberg der Rakschas, der buddhistischen Unholde.

Ghianghia-soumra.[1]

Elle est à l'Ouest des nomades de *Djochout*. Ses sources viennent du Nord-ouest des montagnes *Chakou-yara-mala*, *Djakghiara*[2] et *Niri*.[3] Ce sont quatre ruisseaux qui vont à l'Orient, se réunissent à cent lys de leurs sources, et font une rivière qui prend son cours vers le Sud. Après avoir coulé l'espace d'environ cinquante lys, elle reçoit les eaux d'une petite rivière qui vient du côté de l'Ouest, et qu'on appelle *Djar*[4], prend son cours vers l'Est, et après avoir coulé pendant soixante lys, elle se jette dans *Yarou-tsangbou-kiang*.

Naouk-tsangbou.

Elle est au Sud-ouest des nomades de *Djochout*, à trente lys de distance. Elle prend sa source du lac *Sangri*[5], qui est au Nord-est de ces nomades. Elle coule d'abord vers l'Ouest l'espace de deux cens cinquante et quelques lys. Elle reçoit deux rivières du Nord qui viennent des montagnes *Changri-gaba* et *Moukroung*, et du côté du Sud trois autres qui viennent des monts *Ladjouk*, *Dsouroun* et *Yangbam*. A l'Ouest de ce dernier elle coule vers le Sud l'espace d'environ quatre-vingt lys, après lesquels elle reçoit du Nord-ouest les eaux qui viennent des montagnes *Yara* et *Dakroung*, et après avoir coulé encore l'espace de soixante lys, elle se jette dans *Yarou-tsangbou*.

Satchou-tsangbou.

Elle est au Sud-ouest des nomades de *Saga*, à la distance de cent et quelques lys. Elle tire sa source des montagnes *Voro-Gangtsian*, dont il sort six ruisseaux qui prennent leurs cours vers le Sud, et se réunissent à la distance de cent lys de leurs sources, pour former la rivière *Ghiabalan*. Cette rivière, après un cours de cinquante lys vers le Sud, reçoit les eaux de trois ruisseaux qui viennent du Nord-ouest de trois montagnes *Ladjouk*, *Dsouleng* et *Yangbam*, qu'elle a au Nord-ouest; au Sud-ouest il y a la montagne *Angsé-angredsoung*, de laquelle sortent deux ruisseaux, qui se réunissent et se jettent dans le *Ghiabalan*. Après cette réunion elle coule pendant quelque tems vers le Sud-est, fait un coude vers le Sud-ouest, reçoit deux rivières qui viennent des montagnes *Djassa-goungar-tala*, qu'elle a au Nord-est, *Niémou* et *Lousséra-yangou*[6], qu'elle a à l'Ouest, en tirant un peu vers le Sud, et prend le nom de *Satchou-tsangbou*. Elle coule encore l'espace de soixante-dix lys vers le Sud-ouest et se jette dans *Yarou-tsangbou*.

Mantchou[7]*-tsangbou.*

Elle est au Sud-ouest des *Saga*. Elle est formée par les eaux de plusieurs ruisseaux, dont deux viennent des montagnes *Kor-tchoung*[8] et *Piroung*[9], qu'elle a au Nord. Ces deux ruisseaux, après un cours de deux cens lys vers le Sud, se joignent à trois autres qui viennent de la montagne *Gangtchoung-djadak*[10], qui est à l'Est, et à plusieurs autres qui viennent de la montagne *Laktsang-djori*[11], qui est à l'Ouest. Toutes ces eaux réunies

---

[1] ... soumla, Paß der 3 ...
[2] In der ersten Silbe steckt jedenfalls das tibetische Wort l[e]ags, Eisen.
[3] T. I. schreibt Nieh-li = snye-ri?
[4] Nach T. I. lies Tchar.
[5] = zangs-ri, Kupferberg.
[6] T. I. hat Liu-sê-li-yang-ku.
[7] sman-é‘u, Arzneipflanzenfluß.
[8] T. I. hat 絜 hsieh (nicht 科 k‘o) in der ersten Silbe, hsieh-rh = gser, Gold?
[9] T. I. hat p‘ieh-lung.
[10] Nach T. I. lies tchadak.
[11] lag-bzang 'gro-ri, Drachenberg.

prennent le nom de *Mantchou*, et font la rivière qui coule sous ce nom vers le Sud-est, l'espace de quarante lys, après lesquels elle se jette dans *Yarou-tsangbou*.

Sarghé-tsangbou.

Elle est au Sud-est des *Saga*. Elle est formée par les eaux qui sortent du lac *Lab*.[1] Elle prend son cours vers le Sud-ouest; et après avoir parcouru l'espace d'environ quatre cens lys, elle reçoit du côté de l'Est une petite rivière qui vient de la montagne *Lab-gangtchoung*[2], et du côté de l'Ouest il y a les montagnes *Ladjoung*[3], *Wenbi* et *Poutakla*[4] desquelles découlent huit ruisseaux. Toutes ces eaux réunies font une assez grande rivière qui prend le nom de *Dsa-dak*. Elle coule vers le Sud l'espace de trente lys, après lesquels elle reçoit la rivière *Satchou*, qui vient de l'Est, et celle de *Lou*, qui vient de l'Ouest. Elle coule au Sud-ouest l'espace de trente lys, fait un coude de cent vingt lys et se jette dans *Yarou-tsangbou*.

Oïtchou-tsangbou.[5]

Elle tire sa source du lac *Djamtchouk*, qui est à cent quatre-vingt lys au Nord-ouest de la ville de *Djangabrin*.[6] Au sortir du lac, elle prend son cours vers le Sud, et après une centaine de lys, elle entre dans le lac *Lounngangpou*, dans lequel entrent aussi trois autres ruisseaux qui viennent de l'Ouest. De toutes ces eaux réunies se forme une rivière qui prend le nom de *Daktchou*. Elle coule vers l'Est l'espace de cent quatre-vingt lys, après lesquels elle arrive au Nord du pont qu'on appelle *Moukboudjak-samma*.[7] Là elle se joint aux eaux qui viennent du côté du Nord et prend le nom d'*Oïtchou-tsangbou*. Elle coule vers le Sud-est l'espace de soixante et quelques lys, et se jette dans *Yarou-tsangbou*.

Chang.

Elle prend sa source dans les montagnes *Ghiangdjara* et *Dsao-sokbou*, qui sont au Nord-ouest de la ville de *Changnamrin*. Des deux montagnes, que je viens de nommer, sortent deux ruisseaux qui prennent leurs cours vers le Sud-est. Après avoir coulé l'espace de deux cens quarante lys, ils se joignent aux différens ruisseaux qui viennent des montagnes qui sont au Nord-est, et font une rivière qui, après un cours d'environ cinquante lys, se jette dans *Yarou-tsangbou*.

Yangbadsian.[8]

Elle est à l'Ouest de la ville de *Doungor*. Sa source vient de cinq ruisseaux qui coulent de différentes montagnes vers le Sud-est. Après un cours de cent quatre-vingt lys ces ruisseaux se joignent à la rivière *Mantchou*, qui vient de la montagne *Tsinyun*, qui est à l'Est, et à la rivière *Tchoupou*, qui vient de la montagne *Tomba*, qui est à l'Ouest. Toutes ces eaux réunies prennent le nom de *Yangbadsian*, coulent vers l'Est, et après un cours de quarante lys seulement, ils se jettent dans la rivière *Gardjao-mouren*.

Babroung.

Elle est au Nord-ouest de la ville de *Phengdo*. Elle est formée par trois ruisseaux qui viennent de la montagne *Samtan*[9], et qui coulent vers le Sud-est. Ces trois ruisseaux

---

[1]   rab-mts'o, herrlicher See.

[2]   rab-sgangs k'yung-ri, Garuda-Gletscher.

[3]   Nach T. I. lies Latchoung.

[4]   T. I. führt eine Reihe von Bergnamen auf: la-ch'ung-wen-pi-p'u-t'a-k'o-la-k'o, deren Abteilung nicht ganz sicher ist, vielleicht Ratschung, Umbi, Putaklag.

[5]   T. I. schreibt O-i ch'u, Z. hat wei-ch'u, d. i. tib. dbu'i-é'u, mittlerer Lauf.

[6]   Vgl. tib. byang-'amring rdsongs = Stadt an der Nordseite des Berges, im alten Lande Amring. Nach T. I. lies Moukboutchak-samma (= zamba, Brücke?).

[7]   = yangs-pa-can é'u, breiter Fluß.

[8]   Nach T. I. lies Samdan – tib. bsam-gtan, in Betrachtung versunken.

se joignent à une dixaine d'autres, et prennent, après leur jonction, le nom de *Babrowng*. Cette rivière va se jeter dans *Midik-tsangbou*.[1]

Niandjou.

Elle passe à l'Est de la ville de *Goungbou-Dscbragang*. Plusieurs rivières et ruisseaux concourent à la former et à la grossir:

1. La rivière *Mamtchou*; elle sort de la montagne *Chayukgangra*, qui est au Nord-ouest, et coule pendant l'espace de deux cens quarante lys vers l'Est.
2. La rivière *Baroungtchou*[2]; elle vient de la montagne *Bara*[3], qui est au Midi.
3. La rivière *Boulaitchou*; elle vient de la montagne *Khatsidjoukou*, qui est au Nord.
4. La rivière *Outchou*, qui vient de la montagne *On*.

Ces quatre rivières se réunissent en une seule, laquelle coule vers l'Est l'espace de soixante lys, jusqu'au Midi de la ville *Goungbou-Dscbragang*. Là elle reçoit la rivière *Ghianang*, qui vient du côté du Nord et qui entoure la ville de *Djamou*[4] du côté de l'Orient, elle coule vers le Sud-est environ trois cens lys, arrive au Midi de la ville de *Goungbou-Chighé*, reçoit la rivière *Butchou*[5], qui vient du lac *Badsoungdsou*, qui est au Nord-est, et continue son cours pour recevoir les eaux qui sortent de la montagne *Djabou*[6], qu'elle a au Nord-est. C'est alors qu'elle prend le nom de *Niandchou*[7]. Elle prend son cours vers le Sud, tourne ensuite à l'Est de la ville de *Dscbragang*, et après avoir parcouru l'espace de deux cens lys de chemin, elle se jette dans *Yarou-tsangbou-kiang*.

Gangbou-tsangbou.

Elle passe au Nord-est de la ville de *Djamda* du pays de *Goungbou*. Sa source est dans la montagne *Djora*[8], qui est à l'Ouest de *Djamda*, à cent seize lys de distance. De cette montagne il sort un ruisseau qui porte le nom de *Tchouk*. Depuis sa source, il coule vers le Nord jusqu'à trente lys de distance, et entre dans le lac *Djamna-youmtso*.[9] De ce lac sort une rivière qui prend son cours vers le Sud-est, et qui, après avoir parcouru l'espace de deux cens cinquante lys, reçoit les eaux de *Djauglou*, qui vient de la montagne *Djangarsoung*, du côté du Nord, et d'une autre rivière appellée *Sangtchou*[10], qui est formée par les eaux, qui coulent de la montagne *Sangtsian-Sangtchoung*, auxquelles se joignent quatre autres ruisseaux appellées *Etchou*[11], qui viennent des montagnes *Noubou-goungra*, *Char-goungra*[12] etc., qui sont à l'Est dans le pays de *Kab*. Toutes les eaux réunies prennent le nom de *Gangbou-tsangbou* ou de rivière de *Gangbou*, laquelle coule d'abord vers le Sud, tourne ensuite au Sud-est et après un cours de cent quarante lys, passe à l'Ouest de la montagne *Diyar*, entre dans les terres des nomades de *Gangbou*, va à l'Est de *Pipitang-tala*[13], entre sur les frontières des *Kamou*, où elle reçoit une rivière qui vient du Nord,

---

[1] Z. hat einen Fluß Mudik zangbolung — tib. mu-tig gtsang-po klung, reiner Perlenfluß. Vielleicht ist das Zeichen 米 mi ein Fehler für 木 mu.

[2] Baloungtchou = rba-klong-č'u, wellenreicher Fluß.

[3] Bala = 'ba-la, Höhlenberg (Hexenberg?).

[4] T. I. hat dafür Kung-pu cha-mu-ta wie unten = kong-po, Tiefland?

[5] 'ba-č'u, rauschendes Wasser.

[6] Nach T. I. lies Tchab.

[7] Nach T. I. lies Niantchou.

[8] Nach T. I. lies tcho-la.

[9] T. I. ch'a-mu-na, mts'o, tib. der See.

[10] = bzang-č'u, schöner Fluß.

[11] T. I. = 厄 楚 = wei-ch'u = čbui-č'u, mittlerer Lauf, vgl. oben S. 52, Fußnote 5.

[12] nub, Westen, (in K'am gibt es zwei Berge) nub und sar gangla, West- und Ost-Schneeberg.

[13] T. I. schreibt la-p'i-t'ang.

passe à l'Est de la montagne de *Saïmroungra*[1], sort des terres des *Gangbou*, entre dans le royaume de *Lokabou-djan*, et vient par le Sud-est se jeter dans *Yarou-tsangbou*.

Phongtchou-tsangbou.

Se trouve à deux cens cinquante lys au Sud-est du pays des *Saga*. A l'Ouest il y a une montagne qu'on appelle *Chourmou-tsangra*.[2] A l'Est sont les deux montagnes *Sirdjoungma*[3] et *Gouadja*.[4] De ces trois montagnes sortent trois ruisseaux, qui réunissent leurs eaux, forment une rivière qui coule vers le Sud-est l'espace de deux cens cinquante lys; après lesquels elle reçoit les eaux de quatre ruisseaux. Elle prend son cours vers l'Est. droit pendant cent quarante lys, passe au Midi de la ville de *Losikar*, et coule de-là vers le Nord-est pendant soixante lys, tourne au Nord de la montagne *Gangroungtsian*, revient couler vers le Sud pendant l'espace de deux cens lys, sort des frontières des *Tsang*. passe chez les nomades de *Djoularai* et entre dans les frontières du royaume d'*Enetké* ou de l'*Hindoustan*.

Lotchou[5]-tsangbou.

Elle passe à l'Ouest de *Losikar*. Sa source est à deux cens trente lys au Nord-ouest de cette ville. Des montagnes *Djodjou-Giangtsian* et *Djoubourchang-gangri* sortent deux ruisseaux qui, après cinquante lys de cours, se réunissent et forment la rivière qu'on appelle *Lotchou*; elle coule l'espace de quarante lys vers le Sud et se jette dans *Phongtchou-tsangbou.*

Niou-tsangbou.[6]

La source est à cent trente lys à l'Ouest de la ville de *Paridsoung*. Des montagnes *Djora*, *Nasser* et *Ibala* sortent trois ruisseaux, qui, après un cours d'environ soixante-dix lys, se réunissent et font une rivière qu'on appelle *Nioutchou*. Elle coule pendant trente lys vers le Sud-ouest, après lesquels elle reçoit les eaux de trois ruisseaux qui viennent des montagnes *Dingra-miao-dscrinbou*[7] et *Djoumrama*.[8] Ces trois ruisseaux, au sortir de leurs sources, coulent vers l'Est environ quatre-vingt-dix lys, après lesquels ils se réunissent. Ils coulent l'espace de soixante lys, et se jettent dans *Niou-tsangbou*. Cette rivière, après avoir coulé encore l'espace de soixante-dix lys, se jette dans *Phongtchou-tsangbou.*

Lo-tsangbou.[9]

Elle est au Nord-est de la ville de *Losikar*. Elle est formée par quelques ruisseaux qui viennent des montagnes, lesquels, après s'être réunis, font une petite rivière, qui prend le nom de *Lotchou*. Elle coule vers le Sud-est pendant cent quatre-vingt lys, et vient passer au Nord-est de *Losikar*. Deux ruisseaux qui sortent de la montagne de *Largarbou*[10], qui est à l'Ouest, après un cours de quatre-vingt lys vers le Sud-est, se réunissent et font une petite rivière qui prend le nom de *Ghiatchou*. Cette rivière coule vers le Sud-est l'espace de cent trente lys, passe au Nord de *Losikar*, où elle se jette dans *Lotchou*, et prend le nom de *Lo-tsangbou*. Elle coule encore l'espace de dix lys, après lesquels elle se perd dans *Phongtchou-tsangbou.*

---

[1] T. l. sai-mu lung-la.
[2] Vgl. žol-mo gtsang-la.
[3] Vgl. srid-gsum ma'i-ri, Berg der drei Welten.
[4] T. l. kua-ch'a.
[5] lho-č'u, Südfluß.
[6] = nje'u-č'u.
[7] Der zweite Teil des Namens deutet auf rtse rin-po, hohe Spitze.
[8] Vgl. 'grum-la (spr. jumla), Dachspaß.
[9] Vgl. oben lho-č'u.
[10] Nach T. l. lies Largarbou.

Tchang-tchou.[1]

Elle passe à l'Ouest de la ville de *Dinghiya*.[2] Elle est formée par la réunion de plusieurs ruisseaux. Au Nord-est de *Dinghiya*, à la distance d'environ cent dix lys, sont les montagnes *Rinfoura*[3], *Lounggangtsian* et *Soukongangtsian*, de chacune desquelles il sort un ruisseau. Ces trois ruisseaux coulent séparément vers le Sud-est l'espace de soixante-dix à quatre-vingt lys, après lesquels ils se réunissent, et font une petite rivière qui prend son cours vers le Sud. Après avoir coulé pendant l'espace de quatre-vingt-dix lys, elle reçoit les eaux de deux autres ruisseaux qui viennent du Nord-est. Ces deux ruisseaux, après leur réunion, ont pris le nom de *Ghitchou*.[4] Ils ont coulé sous ce nom l'espace d'environ trois cens vingt lys, après lesquels ils se sont réunis à la rivière formée par les trois ruisseaux dont j'ai parlé d'abord. Toutes ces eaux réunies prennent le nom de *Tchangtchou*, qui, après un cours de vingt lys, se jette dans *Phongtchou-tsangbou*.

Pari-tsangbou-ho.

Elle passe au Sud-ouest de la ville de *Paridsoung*. Sa source vient du lac *Gartsé*[5], qui est à cent vingt lys au Nord-est de *Paridsoung*. Elle coule au Sud-ouest l'espace de quarante lys, entre dans le lac *Djamsou*[6], en sort par le Sud-ouest, va passer à quelque distance de *Paridsoung*, où elle reçoit quatre ruisseaux qui viennent du Nord-est, et prend le nom de *Pari-tsangbou*. Après un cours de quatre-vingt lys vers l'Ouest elle se perd dans la rivière *Phongtchou-tsangbou*.

Yarghia-tsangbou.

Elle est à sept cens lys au Nord de *Lassa*. Sa source vient de la montagne *Bassa*[7]-*toungram*. Elle coule vers l'Ouest, passe au Nord de la province d'*Ouei* et entre dans le Royaume de *Katsi*.

Bouroun.[8]

Se trouve à cent cinquante lys au Sud du lac *Khara-noor*.[9] Elle est formée par deux ruisseaux: le premier vient de la montagne *Goungabagama*[10], qui est à l'Est, et s'appelle *Khara*; le second vient de la montagne *Yuk*, et s'appelle aussi *Yuk*. Ces deux ruisseaux prennent leur cours vers le Nord-ouest, et se joignent à quelque distance de leurs sources. Après avoir coulé sous le nom de *Bouroun*, qu'ils ont pris après leur jonction, pendant l'espace d'environ cent lys, ils se joignent aux différens ruisseaux qui sortent du lac *Chouomou*, prennent leur cours vers le Nord-est, et après avoir couru l'espace d'environ cent lys, ils se jettent dans la rivière *Khara-oussou*.

Boukchak.

Sa source vient de la montagne *Kardjangoutsa*[11], qui est à sept cens lys au Nord de *Lassa*. Les eaux qui sortent de cette montagne, forment d'abord une petite rivière qui coule vers le Sud l'espace de trois cens lys, après lesquelles elle se joint à une autre

---

1 = byang-é'u, Nordfluß?
2 Vgl. die Stadt Sting-skyes, »auf einer Flußinsel gelegen».
3 T. I. Lin-fo-la.
4 Vgl. skyid-é'u, Fluß des Glückes.
5 T. I. hat ka-rh-ts'o, also = tib. rgal-mts'o, See mit Furt.
6 Nach T. I. lies Tchamsou.
7 = Rinderland?
8 = mo. bugur-un (müren), Fluß des Kamelhengstes.
9 = mo. schwarzer See.
10 = gungs k'a-pa ga-ma, die Berge im alten Lande Gungs.
11 Nach T. I. k'a-rh-chan-ku-ch'a (kardjangoutcha).

petite rivière qui s'appelle *Chak*[1] et qui vient de la montagne *Douk-choui*[2], qui est à l'Ouest.
Depuis sa jonction, elle coule vers le Sud-est l'espace de deux cens quarante lys, reçoit les
rivières *Koulan*, qui vient de l'Ouest, et *Bouk*[3], qui vient du Nord, continue son cours vers
le Sud-est pendant l'espace de cent lys, après lesquels elle se jette dans le *Khara-oussou*.

Sokdjan-daugoun.

Elle prend sa source de la montagne appellée par les Mongols *Yke-nomkhoun-oubachi-
dabahn*.[4] De cette montagne coulent d'abord six ruisseaux, qui, après avoir serpenté
pendant quelque temps se réunissent et forment une petite rivière qui coule vers le Sud-est
pendant l'espace de deux cens lys, après lesquels elle reçoit les eaux de quatre ruisseaux,
qui viennent des montagnes *Bakhan-nomkhoun-oubachi-dabahn*[4], *Bouka-oola*[5] et du rocher
Tchakhan[6], qu'elle a au Sud-ouest, prend son cours par le milieu des montagnes, entre
chez les *Kamou*; et après avoir couru l'espace d'environ deux cens lys, elle va se perdre
dans *Khara-oussou*.

Akdam.[7]

Sa source vient des deux lacs *Temen*[8] et *Tala*[9], qui sont au Nord de la montagne
Yke-nomkhoun-oubachi-dabahn. Les eaux qui sortent de ces lacs, après avoir coulé vers le
Nord-est l'espace de cent lys, se joignent aux eaux du ruisseau *Yke-akdam* (*Yke* en Mongol
signifie grand et *bakhan* signifie petit), qui vient de l'Est, et à celles du ruisseau *Bakhan-
akdam*, qui vient de l'Ouest. Toutes ces eaux réunies, après un cours de trois cens lys
vers le Nord-ouest se jettent dans *Mourous-oussou*.

Tonkhour.[10]

Elle est au-dessus de l'endroit où le *Kin-cha-kiang* prend son cours du côté de l'Est.
Sa source vient de la montagne *Erdsighen-dabahn*[11], qui est à vingt lys de distance de la
gorge qui conduit au gué *Yke-koukousair*[12], du côté de l'Ouest. Elle coule d'abord l'espace
de quatre vingt lys vers le Nord jusqu'à la montagne *Tonkhour-tolokhui*[13], sous le nom
d'*Ounie*.[14] Elle se joint aux ruisseaux *Koungtchou* et *Hotsing*[15], qui viennent du Sud-ouest,
coule encore vers le Nord l'espace d'environ cent vingt lys, arrive à *Sarloung-tala*[16] et se
jette dans *Mourous-oussou*.

---

[1] – Fluß im alten Lande Šak, wahrscheinlich tib. Žag = Öl. So die geographische Namensliste »*Nord-
Tibet und Lob-Nur-Gebiet*» (nach der Wutschang-Karte), unter Mitwirkung des Herrn Karl Himly hrsg. von
Dr. Georg Wegener, Berlin 1893. Eine sehr wertvolle und gediegene Abhandlung wie alle Arbeiten Himlys,
unter dessen Namen sie stehen sollte; von den 40 Seiten sind 30 rein philologische Arbeit!

[2] Nach T. I. wäre Doukhoui (tu-hui) zu lesen.

[3] = mo. Dämon; vgl. auch Z. S. 132 = 'bog-é'u, Fluß im alten Lande Bok.

[4] Vgl. oben S. 28, Anm. 1, S. 34 u. 37.

[5] buha agula = mo. Stierberg.

[6] Mo. tsagan = weiß, durch mandschurische Schreibung gegangen.

[7] Vgl. oben das gleichnamige Gebirge. Himly bildet agodam = mo. umfangreich.

[8] Mo. temegen, Kamel.

[9] Mo. Ebene.

[10] Mo. tugul, Kalb?

[11] = mo. eljigen dabagan, Eselspaß?

[12] sair (dsair) ist mo. der Eisbruch eines Flusses, yke ist yeke, groß, koukou ist kükü, blau.

[13] Nach Himly = mo. tugul tologai, Kälberhügel.

[14] = mo. üniye, Kuh.

[15] Nach T. I. Hotsin.

[16] Die Wutschang-Karte (Wegener-Himly) verzeichnet hier einen Namen serlung tala und schlägt für den
ersten Bestandteil des Namens eine tibetische Ableitung vor. T. I. hat wie die Handschrift *sarlung*. Vielleicht
eine falsche Umschreibung für sarluk tala = mo. Steppe der Bergrinder (Yaks).

Tsitsirkhanakoukou-oussou.[1]

Sa source est à trois cens lys au Sud-est du gué *Yké-koukousair*. Elle vient des montagnes *Soukbou-soukem*[2], *Dsagatangnouk* et *Outsim-kadadodsa*. Les eaux qui en déroulent forment sept rivières et deux lacs, qui se joignent après un cours d'environ cent lys vers le Nord-est, et prennent le nom de *Tsitsirkhanakoukou-oussou*. Cette rivière est très large et très profonde; on ne saurait la traverser, même en barque. Elle n'a qu'un cours de trente lys, après lesquels elle se jette dans *Mourous-oussou*.

Témetou[3]*-koukou-oussou.*

Elle passe à l'Est de la précédente, à cinquante lys de distance. Elle est formée par deux ruisseaux qui sortent de la montagne *Dakemkamdsaga*[4] et qui se réunissent après soixante lys de cours vers le Nord-ouest. Ils prennent alors le nom de rivière, et après un cours de soixante-dix lys, se jettent dans *Mourous-oussou*.

Katsi-oulan-mouren.[5]

Elle tire sa source de la montagne *Lekor-oulan-dabsoun-oola*[6], laquelle est à quatre cens lys au Nord-ouest de la montagne *Bassa-toungram*. Elle coule vers le Sud-est l'espace d'environ cinq cens lys, après quoi elle se jette dans *Mourous-oussou*.

Toktonaï-oulan-mouren.

Elle tire sa source de la montagne *Sighin-oulan-tolokhaï*[7], qui est à trois cens lys au Nord-est de la montagne *Lekor*.[8] Elle coule vers l'Est pendant l'espace de quatre cens cinquante lys, et va se perdre dans *Mourous-oussou*.

Namtsitou-oulan-mouren.

Elle tire sa source de la montagne *Bayan-khara-derben-oola*, qui est à trois cens lys au Nord-est de *Sighin-oulan-tolokhaï*. Elle coule vers le Sud-est l'espace de six cens lys, et va se perdre dans *Mourous-oussou*. Les trois rivières, dont on vient de parler en dernier lieu, c'est-à-dire *Katsi*, *Toktonaï* et *Namtsitou*, coulent près des bords septentrionaux du *Kin-cha-kiang*, quand il est encore près de la source. Leurs eaux sont très profondes, et on ne peut les passer que difficilement.

Toukhartou-khara-oussou.

Elle est à l'Est de *Kin-cha-kiang*, lorsque ce fleuve prend son cours vers le Sud. Plusieurs ruisseaux ou petites rivières concourent à la former. Sa source vient de la montagne *Gourban-tourkhatou-oola*[9], d'où elle coule vers l'Ouest l'espace de cent cinquante lys, après lesquelles elle reçoit les eaux du *Kossou-tsiboo*[10] et de *Maochin-khorkho*, qui viennent du Sud, celle de *Gabré*[11] et de *Mokhor-khara-oussou*, qui viennent du Nord. Elle coule encore l'espace de vingt lys et va se perdre dans *Mourous-oussou*.

---

[1] koukou oussou (kükü usu) = mo. blaues Wasser.
[2] Vgl. oben S. 34 Soukmou soukem.
[3] Lies temétou-temegetü, mo. wo es Kamele gibt.
[4] Nach T. I. lies Dakmou.
[5] ulagan mören, mo. = roter Fluß.
[6] Nach T. I. Lesir: Lo-hsieh-'rh, die Handschrift hat statt 斜 gelesen 針; ulagan dabsu agula, mo. = Berg des roten Salzes.
[7] Vgl. Wegener-Himly shidshin = mo. shidshing, Harner? ulagan tologaï, mo. = roter Hügel (Kopf).
[8] S. oben Lesir.
[9] gourban = mo. gurban, drei; tourkhatou lies toukhartou.
[10] Nach T. I. lies tsiloo (ch'i-lao) = mo. tschiloga, Stein.
[11] T. I. = ko-pu-lo.

S. IX, 4.

Dsatchou.[1]

Elle est au Nord-est de la ville *Lo-roungdsoung*, à cent soixante lys de distance. Elle prend sa source dans les deux lacs *Tchou-tchoung* et *Tchoutsian*[2], qui sont au Nord-est. Les eaux qui sortent de ces deux lacs se réunissent et forment une rivière qui coule vers le Sud-est pendant l'espace d'environ cinq cens lys, après lesquels elle se jette dans *Lan-thsang-kiang*.

Doktchou.[3]

Elle est à l'Est de la ville *Dsidam*, à quatre-vingt lys de distance. Sa source vient du lac *Charou-tchou-nor* qui est à deux cens lys de *Dsidam*. Des eaux de ce lac se forme une rivière qui prend son cours vers le Sud-est. Après avoir couru l'espace de trois cens lys, elle arrive à *Milila*, entre dans les limites du *Yun-nan*, où elle perd son nom pour prendre celui d'*Ou-liang-ho* 無量河.[4] Elle coule encore l'espace de deux cens lys, et se jette dans le *Kin-cha-kiang*.

Lytchou.[5]

Elle passe au Nord de la ville de *Lytang*, à la distance de trois lys. Sa source vient des montagnes *Lymou* et *Charoutsi*, qui sont à cent cinquante lys au Nord-ouest de *Lytang*. De ces deux montagnes coulent deux ruisseaux qui, se réunissant, forment la rivière *Lytchou*, qui prend son cours vers le Sud-est jusqu'auprès de *Lytang*. Là elle reçoit les eaux de deux ruisseaux ou petites rivières, qui viennent du Nord-est, coule l'espace de trois cens lys vers le Sud-ouest, et va dans les limites du *Yun-nan* se jeter dans *Ou-liang-ho*.

Dountchou.

Sa source est dans la montagne *Gangri-lamar*[6], qui est au Sud-ouest de la ville de *Lytang*, à la distance de cent quatre-vingt lys. Après avoir coulé l'espace de cent soixante lys, elle reçoit la petite rivière *Matchou*[7], qui vient des rochers *Djam-khada*[8], qui sont au Nord-est de *Lytang*, et après avoir coulé l'espace de cent et quelques lys, elle se jette dans le *Kin-cha-kiang*.

Chytchou.

Elle passe à la distance de cent cinquante lys au Sud-ouest de *Lytang*. Sa source est dans la montagne *Gabounai-gangri*, qui est à l'Est de *Gangri-lamar*. Elle coule trois cens lys au Sud-ouest, et se joint au *Dountchou*.

Oitchou.[9]

Elle est à l'Ouest de la ville de *Dsatsergang;* sa source est dans la montagne *Naran*[10], qui est à trois cens lys au Nord de la même ville. Elle coule vers le Sud pendant l'espace de quatre cens lys, arrive au lac *Ghialam* et va se jeter dans *Lou-kiang*.

---

[1] = tib. ts'va-é'u, Salzfluß.

[2] = tib. é'u-é'ung und é'u-é'en, kleines und großes Wasser.

[3] = tib. dogs-é'u, Fluß im Engpaß.

[4] Chines. = unermeßlicher Fluß.

[5] = tib. li-é'u, Kupferminenfluß.

[6] = tib. gangs ri la-dmar, roter Paß am Schneeberge.

[7] = tib. rma-é'u, Name des Huang-ho.

[8] Die erste Silbe ist vielleicht das tibetische 'gram, Felswand. Bei hada haben wir ein mandschurisches Wort für *Felsen*.

[9] = tib. dbui-é'u (in Kam), s. oben S. 53.

[10] Mo. Sonne.

DES LACS; EN THIBÉTAIN YOUMDSOU.[1]

Mapinmou-talai.[2]

Il est à deux cens lys au Nord-est de la ville de *Dakla*, du département des *Ngari*, et à soixante-cinq lys au Sud-est de la montagne *Gangdis*. Il est formé par les eaux qui coulent du pied de la montagne *Langtsian-kabab*. Ce lac passe pour être la source principale du *Setledje*[3], et c'est pour cette raison qu'on l'a honoré du titre de *Talai*, qui signifie *mer* en langue Mongole; il peut avoir cent quatre-vingt lys de tour. Ses eaux sont propres, douces et salutaires, quoique d'une couleur tirant sur le vert. Elles prennent différentes couleurs, suivant la différente élévation du soleil sur l'horizon, mais vers le milieu du jour, elles brillent de toutes les couleurs ensembles et réfléchissent une lumière semblable à celle des éclairs. Ce lac est fermé des quatre côtés par des montagnes qui en sont comme les portes; ce qui a donné lieu au dicton des gens du pays: »Pour en avoir de l'eau, il faut entrer par le milieu des portes«; c'est-à-dire que, pour puiser dans la source même du *Gange*, il faut franchir quelqu'une de ces montagnes.

Langa.

Il est à cent soixante-dix lys au Nord de la ville de *Dakla*, et à trente-quatre lys au Sud-ouest du mont *Gangdis*. Sa largeur la plus grande est d'environ trois cens lys. C'est un des premiers bassins du lac *Mapinmou-talai*, dont les eaux, après avoir coulé quelque tems vers l'Est, s'amassent et forment le *Langa*. De celui-ci se forme la rivière qui coule vers l'Ouest sous le nom de *Langtchou*. L'eau de ce lac est très saine; elle est de couleur tirant sur le noir.

Yamrouk-youmdsou.[4]

Il est à l'Est de la ville de *Nagardsé*.[5] Sa plus grande largeur est de quatre cens soixante lys. Il environne trois montagnes, dont la première s'appelle *Minab*, la seconde *Yabtou*, et la troisième *Sangry*.[6] De ces montagnes coulent quantité des ruisseaux, dont les eaux rassemblées forment ce lac. Il produit une grande quantité de poissons dont les habitans du pays se nourissent. L'eau de ce lac n'a point de couleur fixé; on la voit tantôt blanche, tantôt verte et tantôt noirâtre: quelquefois même elle est très brillante et fait voir toutes les couleurs à la fois.

---

[1] gyu-mts'o, cigentlich = Saphir-(klarer)See. (Viele Seen sind schon vorher erwähnt worden.)
[2] ma-p'am talai, riesiges Meer (mo. — dalai).
[3] S. oben S. 42 Setledy (= Gangga).
[4] T. I. yü-mu-tsu = gyu-mts'o.
[5] Vgl. oben nag'ar-zung in Wei = sna-dkar rdsongs, weiße Nasenstadt.
[6] T. I. mi-na-pa, ya-po-t'u und sang-li.

Ghiamdsou[1]-Ghimdsou.

Au Nord-ouest de la ville de *Djangabrin*. Autrefois, au lieu d'un seul lac tel qu'on voit aujourd'hui, il y en avait deux, dont l'un s'appellait *Ghiamdsou*, et l'autre *Ghimdsou*.[2] Ces deux lacs s'étant réunis en un seul, on a voulu perpétuer la mémoire de son origine, en lui donnant le nom qu'il porte, lequel n'est autre chose que les deux noms réunis. Sa largeur n'est que de soixante lys. Il est très poissonneux.

Lamdsou-simdsou.

Il est à cent vingt lys au Nord-est de la ville d'*Aridsoung*. Sa plus grande étendue est Nord et Sud; elle est d'environ deux cens vingt lys. Il reçoit un ruisseaux qui vient du côté du Nord, et il en reçoit quatre qui viennent du côté du Sud.

Darouk-youmdsou.[3]

Il est à cinq cens cinquante lys au Nord-est des nomades de *Djéba* de la province de *Tsang*. Sa plus grande étendue est d'environ deux cent quatre-vingt lys. Du côté de l'Ouest, il reçoit les eaux d'une rivière qu'on appelle *Nasoui*, laquelle, après un cours de cinq cens lys, vient se perdre dans ce lac. Du côté du Midi, il reçoit dix autres petites rivières qui viennent des montagnes.

Lac de sel Djabouye-saga.[4]

Il est à cent vingt lys de distance au Nord du précédent. Sa plus grande étendue est de cent cinquante lys. Il produit du sel blanc: les habitans du pays des environs n'en mangent pas d'autre. Auprès de ce lac, du côté du Nord, il y en a un autre, qu'on appelle *Langbou*[5], dont l'étendue est de deux cens vingt lys.

Djamtse-Louynak.

Il est à quatre cens dix lys au Nord-ouest des nomades de *Djochout*. Il n'a que dix lys dans sa plus grande largeur. On trouve dans le fond de ce lac du borax en grande quantité.

Lac de sel Goungnoum-tsaga et onze autres.[6]

Au Nord-ouest de *Lassa*, à la distance d'environ sept cens lys, il se trouve plusieurs lacs salés, qui ne sont pas bien éloignés les uns des autres. Ils sont au nombre de onze:

> le premier est *Goungnoum-tsaga*,
> le second *Liyar-tsaga*,
> le troisième *Lioubou*[7]*-tsaga*,
> le quatrième *Yaghen-tsaga*,
> le cinquième *Namoyor*[8]*-tsaga*,
> le sixième *Kougoung-tsaga*,
> le septième *Bilo-tsaga*,
> le huitième *Ghiamsen*[9]*-tsaga*,
> le neuvième *Martsaga*.[10]

[1] rgya-mts'o, großer See.

[2] Nach T. I. war der erstere der östliche, der andere der westliche.

[3] rta-rog yu-mis'o; nach der bei Z. gegebenen chinesischen Erklärung soll rta-rog ein gelbes Pferd bedeuten und der See nach einem Uferfelsen von besonderer Form und Farbe benannt sein.

[4] Nach T. I. ch'a-pu-ych sa-ka. Die Silbe sa in sa-ga ist jedenfalls wie unten tsa in tsaga das tibetische Wort tswa für Salz. tswa-k'a ist eine »Salzmine«.

[5] glang-bu mts'o, Kalbersee.

[6] Nach T. I. heißt es »zehn andere«.

[7] T. I. lü-pu.

[8] T. I. na-mu o-yo-rh; namu ist vielleicht das von einer Karte übernommene mandschurische Wort für »See«.

[9] T. I. chia-mu-ts'o-mu.

[10] T. I. ma-li ts'a-ka.

Ces neuf lacs sont près des bords de la rivière *Yarghia-tsangbou*. Les plus grands peuvent avoir cent quatre-vingt-dix à deux cens lys de largeur, et les plus petits environ cinquante ou soixante. Ils produisent tous du sel, qui fait un objet de commerce parmi les gens du pays. Ce sel est blanc, à l'exception de celui qu'on tire des deux lacs *Kougoung-tsaga* et *Namoyor-tsaga*, qui est d'un rouge tirant sur le rouge.[1] Il y a encore quelques autres lacs dont on n'a pas marqué les noms, parce que le sel qu'on en tire n'est pas, à beaucoup près, aussi bon que celui qu'on tire des autres qu'on vient de nommer, ni en aussi grande quantité. Le sel de tous ces lacs est le seul dont on se sert à *Lassa*.[2]

Tengri-noor.

Il est à deux cens vingt lys au Nord-ouest de *Lassa*. C'est apparémment le plus grand lac qu'il y ait dans ce pays, puisqu'on lui donne plus de mille lys de tour, sur un diamètre d'environ six cens lys. Sa plus grande largeur est d'Orient en Occident. Les Mongols appellent le *ciel* du mot de *Tengri*. Ils appellent de même ce lac, comme s'ils disaient le lac du ciel. Il appartient au pays de *Tsang*. Apparémment que ses eaux ont une couleur à peu près semblable à celle du ciel. Du côté de l'Est il reçoit les eaux de trois rivières, qu'on appelle toutes trois d'un même nom, qui est *Dchakhassoutai;* et du côté de l'Ouest, il reçoit les rivières *Losa* et *Targou-tsangbou*.[3] Ils coulent quelques centaines de lys et se jettent dans ce lac.

---

[1] Lies *noir*.

[2] Bei T. I. steht nur, daß die Bewohner von Lhasa sich dieses Salzes bedienen.

[3] Nach T. I. müßte der erste der drei Flüsse Tchakhassoutai, der letzte Dargou-tsangbou heißen. Der erste Name ist sicher mongolisch (vielleicht tsagasun, Papier) und deutet wegen der palatalen Schreibung auf eine mandschurische Kartenvorlage. Losa 羅𬴂 könnte »Maultier« bedeuten, die mongolisierte Form des chinesischen Wortes lo-tzĕ 騾子.

DES GUÉS DU THIBET.[1]

Pour aller de la *Chine* au *Thibet*, on part de *Si-ning-fou*, on se rend sur les frontières des *Mongols*, nomades du lac *Khoukhou-noor*, on passe la montagne *Bayan-khara-dabahn*, et on entre dans la province d'*Ouei* par le Nord-est. Pour faire ce trajet, on trouve bien des rivières, qui arrêteraient tout court les voyageurs, s'ils n'étaient au fait des lieux où on peut les passer. Il y en a cinq qu'on peut passer a gué, et quatre qu'on ne peut passer qu'en bateau. Voici les noms et la position de tous ces passages.

1. *Khara-oudjour*[2] pour traverser la rivière *Akdam* dans les endroits qui sont près de sa source.

2. *Khourkha*[3], où l'on traverse la rivière *Mourous-oussou* dans les endroits qui sont près de sa source. Ces deux rivières *Mourous-oussou* et *Akdam* se passent à pied et à cheval, suivant qu'on approche plus ou moins de leurs sources. Les lieux désignés sont en tout tems les plus sûrs.

3. *Baidou*.[4] Il est au Nord-est de *Khourkha*, et il sert pour passer la rivière *Mourous-oussou* dans un autre endroit.

4. *Dolon-Olom*[5], à l'endroit où *Mourous-oussou* change son cours de l'Ouest vers le Sud. C'est-là que cette rivière se partage en sept branches; c'est pourquoi on appelle ce lieu du nom de *Dolon-Olom*. Quoique l'eau, ainsi partagée, semble présenter plusieurs gués, il faut être cependant sur ses gardes, surtout après les pluies et les fontes de neiges.

5. *Bamboule*.[6] Il est à l'Est du précédent, apparémment pour passer encore la rivière *Mourous-oussou*.

Ces cinq gués peuvent se passer en tout tems ou à pied ou à cheval. Il n'en est pas de même des lieux dont je vais parler, et qui sont au nombre de quatre, comme je l'ai dit plus haut.

Le premier s'appelle *Yke-koukousair*. Il est au Midi de *Bamboule*, à la distance d'environ cent lys. En hiver et au printems on peut le passer à cheval, mais en été et en automne, on le passe sur des bateaux de peaux, qu'on trouve là toujours prêts.

---

[1] Dieser Abschnitt und der folgende decken sich fast vollständig mit T. I. 津梁 ching-liang »Furten und Brücken».

[2] Die Bedeutung des zweiten Wortes ist nicht feststellbar.

[3] Geht vielleicht auf das mandschurische Wort hôlha zurück, das Dieb, Räuber und im Kriege den Feind bedeutet. Der Name mag auf irgendein Gefecht hindeuten, das einer der mandschurischen Generale Sereng, Erentei und Yansin im Tibetfeldzug 1718—20 dort mit den Dsungaren gehabt haben könnte.

[4] T. I. 拜都, vielleicht eine Rückumschreibung aus dem Mongolischen von dem chinesischen 白波 pai tu, «Weiße Furt».

[5] = mo. dolugan olom, Sieben Furten.

[6] T. I. pa-mu-pu-lo = bamba la?

Le second s'appelle *Bakhan-koukousair*[1]; le troisième, appellé en Chinois *Pe-tha-tou* ou le gué de la pyramide blanche, ce que les Mongols rendent par *Tchakhan-soubarkhan-olom* et le quatrième *Darkhan-koubou*.[3] Ils sont sur les frontières des nomades de *Khou-khou-noor*. Les quatre passages sont en remontant le *Kin-cha-kiang*. L'eau en est très profond.

Les passages qui se trouvent dans le département des *Tsang* sont au nombre de trois: le premier est à quarante lys au Nord-est de la ville de *Jikadsé* et s'appelle *Dakdjouka*[4]: le second appellé *Lodsé* est au Sud-est de la ville de *Djangludsé* et porte le nom de cette même ville; le troisième est à quatre-vingt lys au Sud-est de la ville de *Saka*[5], et s'appelle *Ghinghia-djouka*. Ces trois passages se font sur des bateaux, qu'on tient toujours prêts sur les lieux.

Les passages pour aller chez les *Kamou*, sont

1. *Birmadjou-soum*.[6] On traverse le *Ya-Loung-kiang* à deux cens sept lys au Sud-ouest de *Ta-thsian-lou*.[7] C'est le chemin ordinaire des étrangers de l'Ouest, qui viennent pour acheter des feuilles de thé sur les frontières de la Chine.

2. *Dayan-tsounggour*.[8] Il est sur le *Kin-cha-kiang*, à trois cens quatre-vingt lys au Nord de la ville de *Goundjouk*.[9] Les *Kamou* prennent ce chemin quand ils vont au lac *Khoukhou-noor*.

3. *Dsedjous*[10], pour traverser le *Kin-cha-kiang*. Il est à soixante dix lys au Sud-ouest de *Batang*. C'est par là que les *Thibétains* viennent à *Tatsien-lou*.

4. *Mepoudjok*, pour traverser le *Kin-cha-kiang*, à soixante lys au Nord-ouest de *Ly-kiang-fou*[11] du *Yun-nan*. Les *Kamou* prennent ce chemin quand ils entrent dans la Chine. Il n'y a aucun de ces passages qui puisse se faire à gué: ils se font tous sur des bateaux de peaux.

---

[1] = mo. Groß- und Klein-kükü dsair; kükü ist blau, dsair ist »der Eisgang«.

[2] Lies soubourkhan.

[3] darhan ist eine mongolische Rangstufe, die mit Steuerfreiheit verbunden ist, koubou vielleicht = mo. köbün (köbegün), Kind = Darhan-Sohn.

[4] Die beiden letzten Silben sind vielleicht das tibetische é'u-k'a = Flußufer, das wir auch in den Namen Hor-é'u-k'a und Nag-é'u-k'a finden. Z. gibt für den ersten Ortsnamen die tibetische Form Hor-'jug-k'a, »vor alters Wohnort der Mongolen«.

[5] Nach T. I. lies Saga 薩嘎.

[6] Die letzte Silbe ist jedenfalls das tibetische gsum = drei.

[7] Willkürliche Schreibung.

[8] T. I. ta-yen ch'ung-ku-rh.

[9] Nach T. I. lies Goundjok (kun-cho-k'o).

[10] Nach T. I. lies Dsedjoussou (tzé-chu-su).

[11] Pl. 3737 vgl. oben.

DES PONTS DU THIBET.

Les ponts qui se trouvent dans le Thibet sont de trois sortes: de pierres, de bois et de chaînes de fer. Les ponts de pierre sont faits là comme on les fait ailleurs; il en est de même des ponts de bois. Pour ce qui est des ponts faits avec des chaines de fer, voici comme on m'en a expliqué la construction. Sur chacun des bords de la rivière, on fixe, d'une manière solide, autant de crampons de fer qu'on veut tendre de chaînes de fer sur la surface de l'eau; on accroche chaque chaîne à son crampon, et quand le nombre des chaines est complet, on les couvre d'épaisses planches, ou de simples troncs d'arbres non encore façonnés qu'on place en travers et qu'on attache l'un contre l'autre de manière qu'ils ne puissent pas se séparer. On met sur tout cela un pouce ou deux de terre ou de sable, et le pont se trouve ainsi fait.

DES PONTS QUI SONT DANS LA PROVINCE D'OUEI.

1. Pont de *Phengdo*, pour passer la rivière de *Dam*, à l'Ouest de la ville de *Phengdo*. Il est fait avec des chaines de fer.

2. *Koukou*, pont de pierre du côté de Nord-ouest de *Lassa*.

3. *Rouy*[1], pont de chaines de fer pour passer le *Yarou-tsangbou*[2] à trente lys au Midi de la ville de *Dakbon-Ghimi*.

4. *Ona*, pont de chaînes de fer pour passer le *Gardjao-mouren*, à vingt lys au Nord de la ville de *Mergourga*.[3]

5. *Tchysam*, pont de bois sur la rivière *Yangbadsian*, à sept lys au Sud-ouest de la ville de *Doungor*.

6. *Djououri*[4], pont fait avec des chaînes de fer, pour passer le *Yarou-tsangbou*, à quatorze lys au Sud-ouest de la ville de *Tchoussous*.[5]

Quand les distances ne sont pas marquées, les ponts dont on parle alors, sont ou aux environs ou dans les villes mêmes.

---

[1] T. I. Lu-i.
[2] Hier hat die alte Ausgabe des T. I. die Silbe *tsang* fortgelassen, sie schreibt ya-lu-pu-chiang.
[3] Nach T. I. lies Mergounga.
[4] Nach T. I. lies Tchou-ou-li (ch'u-wu-li).
[5] Nach T. I. lies Tchouchour (ch'u-shu-rh).

DES PONTS QUI SONT DANS LA PROVINCE DE TSANG.

1. Le pont de *Doungor* est de bois et sert pour passer du bord du lac *Yamrouk* à une île montagneuse qui se trouve dans ce lac.[1] Il est à quarante lys au Sud-est de la ville de *Nagardsé*.

2. *Lassa-djouga*.[2] Il est fait avec des chaînes de fer pour passer le *Yarou-tsangbou*, à vingt lys au Nord-ouest de la ville de *Rinben*.[3]

3. *Djakar*[4]-*djachidsai*. Il est fait avec des chaînes de fer et se trouve au bord du fleuve *Yarou-tsangbou*, à soixante lys à l'Est de la ville de *Pangsoukling*.[5]

4. *Soumghia*, pont de pierre pour passer le *Niantchou*, à quatre lys au Sud-est de la ville de *Jikadsé*. La longueur de ce pont est de plus de sept cens toises: il a dix-neuf arches.

5. *Sangar-djaksam*, pont fait avec des chaînes de fer pour passer le *Oitchou*, à cent lys au Nord-ouest de la ville de *Pangsoukling*. A côté de ce pont il y en a un autre de la même construction, qu'on appelle *Mokbou-djaksam*.[6]

DES PONTS QUI SONT DANS LE PAYS DES KAMOU.

1. *Souksam*, pont de bois pour passer le *Khara-oussou*, à soixante-dix lys de la ville de *Soukdsoung*.[7]

2. *Djamyasamba*[8], pour passer le *Khara-oussou*, à quatre-vingt lys au Nord-est de la ville de *Loroungdsoung*.

3. *Djachidaksam*[9], pour passer le *Lang-thsang-kiang*, en remontant vers sa source, à cent vingt lys au Nord-est de la ville de *Dsatsorgang*.[10]

---

[1] Bei T. J. steht nichts von einer Insel.
[2] Nach T. J. lies Sala-djouga.
[3] Nach T. J. lies Linben oder Rinben.
[4] Nach T. J. lies Tchakar.
[5] Nach T. J. lies Pensoukling (tib. p'un-tsogs gling, Ort der Fülle der Vollkommenheiten)?
[6] Nach T. J. lies Moukbou djaksam.
[7] Nach T. J. lies Soksam und Sokdsoung.
[8] samba = tib. zam-pa, »Brücke«. Auch bei den andern Namen haben wir in der Endsilbe sam immer dies selbe Wort zu sehen.
[9] Nach T. J. lies Djachidakdsam.
[10] Nach T. J. lies Dsadsoligang.

Es seien hierunter zum Schluß einige ergänzende Notizen über Furten und Brücken angefügt, die dem Wei-Tsang t'ung-chih, Buch II, entnommen sind:

Über den Tsang-pu chiang (Yaru tsangpo) gibt es unterhalb von Daktse-deking (ta-tse-tè-ch'ing) beim Torauslaß (d. h. wohl: wo er aus Tibet austritt) eine Holzfähre als Passiergelegenheit.

Am Kara Usu gibt es acht Tagemärsche nördlich von Lhasa einen Fellbootverkehr.

Am Pangdo-Fluß gibt es drei Tagemärsche nördlich von Lhasa eine Kettenbrücke und auch Fellboote.

Der Nu-chiang (vgl. oben S. 43) ist bei seinem reißenden und wildbewegten Wasser nicht zu überschreiten.

9. IX, 4.

Am Yeh-tang-Fluß findet sich 185 Meilen von Lhasa entfernt eine Kettenbrücke, die aber jetzt zerfallen ist. Dafür sind Fellboote zur Überfahrt vorhanden.

Der Chin-sha-chiang (vgl. oben S. 45) hat sehr viele Überfahrtsstellen. Bei Ch'un-k'o, Kung-t'o chu-ch'ia und Niu-ho-chu-pa-lung dienen als Fähren Holzschiffe, die von Beamten und Kaufleuten gemeinsam eingerichtet worden sind. Sonst sind es überall Fellboote.

Der Li-chu-Fluß hat etwa zehn Meilen oberhalb Litang eine Brücke, sang-pa (= tib. zam-pa), welche die große Straße nach Batang hinüberführt. Einige 60 Meilen unterhalb bei gyangdsung (chiang-tsung) ist eine Brücke, die gleichfalls sang-pa heißt.

Der Yalung-Fluß hat bei seinem Eintritt in das Gebiet von Hor nur Fellboote als Fähren. Der Kolonialpräfekt Lin Tsung-au 林琮安, der nach Gandun kam, bewerkstelligte seinen Übergang nach Derge mit Holzfähren und Fellbooten und geradeswegs nach Tschamdo. Bei Ober-, Mittel- und Unter-Dschaba bedient man sich ebenfalls der Boote aus Ochsenhaut für die Überfahrt nach Dschandui und Lagun. Auf der oberen und mittleren Fährstelle hat man Holzboote und Fellboote für die Überfahrt nach Litang. Bei der unteren Fährstelle bedient man sich ebenfalls der Boote aus Ochsenhaut zur Überfahrt nach dem Lande des Mu-li-Häuptlings von Hui-yen-ying 會鹽營, sowie nach dem Gebiete von Chung-tien in Yünnan.

DAS GOLDSTROMLAND

IM CHINESISCH-TIBETISCHEN GRENZGEBIETE,

NACH DEM GROSSEN KRIEGSWERK VOM JAHRE 1781 DARGESTELLT

VON

ERICH HÄNISCH

MIT FÜNF AUFNAHMEN DES VERFASSERS UND DREI KARTENTAFELN

»Der Goldstrom ist der Oberlauf des Goldsandflusses.[1] Außerhalb des Gebietes von *Sung-p'an*[2] entspringt ein Fluß namens *Ts'u-ch'in* 促 浸, der über *Tang-pa* in das Land der Eingeborenenfürsten eintritt, von außerordentlicher Tiefe und Breite. Das ist der Große Goldstrom. Daneben gibt es einen andern namens *Tsan-na* 借 納, mit näherer Quelle. Das ist der Kleine Goldstrom. Beide führen (diese) ihre Namen nach den in den Bergen nahe den Ufern vorkommenden Golderzen. Beide Flüsse haben eine Richtung von Nordost nach Südwest. Im Gebiete des Fürsten von *Ming-cheng* vereinigen sie sich zu dem Flusse *Jo-shui* 若 水 von *Ning-yüan-fu*[3], der später in *Hui-li-chou*[4] den Namen *Chin-sha chiang* führt = Goldsandfluß oder auch *Lu-shui* 瀘 水. In der Zeit der *Sui* wurde der Verwaltungsbezirk Goldstrom aufgestellt. Das war das Außenland (Hinterland) von *Jan-mang* der *Han*-Zeit und das Gebiet *Wei-chou*[5] der *Tang*-Zeit. Zur Zeit der *Ming* wurde das Land dem Kolonialpräfekten von *Tsa-ku* unterstellt: Ein Land von steil aufragenden zahllosen Bergen, zwischen denen sich reißende Bergströme dahinwinden. Das Land der Fellboote und der Seilbrücken. Der Strom ist gewunden und geknickt wie ein Faden. Die Berge sind wild[6] und kalt. Es gibt viel Regen und Schnee. Der Boden bringt nur Hirse und Buchweizen. Die Wohnungen der Eingeborenen bestehen alle aus steinernen Türmen. In dem Lande greifen die Gebiete der neun Eingeborenenfürsten ineinander. . . . .«

Das ist die kurze Beschreibung des Landes, die der Schriftsteller WEI YÜAN 魏 源 seiner Darstellung des Eroberungsfeldzuges, im 7. Buche der bekannten *Kriegsgeschichte der Mandschudynastie* 聖 武 記[7], vorausschickt.

Das Goldstromland, gelegen etwa zwischen den Längengraden 101—103 in der Breite 31—32, ist unserer Kenntnis kaum länger als zwanzig Jahre erschlossen: HOSIE hat es in den britischen Konsularberichten beschrieben, ALBERT TAFEL hat ihm ein Kapitel seines schönen Werkes[8] gewidmet, und die Mitglieder der STÖTZNER'schen Reise vom Jahre 1914 haben es verschiedentlich besprochen.[9] Auch die Missionare haben das Land seit ihrer Niederlassung in *Tatsien-lu* zu Beginn des Jahrhunderts wiederholt besucht[10]:

---

[1] Chin-sha chiang (Kinsha-kiang).

[2] Plf. 5977. Die chinesischen Städtenamen werden nach den Nummern von PLAYFAIR, *Cities and towns of China*, 2. Aufl., Shanghai 1910, aufgeführt (hier durch die Abkürzung Plf. bezeichnet).

[3] Plf. 4714.

[4] Plf. 2341.

[5] Plf. 7001.

[6] Eigentlich »tief«.

[7] sheng-wu chi erschienen 1842.

[8] *Meine Tibetreise*, Stuttgart 1914, Bd. II, Kap. 15.

[9] Vgl. O. ISRAEL im *Jahrbuch des Vereins für Chinesische Sprache und Landeskunde*, Schanghai 1917—18, S. 36—53.

[10] Vgl. hierzu J. H. EDGAR, *The marches of the Mantze*, China Inland Mission 1908.

Und doch ist von dem unwegsamen Lande, das den Gegenstand dieses Aufsatzes bildet, bisher nicht viel mehr bekannt als die durchlaufenden Verkehrsstraßen und die an diesen liegenden chinesischen Handels- und Militärkolonien. Denn sein Inneres ist Europäern wie Chinesen gleich unzugänglich.

Zwei mächtige Bergpässe von viereinhalbtausend Meter Höhe leiten von China her in das Gebiet hinüber: Von Osten aus der Richtung *Ch'eng-tu—Kuan-hsien* der *Banlau* und von Süden aus der Richtung *Tatsienlu* der *Dabo*. Man ist diesen steilen Berg aus einem bewaldeten Tale emporgestiegen, um von seiner Paßhöhe den wunderbaren Rundblick zu genießen, den uns TAFEL auf Bild XII seines I. Bandes vor Augen stellt. Dann geht es drüben hinunter durch steinige Halden, breite Wiesen und tiefe Wälder[1] immer an dem Bergbache entlang, der einen bei der Feste *Rumi Dschanggu* an den Goldstrom führt. Auf steil abfallendem Felsufer steht ein mächtiger Kampfturm. — Solche Türme bilden das Wahrzeichen des Goldstromlandes. — Von Norden kommt der Große Goldstrom dahergebraust[1], um hier den vom Berg *Dabo* kommenden Westfluß aufzunehmen, unten am Felsen hart nach Osten umzubrechen und nach einer kurzen Strecke seine Bahn wieder südwärts zu suchen. Von dort führt er dann den Namen »Fluß der großen Fähre«, *Ta-tu-ho*. Wir haben ihn auf der riesigen eisernen Hängebrücke *Lu-ting-ch'iao* gekreuzt, zwei Tagereisen östlich von *Tatsienlu*, und seine braunen Wasser und wilden Ufer schon früher zwischen *Tse-ta-ti* und *Chin-k'ou* 金 口 auf seinem westöstlichen Laufe kennengelernt, wo er den Namen »Verbindungsfluß« *T'ung-ho* führt, haben auch seine Mündung in den *Min* bei der Stadt *Chia-ting*[2] gesehen, wo er selbst noch den klaren grünen *Ya*-Fluß empfangen hat mit den zierlichen Bambusflößen mit geschweiftem Bug und Heck. Dort, wo der Strom unterhalb von *Rumi Dschanggu* nach Süden umbiegt, nimmt er von Osten her den Kleinen Goldstrom auf, an dessen Ufer weiter aufwärts als wichtigste Kolonie und Garnison die Präfektur *Mou-kung* 懋 功 gelegen ist, das alte *Meino (Mi'i-no)*, der Sitz des Königs von *Zanla*.[3] Zieht man vom *Rumi Dschanggu* den Großen Goldstrom hinauf, so gelangt man durch die Fürstentümer *Badi* und *Bawang*[4] nach den chinesischen Kolonien *Ch'ung-hua* 崇 化 und *Sui-ching* 綏 靖, dies letztere die alte Burg *Lho'i* des Königs von *Tschutschen*: Ein wunderbar klarer Fluß, bald als reißendes Bergwasser zwischen dichtbewaldeten steilen Felsen, bald still und freundlich zwischen flachen Ufern dahinströmend. Am Strande bald besetzt mit anmutigen Siedlungen, weißen Häusern mit Fenstern und Balkonen, die aus der Ferne wie hübsche Villenstädte wirken, bald dicht besät mit drohenden Kampftürmen, jetzt ohne Brücken, nur durch Fellboote überschreitbar. Diese beiden Flußläufe, die das Goldstromland, chinesisch *Chin-ch'uan* 金 川, durchqueren, sind durch die mächtige Masse des Berges *Gunggar* getrennt, den man übersteigen muß, um vom *Tschutschen*- nach dem *Zanla*-Land zu gelangen, an einem den Fuß des Berges bewachenden Turme vorbei, mit

---

[1] Siehe Pl. I, Fig. 5 u. 4.

[2] Pl. 705.

[3] Die Schreibung der Ortsnamen in dieser Arbeit beruht, soweit es sich um chinesische oder nur chinesisch überlieferte Formen handelt, auf dem WADEschen System und ist dann an der Silbentrennung und den Bindestrichen kenntlich. Tibetische Namen erscheinen, soweit bekannt, vollgeschrieben und gleichfalls in Silbentrennung nach der Schreibung von JÄSCHKES Wörterbuch oder, nach der Aussprache, wie sie die mandschurische Quelle überliefert, hier nach der Schreibung von GABELENTZ' Mandschu-deutschem Wörterbuch wiedergegeben. Also *Tsan-na* oder *Tsan-la* (chinesisch nach WADE), *btsan-lha* (tibetische Vollschreibung nach JÄSCHKE), *Zanla* (mandschurische Lautschreibung nach GABELENTZ). In der Einleitung sind einige Namen auch in Lautschrift mit deutschen Werten gebracht, wie *Dschanggu* und *Tschutschen*, die später nach der Umschreibung aus dem Mandschu als *Janggu* und *Cucin* erscheinen.

[4] Siehe Pl. I, Fig. 1—3.

ständiger Steigung über die an den Abhängen hingebreiteten Waldungen und Matten mit den weidenden Herden von Pferden und Bergrindern, bis man am Abend die Fünftausend-Meter-Paßhöhe erreicht. Ähnlich liegt der Paß *Banlan*, der uns in östlicher Richtung aus dem Hochgebirge entläßt. Dicht unterhalb des Übergangs finden wir hier eine breite Ebene, genannt *Wan-jen-fên* »Massengrab«, zur Erinnerung an eine der blutigsten Schlachten (chinesischen Niederlagen) aus dem Eroberungskriege. In diesem Lande zwischen den Bergen *Dabo* und *Banlan*, das von den Chinesen als *ts'ao-ti*, »Grasland«, bezeichnet wird, findet sich das chinesische Element, meist Einwanderer aus der Provinz *Hupei*, in den wenigen Flecken als Beamte, Soldaten und Händler in gutgezimmerten Holzhäusern, als Siedler nur verstreut im Tale angebaut. Demgegenüber die Eingeborenen in festen Steinhäusern, *chai-tzĕ* genannt, mit Außenfenstern und Balkonen, flachen mit Gebets-flaggen geschmückten Dächern, die von außen auf eingekerbten Baumstämmen erstiegen werden. Die Bewohner, ein hochgewachsenes stämmiges Bergvolk, gekleidet in Turban, Rock, tibetische weite Hose, Sandalen, mit umschnürten Unterschenkeln oder in tibetischen rotschäftigen Lederstiefeln. Von Beruf sind sie fast durchweg Viehzüchter. Sie werden zu den weiter unten zu besprechenden 18 Eingeborenenstämmen gezählt und gehören ethnologisch wohl zu den Tibetern. Doch sind sie sicher keine reine tibetische Rasse, sondern gehen in weitem Maße auf die Urbevölkerungsschicht zurück, möchten also viel-leicht zu den Lolos und auch zu den Wildstämmen der Yünnan-Provinz Beziehungen auf-weisen. Es fehlt aber noch Klarheit über diese Frage. Sie besitzen noch ihre alte Volks-religion, die auch als *Bon* bezeichnet und von den »schwarzen Lamas« vertreten wird. Doch überwiegt die gelbe Kirche und damit auch die tibetische Kultur. Ihre Landes-sprache unterscheidet sich beträchtlich vom Hochtibetischen. Die geographischen Namen im Lande sind daher durchaus alle mit dem Tibetischen zu lösen. Selbst da, wo wir sie in tibetischer Schrift erhalten haben, mag es sich oft um eine lautliche Wieder-gabe nichttibetischer Eingeborenenwörter handeln. Der Schreiber des Aufsatzes stellte u. a. manche sprachliche Sonderheiten fest, von denen einige Beispiele hierunter gegeben seien: Zahlenreihe 1—10 *zi 'ŋ̍ su 'ḍa mña 'tchüĕ zniĕ li ṅga zra*, 11 *ŏwrĕ*, 12 *ŏmñĕ*, 13 *ŏsŭ*, 20 *äwḍa*, 30 *śu-sk'a*, 40 *'ḷa-sk'a*, 100 *ŏ-śĕ*, Wasser *u-śa*, Haus *yŏ*, Butter *stŏ*, Mensch *dsĩ*, Pferd *rĩ*, Maultier *drc*, Rind *hsŭ*, Hund *k'a*, Buch *ŏmñä*.[1] Hier ist die Ver-wandtschaft mit dem Hochtibetischen zu erkennen bei den Zahlen 1, 2, 3 und 5. Das Wort *dre* für Maultier ist rein tibetisch. Die andern Wörter sind alle fremd. Es wird in dem der Arbeit zugrunde gelegten großen Kriegswerke berichtet, daß die in den Meldungen erwähnten Ortsnamen zum großen Teile in Peking, wahrscheinlich von den dortigen amtlichen Dolmetschern für das Tibetische, nicht verstanden und bei der Anfertigung von Karten dem *Tschangkia Hutuktu*, dem lamaistischen Nuntius in Peking, zur Feststellung vorgelegt worden seien. Dieser habe sie dann gelöst und in die richtige Form gebracht. Tatsächlich wird er ihnen dabei wohl Gewalt angetan und damit den Wert der Karten, die uns übrigens noch nicht bekanntgeworden sind und jedenfalls noch in den Pekinger Archiven ruhen, stark beein-trächtigt haben. Jedenfalls dürfte bei Abweichungen die Schreibung in den Original-berichten vom Kriegsschauplatz vorzuziehen sein. Daß dort bei der Aufzeichnung der Ortsnamen sehr sorgfältig zu Werke gegangen wurde, bezeugt ein Kaiserlicher Erlaß an den Generalstab vom Tage *jen-tzĕ* des I. Monats 37. Jahres der Regierung KIENLUNG (1772)[2]:

---

[1] *c* ist hier der französische Laut, die Silbe *tchüĕ* deutsch zu sprechen, *hsŭ* nach WADE.
[2] Buch XVI des Kriegswerks, S. 53/54.

Die mir von General KUEI LIN 桂林 eingereichte Landkarte der Eingeborenenfürsten weist in den Ortsnamen zahlreiche Irrtümer auf. Da unter den nicht feststellbaren Eingeborenen-Ortsnamen viele sind, bei denen man im allgemeinen die tanggutische[1] Sprache zugrunde legen kann, so habe ich den *Tschangkia Hutuktu* beauftragt, sie im einzelnen zu vergleichen und in die mandschurische Sprache zu übertragen. Danach habe ich sie nach sorgfältiger Nachprüfung in den Plan eingezeichnet. Man soll dies den Generalen WENFU und KUEI LIN mitteilen und sie anweisen, daß sie von jetzt ab in den Fällen, wo man die betreffenden Formen solcher Orte in tibetischer Schrift nicht verstehen kann, die Aussprache der Namen bei den Eingeborenen der betreffenden Plätze genau erkunden und dann in mandschurischer Umschreibung wiedergeben.

Da in diese mandschurischen Karten sicherlich auch manche mandschurische Bezeichnungen aufgenommen worden sind, die nach dem Muster der Vorgänge bei der sonstigen chinesischen Kolonialkartographie fälschlich als Bestandteile der Ortsnamen in chinesische Karten übergegangen sein mögen, soll hierunter eine kurze Probe der mandschurischen geographischen Nomenklatur gegeben werden:

alin Berg	*buten, cikin* Abhang	*kamni* Engpaß, Schlucht
hada Felsen	*meifehe* Abhang	*ula, bira* Fluß
wehe Stein	*hailashon* steiler Abhang	*yohoron* Bergspalte, Bergstrom
dekcu Anhöhe	*haiha* schräge Bergseite	*birgan* Graben
ala Hochfläche	*haksan* steile, gefährliche Stelle	*dalin, ekcin* Ufer
cokcohon, eneshun Hügel	*antu* Vorderseite (Sonnenseite)	*holo* Tal
cokcihiyan Felsgipfel	des Berges	*šeri, sekiyen* Quelle
fiyeleku Gipfel	*boso, gencehen* Rückseite des	*hôcin* Brunnen
fisa Rücken	Berges	*bujan, šuwa* Wald
oyo Dach	*dooha* Brücke	*omo* See

Das Goldstromgebiet wird, wie oben gesagt, oft mit dem Namen »Land der 18 Eingeborenenfürsten«, *shih-pa t'u-sze* 十八土司, belegt. Die Namen dieser 18 Fürsten bzw. Eingeborenenstämme, deren Länder übrigens zum Teil an das eigentliche Goldstromgebiet nur gerade heranreichen, werden kaum an zwei Stellen gleichlautend aufgeführt. Das hat seinen Grund zum Teil darin, daß in den letzten 200 Jahren manche Stämme verschwunden, unterworfen, andere wieder gespalten sind. Auf der beigegebenen Übersichtskarte aus den Kaiserlichen Handbüchern *Ta-Ch'ing hui-tien* 大清會典[2] ist nur eine beschränkte Anzahl aufgeführt.

Das dieser Arbeit zugrunde gelegte Kriegswerk ergibt folgende Namen: *Cucin, Zanla, Okši,* drei *Zagu (Somo, Jokz'ai, Sunggak), Cosgiyab, Gebšiza, Kungsa, Mašu, Burakdi (= Badi), Bawang, Yüko, Damba, Giyalung, Muping, Mingjeng* und *Wasse.* Das wären 18. Außerdem werden noch aufgeführt im Westen *Hor ganze, Jandui* und *Derget* und schließlich die kleineren Stämme *Cowe, Beli, Narincang* und *Iomo.* Im Laufe der Zeit haben sich wie gesagt manche Stämme verschoben, manche sind in andern aufgegangen. Der englische Reisende COLBORNE BABER hat folgende Stämme erfragt, von denen allerdings nur wenige Schreibungen auf obige Namen zurückgeführt werden können: *Dji-la (= Ja-la? = Mingjeng), Mu-p'ing, Djia-k'a?, Wo-je (Okši), Rabten* »which includes Tsen-la« *(Zanla), Tam-ba (Damba), So-mung (Somo), Djiu-tse (Jokz'ai?), Zur-ga (Sunggak?), Tchro-shiop (Cosgiyab?), Pa-ung (Bawang), Tchra-tin?, Gé-shie (Gebšiza), Mazu (Mašu), Kung-sar, Pé-ré (Bele), Tchran-go (Janggu), Djé-gu (Zagu?).*

[1] d. h. tibetische.
[2] s. Pl. II.

Die Stötznersche Expedition, die eine Skizze der Stammeswohnsitze mitgebracht hat, errechnet die Zahl 18 durch Einbeziehung der weit nördlich, zum Teil schon im *Kansu*-Gebiet wohnenden *Ngolok* und *Ngaba*, sowie einiger chinesischer Verwaltungsbezirke, die an sich mit der Stammeseinteilung nichts zu tun haben. Es mag eben die alte Zahl 18 gar nicht mehr vorhanden sein.

Wei Yüan spricht in seiner Eroberungsgeschichte des Landes von nur 9 Fürsten bzw. Stämmen. Von diesen waren in der Eroberungszeit die beiden bedeutendsten die *Zanla* am Kleinen und die *Cucin* am Großen Goldstrom. Die *Zanla*, von den Chinesen mit den Zeichen 贊 拉 *tsan-la*, oder auch 贊 納 *tsan-na* nach der mundartlichen Aussprache der aus *Hupei* stammenden Siedler, wiedergegeben, schreiben ihren Namen im Tibetischen, nach den Steininschriften, *btsan-lha* mit der Bedeutung »Dämonen«. Der Name *Cucin*, von Wei Yüan durch die Zeichen 促 浸 *ts'u-ch'in* umschrieben, denen ebenfalls *Hupei*-Mundart zugrunde liegt, ist nichts anderes als das tibetische *c'u-c'en (tschu-tschen)*, »Großes Wasser«, die Bezeichnung für den Großen Goldstrom. Nach der chinesischen Verwaltungseinteilung unterstehen die nördlichen und östlichen Teile des Gebietes den Präfekturen *Li-fan (Mao-chou)* und *Chiung-chou*[1], die südlichen der Präfektur *Ya-chou*[2] der chinesischen Provinz *Szetschuan;* die westlichen leiten in das Hinterland der Provinz über und werden von dem Kolonialpräfekten in *Tatsienlu* verwaltet. Das eigentliche Goldstromland dagegen wird eingenommen von der Kolonialpräfektur *Mou-kung*[3] 懋 功, in der *Hupei*-Aussprache der Ansiedler *Mong-kung* gesprochen, die wieder in die Unterpräfekturen *Fu-pien* 撫 邊, *Ch'ung-hua* und *Sui-ching*[4], am Orte gesprochen *Ts'ung-hua* und *Hsü-ching*, zerfällt. Dieser Name *Hsü-ching* wird wieder mit der tibetischen Bezeichnung des Gebietsteiles *c'u-c'en* (s. o.) in Verbindung gebracht. In *Rumi Dschanggu* sitzt ein chinesischer Beamter, der dem Präfekten in *Tatsienlu* untersteht. Die Verteilung der Chinesen über das Land stellt sich folgendermaßen dar: An den Straßen und in den Marktplätzen finden sich chinesische Siedler als Herbergswirte und Transportunternehmer, meist Mohammedaner, sowie als Händler. Auch bei den großen Lamaklöstern gibt es oft ganze Straßen mit chinesischen Händlern und Gewerbetreibenden, die die Klöster mit ihren Bedürfnissen versorgen. Chinesische Ackerbauer sieht man nur sehr vereinzelt. Die Viehzucht scheint ausschließlich in den Händen der Eingeborenen zu liegen. In den Städten und Märkten überwiegen die Chinesen. Diese haben ihre chinesischen Häuser gebaut und führen ihr chinesisches Leben. Die Städte weisen dann neben den Amtsgebäuden auch chinesische Schulen und Tempel auf, etwa einen Kriegsgott-Tempel *Kuan-ti miao* 關 帝 廟 und einen Tempel der *Kuan-yin*. Öfter findet man einen Tempel des *Wu-hou* 武 侯, des Kriegsherzogs, worunter der berühmte General Chu-ko Liang 諸葛亮 aus der *Han*-Zeit verstanden wird, dem die Geschichte große Kriegstaten gegen die Eingeborenen dieser Gebiete zuschreibt. Die Häuser der Eingeborenen, die entweder in Dörfern zusammengeschlossen oder einzeln an den Bergen liegend erscheinen — im letztern Falle werden sie von den Chinesen als *chai-tzŏ* 寨 子, »Blockhäuser oder Burgen«, bezeichnet — unterscheiden sich von den chinesischen Gebäuden auf den ersten Blick durch ihre Fenster und Balkone. Weitere Wahrzeichen des Landes sind die lamaistischen Baudenkmäler: Tempel, Mönchsgräber, Gebetsmühlen, Hängebrücken und Fellboote und schließlich als besondere

---

[1] Plf. 3691, 4498, 1309.

[2] Plf. 7211.

[3] Plf. 4496.

[4] *Fu-pien* und *Sui-ching* sind Namen, die an die Unterwerfung der Grenzgebiete erinnern und sich auch in andern chinesischen Kolonialländern finden.

10. IX. 4.

Eigentümlichkeit der Gegend die großen Kampftürme, *de'o* genannt, chinesisch durch *tiao* 刁[周],
»steinernes Haus«, wiedergegeben, mandschurisch *yerutu*, die im Landschaftsbilde etwa die
chinesische Pagode vertreten.[1] Bei Kriegszustand gaben die Einwohner ihre Häuser und
Dörfer auf und verteidigten sich in diesen Türmen[2], die stets an wichtigen Geländepunkten
errichtet waren, manchmal einzeln wie der berühmte Turm bei *Marbang* (vgl. eine Aufnahme
des Verfassers in Tafels Buch, Bd. II, Taf. LV) oder in ganzen Reihen, wie auf dem ersten
Bilde[3] dieses Aufsatzes zu sehen. Es dürfte bekannt sein, daß der chinesische Kaiser seinerzeit
zur Einübung seiner Sturmtruppen Modelltürme bei Peking errichten ließ, die noch heute
stehen, und daß bei den nicht viel späteren Kämpfen mit den Ureinwohnern in *Hunan* und
Kweitschou die Chinesen ihrerseits solche Türme erbauten, um sich in den eroberten Gebieten
zu halten. Man findet daher in den Präfekturen *Fêng-huang* 鳳凰 und *Ch'ien-chou* 乾州[4]
in West-*Hunan* heute noch eine große Menge von diesen Gebäuden. Und gerade diese
Kriegstürme waren es, die die Eroberung des Landes so außerordentlich schwierig gestalteten.

Die beiden mächtigsten Stämme *Cucin* und *Zanla* hatten um die Mitte des 18. Jahrhunderts durch ihre Widerspenstigkeit den chinesischen Kaiser zum Eingreifen gezwungen
und damit schließlich die Unterwerfung des ganzen Goldstromlandes herbeigeführt. Eine
genauere Beschreibung dieses Feldzuges, dessen siegreiche Beendigung als besonderes
Ruhmesblatt in der chinesischen Kriegsgeschichte gilt, der auch überhaupt eine eigene
Würdigung verdient, soll vom Verfasser dieses Aufsatzes an anderer Stelle geboten werden.
Hierunter sei nur eine Zusammenfassung der Ereignisse gegeben:

Seit dem fünften Jahre der Regierung KANGHI, d. i. 1666, stand das Land dem Namen
nach unter chinesischer Oberhoheit. Kriegerische Verwicklungen unter den einzelnen
Stämmen veranlaßten die Provinzialregierung von *Szetschuan* im Jahre 1730 zu einer Straf-
expedition gegen die allem gütlichen Zureden unzugänglichen Fürsten, die nach vierjährigem
Kämpfe sich dem chinesischen Machtwillen beugen mußten. Aber schon nach wenigen
Jahren war die Lehre vergessen. Neue Unruhen im Lande forderten eine um so entschie-
denere Unterdrückung, als der Kaiser die widerspenstigen Fürsten vordem mit Milde
behandelt und ihnen keine andere Strafe als die Anerkennung der chinesischen Oberhoheit und das Gelöbnis der Urfehde auferlegt hatte. Eine neue Expedition in großem
Stile wurde eingeleitet. Der Einmarsch der chinesischen Heere im Anfange des Jahres 1772
geschah wie vordem von Osten her über *Wen-ch'uan*[5] und den *Banlan*-Paß, von Süden
her über *Tatsienlu* und den *Dabo*-Paß. Vom *Banlan* kämpfte man sich langsam vor über
Damba zung, *Ziri*, den Berg *Rabcuk*, *Meimei k'a*, den Tempel *Dungma*, *Serkwi*, *Biyesman*,
den Berg *Gunggar*, *Luding zung*, *Deo u* und den Berg *Kamser*. Alle festen Punkte, eine
Unmenge von Pässen, Sperren, Burgen und Tempeln mußten genommen werden, bevor man
zum Angriff auf *Meino* schreiten konnte, den Hauptsitz der Feinde in Klein-Goldstromland.

---

[1] Wir haben in diesem Worte *de'o* — so findet es sich in den tibetischen Inschriften — höchst wahrscheinlich ein, nichttibetisches, Eingeborenenwort vor uns. Das chinesische Wort *tiao* ist im *Kanghi*-Wörterbuch,
in der Bedeutung »steinernes Haus« ohne Textbeleg, nur mit Verweisung auf das alte Wörterbuch *Pien-hai* aufgeführt: also ein ungebräuchliches Zeichen. In späteren Wörterbüchern wird es gerade auf diese Türme im
Goldstromlande bezogen. In seiner chinesischen Bedeutung »steinernes Haus« könnte es wohl auf die tibetischen
Burgen angewandt werden, aber nicht auf die Kriegstürme, die den Chinesen etwas ganz Neues waren. Es ist
anzunehmen, daß sie für diese das Eingeborenenwort beibehalten und zur Schreibung das ungebräuchliche, also
prägnante, lautähnliche Zeichen *tiao* wählten.

[2] Sie spielten also eine ähnliche Rolle wie die Pfandhaustürme in der Kantonprovinz.

[3] Pl. I, Fig. 1.

[4] Plf. 1722 u. 922.

[5] Nordöstlich von *Kuan-hsien* gelegen, fehlt bei Plf.

Erst am Ende des Jahres stand man vor der Stadt. Nach anfänglichen Erfolgen gab es schwere Rückschläge. So war im Sommer eine Abteilung von 3000 Mann in *Molung geu* von den Feinden umzingelt und niedergemacht worden. Und auch die Einnahme der Hauptfesten von Klein-Goldstromland, *Meino* und *Dimda*, brachte noch keine Entscheidung, da der Fürst SENGGE SANG nach der Residenz *Le'uwei* in Groß-Goldstromland entkommen war. Im nächsten Jahre, 1773, erfolgte dann der Angriff auf dieses Land, von drei Seiten, Südwesten, Südosten und Osten. Aber der Vormarsch der Südost-Abteilung WENFU, von Klein-Goldstromland her über den Paß *Gunggar*, kam bald zum Stehen, da der Führer seine Kräfte mit Einzelunternehmungen gegen die zahlreichen Türme verzettelte, während er selbst mit dem Haupttrupp in dem befestigten Lager *Mugom* liegenblieb. Die Folge war eine neue Erhebung in Klein-Goldstromland, Überwältigung der Etappen im Rücken der Abteilung und schließlich ein Überfall auf WENFU's Lager, bei dem der General mit seiner gesamten Truppe, über 3000 Mann, niedergemacht wurde. Der Kaiser, der angesichts der langsamen Fortschritte bereits einen Abbruch des Feldzuges erwogen hatte, kam nach dieser schweren Niederlage zu dem Entschlusse, den Feldzug jetzt unter allen Umständen zu einem siegreichen Ende zu führen. Er nahm einen Wechsel in den Führerstellen vor und gab die Losung zu einem erneuten Vorstoß, der dann auch Klein-Goldstromland bald wieder völlig in chinesische Hand brachte und danach einen Einbruch in Groß-Goldstromland ermöglichte. Hier waren *Le'uwei* und *Gara'i* die beiden feindlichen Hauptstützpunkte. Ihre Einnahme erforderte bei den ungemein starken Befestigungen und der todesmutigen Verteidigung ganz gewaltige Anstrengungen. Erst nach zwei Jahren, im Spätherbst 1775, brachte man die Feste *Le'uwei* zu Fall und erst im Frühling des nächsten Jahres, 1776, die Feste *Gara'i*, in der nun auch die feindlichen Führer SONOM und SALBUN gefangen wurden, die Fürsten von Groß-Goldstromland. Der vordem zu ihnen geflüchtete Herrscher von Klein-Goldstromland, SENGGE SANG, war von ihnen ermordet, und seine Leiche war ausgeliefert worden.

Der vierjährige Feldzug findet sich in dem oben angeführten Kriegsbuch *Sheng-wu-chi* kurz beschrieben. Doch gibt es noch ein Sonderwerk mit einer ausführlichen Darstellung, auf welches ebenfalls eingangs bereits hingewiesen wurde. Es trägt den Titel *Ch'in-ting p'ing-ting liang Chin-chu'an fang-lio* 欽訂平定兩金川方略, »Auf Kaiserlichen Befehl verfaßtes Generalstabswerk über die Unterwerfung der beiden Goldstromländer«. Es ist im Jahre 1781 in 152 Büchern erschienen. Diese Sammlungen amtlicher Schriftstücke zu den großen Feldzügen des Mandschuhauses bilden die eigentlichen Quellen für die Kriegsgeschichte dieser Zeit. Es ist dabei ein glücklicher Umstand, daß die großen chinesischen Nebenländer dem Reiche unter einem fremden Herrscherhause zugeführt wurden, und zwar zu einer Zeit, als dieses noch seine eigene Sprache pflegte. So sind die Kriegsberichte auf Inschriften und in der Literatur auch in mandschurischer Sprache überliefert worden, insonderheit sind die meisten großen Kriegswerke in Doppelausgaben, chinesisch und mandschurisch, erschienen. Das ist von großer Bedeutung für die Schreibung der fremden Eigen- und Ortsnamen, die in der chinesischen Schrift arg verstümmelt sind, während sie in der mandschurischen Lautschrift uns getreu nach der Aussprache überliefert werden.[1]

---

[1] Wenn P. PELLIOT in seinem neuen Aufsatz *Les Conquêtes de l'Empereur de la Chine*, T'oung Pao, Vol. XX, S. 259, den Wert der mandschurischen Umschreibungen von nichtchinesischen Namen einschränken will, so möchte ich mich ihm hier betreffs der Biographien der Tributärfürsten wohl anschließen, wenn er damit das mir vorliegende *tulergi golbi monggo hoise aiman-i wang gung sai ulabun* meint. Dies Werk stammt aus der Mitte des 19. Jahrhunderts, einer Zeit, in der die mandschurische Sprache keine literarische Rolle mehr spielte und wohl nur noch aus dem Chinesischen übersetzt wurde. In der Mandschuliteratur der Kienlung-Zeit sind mir mandschurische Umschreibungen fremder Namen auf Grund chinesischer Transkriptionen bisher nicht aufgefallen.

Bei einem Werke vom Umfange des vorliegenden wird man eine sehr genaue Darstellung des Feldzugs, daher eine große Menge von Eigen- und Ortsnamen erwarten dürfen. Tatsächlich werden in dem Werke wohl ungefähr alle Plätze, Berge, Flüsse und Pässe aufgeführt sein, die sich in dem verhältnismäßig kleinen Lande überhaupt finden. Denn es gibt wohl keinen Punkt des Landes, um den nicht gekämpft worden wäre. Ein Auszug des geographischen Stoffes dürfte also eine ziemlich erschöpfende Beschreibung des Landes ergeben, jedenfalls eine genauere, als wir von irgendeinem andern Literaturwerk erwarten können. Nun führt uns ja die zugrunde liegende Handlung um 150 Jahre zurück. Von den damaligen Städten, Dörfern und festen Plätzen der Eingeborenen sind sicher manche zerstört und heute nicht mehr vorhanden, manche haben ihre Namen gewechselt, manche neue chinesische Siedelungen sind dazu gekommen. Doch muß immer noch reichlicher Stoff übrigbleiben, der noch für heute seinen Wert behält. Leider ist das besagte Kriegswerk ein sehr seltenes Buch, das in den europäischen Büchereien kaum zu finden sein dürfte. Bei WYLIE, Notes on Chinese literature, new ed. 1901, ist es auf S. 28 aufgeführt. MOELLENDORFF gibt in seiner mandschurischen Bibliographie unter Nr. 164 die mandschurische Ausgabe an als in der Bibliothek in Petersburg vorhanden. — Der Verfasser dieses Aufsatzes befindet sich im glücklichen Besitze der ersten Hälfte dieser mandschurischen Ausgabe, nämlich des Einleitungsbandes und der Bücher 1—72, welche die Vorgeschichte vom Jahre 1759 an und den ersten Teil des Krieges vom V. chinesischen Monat 1771 bis zum VIII. chinesischen Monat 1772 umfassen. Das ist in der Hauptsache die Zeit der Kriegshandlungen im Klein-Goldstromlande, die aber auch nach dem Groß-Goldstromlande hinübergreifen. Aus diesem Abschnitt ist der geographische Inhalt, wohl erschöpfend, herausgezogen und zusammengestellt worden.[1] Natürlich ließe er sich durch Ausnützung der auch recht reichhaltigen chinesischen Nebenquellen, vor allem der großen Aktensammlung *Tung-hua-lu* 東華錄, für die fehlende Hälfte ergänzen.[2] Doch wurde hiervon abgesehen, da die einheitliche Schreibung dabei gestört würde, wenn auch selbstverständlich diese Quellen zur Textinterpretation verwandt wurden.

Nur zwei chinesische rein geographische Stoffe wurden verwertet und der eigentlichen Arbeit vorangestellt: Die Abschnitte Groß- und Klein-Goldstromland (die Präfekturen *Argu* und *Meino*) aus der großen Reichsgeographie *Ta-Ch'ing I-t'ung chih* 大清一統志, und zwar der Ausgabe in 500 Büchern, Buch 321—323[3], sowie zwei vom Verfasser von Ort und Stelle mitgebrachte amtliche Karten. Hier mußte in vielen Fällen die chinesische Schreibung verwandt werden, nach WADEscher Umschreibung mit Silbentrennung und Bindestrichen. Bei unzweifelhaft chinesischen Namen sind die chinesischen Zeichen, soweit feststellbar, dazugefügt worden, ebenso bei denjenigen tibetischen Namen, die ohne weiteres erkennbar oder aus tibetischen Inschriften herzuleiten waren, die tibetischen Vollschreibungen.

I. A-rh-ku t'ing 阿爾古廳[4], der Sitz des Fürsten von Groß-Goldstromland, 1210 *Li* westlich von der Provinzialhauptstadt von *Szetschuan*. Die Ausdehnung des Gebiets beträgt von Osten nach Westen 260 *Li* und von Norden nach Süden 300 *Li*. Es grenzt an folgende Eingeborenenstaaten: Im Osten an Klein-Goldstromland bei einer Entfernung von 110 *Li*, im

---

[1] Über 400 Ortsnamen, ein reicher Stoff auch für sprachliche und etymologische Forschungen. Der hierzu gehörige Stoff aus der Übersichtsdarstellung des Einleitungsbandes ist ziemlich dürftig.

[2] Hierzu gehören die Teilkarten Nr. *II* und *III* auf Pl. II. Nr. *IV* ist als Anschlußkarte dazu gesetzt worden.

[3] Vgl. unten *Argu*.

Westen an *Cosgiyab* bei 150 *Li*, im Süden an *Burakdi* bei 210 *Li*, im Norden an *Damba* bei 90 *Li*, im Südosten an Klein-Goldstromland bei 180 *Li*, im Nordosten an *Jok꞉ai* bei 180 *Li*, im Südwesten an *Gebśiza* bei 150 *Li*, im Nordwesten an *Cosgiyab* bei 180 *Li*. Von der Präfektur bis Peking sind es 5700 *Li*.

Verwaltungsgeschichte. Nach dem Tributbuche des Yü gehörte es zur Provinz *Liang-chou* 梁 州 und war eigentlich der Stamm (das Land) der *Ti-kʻiang* 氐 羌. In der *Ming*-Zeit war ein gewisser HA-I-LA-MU (alte Schreibung *Ha-i-ma-i* 哈 衣 麻 衣), der zum lamaistischen Abt *yen-hua chʻan-shih* 演 化 禪 師 ernannt wurde und dies Gebiet erblich in Besitz nahm. Im 61. Jahre *Kanghi* (1722) unterwarf sich der Häuptling (土 合 *tuśe*) SCHALBUN dem chinesischen Kaiser und trat in seine Dienste. Er erhielt im darauffolgenden Jahre den Rang eines Kolonialpräfekten und im Jahre 1730 das Siegel mit dem Titel verliehen. Im 7. Jahre *Kienlung* (1742) erbte sein Sohn LANGKA den Rang und nannte sein Land »Goldstrom». Er suchte den ganzen Stamm an sich zu ziehen und unternahm Einfälle in die Grenzländer. Darauf ging ihm eine Kriegserklärung des Kaisers zu, und der Feldzug zu seiner Niederlage wurde mit aller Macht betrieben, so daß LANGKA im Frühjahr 1749 sich unterwarf und um Gnade bat, worauf der Kaiser ihm verzieh und seine Strafe erließ. Aber später fiel sein Sohn SONOM, der von noch gewalttätigerer Natur war, über die Häuptlinge der *Gebśiza* her. Der Kaiser ließ seine Generale ins Feld rücken, um SONOMS Nester auszufegen. Im Frühjahr 1776 wurde SONOM mit drei Brüdern, seiner Mutter AZʻANG und seiner Tante ACING in Gefangenschaft eingeliefert. Dabei wurde an diesem Platze (seiner Residenz) die Präfekturstadt *Argu* errichtet und unmittelbar unter die Provinzialverwaltung von *Szetschuan* gestellt.

Bodenbeschaffenheit. In Goldstromland gibt es zwei Nester[1], eins in *Leʻuwei* 勒 烏 圍 und eins in *Garaʼi* 噶 拉 衣, gewöhnlich *yai-kua-rh* 崖 栝 耳[2] genannt. Sie sind 120 *Li* voneinander entfernt. Der *Lu*-Fluß 瀘, der von Nordwesten aus dem Lande des *Zʻunggak*[3]-Fürsten kommt, fließt zwischen (beiden Nestern) hindurch. Hohe Berge ragen dort steil empor, schwindelnde Wege winden sich hin und her, Türme und steinerne Schanzen sperren die Räume dazwischen. Zwischen *Garaʼi* und *Karsar*, einer Entfernung von einigen 40 *Li*, liegen die Berge *Gunggar*, *Mugom*, *Si ling* 昔 嶺 und *Scrli*, alles gezackte Reihen mit Gipfeln wie Schwerter und Spieße. In drei Jahreszeiten liegen hier hohe Schneewehen, die erst im Sommer schmelzen. Wolken und Nebel verdunkeln das Land. Das Klima ist äußerst ungünstig. Wenn man von *Si ling* nach Westen geht, ist der äußerste Punkt (wieder) das Nest *Garaʼi*. Hier ragen die Türme auf, die Burgen stehen dicht. Der Ort ist von flachen Häusern umgeben und lehnt sich mit dem Rücken an hohe Berge. Rechts und links stehen überall Felsklippen. Mit der Vorderseite liegt er am Großen Goldstrom. In der Nähe dieses Nestes auf eine Strecke von einigen 10 *Li* werden die Wege noch viel gefährlicher. Auf der Strecke von *Leʻuwei* nach *Damba*, einige 50 *Li*, liegen die Berge *Murjin kang* 岡[4], *Geśizung kang* und *Źi pang*. Dicht an dem Neste stehen mehrere *Li* weit einzwängende Felsen, wie aus der Erde gewachsen, dicht am Flusse steil in die Höhe. Dieses Nest ist ebenso fest und geräumig wie *Garaʼi* und ebenfalls von Wohnhäusern umgeben. Dazwischen liegt *Mei o geo*, von wo aus es geradeswegs nach *Dimda* und *Buranggo zung* in Klein-Goldstromland geht. Das ist der Ort, wo die Eingeborenen herauskommen und verschwinden.

---

[1] Mit »Nest» bezeichnen die Chinesen die schwer zugänglichen Festen und Schlupfwinkel der Eingeborenen.
[2] Die Zeichen sind falsch gestellt. Sie sind zu lesen *Kʻua-rh-yai*, also eine chinesische Umbildung des Namens auf *yai* »Schlucht».
[3] Der Name kommt meist in der Form *Sunggak* vor.
[4] Die Silbe *kang* in der Bedeutung Bergrücken ist hier wohl chinesische Zusatzbezeichnung.

Kultur. Im allgemeinen baut das Volk Hafer und Buchweizen, züchtet Rinder und Schafe, baut Häuser und errichtet Türme, die es aber nicht mit Hecken und Palisaden umgibt. Seine Speise ist *tsan-pa* 糌 粑 [1], sein Getränk Buttermilch 乳 酪 und Bergtee. Die Reichen kleiden sich in rote Wolle und geblümte Seidenstoffe, die übrigen alle in Filz und Schaffelle. Sie halten Lamaistenmönche. Heilkunde und Arzneipflanzen kennen sie nicht. Sie achten Eide und Verträge und schneiden Holzkerben als Beweismittel. Sie brennen Schafblasen und zerreißen sie, um das Los zu befragen und danach Glück und Unglück vorauszubestimmen. Die Leichen bestatten sie entweder im Wasser oder sie verbrennen sie. Sie achten auf die Worte der Lamas. Bei den Heiraten gehen sie nach dem Vermögen und schließen den Vertrag ab nach Rindern, Schafen und Pferden. Männer und Frauen halten gemeinsame Vergnügungen, wobei sie sich an den Händen fassen [2] und (tibetische) Lieder in ihrer Sprache singen. Bei ihren Weingelagen machen sie Musik, was sie »in den Topfladen springen» nennen 跳 鍋 庄. [3] Ihrer Natur nach sind sie eigennützig und streitsüchtig. Sie achten das Leben gering und machen sich nichts aus dem Tode. An zerklüfteten Felsrändern entlang und steilen Abhängen wandeln sie gleich wie auf breiten Fahrwegen. Alle schweren Lasten tragen sie auf dem Rücken, das Tragen an der Tragstange kennen sie nicht. Die Frauen tragen große Ringe in den Ohren, und auch die Männer haben Ohrgehänge. Von 12 Jahren an führen alle ein kurzes Messer an der Lende. Sie sind vertraut mit Gewehr und Hakenspeer, Armbrust und Geschoß, verstehen sich aber nicht gut auf Bogen und Pfeil. — In den Gebirgsreihen und Felsschichten gibt es schwere Nebel und hohe Winde. Die Dünste auf den Bergen sind voller Pestilenzhauch. Es herrscht viel Kälte und wenig Hitze. Im Frühjahr und Sommer dauern die Regen- und Schneefälle wochen- und monatelang. Selten ist klares Wetter. Bei jedem Regen gibt es Gewitter mit mächtigem Donner. In dem Leuchten der Blitze hallt es von allen Seiten. Erst im 8. oder 9. Monat klärt sich das Wetter. Im Winter liegt tiefer Schnee, die höheren Täler weit und breit vergletschert, die Wege sind dann unterbrochen. (Aus der illustrierten Beschreibung des Goldstromlandes.[4])

Feste Städte. Präfekturstadt *A-rh-ku*, Stadtmauer noch nicht gebaut.

Bevölkerung. In Zivilberufen Beschäftigte und angesiedelte Besatzung (Chinesen) = 56 Hausstände mit 194 Männern und Frauen. Eingeborene = 679 Hausstände mit 3658 Männern und Frauen.

Ackerland und Abgaben. Neu unter den Pflug genommenes Ackerland über 69168 Morgen. Abgaben noch nicht erhoben, die Höhe der Steuersumme auch noch nicht festgesetzt.

Berge und Flüsse. *So-wu*, 150 *Li* östlich der Stadt. Im 41. Jahre *Kienlung* (1776), als die Unterwerfung des Goldstromlandes abgeschlossen war, erging eine Kaiserliche Anweisung, dem *So-wu*-Berge und dem Goldstrom beiden Opfer darzubringen und sie in die Liste der Frühling- und Herbstopfer einzureihen. *Giyaso*, 150 *Li* westlich der Stadt. Seine Gipfel stehen dicht und in Schichten übereinander, mit außerordentlich steilen Abgründen. *Zugu*, 90 *Li* nördlich der Stadt, stößt an das Gebiet des Fürsten von *Damba*.

---

[1] *tsam-pa*, der Mehlbrei der Tibeter.

[2] Nach chinesischer Anschauung ein besonderer Verstoß gegen die Sitte. Die gemeinsame Feier an sich ist schon unschicklich.

[3] *t'iao kuo-chuang*. Es mag sich um ein Eingeborenenwort handeln, das in der chinesischen lautlichen Wiedergabe als Wortspiel benutzt worden ist.

[4] Das Buch ist nicht bekannt geworden.

Gunggar, 240 *Li* südöstlich der Stadt. Er grenzt an *Nio cang* in Klein-Goldstromland. Seine Gipfel stehen dicht im Kreise wie ein Gürtel. Es herrscht dort das ganze Jahr hindurch Regen und Schnee. *Danggar*, 260 *Li* südöstlich der Stadt, ein Querzug von über 20 *Li*, stets verhüllt von Wolken und Nebel. *Ži pang*, 70 *Li* nordwestlich der Stadt. *I hi*, 100 *Li* nordwestlich der Stadt, grenzt an das Gebiet des Fürsten von *Cosgiyab*. *Siling*, 190 *Li* östlich der Stadt.

Goldstrom. Seine Quelle entspringt jenseits von *Mao-niu-hsi* 氂 牛 漵 (Yakrinderdamm) im Nordwesten von der Grenzgarnison *Sung-p'an*. Durch die Länder der Stämme *Cosgiyab*, *Z'unggak* und *Damba* strömt er in das Gebiet des Fürsten von Goldstromland ein. An der Präfekturstadt vorbei in westlicher Richtung gelangt er nach *Gara'i*, wo er die Gewässer vom *Gungga*-Berge, dann über *Marbang*, *Badi* und *Bawang* in südwestlicher Richtung vorbei an *Janggu*, wo er die Gewässer des *Mengbai*-Berges aufnimmt. Danach tritt er, in südlicher Richtung fließend, in das Land des Fürsten von *Ming-jeng* ein, strömt durch das Gebiet von *Tatsienlu*, wo er einzelne kleine Bergwasser aufnimmt, und nimmt seinen Lauf in südlicher Richtung durch die Brücke *Lu-ling-ch'iao*, in das Gebiet von *Ch'ing-ch'i-hsien*.[1] Im Jahre 1776 wurde er in die Opferliste aufgenommen, zum Opfern im Frühling und Herbst.

Grenzpässe und Engen 關 隘. *Karsor*, südlich der Stadt. Weiter westwärts liegt der *Langla*. Beide besitzen einen Kriegsturm und eine Sperre. Jetzt sind dort Poststellen eingerichtet. *Gara'i*, gegenüber der Stadt auf der andern Flußseite, ein wenig nach Osten, ein Nest des Goldstromlandes. Das Gelände ist dort sehr gefährlich. Jetzt befindet sich an dem Platze eine Proviantzweigstelle. *Dusung* 獨 松[2], westlich der Stadt. Weiter nach Norden liegt *Gaza* 甲 咱. An beiden Orten sind jetzt Poststellen eingerichtet. *Le'uwei (Lo-wu-wei)*, gegenüber der Stadt auf der andern Flußseite, ein wenig nach Westen, ein Nest des Goldstromlandes. Bei seiner Bezwingung im Jahre 1775 wurde eine vom Kaiser verfaßte Inschrift über die Eroberung des Goldstromlandes (hier) in *Le'uwei* in Stein gemeißelt. Jetzt liegt an dem Orte eine starke Besatzungstruppe. *Mabang*[3], an der Grenze des Präfekturgebiets, westlich des Flusses. Jetzt ist dort ein Proviantamt eingerichtet. *Sui-ching-ying* 綏 靖 營, an der Präfekturgrenze, im Jahre 1776 errichtet, im Jahre 1780 vom Kaiser mit diesem Namen bezeichnet.[4] *Ch'ung-hua-ying* 崇 化 營 befindet sich am Platze von *Gara'i*. *Ch'ing-ning-ying* 慶 甯 營 liegt westlich der Präfekturstadt an dem Platze von *Ju-chai* 茹 寨. Die letzten beiden Lager sind ebenso wie *Sui-ching* eingerichtet.

Fähren und Brücken. Flußübergänge von *Gara'i*, *La-kio (Lagô)*, *Kuang-fa-sze*, *Dusung*, *Le'uwei* und *Ju-chai*. Diese Flußübergänge sind alle nach den Ortschaften benannt und besitzen Fährboote. Brücke *Kakagio* 卡 卡 角, Brücke *Ch'en-kio kou*, Brücke 1 und 2 am Fuße des *Manai*-Berges. Diese sind alle aus Seilen gemacht, von verschiedener Länge, 400—500 Fuß. Brücke *T'ao-wu*, *Shuang-tiao ch'iao*, Brücke vom doppelten Kriegsturm 雙 碉 橋, *Teng-la ch'iao* 登 菩 橋. Diese sind alle Holzbrücken von verschiedener Länge (10—30 Fuß).

Tempel. *Kuang-fa-sze* 廣 法 寺 = Tempel der Ausbreitung des Glaubens, westlich der Präfekturstadt am Orte *Gara'i*. Das war früher der alte *Yung-pu Lama*-Tempel

---

[1] Plf. 1235.

[2] Der Name, hier jedenfalls eine Umschreibung aus dem Tibetischen, kommt in China häufig als Ortsname vor; einzelnstehende Föhre.

[3] Lies *Marbang*. Dort steht einer der höchsten Kriegstürme des Landes. Vgl. oben S. 74.

[4] Vgl. das Kartenbild Pl. IV.

雅市喇嘛寺. Im 41. Jahre der Regierung *Kienlung* von unserer Dynastie (1776) bei der Niederwerfung des Goldstromlandes war er neu aufgebaut worden. Der Kaiser verlieh ihm seinen Namen sowie ein eigenhändig geschriebenes Querschild mit der Inschrift "Weite Verbreitung der rechten Lehre", 正 教 恒 宣 *cheng-chiao heng-hsüan*.[1] Landeserzeugnisse. Yakrinder, Fasanen, Lattich, Fieberheilpflanze.

II. Meino t'ing 美 諾, früher Sitz des Fürsten von Klein-Goldstromland.[2] Es liegt 860 Meilen westlich von der Hauptstadt der Provinz *Szetschuan*. Die Ausdehnung des Landes von Osten nach Westen = 175 *Li*, von Süden nach Norden = 570 *Li*. Es grenzt an folgende Eingeborenenstaaten: Im Osten an *Oksi*, 35 *Li* (von der Präfekturstadt entfernt), im Westen an Alt-Goldstromland, 140 *Li*, im Süden an *Muping*, 180 *Li*, im Norden an *Somo*, 390 *Li*, im Südosten an *Wasse*, 210 *Li*, im Nordosten an *Zagu*, 300 *Li*, im Südwesten an *Mingjeng*, 210 *Li*, im Nordwesten an *Jokz'ai*, 420 *Li*. Von der Präfekturstadt bis Peking sind es 5700 *Li*.

Verwaltungsgeschichte. Nach dem Tributbuche des Yü gehörte es zur Provinz *Liang-chou*. Zur *Han*-Zeit bildete es das Gebiet der *Man*-Völker des Südwestens. Zur *Tang*-Zeit nahmen die *T'u-fan* das Land in Besitz. Seit der *Ming*-Zeit heißt es "Goldstromland". Der Fürst wurde mit der Würde eines lamaistischen Abtes belehnt, die er bis auf Pu-rh-ki-hsi vererbte. Unter der regierenden Dynastie, im 7. Jahre *Schuntschi* (1650), unterwarf sich der Fürst dem Reiche. Man übertrug das Fürstenamt einem Angehörigen der regierenden Familie von (Groß-)Goldstromland. Die Eingeborenen nennen den Großen Goldstrom *Ts'u-ch'in* und den Kleinen Goldstrom *Tsan-la (Zanla)*. *Ts'u-ch'in* bedeutet "Ufer des Großen Flusses", *Tsan-la* "Ufer des Kleinen Flusses".[3] Das soll also heißen, daß derselbe Volksstamm zu einem Teile am Ufer des Großen, zum andern Teile am Ufer des Kleinen Flusses wohnt. Als im Jahre 1748 der Häuptling Lang-örh-ki, der sich heimlich an (Groß-)Goldstromland anschließen wollte, den Fürsten Z'ewang mit Krieg überzog, marschierte der Statthalter Fuheng gegen ihn. Jener ergab sich und wurde hingerichtet. Als dann Z'ewang alt geworden war, und sein Sohn Sengge Sang, ein niederträchtiger und gewalttätiger Mann, wiederholt die Stadt der *Oksi* belagerte und dann sogar über den Fürsten von *Mingjeng* herfiel, beschloß der Kaiser im Jahre 1774, ihn mit Heeresmacht zu bekriegen. Es wurde eine Steintafel mit einer vom Kaiser verfertigten Inschrift über die Besiegung des Goldstromlandes in *Meino* gesetzt.[4] Im Jahre 1776 wurde an diesem Platze die Präfekturstadt als Garnison errichtet und unmittelbar der Provinzialverwaltung von *Szetschuan* unterstellt.

Feste Städte. *Meino*, Stadtmauer noch nicht gebaut.

Bevölkerung. In Zivilberufen Beschäftigte und angesiedelte Besatzung (Chinesen): 113 Familien, 280 Seelen, Männer und Frauen. Dazu Eingeborene: 948 Familien mit 4423 Seelen.

Ackerland und Abgaben. Neu unter den Pflug genommenes Ackerland 48492 Morgen. Abgaben noch nicht erhoben. Höhe der Steuersumme auch noch nicht festgesetzt.

---

[1] Die Inschrift, die heute über dem Eingangstor des Tempels zu lesen ist, enthält außer dem chinesischen Namen *K'uang-fa-sze* noch seine mandschurische, tibetische und mongolische Übersetzung: *šajin be badarambuha juktehen, bstan-'p' el-glñ, šajin-i badaragulhu süme*

[2] Stamm *Zanla*.

[3] Über die richtige Bedeutung dieser beiden tibetischen Namen vgl. oben S. 73.

[4] Eine Abreibung davon wurde vom Verfasser des Aufsatzes mitgebracht.

Berge und Flüsse. Berge: *Mordo*, 160 *Li* westlich der Stadt. Im Jahre 1776, anläßlich der Siegesfeier für die Niederwerfung des Goldstromlandes, wurde der Berg auf Kaiserliche Verordnung durch Opfer geehrt und in die Liste der Frühlings- und Herbstopfer eingereiht. Früher befand sich auf ihm ein Lamatempel. *Balang*[1], 210 *Li* östlich der Stadt, bildet die Grenze nach dem Fürstentum *Wasse*. *Pieh-pang*[2], 240 *Li* östlich der Stadt, Grenze nach der Präfektur *Zagu*. *K'ung-ch'ia (K'ung-k'a)* 壟 卡[3], 140 *Li* westlich der Stadt, bildet die Grenze mit *Ts'u-ch'in (Cucin)*. *Shan-kio (Samgigo)*, 390 *Li* östlich der Stadt. *Jih-rh* 日 閣, 390 *Li* nördlich der Stadt, bildet die Grenze nach dem Fürstentum *Somo*. *Mengbai* 孟 拜, 420 *Li* nordwestlich der Stadt, heißt auch *Mengbi* 夢 筆, bildet die Grenze nach dem Fürstentum *Jokz'ui*.

Der Kleine Goldstrom entspringt auf dem Berge *Mengbai*, nordwestlich des Präfekturgebiets, fließt in südöstlicher Richtung an *Dabanjao* vorbei, nimmt bei *Sala* die Wasser des Berges *Jih-rh* auf, fließt dann südwärts nach *Mardang* und *Dimda*. Bei *Mubo*[4] empfängt er die Gewässer des Berges *So-wu*[5] und nimmt dann wieder einen südlichen Lauf. Bei *Meng-ku-chai* 猛 固 寨 empfängt er die Gewässer des Berges *Balang* und nimmt danach südwestliche Richtung. Nördlich der Präfekturstadt nimmt er die Wasser des Berges *Gungga* 功 噶[6] auf. Dann wendet er sich wieder nach Südwesten, empfängt die kleinen Bergbäche des Nord- und Südberges, um dann im Gebiete des Fürstentums *Mingjeng* bei dem Orte *Pien-ku* 邊 谷[7] *(Biyangu)* in den *Ta-tu*-Fluß zu münden. Der *Ta-tu*-Fluß ist der Unterlauf des (Großen) Goldstromes.

Grenzpässe und Engen. *Minggo*-Brücke, 30 *Li* östlich der Stadt, bildet die Grenze nach dem Fürstentum *Oksi*. Jetzt ist dort eine Poststelle eingerichtet. *Ziri chai*, 90 *Li* östlich der Stadt. Jetzt befindet sich dort eine Poststelle. *Mu-rh chai*, 120 *Li* östlich der Stadt, eine Schlucht mit ungewöhnlich steilen Wänden, jetzt als Poststelle eingerichtet. *Jih-lung-chai*, 150 *Li* östlich der Stadt, jetzt eine Poststelle. *Sung-lin-k'ou* 松 林 口 (Föhrenwaldschlucht), 180 *Li* östlich der Stadt, der Platz stellt die Verbindung dar nach *Ta-i-p'ing* 大 邑 坪[8] und bildet die Kehle (den Zugangsplatz) von *Meino*. Jetzt als Poststelle eingerichtet. *Tsé-rh-kiao-chai*, 30 *Li* nördlich der Stadt, jetzt eine Poststelle. *Ch'ung-tê* 崇 德[9], 60 *Li* nördlich der Stadt, jetzt eine Poststelle. *Hsiao-niu-ch'ang* 牛 小 厰 (kleiner Kuhstall), 78 *Li* nördlich der Stadt, 15 *Li* darüber hinaus liegt *Ta-niu-ch'ang* (großer Kuhstall). Jetzt eine Poststelle. *Dabanjao* 大 板 昭, westlich der Stadt, jetzt ein Proviantamt. *Dimda*, desgl. *Janggu* 章 谷, desgl. Das Militärlager *Mou-kung* 懋 功, im Stadtgebiet, im Jahre 1776 errichtet, im Jahre 1780 vom Kaiser mit diesem Namen bedacht. Das Militärlager *Fu-pien* 撫 邊, am Platze von *Dimda*, die Errichtungsgeschichte ist dieselbe wie die von *Mou-kung*.

Fähren und Brücken. Fähre bei der Kolonie *Janggu*. Fähre *Ting-kin* 定 金. Brücke bei der *T'ai-p'ing* 太 平-Fähre, südwestlich der Stadt, es befindet sich dort ein

---

[1] Chinesische Schreibung *Pa-lang-la*, mandschurische Lautschreibung *Balangla*, der tibetische Name nach der Inschrift *Blangla* = Paß (la) auf dem (die Götter das Opfer annehmen werden? Die heute übliche Aussprache des Namens ist *Banlan*.

[2] = *Bivangla?*

[3] Vgl. unten *Gunggarla*.

[4] Vgl. unten *Mu-p'o*, Pl. III Nr. 20.

[5] Vgl. unten *Sobu*.

[6] Zu unterscheiden von *Gunggar*.

[7] Die chinesische Schreibung bedeutet *Grenztal*.

[8] Die chinesische Schreibung bedeutet *Ebene der Hauptstadt*.

[9] Chinesisch *Erhabene Tugend*.

II. IX, 4.

Fährboot. Die Brücken *Bangko, Unggurlung, T'ien-ch'u* 田楚. Diese drei sind alle Seilbrücken und jede über 200 Fuß lang. Die Brücke *Menggu* Nr. 1 und 3, die Brücken *Yün-ts'ang* 匀藏 und *K'ang-ta*. Diese sind alle Holzbrücken. Die *Yün-ts'ang*-Brücke ist 120 Fuß lang, die andern alle über 50 Fuß.

Tempel. *Sheng-yin-sze* 勝因寺, auf einem Bergabhang südlich des Präfekturyamens. Im Jahre 1776 auf Antrag beim Kaiser gebaut unter dem Namen *Meidu*-Lamatempel, im Jahre 1780 vom Kaiser mit dem gegenwärtigen Namen bedacht.

Erzeugnisse. Yakrinder, Fasanen, Lattich, Fieberheilkraut.

— · — · —

Die Handbücher (志書 *chih-shu*) für diese beiden Verwaltungsbezirke konnten nicht ausfindig gemacht, ja es konnte nicht einmal mit Sicherheit ermittelt werden, ob solche überhaupt schon vorliegen. Wenn bekanntermaßen Verwaltungshandbücher schon im allgemeinen schwer zu erlangen sind, werden im besonderen die aus den Grenzgebieten noch strenger zurückgehalten. Es gelang dem Verfasser des Aufsatzes aber, zwei Landkarten von dort mit heimzubringen, die nebenstehend in verkleinertem Maßstabe wiedergegeben sind. Die Karten messen jede 45:92 cm. Sie sind mit Tusche gezeichnet, der Fluß und die Berge mit Wasserfarben grün, die Gebäude grün oder braun angelegt. Die Kartenzeichnung ist chinesischer Art, perspektivisch von dem die Mitte durchlaufenden Flusse orientiert. Die Karte Pl. III Lager *Fu-pien* (am Kleinen Goldstrom) ist bei weitem feiner gezeichnet als Pl. IV, Lager *Sui-ching* (am Großen Goldstrom). Der Kleine Goldstrom auf Pl. III trägt nur Brücken, der Große Goldstrom auf Pl. IV nur Fähren. Beide Karten zeigen neben chinesischen Häusern mit Yamenmasten tibetische Steinburgen mit Flaggen sowie zahlreiche Kriegstürme. Während auf Pl. III sowohl das Militärlager als auch die Kolonie sowie mehrere Einzelposten sauber gezeichnete Maueranlagen aufweisen, sind auf Pl. IV selbst bei dem Militärlager die Mauern nur schwach angedeutet. Beide Karten sind, wie gesagt, nach den Flüssen orientiert, Pl. III regelmäßig nach den Hauptrichtungen, Pl. IV nach den Zwischenrichtungen. Die Namensbezeichnungen sind nach chinesischer Art durch aufgeklebte rote Zettel gegeben, diese erscheinen auf Pl. III, sind jedoch hier, da die schwarze Schrift auf rotem Grunde im Lichtbilde nicht hervortritt, durch Nummern gekennzeichnet worden. Von der anderen, durch Wasser etwas verwaschenen Karte, sind die Zettel losgelöst und ihre Plätze ebenfalls durch Nummern bezeichnet worden. Die entsprechenden Zettelaufschriften folgen hierunter.

Pl. III. Lager Fu-pien *(Dimda)* am Kleinen Goldstrom.

1. Norden. Zum Berge *Menghi*, der Grenze des Fürstentums *Jokz'ai*, vom Lager 220 *Li*. Es führen Wege nach *Wei-chou, Sung-p'an* und *Cosgiyab*.
2. Poststelle *Mardang*, vom Lager 70 *Li*.
3. Gedächtnishalle für den Herzog *Tung (Tung T'ien-p'i* 董天鴉).[1]
4. Chinesischer Kriegsgott-Tempel.
5. Militärlager *Fu-pien*.
6. Magazin.
7. Brücke *Teng-ta*.[2]
8. Pulverfabrik.

---

[1] Ein Heerführer aus dem Eroberungsfeldzuge.
[2] Vgl. unten S. 95 *Demda*.

9. Osten. Zum Berge *K'o-ku* in der Kolonie *Biyesman*, Grenze von *Okśi* vom Lager 160 *Li*.
10. Wagnerei.
11. Hauptmannsposten der Kolonie *Pa-chio-tiao* mit Eingeborenenburg (achteckiger Kriegsturm).
12. Süden. Zum Posten *Minggo zung* im Bezirk *Mou-kung*, vom Lager 120 *Li*.
13. *Meng-ku*, Brücke Nr. 1.
14. Posten *Minggo zung*, 1 Sergeant.
15. *Meng-ku*, Brücke Nr. 2.
16. Poststelle *P'o-tiao* (zerstörter Kriegsturm), vom Lager 90 *Li*.
17. Posten *Pa-chio-tiao* (vom Achteckigen Turm), 1 Unteroffizier.
18. Untere Poststelle vom Posten *Pa-chio-tiao*, vom Lager 50 *Li*.
19. Poststelle »Lamatempel«, vom Lager 30 *Li*.
20. Poststelle *Mu-p'o*, vom Lager 20 *Li*.
21. Hauptmannsposten der Kolonie *Biyesman* mit Eingeborenenburg.
22. Untere Poststelle vom Posten *Jangu*, vom Lager 5 *Li*.
23. Kolonie *Fu-pien*.
24. Westen. Zum Bergrücken *Tsa-ma (Zama)*, der Grenze des Bezirks *Sui-ching*, vom Lager 120 *Li*.
25. Posten *Jangu*, 1 Unteroffizier.
26. Poststelle *Shuang-tiao* (Doppelturm), vom Lager 20 *Li*.
27. Doppelturm-Brücke.
28. Poststelle *T'ao-wu*, vom Lager 50 Meilen.
29. Brücke *T'ao-wu*.
30. Untere Poststelle vom Posten *Dabanjao*, vom Lager 160 *Li*.
31. Posten *Dabanjao*, 1 Leutnant.
32. Poststelle *Karsa*¹, vom Lager 130 *Li*.
33. Poststelle *So-lo-p'o-ku*, vom Lager 160 *Li*.
34. Untere Poststelle vom Posten *Sala*, vom Lager 90 *Li*.
35. Posten *Sala*, 1 Unteroffizier.

Pl. IV. Militärlager Sui-ching, am Großen Goldstrom.

1. Südwest. Grenze nach (dem Fürstentum) *Gebśza*.
2. Südwest; zur Garnison *Fou-ho* 付 和, Grenze mit *Gebśza*, 190 *Li*.
3. Poststelle *K'a-la* Fähre.
4. Posten *Tu-sung*. 2. Amt der rechten Abteilung, 1 Unteroffizier: Es untersteht der Kolonie *Sui-ching* und grenzt an den Ort *Niu-ch'ang* von der Kolonie *Ch'ung-hua*, von dem es 10 *Li* entfernt ist. Die Entfernung vom Lager beträgt 50 *Li*. Es sind hier hingelegt an Wachmannschaften = 25 Mann.
5. Unteroffiziersblockhaus von der Kolonie *Ka-wu*-Paß.
6. Südwest. Grenze nach der Kolonie *Ch'ung-hua*.
7. *Tu-sung*-Graben. Unterhalb dieses Berges teilt er sich in die einzelnen Gräben *Jengdi*, *Mu-shu*, *Hsia-tsu*, *Tu-tsu*. Sie bilden die wichtigen Verkehrswege für die Eingeborenen. Eine früher hier befindliche Holzsperre 木 卡 war ursprünglich als Schutz gegen Räuber errichtet. Von hier bis zum Posten *Tu-sung* sind es ungefähr einige 30 *Li*.
8. Kriegstempel.

---

¹ Vgl. oben S. 79 *Karsar?*

9. Poststelle *Ka-ku* 噶 谷. Vom Lager 40 *Li*, bis zum Posten *Tu-sung* 10 *Li*.
10. Kriegstempel.
11. Posten *Chia-tsa (Gazai)*[1], 2. Kompanie der linken Abteilung, 1 Unteroffizier. Er untersteht der Kolonie *Sui-ching*. Bis zur Poststelle *Ka-ku* sind es 10 *Li*, vom Lager 30 *Li*. Wachmannschaften = 20 Mann.
12. *Yü-k'o* 余 科.[2]
13. *Shuang-tiao* (Doppelturm).
14. *Chao-pi* 照 眸.
15. Leutnantsblockhaus von *Pa-pu-li(ri)* 巴 布 里.[3]
16. Pulverfabrik.
17. Kolonialpräfektur-Yamen.
18. Untere Poststelle, vom Lager 5 *Li*.
19. Zehntausendmeilen-Mauer. Vom *So-wu*-Berg etwa 20 *Li*. Oben ist aus Steinen ein Umfassungswall gebaut, im Durchmesser über 1 *Li*. Unterhalb dieses Platzes gibt es ewigen Schnee und im Winter nicht schmelzendes Eis. Aber zur Zeit, wenn der Weg zwischen den beiden Lagern *Sui-ching* und *Fu-pien* frei wird, gibt es hier einen Träger- und Handelsverkehr.
20. Südost. Bis zu der Stelle, wo der Rücken des Zehntausendmeilen-Mauer-Berges an das Gebiet von *Fu-pien* grenzt, sind es 135 *Li*.
21. *Giyaso*-Berg. Oben vom Berge *Tan-kieh* bis zu diesem Berge etwa 78 *Li*. Er ragt massig empor unter den Bergen in Ost und West. Oben stößt er an die Milchstraße, nach unten blickt er hinab auf die ausgebreiteten (anderen) Berggipfel, die alle niedriger sind als er und deren keiner ihm gleichkommt. Er ist tatsächlich die Paßsperre und das Schloß des *Sui-ching*-Gebietes. Auf seinem Gipfel befindet sich eine ebene Platte, auf der 100 Mann den Paß sperren können. Dies war der wirkungsvollste Stützpunkt in der Goldstrom-Expedition, der dafür auch in die Opferliste eingetragen wurde. *Cosgiyab* grenzt hier an die Fürstentümer *Gebśiza* und *Badi*. Oben ist *Gebśiza*, unten *Badi*. Die Grenzen greifen ineinander wie Hundezähne, so daß ihre Verteidigung recht schwierig ist.
22. Nordwest. Zur Grenze des Fürstentums *Cosgiyab* = 90 *Li*.
23. Wohnsitze und Weiden der Eingeborenen.
24. Militärlager *Sui-ching*. Die Zahl der Offiziere, Unteroffiziere, Reiter und Fußsoldaten beträgt auf dem Papier 280 Mann. Mit Abrechnung der auf die 5 Militärposten und die Poststellen detachierten Abteilungen bleiben tatsächlich im Lager nur 150 Mann zurück.
25. Hauptmanns-Yamen.
26. Kommandantur.
27. Kriegstempel.
28. Exerzierhaus.
29. Bergrücken *Ka-rh-kuang*. Von dem Blockhaus *Ko-rh-wa-kio* über den Bergpaß *Kou-tu* 溝 度 嶺, bis hierher sind es etwa 67 *Li*. Hinter dem Blockhause ist massiges Gebirge und dichter Wald. Der Berg grenzt an das Gebiet des Militärpostens *Dabanjao* vom Lager *Fu-pien*. Hierin ist ein leichtes Versteck für Verbrecher und Banditen. Daher haben die Wachen hier doppelte Aufmerksamkeit nötig.

---

[1] Vgl. oben S. 79 *Gazapu*.
[2] Stammesname.
[3] *Babu*-Berg.

30. Osten. Grenze nach der Zehntausend-Meilen-Mauer im Kolonialbezirk *Fu-pien.*
31. Berg *So-wu.* Über Blockhaus *Ka-rh-kuang* herum nach dem Berge *So-wu* sind es 90 *Li.*
Das ist auch ein Berg, der uns in der Goldstrom-Expedition außerordentlich vor-
wärts geholfen hat und dafür in die Opferliste aufgenommen wurde. Die Berge
stehen dort auf eine lange Strecke einander gegenüber, werden aber allmählich
niedriger.
32. Posten *T'a-kio-lo.*[1] 1. Abteilung der rechten Kompanie, 1 Sergeant. Gehört zur
Kolonie *Sui-ching,* (der Bezirk des Postens) grenzt an *Dabanjao* in der Kolonie
Fu-pien. (Bis zu dieser Grenze sind es) 135 *Li.* Vom Lager ist es 15 *Li* entfernt.
Es ist hier ein Verteidigungswerk angelegt, mit 20 Mann starker Besatzung.
33. Inschriftenpavillon.
34. Fährstelle *Le'uwei (Lo-wu-wei).*
35. *Shen-hsien-pao* 神仙包.[2]
36. *Ihi*-Berge. Diese Berge sind von dem Bergrücken am Posten *Zipang* wohl über 100 *Li*
entfernt. Die Natur dieser Berge ist felsig und hoch, das Gelände ist äußerst gefährlich. In früherer Zeit gab es dort viele Militärlager. Es ist hier auch ein
wichtiger Abkürzungsweg für die Eingeborenen. Man kann ohne Verwendung
großer Streitkräfte die wichtigen Stellungen halten. Es sind hier Verteidigungs-
werke angelegt.
37. *Tan-kieh*-Berg. Von den *Ihi*-Bergen ist es nach der Auskunft der Eingeborenen eine
Entfernung von 60—70 *Li.* Aufwärts verbindet es mit *Ihi,* abwärts mit *Giyaso.*
Auf diesem Berge gibt es eine zur Zeit der Eroberung des Goldstromlandes gebaute
steinerne Sperre, die allein oben stehengeblieben ist. Es ist eine Sperre für die
Eingeborenenstämme des Graslandes. — In diesen Bergen gibt es mehrere Ketten
großer Paßrücken. Das ist der Ort, wo die Wilden des *Yüko*-Stammes mit ihren
Zelten nomadisieren. Sie wechseln zwar auf Pfaden über diesen Berg hinüber,
unter großen Beschwerden bei der Länge des Weges und der Unfruchtbarkeit des
Berges. Ihr regelmäßiges Erscheinen und Verschwinden aber geschieht immer durch
die Gebiete *Ts'ang-tu* und *Chou-sou* im *Cosgiyab*-Lande.
38. Leutnant(sposten) von der Ansiedlung *Ju-chai* 如寨.
39. Posten *Galdan*-Tempel, 1 Sergeant von der 1. Kompanie der linken Abteilung. Gehört
zur Kolonie *Sui-ching.* Grenzt an Kolonie *Fu-pien,* eine Entfernung von 130 *Li.*
Vom Lager 30 *Li* entfernt. Hier ist ein Verteidigungswerk angelegt, mit 25 Wachmannschaften.
40. *Kiu-pa-so* 九把鎖.[3] Über *Yang-chia-tiao* (Turm der Familie YANG) bis hierher etwa
80—90 *Li.* Hinter dem Berge liegt ein Ort, der zu dem Posten *Dabanjao* vom
Lager *Fu-pien* gehört, namens *Hsiung-chia ta-ti* 熊家大地.[4] Das ist der Hauptweg,
auf dem seinerzeit der Vormarsch erfolgte. Vor dem Berge ist Gebiet des Lagers
(Sui-ching). Die beiden Blockhäuser *Ka-rh-kuang* und *Ko-rh-wa* unterstehen beide
dem Kommando des Lagers.
41. *Yang-chia-tiao* (Turm der Familie YANG). Über *Lung-wo* (Drachennest) bis hierher etwa
50—60 *Li.* Hinter dem Berge liegt ein Ort, der heißt *Lo-pu-cha.* Ein wenig tiefer
liegt *Kiu-pa-so.* Das ist der Ort, wo beim Vormarsch zur Eroberung des Goldstrom-

---

[1] Vgl. unten *Tekyur.*
[2] Rein chinesischer Ortsname (taoistischer Ausdruck).
[3] Die Zeichen der chinesischen Umschreibung bedeuten »die 9 Türschlösser«.
[4] Chinesische Ortsbezeichnung: Großer Platz der Familie HSIUNG.

landes das Lager aufgeschlagen wurde. Alle die alten Wälle und zerstörten Sperren sind dort noch zu sehen, dicht wie Fischschuppen. Hinter dem Berge *Kiu-pa-so* ist wieder ein Ort, der heißt Siegeshöhe. Die Eingeborenen sagen, der Name komme daher, daß das kaiserliche Heer dort einen großen Sieg errungen habe. Vor dem Berge liegt dann das dem Lager unterstehende Blockhaus *Ko-rh-kio*. An diesem Platze ist ein Verteidigungswerk angelegt, das Aufstände der Eingeborenen in der Südecke zum Stehen bringen kann.

42. Leutnant(sposten) von der Kolonie *Ko-rh-wa-kio*.

43. Posten *Ko-rh-t'i'*, 1 Unteroffizier der 2. Kompanie, rechte Abteilung. Er untersteht der Kolonie *Sui-ching*, und sein Bereich grenzt an das Fürstentum *Damba*, bei einer Entfernung von 140 *Li*. Vom Lager ist er 50 *Li* entfernt. Es ist hier ein Verteidigungswerk angelegt. Die Besatzung an Verteidigungs- und Angriffstruppen beträgt 25 Mann.

44. Fährstelle von *Ju-chai*.

45. Lager *Ch'ing-ning* 慶寧.

46. *Ts'ang-tu* 蒼都.[2]

47. Bergrücken *Zipang*. Dieser Ort ist von *Sui-ching* 60 *Li* und vom Lager *Ch'ing-ning* 30 *Li* entfernt. Das Gelände dort ist höher als *Kuan-chai* in *Cosgiyab*. Der Ort ist wirklich das Ein- und Ausgangstor für die dortigen Eingeborenen und andere. Das Verteidigungswerk ist sehr leicht zu halten. Die Eingeborenen von dort behaupten von der Gestalt dieses Berges, daß er sich gerade hinein nach Tibet erstrecke. Vom Gipfel des Berges kann man in westlicher Richtung den jenem Fürsten unterstehenden Stamm *Ts'ang-tu* erblicken.

48. *Chou-sou* 周叟 *(Jeo-seo)*.[3]

49. *Lung-wo* (Drachennest). Dieser Ort ist von *Sui-ching* 85 *Li* entfernt. Es ist der Grenzpunkt zwischen dem dem Lager *(Sui-ching)* unterstehenden Posten *Ko-rh-t'i* und dem dem Brigadebezirk *Wei-chou* unterstehenden Fürstentum *Damba*. Getrennt werden sie durch den Großen Goldstrom. Diesseits von *Damba* liegen die Fürstentümer *Sung-kang*[4] und *Jokz'ai*. An diesem Orte und am *Yang-chia*-Turm hat man durch Errichtung von Verteidigungswerken die Möglichkeit zu Verteidigung und Angriff.

50. Fürstentum *Damba*.

51. Nordostgrenze an *Damba*.

52. Nordost. Nach dem Bergrücken *Zagu*, der Grenze mit dem Gebiete des dem Brigadebezirk *Wei-chou* unterstehenden Fürstentums *Damba*, 140 *Li*.

53. Nordwest. Grenze an *Cosgiyab*.

Da mit den beiden Übersetzungen aus der Reichsgeographie bereits eine kurze systematische Beschreibung des Landes gebracht wurde, ist bei dem aus dem Kriegswerk geförderten Stoff von dieser Form abgesehen und dafür die einer Liste der Ortsnamen mit Beschreibungen gewählt worden, — davorgestellt eine gesonderte Aufführung einiger wichtiger Anhaltspunkte. Der Stoff ist ganz ungleich verteilt. Daher haben einzelne Orte ausführlichere, andere kürzere Beschreibungen erhalten, für einige kam nur gerade die

---

[1] Es finden sich auf diesen Karten einzelne Namen, die in dem Kriegswerk fehlen.

[2] Stammesname.

[3] Stammesname.

[4] Vgl. oben S. 77 *Z'unggak*.

Angabe der Lage heraus. Wiederholungen derselben Beschreibung an verschiedenen Orten haben sich nicht ganz vermeiden lassen.

Die nachgesetzten Stellenvermerke beziehen sich auf das Kriegswerk, so daß die Zahl vor dem Komma den Band (*chüan*, mandschurisch *debtelin*)[1], die Zahl danach das Blatt bezeichnet mit der Vorder- oder Rückseite a, b.

Zur Veranschaulichung sei die Probe einer zusammenhängenden Ortsbeschreibung im umschriebenen mandschurischen Text und deutscher Übersetzung vorausgestellt:

Aus dem Bericht der Generale WENFU, UDAI und AGÔI vom Tage *wu-wu* I. Monats des 37. Jahres KIENLUNG (1772):

... ne jugôn tuwanara niyalma amasi jifi alaha bade. Damba Zung ni bakcin julergi ergide. Bumbur Sangg'ang sere emu ba bi. ere alin be dabaci. uthai Meino de isinaci ombi. geli Ziri-i amargi alin-i boso. Sebser deri olime. Okśi-i fere śancin de isinaci ombi seme alahabi: amban be baicaci. Bumbur Sangg'ang sere ba. uthai onggolo Dung Tiyan-bi-i Giyagin Da deri afame gaiha Nio Cang sere bade hanci. amala Nio cang be ufaraha turgunde ere jugôn deri dosime mutehekô. tere sidende ilan amba dabagan bi. iktaka nimanggi labdu bime. inu umesi haksan. aika ere ilan dabagan be dabame muteci. alin be jafame julesi ibeme. mangga ilan duin inenggi uthai Meino de isinaci ombi ... jai Sebser oci. amargi alin-i boso ergi de bi. bujan śuwa śumin fisin. haksan hafirahôn. yabure de mangga. aika ere jugôn deri olime yabuci. Okśi-i fere śancin de isinaci ombi: 17, 7ᵇ ff.

Eben sind die zur Wegeerkundung ausgegangenen Streifwachen zurückgekehrt und melden: »Auf der Südseite gegenüber *Damba zung* liegt ein Ort namens *Bumbur sanggang*. Wenn man den dortigen Berg übersteigt, so kommt man nach *Meino*. Weiter kann man an der Rückseite des Nordberges von *Ziri*, auf einem Umwege über *Sebser*, nach der Nordschanze von *Okśi* gelangen.« Wir (die Generale) bemerken dazu, daß der Ort *Bumbur sanggang* in der Nähe des Ortes *Nio cang* gelegen ist, den vordem *Tung T'ien-pi* auf dem Wege über *Giyagin da* im Kampf erobert hatte. Da *Nio cang* später wieder verlorengegangen war, hat man auf diesem Wege nicht mehr vorgehen können. Es gibt auf dieser Strecke drei große Paßübergänge. Da dort hoher Schnee in Masse liegt, ist der Weg äußerst gefährlich. Gelänge es, die drei Paßübergänge zu überschreiten, so könnte man sich der Berge bemächtigen und nach Süden vorrückend in knapp 3—4 Tagen in *Meino* sein ... Weiter *Sebser*. Das liegt an der Rückseite des Nordberges. Es gibt dort dichten Wald und Unterholz, steile Abhänge und enge Strecken, die schwer gangbar sind. Wenn man auf diesem Wege heruntergeht, gelangt man nach der Nordschanze von *Okśi*.

Als wichtigste Grenzpunkte und Grenzlinien zwischen den einzelnen Landesteilen finden sich angegeben: *Balang*-Paß zwischen *Okśi* westlich und *Wasse* östlich, *Deo u*-Paß zwischen *Okśi* südlich und *Zanla* nördlich, *Gunggarla*-Paß zwischen *Zanla* östlich und *Cucin* westlich (im Norden), *Janggu* zwischen *Zanla* östlich und *Cucin* westlich (im Süden), Kleiner Goldstrom zwischen *Zanla* nördlich und *Mingjeng* südlich, Großer Goldstrom zwischen *Cucin* östlich und *Gebśiza* westlich.

An Flüssen werden außer dem Großen und Kleinen Goldstrom erwähnt: *Ergu* und *Garma*, Nebenflüsse des Großen Goldstromes, *Gezang* und *Giyager*[2] desgl. *Giyamcu* ist jedenfalls der bei *Rumi Janggu* in den Großen Goldstrom einmündende vom *Dabo*-Berg herab-

---

[1] Römisch I gilt für den Einleitungsband mit der kurzen zusammenfassenden Darstellung.
[2] eigentlich Landschaftsnamen.

kommende sogenannte »Westfluß«. Außerdem werden eine ganze Anzahl von Bergströmen erwähnt: *yohoron*, chinesisch: *kou*, eigentlich Bergspalten, die natürlich gemeinhin Flußbetten bilden, z. B. *Namgiyor zung*, *Z'ula giyok* u. a. m. An Brücken scheint das Land zu der damaligen Zeit nicht sehr reich gewesen zu sein. Der Verkehr über die Flüsse wurde auf Fellbooten und Fähren bewerkstelligt. Ein großer Teil der im Kriegswerk erwähnten Brücken ist wohl erst von den chinesischen Truppen gebaut worden. Es werden folgende aufgeführt: eine bei *Janggu* 53, 35ª; eine über den *Gezang*-Fluß 46, 36ᵇ; eine bei *Muc'i* 57, 66ᵇ; eine bei *Mubo* über den Bergstrom *Z'ula giyok* 62, 67ᵇ; eine bei *Zikar*, nicht weit von *Mei mei k'a* 38, 24ª. Einige Brücken sind mit Namen genannt: *Giyar ži sang* I, 17ᵇ südwestlich von *Le'uwei*; *Samgom*[1] westlich von *Meino*, bei *Minggo zung* nahe *Demdan* 44, 42ᵇ; *Gen-da kiyoo*[2], chinesischerseits des *Balang*-Passes, nicht weit vom Passe *O-lung-kuan* 16, 43ᵇ; *Sin-kiyoo*[3] nicht weit von *Kodo* bei *Minggo zung* 63, 2ª.

An Wasserstellen finden wir zwei Quellen westlich des *Dartu*-Berges, der nicht weit von *I hi* gelegen ist 52, 7ᵇ; weiter heiße Quellen bei einem Orte *Dangli*, der im *Gebšiza*-Lande zu liegen scheint 6, 10ª. Während es heißt, daß Salpeter für die Pulverbereitung im *Cucin*-Lande leicht zu finden sei, sollen Schwefelquellen durchaus nicht so häufig sein. Im *Gebšiza*-Lande wird eine solche bei *Moze geo* aufgeführt 60, 49ᵇ. Vom Berge *Gunggarla* wird an einer Stelle 51, 36ª gesagt, daß dort sehr ergiebige Kohlenminen vorhanden seien: *Gunggarla-i moo yaha-i nemu umesi elgiyen fulu*. Von Tempeln, die in dem Feldzuge die Rolle von Festungen spielten, ist eine ganze Anzahl genannt: der Tempel *Bodi* im *Cucin*-Lande, Tempel *Daido* bei *Mubdo*, nicht weit von *Buranggo zung*; *Galdan* am Großen Goldstrom[4]; *Gero*, wohl mit *Gero șena* identisch, im *Cosgiyab*-Lande, nach dem *Gebšiza*-Gebiet zu gelegen: *Meidu*, etwa 3—4 *Li* nördlich von *Meino*; *Meilo* bei *Dungma*, nicht weit von *Mei mei k'a* und *Biyesman*; *Kunser* auf dem gleichnamigen Berge bei *Le'uwei*; *Lenggiyo* dicht bei dieser Stadt; *Mubo* bei *Z'ula giyok*; *Narbub* auf dem Berge *Mordo*, bei *Kaya*; *Ragu* auf dem gleichnamigen Berge unterhalb des Tempels *Kunser*; *San Zang* unweit *Giyomgiyao?*; *Z'erdan sem* am Flußufer beim Berge *Banggiya*. Ein Tempel, ohne Namensangabe, wird bei *Minggo zung* in der Nähe einer Brücke[5] erwähnt.

LISTE DER AUS DEM KRIEGSWERK ZUSAMMENGESTELLTEN ORTSBESCHREIBUNGEN.

Adung, Burg bei *Biyesman*, 1—2 *Li* unterhalb von *Mei mei k'a* 31, 41ᵇ.

Agiye, Burg am *Kobkioi*-Berge, nicht weit von *Gara'i* I, 17ᵇ.

Akamya, Burg westlich jenseits von *Ziri* 21, 17ᵇ. Der Ort *A.* liegt an einem wichtigen Wege des Nord- und Südberges[6], liegt auf einem hohen Bergpfad am Saume des Berges *Dersu* 23, 43ᵇ. Wenn man diesen Platz einnimmt, kann man die Feinde in *Ziri* vernichten und geradeswegs auf *Meino* vorstoßen 19, 24ª. Wenn man von *A.* aus *Buranggo zung* nehmen will, muß man über den Grat des *Biyesman*-Berges 29, 12ᵇ.

Akar, Burg nicht weit von *Biyesman* 31, 41ᵇ.

---

[1] In der ersten Silbe steckt wohl das tibetische Wort für Brücke *Zam-ea*.
[2] *kiyoo* ist das chinesische Wort *ch'iao* = Brücke.
[3] = chines. Neue Brücke.
[4] Vgl. Nr. 39 auf Pl. IV *(Sui-ching)*.
[5] Vgl. Nr. 13 auf Pl. III.
[6] Zwischen Nord- und Südberg von *Dersu*.

Argu[1], Festung im *Cucin*-Lande. MINGLIVANGS Heeresabteilung rückte von *Langgu* vor, bemächtigte sich des Bergrückens unterhalb des *Zisman*-Berges, sowie der Orte *Namdi* und *Se tiyei an*, drang dann von neuem oberhalb von *Zisman* nach *Giyaso* durch und nahm *A.* in Besitz I, 19/20,

Ayang, Ort am Flußufer gegenüber dem *Gargin*-Berge 19, 9[b].

Babu[2], Ort zwischen *Argu* und *Gara'i*, unweit *Langgu* und *Dusung* I, 20[a].

Badu, eine Schanze vor dem Ausgang des *Gunggarla*-Passes 51, 11[a].

Bajagu, Ort im *Cucin*-Lande 2, 47[b].

Bajan, Ort (Berg?) bei *Le'uwei* im *Cucin*-Lande I, 16[b].

Bal, Ort im *Gebsiza*-Lande 1, 42[b].

Bala, Burg bei *Biyesman* 31, 41[b].

Balangla, von *Ch'eng-tu* über 800 *Li*, im *Wasse*-Land 6, 20[a]; (der Paßweg) ist steil und eng ... Von dem westlich des *B.* gelegenen *Zi rung zung* bis nach *Damba zung* führen alle Wege durch. Es ist ein äußerst wichtiger Platz. Wenn man *Zi rung zung* und *Damba zung* nicht nehmen kann, muß man unbedingt nach *B.* eine größere Truppenabteilung legen. Man muß auch verhüten, daß die Feinde durch eine Umgehung (des *B.*-Passes) die Verbindung nach *Biwangla* und *Dermi*, sowie den innerhalb von *B.* (d. h. nach China zu) gelegenen Orten, dem Berge *Deng zang*, *San zen geo*, dem Passe *O-lung-kuan* und der Brücke *Gen da kiyoo* unterbrechen 16, 43[a] ff.

Balang so, ein Ort des *Cosgiyab*-Landes, der damals vom *Zanla*-Stamm besetzt war 41, 30[a]; 42, 8[a].

Bang giya, ein Berg am Großen Goldstrom? Es heißt in einem Bericht des Generals AGÖI vom Tage *ting-sze* XI. Monats 1771: eine Abteilung rückte auf dem Grat des *B.*-Berges vor, eine andere marschierte am Rande des Bergstromes entlang, stieg dann hinauf auf die Höhe des *B.*-Berges, überschritt ihn hinter den Feinden herumkommend, worauf sich beide Abteilungen vereinigten und nun im Kampfe die auf dem Rücken des *B.*-Berges befindliche Steinburg und den großen Turm und alle dort vorhandenen Steinbefestigungen eroberten. Eine andere Abteilung ging am Ufer des Stromes entlang vor. Während sie um den Lamatempel *Z'erdan sem* kämpfte, griff die Abteilung, die den *B.*-Berg erobert hatte, in der Richtung nach abwärts umfassend an ... und eroberten den Lamatempel von *Z'erdan sem*. Die erste Abteilung ging dann weiter auf den *Gunggar*-Berg zu 43, 19[b] ff.

Bangko.[3] Die Natur des südlich von *Gargin* gelegenen Ostberges, seines Rückens, ist außerordentlich schmal und steil. Unten fällt er nach dem großen Strome ab. Abhänge und Felsen ragen steil in die Höhe. Wege fehlen völlig. In einem Tale vor der früher eroberten Steinschanze sind mehrere Türme und Schanzen gebaut. Der Name dieses Ortes heißt *B.* 19, 7[a]. Eine Erwähnung 67, 24[a].

Bawang[4], Name eines Stammes und Landes am Großen Goldstrom, oberhalb von *Rumi janggu*. Erwähnungen 19, 41[b]; 25, 41; 29, 62[b]; 48, 11[b].

Begar giyok, Feste 120 *Li* nordwestlich von *Meino*. Es heißt an einer Stelle 44, 28[b], der Stammeshäuptling SENGGE SANG wolle sich, wenn er *Meino* nicht halten könne, nach *B. g.* zurückziehen. Von *Meino* führt ein Weg über *B. g.* nach *Buranggo zung* 45, 43[b].

---

[1] Vgl. S. 76 *A-rh-ku* u. Pl. II, *H*.
[2] Als Berg *Baburi* vgl. Pl. IV, 15.
[3] Vgl. S. 82 oben.
[4] Vgl. Pl. I, 1 u. 2; II, *I*.
12. IX. 4.

Nördlich von *B. g.* und südlich an *Z'ula giyok* vorbei geht es zu dem großen Berge *Ungguda* 49, 47[b]. Es gibt einen Wegetreffpunkt südlich des Bergstromes von *Z'ula giyok* und nördlich des Turmes von *B. g.* 47. 12[a]. Westlich von *Daba geo* ist der Berg *Punglur.* An dem Bergstrom entlang kommt man südwärts nach dem Turm *B. g.* Wenn man von dort nach Westen geht, kommt man an die Grenze von *Cucin*, geht man nach Norden, so kommt man nach *Buranggo zung* 45, 37[a,b].

Be tu kan, eine Station an der Grenzecke von *Zanla* und *Cucin* 39, 47[b].

Bezu, Burg im *Gcbbiza*-Lande 58, 2[b].

Biwangla, wichtiger Paß nördlich von *Balangla* 22, 2[a], dürfte mit dem *Bipeng*-Berge auf den chinesischen Karten identisch sein.[1] Erwähnt 7, 28[b]; 16, 43[b].

Biyan gu[2] im *Mingjeng*-Lande 10, 22[a]. Von *B.* nach *Gezung* sind es nicht mehr als 30 *Li.*

Biyesman[3] im *Zanla*-Lande, nördlich von *Damba zung* 16, 36[a], nördlich von *Meino* 46, 1[a]. Bei *B.* liegen 5 Burgen 37, 36[b]. Als man nach Eroberung von *Ziri* den Feinden den Rückweg über *Mei o geo* verlegen wollte, hatte man die Möglichkeit, entweder über *Oksi* und *Minggo zung* oder auf dem *B.*-Wege vorzugehen 68, 20[a].

Bodi, Lamatempel im *Cucin*-Lande 2, 53[a].

Bolgen, Berg in der Nähe des Berges *Murasgo* 42, 15[b].

Boogo noor im *Cucin*-Lande 2, 52[a].

Borugu im *Damba*-Lande 2, 52[b], 3, 52[a].

Bulak, Burg im *Zanla*-Lande bei *Nara giyo*, auf der Südseite des Kleinen Goldstroms. General WENFU meldet: »Ich teilte meine Truppen, schickte heimlich nach dem Südwehr des Flusses, ließ dort eine Brücke schlagen, worauf HAILANCA und DERSEMBOO den Fluß überschritten, geradeswegs den Südberg erstiegen und die beiden Burgen *Bulak* und *Jakor* im Kampfe nahmen . . . ESENTEI ging während der Nacht ebenfalls über den Fluß, gelangte nach *Nara giyo* auf dem Südberge und eroberte die sämtlichen dortigen Burgen und Schanzen der Feinde« 43, 30[a/b].

Bumbur sanggang im *Zanla*-Lande, nahe bei *Niö eang.* Dazwischen liegen drei große Berge, die sehr gefährlich sind, da tief verschneit. Gelingt es, diese drei Pässe zu überschreiten, so kann man den Berg *(Mardik?)* nehmen und in knapp 3—4 Tagen nach *Meino* kommen 17, 8[a]. *B. s.* liegt nicht weit von *Meino.* Wenn man in nordöstlicher Richtung einige 40 *Li* vorgeht, kann man *Damba* entsetzen 9, 52[a]. Von *B. s.* führt ein Weg über *Sebser* nach *Ziri* 19, 38[a]. *B. s.* liegt südlich des *Mardik*-Berges: Am Orte *Mardik* befindet sich dichter Wald und ein langgestreckter Berg, der in westlicher Richtung nach *Z'ebdan* hinreicht, in südlicher Richtung *B. s.* nahe liegt 36, 32[a,b]. Ein sehr langgestreckter Bergrücken der Gegend von *Mardik* und *Gungga.* Dieser stößt im Osten an die Grenzecke von *B. s.* 41, 40[b]. Auf dem Bergrücken nördlich von *Rabcuk* und südlich von *B. s.* läuft ein kleiner Weg, auf dem herumgehend man nach Einnahme des gegenüberliegenden Felsens nach *Muramba* hinuntersteigen kann 29, 40[a]. *B. s.* liegt an der Südseite des Flusses, gegenüber von *Damba zung.* Wenn man den Berg von *B. s.* überschreitet, kommt man nach *Meino* 17, 7/8.

Burak, Burg nicht weit von *Minggo zung*, auf dem Südberge des *Daksu*-Berges, am Kleinen Goldstrom 44, 41[a].

Vgl. S. 81 u. Pl. II, *III* u. *IV.*

[2] Vgl. S. 81.

[3] Vgl. Pl. II, *I;* III, 21.

Burakdi[1], Name eines Stammes und Landes am Großen Goldstrom, oberhalb von *Barwang*. Erwähnungen 2, 40ª; 19, 41; 25, 41.

Buranggo zung[2], wie *Dimda* ein altes Nest des Fürsten von *Zanla*. An diesen Ort hatte der Fürst SENGGE SANG von *Meino* aus seine Familie in Sicherheit gebracht. Er setzte sie nördlich von der Burg in ein Boot, führte sie über den Strom und brachte sie nach *B. z.* 45,30. Von *B. z.* bis zur Mündung des *Z'ula giyok*-Baches sind es kaum ein Dutzend *Li*, bis in das Innere (an den Oberlauf) des Baches sind es auch nur 60—70 *Li* 50, 25ᵇ. Das Gebiet von *B. z.* und *Mei o geo* sind nicht die einzigen Stellen, die eine Verbindung mit *Cucin* haben, sondern auch die Plätze im Norden, wie *Zeng teo geo*, *Mardang*, *Da ban jao* und *Karsar*, die haben alle Verbindung mit *Cucin*. Und der Bach *Z'ula giyok* im Südwesten, der reicht auch noch an die Grenze 50, 27ª,ᵇ. Von *B. z.* nördlich bis nach *Zeng teo geo* ist das Gelände weit und ausgedehnt (eine Ebene?) 50, 46ᵇ. — Über einen Marsch von *B. z.* nach *Gunggarla*: am Tage des Aufbruchs wurde sogleich an der östlichen Schlucht von *Z'ula giyok* der Berg überschritten und in westlicher Richtung auf dem Hauptwege von *Nio cang* vorgegangen. Diese östliche Schlucht des *Z'ula giyok*-Baches, die von *B. z.* nur ein Dutzend *Li* entfernt ist ... Von *B. z.* nach *Si ling* sind es 7 Tagemärsche, der Weg geht über die Burg *Mubo* am Bergstrom *Z'ula giyok* entlang nach *Mugang* und *Si ling* 52, 44—45.

Burungkaza, eine Burg mit Turm nicht weit von *Sengge zung* 44, 31ª.

Ci zu, Ort im *Barwang*-Lande? vgl. *Elgui* 4, 26ª.

Cun, Name eines Eingeborenenstammes, bei den *Jan dui*? 1, 16ª.

Cung de[3], Name der Poststelle von *Daba geo* (s. auch dieses). Es ist ein sehr wichtiger Platz, von dem es gerade Wege nach den Orten *Meino*, *Buranggo zung*, *Z'ula giyok* und *Begar giyok* gibt 49, 48ª. Von *Meino* über *C. d.* und *Nio cang* hinaus, das ist der Weg nach *Karsar* vom Vormarsch gegen *Cucin* aus den Jahren 12 und 13 (1747 und 1748) 46, 1ᵇ.

C'i mu, Ort bei *Meino* 45, 24ᵇ.

Daba, im *Cucin*-Lande erwähnt 2, 51ᵇ; 49, 38ᵇ.

Daba geo[4], vgl. *Cung de*, eine wichtige Wegkreuzung im *Zanla*-Lande; der *Zanla*-Fürst SENGGE SANG hatte auf seiner Flucht aus *Meino* seinen Weg über *D. g.* genommen. Auf der Innenseite dieses Bergstromes gibt es zwei Wege. Der eine führt nach dem Passe *Gunggarla* im *Cucin*-Lande, der andere nach *Buranggo zung*. So lautet die Aussage der befragten Gefangenen. Der Berg westlich von *D. g.* heißt *Punglur*. Wenn man über den Bergstrom hinüber in südlicher Richtung nach *Begar giyok* geht und danach

---

[1] Vgl. Pl. I, Fig. 3. Der Name, dessen tibetische Schreibung fehlt, entspricht der chinesischen Form *Badi*. Man wird also auf ein tibetisches Wort *bragdi* schließen können, vielleicht *brag-'dre*, was »Felsen-Dämon« bedeuten würde. Tafel I. c. II, S. 224, Anm. 3, gibt die Aussprache *Brasdi*. Da die mandschurische Umschreibung bei doppelkonsonantischem Anlaut stets einen Vokal einschiebt, hätten wir entsprechend der Erweiterung *Balang* aus *blang*, für *Bulak = blag*, *Buranggo = branggo*, *Burungkaza = brungk.*, *Derunggiyo = drungg.* usw. vorauszusetzen. Da andererseits das Tibetische die Mouillierung des Konsonanten durch einfaches *y*, das Mandschurische dieselbe durch *iy* wiedergibt, müssen den mandschurischen Schreibungen wie *Biyan, Biyesman, Giyaso* u. dergl. die tibetischen Formen *byan*, *byesm.*, *gyato* zugrunde liegen.

[2] Die tibetische Inschrift schreibt für *Buranggo zung* allerdings *P'ru mu mgo rdsong*. Ob wir es hier im Text mit einer stark dialektischen Aussprache des tibetischen Wortes oder bei der Inschrift mit einer tibetischen Nachbildung eines Eingeborenenwortes zu tun haben (vgl. S. 71 unten), sei dahingestellt.

[3] Vgl. S. 81, Anm. 9.

[4] In dieser Silbe *geo* haben wir jedenfalls das chinesische Wort *kou* für »Graben, Wasserspalte« zu sehen, das dem mandschurischen *yohoron* entspräche; vgl. oben S. 88.

sich gegen Westen wendet, so kommt man an die *Cucin*-Grenze. Wenn man sich nach Norden wendet, kommt man nach *Buranggo zung* 45, 37. Nördlich an *Begar giyok* und südlich an *Z'ula giyok* vorbei, über den großen Berg *Ungguda* hinüber und dann den Abhang hinab, da liegt *D. g.* . . . . Auf der Strecke von *D. g.* bis zum Passe *Gunggarla* liegt im Osten ein großer Berg. Es ist ein langer, weiter Weg, und es gibt dort auch viele kleine Wege, auf denen die Leute aus dem *Zanla-* und *Cucin*-Lande hin und her verkehren 49, 48 ff.

Da ban joo (auch jao)[1] im *Zanla*-Lande. Nahe an der Nordburg[2] von *Somo* gibt es einen Weg, der nach dem Orte *Da ban joo* in *Zanla* führt 36, 13[b]. Links (östlich?) von *Na yön da* geht ein Weg, der über den Bergrücken nach *Da ban jao* führt. Den Bergrücken hinunter geht es nach *D.* 38, 26[b]. *D.* in der Nähe von *Damba* gelegen 63, 14. Gerade südlich von *D.* ist eine Bergschlucht 63, 13[a].

Dabsang, eine Landschaft im *Gebśiza*-Lande? 1, 42[b].

Da i, Burg in der Umgebung von *Minggo zung* 46, 2[a].

Daido, Lamatempel, nicht weit von *Mubdo*, bei *Buranggo zung* 46, 11[b].

Dajak giyo, Berg nicht weit von *Mugom*. Nach dem Falle des dortigen großen Heerlagers, bei dem der Oberfeldherr WENFU seinen Tod fand, gelang es den Resten des chinesischen Heeres, nach dem Berge *D. g.* über den Bergstrom hinweg nach dem Passe *Gunggarla* zu entkommen 63, 28[a]. *D. g.* war mit der Schlucht des *Gunggarla*-Berges und *Si ling* ein Hauptstützpunkt der Feinde 59, 44[b]. Der hohe Berg an der westlichen Schluchtöffnung von *Z'ula giyok*, das ist das Dach des Berges *D. g.* Dieses Bergdach ist ein strategisch sehr wichtiger Platz und äußerst schwer gangbar 57, 32. Der Rücken des Berges ist sehr lang und mit dichtem Walde bewachsen 57, 26[b]. In einem Bericht des Generals WENFU finden sich drei Vormarschwege aufgeführt: In südlicher Richtung vorgegangen, dann gerade bergab, geht es nach dem westlichen Vorberge von *D. g.* Wenn man oben geradeswegs den Südberg erobert, dann kann man nach *Karsar* kommen. Wenn man den Bergstrom überschreitet und südwärts vorgeht, dann kann man mit einer Umgehung am Fuße des Berges *Si ling* vorbeikommen. Aber dort überall gibt es dichten Wald und unzählige Pfade (auf denen feindliche Überfälle zu gewärtigen sind) 57, 28[b]. Am Abhange des westlichen Bergfußes von *D. g.* findet sich eine tiefe Felsspalte und dichter Wald, abfallendes Ufer und steiler Felsen 57, 30. Wenn man südwärts vorgeht, ist man nicht weit von *Karsar* entfernt. Wenn man über den Bergstrom hinüber westwärts vorrückt, dann kann man um den Fuß des Berges *Si ling* herum nach der Burg *Serli* kommen. Steigt man bis zu dem nördlichen Fuße des *D. g.*-Berges hinab und dringt dann am Bergflusse vor, so kommt man bei *Si ling* vorbei. Steigt man bis zu dem südlichen Fuße des *D. g.*-Berges hinab und rückt dann vor, so kann man gegen *Karsar* vorgehen 58, 4 ff. Am Bergstrom von *D. g.* abwärts nach der Burg *Desdung:* Der Bergstrom führt südwärts nach *Karsar*, westwärts kommt man nach *Serli*. Dazwischen (auf dem Wege) ist dichter Wald 58, 7 ff. Es gibt einen Weg, auf dem man den *D. g.*-Berg schräg in die Höhe steigen kann 59, 6[a]. Wenn man über *D. g.* vorgeht und (unter Vermeidung von *Karsar*) den Bergstrom überschreitet und westwärts um den Fuß des Berges *Si ling* herumgeht, so kann man nach der Burg *Serli* gelangen. Aber der Nordweg ist recht weit, und noch dazu ist der Bach auf diesem Wege sehr tief und mit dichtem Walde bestanden, dessen Niederhauen große Mühe macht und dem auch mit Feuer nicht gut beizukommen ist 59, 10/11.

---

[1] Vgl. Pl. II, *I* u. *III*; III, 31; sowie S. 81.

[2] *fere śancin* = Burg mit nach Norden gerichteter Mauer.

Bei *D. g.* befindet sich eine Quelle: die Soldaten von *D. g.* mußten über 20 *Li* hin und her zurücklegen, um zum Bach hinabzusteigen und Wasser zu holen, was sehr beschwerlich war. Da sah man, daß die Feinde südlich von der Burg Wasser holten 60, 6—8. Der Bergrücken von *D. g.*, genau nördlich vom Schluchtausgang des *Gunggarla*, liegt zwischen *Karsar* und *Mugom.* Er ist mehrere Dutzend *Li* lang. Im Süden, durch einen Bergbach getrennt, liegen dann die Orte *Samka* u. a. 56, 33a.

Daklo, Burg nicht weit von *Buranggo zung* 46, 12b.

Daksu, Berg bei *Minggo zung.* Über den Fuß des Berges *D.* hinüber gelangt man nach *Minggo zung* 43, 2a. Aus einem Bericht der Generale WENFU und FENGSENGGE: Nachdem wir uns wiederholt die Frage überlegt haben, wie wir nach Wegnahme der feindlichen Burgen, Türme und Schanzen auf dem *D.*-Berge nun *Minggo zung* erobern könnten, kamen wir zu dem Ergebnisse: Wenn wir über den Südberg vorgehen wollen, werden wir den nicht leicht überschreiten können, da der Bergstrom dreimal den Weg kreuzt. Am Nordberge wieder gibt es keinen durchgehenden Weg. Wenn wir aber vom Rücken des *D.*-Berges hinab vorgehend den Fluß überschreiten und dann auf dem Hauptweg am Südufer entlang mit geteilten Truppen marschieren und die Feinde überraschen, so daß sie sich nicht gegenseitig unterstützen können, so möchte es gelingen, den Ort *(Minggo zung)* zu nehmen ... Es sollte dann eine Abteilung den Nordberg (von *D.*) hinabsteigen, eine Brücke schlagen, den Fluß überschreiten, geradeswegs über die Orte *Burak* und *Jandegu* auf dem Südberge dessen Rücken überschreitend vorgehen und sich des Ortes *Minggo zung* bemächtigen. Eine andere Abteilung sollte ebenfalls den Nordberg hinabsteigen, über den Fluß gehen und dann über *Nara giyo* hinauf geradezu vorgehen. Eine andere sollte nach dem Südberge marschieren und von *Gesidi* gerade abwärts vorgehen. Die letzte sollte den Fluß überschreiten an dem mitten am Südberge gelegenen Orte *Orji* hinauf geradeswegs angreifen und den Feinden den Weg verlegen. Die erste Abteilung ging dann auch den Rücken des *D.*-Berges hinab weiter vor, besetzte die Brücke von *Minggo zung*, eroberte geradeswegs *Demda*, nahm drei Burgen mit Türmen und sieben Schanzen. Einige zweihundert Feinde, die aus der Schlucht zum Gegenangriff herausgestürzt kamen, schlug die Abteilung im heftigen Kampfe in die Flucht, wobei eine Menge Feinde getötet und verwundet wurden oder ins Wasser fielen und ertranken 44, 40—42.

Damba[1], Land eines Eingeborenenstammes bzw. Residenz des Fürsten. Das *Damba*-Land stößt an *Cucin* 49, 41. Es grenzt an *Cosgiyab* 51, 5b, und stößt an *Zagu* 61, 32b. Von *Somo* bis *D.* sind es 17 Poststellen, bis zum (damaligen chinesischen) Heerlager von *Cosgiyab* weitere 5—6 Poststellen 50, 28a. Wenn man im Norden über *D.* hinausgeht, kommt man an die Grenze von *Golok* 50, 41b. Das Gebiet von *Damba* ist zwar an seiner Nordgrenze von dem Eingeborenenstamme der drei *Zagu* eingeengt, aber in der näheren Umgebung gibt es viele gangbare Wege von *Cucin (hanci surdeme bade, Cucin-i yabuci ojoro jugôn labdu)* 50, 43. Im *D.*-Gebiet gibt es zahlreiche Schluchten und Pässe, die nach *Cucin* führen 54, 27a. *D.* ist vom Lager in *I hi* über 100 *Li* entfernt, dazwischen liegen hohe Berge und tiefe Flüsse 53, 9a. Das Gebiet von *D.* bildet den nördlichen Zufuhrweg für das Lager von *I hi*, es liegt dicht bei *Cosgiyab* 52, 53a. *D.* liegt nahe an *Zeng teo geo* 38, 47a. Die Zufuhr nach *Damba* geht über *Tatsienlu* und *Zelung* unmittelbar 59, 16b.

Damba Borugu erwähnt 2, 52b.

Damba zung im *Oksi*-Lande, südwestlich von *Balangla* 6, 51b, hat also nichts mit *Damba* zu tun, vier Tagemärsche entfernt von der Fürstenburg von *Zanla* 5, 52a. Von *D. z.*

---

[1] Chines. *Tang-pa.* Vgl. Pl. II, *I;* IV, 50.

nur durch den Fluß getrennt liegt *Muramba* 18, 42ª. Auf dem *D. z.* gegenüberliegenden Ufer, in südlicher Richtung, ist ein Ort *Bumbur sanggang*. Wenn man den Berg dort überschreitet, kommt man nach *Meino* 17, 7/8. Auf dem Rücken des nordöstlichen Berges von *Giyagin da* ist ein Weg, der nach *D. z.* führt 13, 28ᵇ.

Dandung im *Gebšiza*-Lande? 1, 9ª.

Dangga, vgl. *Margu*, nicht weit von *Gara'i* I, 19ᵇ.

Danggarla[1], wichtiger hoher Gebirgspaß im *Cucin*-Lande, an der Grenze. Von *Ya-chou* bis zum Lager von *D.* sind es 22 Stationen 58, 24ᵇ. Wenn man an der Mündung des Bergstromes von *Namgiyor zung* den Berg hinaufsteigt, kommt man nach etwa 40 *Li* nach *Nawei* und *Najam*. Von dort nach Norden zu bergaufwärts kommt man nach einem Marsche von über 30 *Li* schließlich an ein mächtiges Gebirge, das sich in der Ferne an den *Gunggarla* anschließt. Das ist der *D.* 48, 6 7. Bis zum *Gunggarla* sind es etwas über 100 *Li* 57, 52ª. Der Rücken des *D.* mißt in der Länge über 20 *Li* 50, 4ª. Der Rücken des *D.* streckt sich von Ost nach West auf etwa mehrere Dutzend *Li* hin ... »Im vorigen Jahre waren auf dem Wege von *Sengge zung* nach *Meino* die Pfade dieses Berges außerordentlich gefährlich. An den engen Stellen konnte man wohl zu Fuß gehen, aber nur gestützt« 60, 20. In den Bergspalten wächst dichter Wald 60, 52ª,ᵇ. Auf dem Wege nördlich von *D.* liegen wichtige Pässe 68, 39/40. Unterhalb des Bergrückens von *D.* liegen die 9 Burgen von *Kejeo*. Dieser Platz ist eben und hat viele Burgen ... Wenn man am Stromufer entlang nach Nordosten geht, gelangt man nach einem Orte *Sengda*. Wenn man auf dem Umwege über das Gebiet von *Sengiyab*, das zu *Bawang* und *Burakdi* gehört, vorgeht, kann man zwar auch nach *Sengda* gelangen. Aber die 9 Burgen von *Kejeo* liegen an dem Nordabhange des *D.*, und *Sengda* liegt unten am Berge 55, 18/19. Die Zufuhr für das Lager von *D.* kommt über *Muping* 58, 26ª.

Dangiyan, Name einer Burg mit Kriegsturm, bei *Gaca* 44, 2ᵇ.

Dangli, Ort mit heißen Quellen 6, 9/10.

Danja, Ort oberhalb von *Dugung* 44, 2ª.

Danjam, Ort nicht weit von *Le'uwei*, südlich einer Felsspalte, auf deren Nordseite der Ort *Daslam* liegt I, 16ᵇ.

Danjin, ein Ort oberhalb von *Dugung* 44, 2ª.

Dargiyei, Burg unterhalb von *Biyesman*, etwa 2 *Li* entfernt 31, 41ᵇ.

Dartu, Berg bei *I hi* im *Cosgiyab*-Lande, ein wichtiger Engpaß der Feinde 62, 3ª. Der Rücken des Berges ist gleichsam, wie *Ži pang*, die Tür von *Cucin*. Am Fuße des Berges steht dichter Wald 53, 1. Von *Ži pang* ist er nur 67 *Li* entfernt 51, 47ᵇ, von den feindlichen Nestern von *Le'uwei* nur 60—70 *Li*. Es ist ein wichtiger Engpaß für den Angriff der *I hi*-Abteilung auf *Le'uwei* 69, 1. Westlich von *D.* finden sich zwei Quellen 52, 7ᵇ.

Daryuk, Burg unterhalb von *Biyesman*, etwa 12 *Li* entfernt 31, 41ᵇ.

Daslam, Ort nicht weit von *Le'uwei*, nördlich von einer Felsspalte, gegenüber *Danjam* I, 16ᵇ.

Dasri, eine Turmburg nicht weit von *Da u* I, 18ᵇ; vgl. *Molugu*.

Dašihi, Burg nicht weit von *Sengge zung:* Wenn man über die Mündung des Bergstromes von *Namgiyor zung* hinausgeht, so findet sich an der Nordseite eine Strecke Weges an einem abschüssigen Felsen. An der Südseite ist der Große Strom. Und jenseits des Stromes liegen die Burgen *D.* und *Žung jai* 77, 22ᵇ.

---

[1] Vgl. S. 79 u. Pl. II, *I* u. *III* (*Dangga*).

Da u, wie *Sengge zung* ein wichtiger Ort in *Zanla* 14, 56ᵇ. Von *Yoza* nach *D.*
sind es 60—70 *Li* 34, 15ᵃ. Von dem Paßübergang des Berges *Molung geo* ist er auch nicht
weit entfernt. Es ist ein sehr wichtiger Platz auf dem Wege nach *Meino* 19, 34ᵃ. Von *D.*
auf dem Wege *Gidi* und *Dandung* nach *Muc'i* 39, 37/38. Von *D.* und *Dawei* aus wurden
die Burgen *Molugu* und *Dasri* erobert I, 18ᵇ.

Dawei[1] bei *Da u,* noch heute ein wichtiger Platz auf dem Wege vom *Balangla* nach
Mou-kung. Erwähnt I, 18ᵇ.

Degu, ein Ort westlich von *Unggurlung,* erwähnt als *Burakni D.* 41, 26ᵃ. Ob es
sich um einen zusammengesetzten Namen handelt, oder ob hinter *Burakni* eine Interpunktion
im Druck ausgefallen ist, wir also zwei selbständige Namen zu lesen hätten, ob schließlich
das an sich sehr deutlich im Druck erscheinende Wort *Burakni* ein Fehler und *Burakdi*
zu lesen ist, kann nicht entschieden werden. An sich wäre der Fehler graphisch erklärlich
und auch inhaltlich, da die Länder *Bawang* und *Burakdi* kurz vor dieser Stelle erwähnt
werden. Es würde also vielleicht sich um einen Ort *D.* im Lande *Burakdi* handeln.

Degung, Burg oben auf der Nordseite des *Gunggar*-Berges 43, 20ᵇ.

Dek, Ort im *Cucin*-Lande. Der Druck ist nicht ganz klar. Der Name ist vielleicht
Dena zu lesen 2, 48ᵇ.

Demda[2], Burg bei *Minggo zung.* Man ging über den Fuß des Berges *Daksu* vor
und eroberte beim Kampfe um *Minggo zung* geradeswegs die Burg *D.* 43, 30ᵇ. Von dem
Rücken des Berges *Daksu* abwärts vorgehend bemächtigte man sich der Brücke von
Minggo zung und nahm sogleich *D.* im Kampfe 44, 42ᵇ. An der zweiten Stelle könnte
das etwas undeutlich gedruckte Wort auch *Demdan* gelesen werden.

Deng cun, Ort unweit *Mugom* 64, 5ᵇ und des Lamatempels *Mubo* 62, 11ᵃ.

Dengge, Berg bei *Na yön da* und dem Berge *Gogar* 38, 48ᵇ. Vielleicht aber ist
das Wort kein Name, sondern ist von dem mandschurischen Wortstamme *»den»* abzuleiten
und bedeutet dann der »hohe Berg« oder die »höchste Kuppe des Berges«.

Deng i, einer von 5 zusammenstehenden, mit mehr als 60 Türmen und 17 Schanzen
befestigten Bergen, in der Nähe von *Kaya* 16, 32ᵃ.

Deng ženg, Ort unten am Berge *Balangla* 7, 2ᵇ. Der Ort *D. ž.* am Fuße des *Balangla*
ist der Nordweg von *San sen geo.* Es ist ein sehr wichtiger Ort 7, 28ᵇ. Es liegt zwar
eine Meldung des Generalmajors *Fucang* vor, nach der er auf den Ort *D. ž.* vorgerückt
sei, aber tatsächlich hat er sich kaum einige Dutzend *Li* von *San sen geo* entfernt 11, 12ᵃ.
Bis auf die Höhe des Berges *Balangla* sind es einige 50 *Li* 8, 7ᵃ.

Deo u, Ort und Berg an der Grenze zwischen *Oksi* südlich und *Zanla* nördlich.
Das Joch des Berges bildet die Grenzlinie. In *Biyesman* war früher ein Häuptling gewesen,
später aber war der Ort von *Zanla* in Besitz genommen worden. Dort ist ein Weg, der
nach *Dimda* und *Buranggo zung* führt. Wenn man *Deo u* nicht schleunigst einnehmen
könnte, sollte man mit einer Abteilung auf dem *Biyesman*-Wege vorrücken 40, 39. Der
Rücken des Berges *Deo u* im *Oksi*-Lande reicht geradeswegs an den Turm *Begar giyok*
sowie an *Dimda* . . . Es ist ein sehr wichtiger Platz 68, 55ᵇ. Wenn man von dem am
Nordberg von *Loding zung* gelegenen Orte *Mei mei ka* nach der Brücke *Žikar* hinuntersteigt, dann führt am Rande des Berges entlang ein kleiner Weg. Der Ort dort heißt *Deo u.*
In der Nähe kann man nach *Kangsar* gelangen und in der Ferne nach *Minggo zung* 38, 36ᵇ.

---

[1] Vgl. Pl. II, *l.*
[2] Vgl. S. 79 u. Pl. III, 7 *(Teng-la).*

Dereng, Ort unweit *Dartu.* Erwähnt I, 14^b.

Derla, Schanze am Fuße des Berges *Gunggarla.* Wenn man vom Rücken des Berges *Mugom* aus nordwärts sich nach dem Paßloche des Berges *Gunggarla* umsieht, so befindet es sich erst recht im Norden des Berggrats. Von dem Paßloche abwärts liegen die drei Schanzen *Badu, J'ihu* und *D.* 51, 10, 11.

Dermi, Ort unweit des Berges *Balangla.* An dem Nordberge des *Balangla* ist ein kleiner Weg nach *D.* Westlich von *Balangla* und östlich von *Damba zung* ist ein Ort *Zi rung zung.* Nördlich von dort geht es nach *Biwangla,* südlich nach *D.* 22, 2ᵃ.

Dersu, hoher Berg, von *Ziri* aus jenseits des Berges *Tekyur.* Wenn man an dem Rücken des Berges *D.* hinabsteigt, dann kommt man nach *Akamya* 21, 19ᵇ. Erwähnt werden neuerrichtete feindliche Türme und Schanzen auf der Strecke von *D.* bis zum Rücken des *Gungga*-Berges 37, 37ᵃ.

Derunggiyo, Burg auf dem äußersten Ende des Südberges (von *Ziri?*). Jenseits von *D.* ist wieder ein großer Berg. Von dem Rücken dieses Berges hinab kann man unmittelbar jenseits der Burg *Ziri* und diesseits der Nordburg von *Okśi* in die *Akamya* genannte Burg hineinfallen 19, 20.

Desdung, Burg nicht weit vom Berg *Dajak giyo:* Als wir auf dem Berge *Dajak giyo* entlang zogen, haben wir auf einem Marsche von über 10 *Li* die an beiden Seiten im Walde im Hinterhalt liegenden Feinde insgesamt herausgetrieben, und als wir dann geradeswegs bergab vordrangen, erblickten wir die Burg *D.* Als unsere Truppe kämpfend herangekommen war, gaben die Feinde die Burg auf und flüchteten sich in eine große Holzburg *(moo-i hoton)* (mit Palisadenverhau?). So nahmen wir die Schanze im Kampfe. Jene große Holzburg lag oben auf einem hohen Felsen. Um sie herum hatte man einen tiefen Graben gezogen und dichte Palisaden angelegt, eine gute Hilfe für die Verteidigung ... Wenn man über den Bergfuß an der Nordseite hinabsteigt und durch die Bergspalte kämpfend vorgeht, kann man in einem Umweg an *Si ling* vorbeikommen. Wenn man über den Berg-fuß an der Südseite hinabsteigt und kämpfend vorgeht, kann man oben geradeswegs *Karsar* angreifen 58, 4 ff.

Dimda[1], ein altes Nest des Oberhäuptlings von *Zanla,* ebenso wie *Buranggo zung* 26, 27ᵇ. Ein sehr schwer zugänglicher Platz 62, 29ᵃ. Es liegt weiter entfernt von dem damaligen Militärlager von *Danggarla* als von dem von *Mugom* 62, 36ᵇ.

Dingdaśi noor, Berg nördlich der alten Burg von *Okśi* 42, 1ᵇ.

Doger, Ort im *Cucin*-Lande. Erwähnt 3, 52ᵇ.

Dugum, Ort bei *Argu* I, 20ᵃ.

Dugung, Ort und Berg auf der Strecke von *Bang giya* nach dem Gebiet von *Nawei* und *Najam* 44, 1ᵃ. Vom Rücken des Berges abwärts liegt eine Burg *Laza,* von *D.* auf-wärts eine Burg *Danja* 44, 2ᵃ.

Dunggu, wichtiger Engpaß im *Mingjeng*-Lande 7, 3ᵃ. Vom *Gebśiza*-Lande durch einen Berg getrennt 8, 23ᵇ. Von *Kaltar* bis in die Gegend von *Moonio, D., Gangca* und *Janggu* sind es ungefähr 3—4 Tagemärsche 10, 25ᵇ.

Dungma, Ort in der Nähe des *Rabcuk*-Berges: Wir wollen die Orte am Nordberge (von *Rabcuk?*) *Zaza, Serkioi* und *D.* vorher einnehmen, die von *Biyesman* kommende Straße absperren und es dahin bringen, daß die Feinde sich nicht mehr halten können ...

---

[1] Das heutige *Fu-tien.* s. S. 77, 81 u. Pl. II, *I* u. *III.*

Nördlich von *Mei mei ka* (?) stößt der Weg an die Burgen *Zazan, Serkioi, D.*, den Lamatempel und *Giyardo* 27, 3. Die 3 Burgen *D.*, *Serkioi* und der Lamatempel liegen zwischen
Mei mei ka und *Biyesman* 29, 51ª.

E Diyoo[1], Ort im *Damba*-Lande 4, 19ª.

E ja, Ort bei *Luka*, Lage unbestimmt 19, 14ª.

Elgui, Ort unbestimmter Lage 4, 26ª.

E lung giyo, jedenfalls chinesisch: *O-lung-chio* = Ecke des kauernden Drachen, innerhalb (d. h. auf der chinesischen Seite) der Schlucht von *San šen geo* 7, 35ᵇ.

E po, Ort im *Cosgiyab*-Lande 2, 44ᵇ, nicht weit von *I hi* I, 12/13. Der Weg von *E.*,
von der Nordschanze von *Cosgiyab* aufgebrochen bis *Le'uwei* nur 2 große Tagemärsche,
ziemlich eben und leicht gangbar 25, 41ᵇ. Der Rücken des Berges von *I hi* bildet einen
Weg, auf dem man über *E.* gegen *Le'uwei* vorgehen kann 41, 26ᵇ. Südlich von *Muc'i* bis
zur Grenzlinie des Gebiets von *E.* sind es über 70 *Li* 40, 24ª.

Erben, Palisadenburg bei dem Nordberge von *Kamser* 42, 15ᵇ.

Ergu, Fluß 15 *Li* südlich von *Muc'i*. Wenn man den Fluß (auf dem Wege von *Muc'i*)
überschreitet, ist man bei der Nordschanze von *Le'uwei* im *Cucin*-Lande 40, 24ᵇ.

Erti, Ort bei *Le'uwei*, erwähnt I, 15ᵇ.

Fe šancin, d. h. die alte Burg im *Okši*-Lande, unweit *Muramba?* 36, 31ᵇ.

Gabgiye, Burg im *Cucin*-Lande 58, 6ª.

Gaca, Ort unweit von *Sengge zung* 42, 31ª. Halbwegs von *Z'erdan sem* nach *Sengge
zung* gelegen 44, 31ª.

Ga gang, Berggipfel unweit des *Kaya*-Passes 16, 32ª.

Gajung, Ort in *Zanla*, unweit *Janggu* und *Yoza?* 8, 11ᵇ; 10, 5ª. Nördlich des Berges
von *G.* gibt es einen nach *Zanla* führenden Weg, aber man muß bei *Bawang* und *Burakdi*
vorbei, und wenn man durch das Gebiet von *Cucin* hindurchkommt, ist da noch ein Schneeberg, den man kaum umgehen kann 11, 47ᵇ.

Galangga, Burg im *Cucin*-Lande I, 15ª, 22, 42ª.

Galdan[2], Tempel unweit *Galangga?*

Galtar, Lage unbestimmt, erwähnt 44, 12ᵇ; vgl. unten *Kaltar*.

Gangca (Gang ca), Ort in der Nähe von *Moonio* und *Dunggu*, vom *Gebšiza*-Lande
durch einen Berg getrennt 8, 23ᵇ. Von *Kaltar* nach der Gegend von *Moonio*, *Dungu* und
Gang ca sind es ungefähr 3—4 Tagemärsche.

Gan hai ze, chinesischer Name (»ausgetrockneter See«), Lage unbestimmt, erwähnt
56, 21,22.

Ganpu, Lage unbestimmt, genannt mit *Zagu nao* und *Meng-dung* 57, 45ª.

Ganze, Orts- und Stammesname?, erwähnt 1, 18ª,ᵇ.

---

[1] Augenscheinlich ein chinesischer Name. Der zweite Bestandteil ist sicher das Zeichen *tiao*, hier aus
dem Chinesischen umschrieben, während die Form *do* aus der Eingeborenensprache genommen wäre. Also
vielleicht 把 *o-tiao*, der »eroberte Turm«; vgl. den Namen *P'o-tiao*, der »zerstörte Turm«, vgl. Pl. III, 16.

[2] Vgl. *Gardan sze* Pl. II, *I* u. IV, 39. Der Name ist tibetisch *dga-ldan*, »freudenreich«. Den gleichen
Namen trägt das von dem Reformator TSONGKHAPA in der Nähe von *Lhasa* erbaute berühmte Kloster.

13. IX, 4.

Gara'i[1], wie *Le'uwei* gleichsam das Herz des *Cucin*-Landes. Ein Weg über *Gunggarla* zum Vorrücken auf *Karsar* und Angriff auf *G.* Ein anderer wichtiger Weg zum Vorrücken auf *G.* geht von *Sengge zung* über *Nawei* und *Najam* auf *Danggarla* vor 46, 33/34. Der Häuptling YUNGJUNG von den *Cucin* kam aus *G.* über *Bawang*, *Burakdi* und *Gebšiza* über den Strom nach *Janggu* 16, 20b. Es gibt vier Wege nach *G.*: 1) Der *Sengge zung*-Weg: südlich von *Meino* her über die neun Schanzen von *Ke jeo*, 6—7 Tagemärsche, ein schmaler und gefährlicher Weg. 2) Der *Gebšiza*-Weg: Von der Nordschanze von *Gidi* nach *Jengdi*, von dort 4—5 Tagemärsche. 3) Der *Marbang*-Weg: Von *Janggu* über *Burakdi* und *Bawang* nach *G.*, ein gefährlicher und schmaler Weg von 5—6 Tagemärschen. 4) Der *Giyaso*-Weg: Von der Nordschanze *Meker* in *Cosgiyab* aufbrechend, bis *Le'uwei* 3 Tagemärsche. Diese Straßen werden aber alle durch den großen Strom unterbrochen. Und auf dem Wege liegt auch ein Ort *Mayagang* mit sehr vielen Türmen und Burgen, dessen Eroberung großen Kraftaufwand erfordert 25, 41 ff. Von *Si ling* nach *G.* führt ein kleiner aber naher Weg 50, 18b. Auch von *Zeng da* gibt es eine Verbindung nach *G.* Der Weg ist auf der Karte ziemlich eben eingezeichnet 52, 43ª. Von *Meino* bis *G.* sind es 5 Tagemärsche.

Gargin, Berg südlich von *Giyamu* am Ufer des Stromes 16, 33ª. Der Rücken des Südost-Berges von *G.* hat steil aufragende Gipfel, zwei Berge bilden eine Umfassung. Wenn man den Rücken der Berge übersteigt, ist es nicht mehr weit von *Da u* 18, 31b. Nördlich von *G.* ist der Rücken eines Querberges 17, 30ª. Nördlich des Bergrückens im Norden von *G.* ist ein Paßübergang, genannt *Molung geo*. Dort ist ein Abkürzungssteg. der nach *Da u* hinüberführt. Die Gestalt des Bergrückens von *G.* ist äußerst abschüssig und steil. Unten beugt er sich zu dem großen Strom hinunter. Der Abhang und der Gipfel ragen steil empor, völlig ohne Wege. Vor der vordem erstürmten Steinschanze in der Schlucht des Berges sind mehrere Türme und Burgen gebaut. Der Ort heißt *Bangko*. Am jenseitigen Ufer des Flusses liegt *Azang* 19, 7—9. Von *Giyamu* stiegen wir in die Bergspalte hinab, danach hängend und kriechend den jenseitigen Berg hinauf und legten dann am Fuße des *G.*-Berges einen Hinterhalt 19, 5/6.

Garma[2], Fluß 20 *Li* südlich von *Muc'i* 40, 24b, Ort in *Cosgiyab*, der zusammen mit *Muluzung* von den drei *Zagu* besetzt war 41, 30ª.

Gašari, Burg in der Umgegend von *Minggo-zung* 46, 2b.

Gazapu[3], Berg bei *Marbang* I, 20b.

Gebšiza[4], Stammes- und Ländername.

Gegiyang, Ort auf dem Nordwege für den Vormarsch der *Cosgiyab*-Abteilung 68, 11ª.

Gegiyata, Ort im *Gebšiza*-Lande, an dem den *Cucin*-Leuten der Rückzugsweg verlegt werden sollte 1, 28b.

---

[1] Vgl. S. 77, 79, sowie Pl. I, *I* u. *II.* Auf der Übersichtskarte findet sich der in der allgemeinen Beschreibung S. 77, Anm. 2, erwähnte Name *Kua-rh-yai* als *Goryai* noch gesondert als Berg neben dem Ort *Gara'i* eingetragen. Wahrscheinlich ein Irrtum. Von den Namen *Gara'i* und *Garma* kommt auch eine Schreibung mit dem harten mandschurischen *g* vor. Bei den chinesischen und tibetischen Fremdnamen handelt es sich vor *a* und *o* stets um den in der mandschurischen Sprache nicht vorkommenden weichen Laut, der nach der GABELENTZ'schen Umschreibung eigentlich mit *g'* und *k'* wiedergegeben werden müßte.

[2] Vgl. S. 87, Anm. 2.

[3] Vgl. S. 79 u. Pl. IV, 11.

[4] Vgl. S. 72 u. Pl. II, *I* u. *II*; IV, 1. Die tibetische Schreibung des Namens lautet *dge-bšes-rtsas*. *Dge-bšes* bedeutet nach JÄSCHKE, A Tibetan-English Dictionary, London 1881, S. 568, einen Laienbruder.

Gejin, Ort, 10 *Li* westlich von *Giyalu*. Wenn man von dort aus den Berg in einem Bogen überschreitet, gelangt man nach dem Berge *Giyaza* bei *Jeng di* 43, 10ᵇ.

Gelgu, Ort bei *I hi* und *E po* I, 13ª.

Gelukgu, Ort, über den ein Weg zum *Cucin*-Lande führt, nicht weit von *Sengiyab*, *Giyarmu* und *Sengge zung* 36, 46.

Gen da kiyoo, Brücke auf der chinesischen Seite des *Balangla* 16, 43ᵇ.

Genggete, Burg bei *Marbang* I, 21ª.

Gerge pu, Ort im *Gebśiza*-Lande. Über diesen Ort sollte die Truppe von *Gidi* auf *Giyarlung* vorgehen 40, 20ᵇ.

Gerhi, Ort auf dem Wege von *Murjingang* nach *Le'uwei* 4, 4ᵇ.

Gero, Tempel im *Gebśiza*-Lande, der Ort, den die *Cosgiyab*-Leute besuchen, wenn sie zum Handel nach *Tatsienlu* gehen 1, 9ᵇ.

Gero sena, Lamatempel im *Gebśiza*-Land = *Gero*-Tempel? 1, 2.

Gerukgu, Ort am *Giyarma*-Berge 41, 3ª. Es handelt sich jedenfalls um denselben Ort wie *Gelukgu*.

Geśidi, Ort südlich vom Berge *Sem sengge*, erwähnt bei dem Angriffe auf *Minggo zung* 42, 2ª. Die Generale HAILANCA und ESENTEI gingen um Mitternacht über den (Kleinen Gold-)Strom und bemächtigten sich, nach *Nara giyo* gelangt, der feindlichen Burgen und Schanzen insgesamt und stießen dann nach *G.* vor 43, 30ᵇ.

Gezang[1], Ort im *Damba*-Lande 4, 19ᵇ. Die Strecke von der *G.*-Brücke nach *Gidi* und *Dandung* 49, 36ᵇ.

Gezung, Berg unweit *Kaya*: Auf der Strecke von *Kaya* nach *G.*, wo längs des Stromes die Füße der beiderseitigen Berge sich umfassen und vermischen, wird der Weg noch enger und gefährlicher. Von der Schlucht des Berges *G.* an aufwärts hatten die Feinde auf dem Fuße der beiderseitigen Berge Blockhäuser und Schanzen gebaut und so den Weg gesperrt 32, 1.

Gidi, Ort im *Gebśiza*-Lande: Von *Da u* auf dem Wege *G.* und *Dandung* nach *Muc'i* 39, 37ᵇ, von der *Gezang*-Brücke nach *G.* und *Dandung* 49, 36ᵇ, von der Nordschanze von *G.* über *Jeng di* nach *Gara'i* ungefähr 4—5 Tagemärsche 25, 40. Für die *Gebśiza*-Straße sind die Proviantsammelplätze *G.* und *Dandung* 44, 17ᵇ. Ein Weg nach dem *Cosgiyab*-Lande über *Janggu* und *G.* 46, 35ª.

Gio[2], Burg westlich von *Meino*, südlich des Stromes, östlich von *Źung jai*, nahe der Burg *Marli* gelegen. Erst nach Einnahme dieser Burgen ist der Weg südlich des Stromes nach *Meino* frei 64, 41ᵇ. An einer andern Stelle erscheint die Burg unter dem erweiterten Namen *Gio jai* 65, 8ᵇ.

Gio ze jai, Ort ohne nähere Angabe der Lage, genannt im Zusammenhange mit *Zagu nao*, *Gang pu*, Ober- und Unter-*Meng dung* 57, 45ª. Jedenfalls ein chinesischer Name.

Giyaba, Berg südlich des Berges *Gung ya* 44, 37ª. Erwähnt beim Angriff auf *Minggo zung* 45, 14ª.

Giyager, Fluß, erwähnt bei *Gezang*. Im Gebiet von *Cucin* und *Damba*? 4, 19ª.

---

[1] Vgl. S. 87, Anm. 2.
[2] Vielleicht identisch mit *Jio*; denn 70, 2ª haben wir die Zusammenstellung *Jio* und *Marli*, 64, 42ª *Gio* und *Marli*.

Giyagin da, Berg in *Muping* bei *Nio cang* 7, 11 [b]. Von *Ch'eng-tu* 800 *Li* entfernt 15. 20 [b]. Auf dem Rücken des Berges nordöstlich von *G. d.* führt ein Weg nach *Damba zung.* Wenn man über den Bergrücken vorgeht, findet man jetzt (Februar) hohen Schnee 13, 28 29. Neben diesem Weg ist ein anderer nach *Pu sung gang.* Der führt durch dichten Wald. Von *Siyoo guzan ze (hsiao-kuan-tze)* bis nach der Gegend von *Yoo ji* geht es immer am Bergrand entlang. Über *Yoo ji* hinaus kommt man dann geradeswegs nach *G. d.* . . . Auf dem Wege von *G. d.* ist das Wetter jetzt (Oktober) noch ziemlich warm, aber außerhalb des Passes *O-lung-kuan* ist schon Eis gefroren. Nordöstlich von *G. d.* geht ein Weg nach *Damba zung* ab, nordwestlich nach *Muping* 8, 34 35.

Giya giyo, Ort im *Cosgiyab*-Lande, mit *E po* zusammen erwähnt 2, 44 [a]. Der nördliche Weg für den Einmarsch in *Cosgiyab* 68, 11 [a].

Giyalu, Ort nicht weit von *Giyarlung*, auf demselben Bergrücken 49, 36 [a]. An einer andern Stelle wird von Pässen gesprochen, die von *Gidi* nach *G.*, *Dandung* und *Cosgiyab* führen 49, 37 [b]. Zum Vormarsch auf *Giyarlung* muß man über *G.* Südlich von *G.* stehen an der Ost- und Westseite zwei steile Bergrücken einander gegenüber. Der Ort ist wahrlich der wichtigste Zugangspaß auf der Nordstraße nach dem *Cucin*-Lande 41, 12 [b]. Wenn man bei *G.* den Strom überschreitet und etwa 3 *Li* marschiert, so liegen auf dem Marsche nach der Schlucht des Berges *Jeng di* und dem Angriffswege gegen *Giyarlung* noch Orte, die immer noch durch feindliche Türme und Blockhäuser gesperrt sind? 41, 13. Wenn man *G.* wegnimmt, dann kann man entweder geradeswegs zum Angriff auf *Jeng di* schreiten oder um *Giyarlung* kämpfen 42, 12 [b].

Giyambei, Berg an der *Cosgiyab*—*Cucin*-Grenze 2, 51 [b].

Giyamcu[1], Fluß, wohl der »Westfluß« genannte Nebenfluß des Großen Goldstromes, der vom *Dabo*-Berge herabkommt und bei *Rumi Janggu* einmündet: »Die 3000 Mann Truppen aus der Provinz *Kansu* sind zwar über *Tatsienlu* hinausmarschiert, aber da die Brücke über den *G.*-Fluß zerstört ist, können sie nicht ohne weiteres hinüber« 32, 3 [a]. Die Truppen sind verteilt als Besatzungen für die Mündung des *G.*-Flusses, 9 wichtige Zugänge wie *Janggu* u. a. sowie die neu genommenen, an der Ostseite des Flusses gelegenen Türme und Schanzen von *Jagungla* u. a. a. O. 10, 4 [b].

Giyamu, Ort in *Zanla*. Östlich gegenüber von *Kaya*. Um geradeswegs nach *G.* zu gelangen, muß man über den Rücken des Berges nördlich des Lamatempels seinen Weg nehmen und dann im Bogen hinter dem Berge herumkommen. Da aber der Berg sehr steil und schwer gangbar ist und mehrere Türme reihenweise dort stehen, so beschießen wir ihn jetzt mit schwerem Geschütz. Nach seiner Einnahme würde ich dann eine Abteilung aussenden, die den Bergpaß auf einem Umweg überschritte, und würde dann versuchen, (den Ort *G.*) unversehens durch Kampf einzunehmen. Wenn wir *G.* erobern, dann können wir nicht nur, indem wir um *Kaya* herumgreifen, es von vorn und hinten bedrängen und dabei die feindlichen festen Türme umgehen, sondern auch den Feinden den Rückzug abschneiden 12, 57. Beim Angriff auf *Kaya:* Eine Abteilung sollte über den Bergrand im Westen hinüber am Fluß entlang vorgehen und (mit der vom Lamatempel vorgegangenen) gemeinsam die Orte *Gosung* und *G.* wegnehmen 16, 2. *G.* liegt südwestlich von *Gosung*, von dem es durch einen Fluß getrennt ist 16, 1.

Giyardo, Burg nördlich von *Mei mei ka* 24, 53; 27, 3.

---

[1] Vgl. oben S. 70 u. 87, sowie Pl. 1 in Bild 4 zur linken Hand.

Giyari, Berg an der Grenze der Länder *Janggu*, *Gebśša* und *Bawang?* Es wird berichtet, daß die beiden erstgenannten Stämme diesen Berg befestigt hätten, um dadurch den *Bawang*-Stamm gegen die Angriffe von *Cucin* und *Burakdi* zu unterstützen 4, 25/26.

Giyarlung ba[1], Ort im *Cucin*-Lande, wichtiger Engpaß an der *Cucin*-Grenze 30, 7, früher zu *Cosgiyab* gehörig, liegt nahe *Giyalu*, mit diesem Ort auf demselben Bergrücken 49, 35/36. Nahe dabei ein Ort *Segen* 47, 13[a].

Giyarmu, Berg nahe dem *Cucin*-Lande. Von *Molung geo* bis zum Berge G. über 100 *Li* 40, 26[b]. Der Rücken des Berges *G.* hat in der Länge einige Dutzend *Li*. Auf dieser Strecke finden sich mehrere Erhebungen und hohe Felsen. Der vierte und fünfte Felsen sind besonders steil. Wenn man sich dieser beiden Felsen bemächtigt, dann liegen die Klippen, die Türme und Schanzen von den Bergen der ganzen Südgegend alle unter einem 41, 1.

Giyarsa, Burg etwa 2 *Li* unterhalb der Burg *Mei mei ka* 31, 41.

Giyartang, Ort im *Derget*-Lande, erwähnt 60, 31[b].

Giyar ži sang, Brücke südwestlich von *Le'uwei?*, ein wichtiger Weg nach *Gara'i* I, 17[b].

Giyaso[2], Berg in der Nähe von *I hi*, liegt mit *Ži pang* und *E po* an dem Vormarsch-wege nach *Le'uwei*. Der Berg ist steil, und der Auf- und Abstieg außerordentlich schwierig 41, 26. Oberhalb von *Žisman* geht es nach *G.* I, 20[a]. *G.* bildet einen Zugangsweg nach dem *Cucin*-Lande: Wenn man von der Nordschanze *Meker* von *Cosgiyab* abmarschiert, sind es bis *Le'uwei* 3 Tagemärsche und dann bis *Gara'i* wieder 3 Tagemärsche. Aber beide Orte liegen jenseits des großen Stromes, und unterwegs gibt es noch einen Ort *Mayagang*, dessen Einnahme bei seinen zahlreichen Türmen und Burgen große Anstrengung erheischt … Der Weg über *E po* ist ziemlich eben und kann mit dem von *G.* nicht verglichen werden 25, 41/42.

Giyaza[3], Berg bei *Jeng di*. Wenn man von *Gejin* den Berg in einem Umweg über-steigt, kommt man nach dem Berge *G.* bei *Jeng di* … Von *Gejin* bis zum Berge *G.* sind es etwa über 100 *Li*. Auf dem Wege liegen 2 Schneeberge 43, 10,11.

Giyomgiyao[4], Ort nördlich der *Cucin*-Grenze. Links und rechts von dem Berge sind 2 Spalten, die beide zum *Cucin*-Lande führen 56, 24. Einer führt nach *Že şe lo* in *Cucin*, der andere nach *Oban* in *Cucin* 56, 18[b]. Der Ort *G.* bildet den Nordweg zu den beiden Heerlagern in *I hi* und *Ži pang*. Der Platz ist breit und ausgedehnt und mit dichtem Gebüsch und dickem Walde bestanden 54, 26. Eine Patrouille aus *G.* kam an den Schlucht-ausgang des *Oban*-Berges, überschritt den Fluß und machte sich daran, Brennholz zu schneiden, als sie plötzlich aus dem Walde heraus überfallen wurde … Die Feinde, über-wältigt, flohen schließlich durch die Schlucht 56, 19.

Giyön ni, Berg am Großen Goldflusse; nahe dem Berge *Mus gunggak?* I, 14[a].

Gogar, Berg im *Zanla*-Lande?, über 50 *Li* von *Na yön da* in Feindesland hinein. Der General TUNG T'IEN-PI meldet, daß er dort die Feinde gerade beim Schanzenbau über-rascht, überfallen und in die Flucht geschlagen, darauf sich des Rückens des *Dengge*-Berges

---

[1] Die Silbe *ba* gehört hier zum tibetischen Namen und ist nicht etwa das mandschurische Wort für »Ort«. Vgl. die Stelle *G. ba sere ba*, »der *G. ba* genannte Ort« 47, 14[a].

[2] Vgl. S. 78, Pl. II, *I u, II, IV*, 21.

[3] Vgl. *Gaza* S. 79.

[4] Daß der Name so und nicht *Giyomgiyab* zu lesen ist, ergibt sich aus einer Variante *Giyomgiyoo*, deren letzte Silbe nur für *giyao* stehen kann.

(des höchsten Berges?) bemächtigt habe, und fährt fort: Da ich feststellte, daß aut dem Rücken des Berges *G.* noch 7 feindliche Schanzen standen, so haben wir noch am selben Tage (5. IX. 37. Jahr = 1772) weiter von der Westseite geradeswegs den Berg erstiegen und seinen Grat erobert . . . Ich möchte jetzt auf dem *Dengge*-Berge einen Halt machen und dann die Abteilung von *Kanjo geo* in Eile heranziehen und nach Vereinigung mit ihr in einem raschen Angriff einen baldigen Erfolg erzielen. — Eine spätere Meldung desselben: Ich habe trotz tagelang fortdauernder Kämpfe um den Grat des Berges *G.* ihn immer noch nicht in die Hand bekommen können. Aber ich habe erkundet, daß auf der rechten Seite des *Dengge*-Berges ein Weg ist, auf dem man die feindlichen Schanzen umgehen kann. Dann können wir uns mit der Abteilung von *Kanjo geo* vereinigen. Nun erhalte ich Nachricht von dieser Abteilung, daß sie bereits den Grat des Berges *Zama* im *Zanla*-Lande besetzt habe. Wenn man auf diesem Wege herum den Berg überschritte, dann hätten die auf dem Gipfel des *G.*-Berges sitzenden Feinde ihre strategische Stellung verloren . . . 38, 47—49.

Gojeo, Berg in der Nähe von *Da u.* Nördlich vom *G.*-Berge ist der Ort, wo im IV. Monat der General HsÜEH TSUNG seine Niederlage erlitt: Als wir jetzt den Ort im Kampfe genommen haben, sahen wir, daß an dem Felsen und auf der Flußinsel immer noch die Gebeine der damals gefallenen Soldaten herumliegen. Wir haben sie beerdigen lassen und die Generalmajore INGTAI und WANG WAN-PANG mit Wahrnehmung der Opferriten beauftragt 44, 8. Wir haben den Übergang des Berges von *Da u* und den Abhang trotz langwieriger Kämpfe nicht nehmen können. Aber die Generale INGTAI und WANG T'ENG-LUNG haben durch Kundschafter erfahren, daß nördlich des *G.*-Berges noch ein kleiner Zugangsweg ist 32, 13.

Gokdo[1], Berg bei *Le'uwei,* erwähnt I, 16ᵃ.

Gologolo, Burg bei der Burg *Dungma* 30, 32.

Golok, Volksstamm nördlich der Länder *Damba* und *Zung gak.* Der Stamm zerfällt in 3 Teile: Ober-, Mittel- und Unter-*G.* Mittel-*G.* zählt nur einige hundert Familien.

Gosung, Ort bei *Kaya.* Der Berg von *Kaya* hat steile Felsgipfel und Abhänge. Er befindet sich im Südwesten von *Giyamu* und *G.* Dazwischen fließt ein Strom 40, 1/2.

Gošu, Schanze bei *Biyesman* 31, 41ᵇ.

Gozung, wichtiger Engpaß in *Ming jeng,* neben *Tai ning, Mooino, Dunggu* und *Janggu* 7, 3ᵃ.

Guga[2], Ort nördlich von *Janggu?* Erwähnt 71, 22ᵇ.

Gumbur, Ort unweit *Mugom?* 50, 56ᵇ.

Gumburi, Ort unweit *Karsar?* 61, 41ᵃ.

Gungbur, Berg, den man auf dem Wege vom Westauslasse der Bergspalte von *Z'ula giyok* nach *Su lin keo* und *Mugom* überschreitet 52, 45.

Gungga[3], Ort in der Nähe von *Mardik* 36, 32ᵇ.

Gunggarla[4], wichtiger Paß an der *Cucin-Zanla*-Grenze. Östlich der Schluchtöffnung des Berges *G.* ist *Zanla*-Gebiet. Wenn man nördlich der Schlucht den Berg überschreitet und weitergeht, dann ist man schon mehrere Dutzend *Li* im *Cucin*-Gebiet 52, 46ᵃ. Der

---

[1] Die Silbe *go* ist hier ausnahmsweise mit dem mandschurischen Gaumen-*g* geschrieben.

[2] Vgl. Pl. II, *II.*

[3] Vgl. Pl. II, *I.*

[4] Vgl. S. 77, 79, Pl. II, *I.*

Berg ist von Süden nach Norden über 100 *Li* lang 54, 46. *G.* ist der Ort, wo sich die Gebiete von *Cucin* und *Zanla* treffen. Dieser Berg gleicht dem *Balangla*, aber seine Gestalt ist noch höher und steiler und seine Erddünste (na-i sukdun) sind noch kälter. Der General Wznfu, der diese Erkundung eingeholt hatte, schreibt daraufhin: Ich habe mir überlegt, daß in Anbetracht davon, daß wir etwas in Eile sind und keine Zeit zu verlieren haben, es näher und bequemer wäre, wenn wir am 22. und den folgenden Tagen des XII. Monats mit der Truppe aufbrächen und an dem Treffpunkt südlich der Schlucht *Z'ula giyok* und nördlich des Turmes *Begar giyok* einen Weg suchten, um geradezu auf *Nio cang* loszumarschieren, als wenn wir wieder nach *Meino* umkehrten und von neuem nach *G.* marschierten 47, 12.[1] Die Zufuhr für die Truppen in *G.* geht gewöhnlich über *Meino* 52, 58ᵃ. Wenn man von *Meino* den Reis nach *G.* schafft, so sind es über 100 *Li.* Nun ist die Strecke von *G.* nach *Z'ula giyok*, obgleich auf Abkürzungswegen, doch noch etwa 60—70 *Li* 50, 25ᵃ. Von *Nio cang* sind es 20 *Li* 49, 52. Von *Danggarla* etwas über 100 *Li* 57, 52ᵃ. Wir haben über *G.* den Berg überschritten und sind dann in östlicher Richtung nach der Schlucht *Z'ula giyok* marschiert 53, 24ᵇ. Von *G.* nach *Z'ula giyok* ist ein neuer Weg angelegt 53, 40ᵇ. *G.* liegt genau westlich von der Schluchtöffnung des *G.*-Berges. Das dazwischenliegende Gelände westlich von *Badu*, *Jigu* und *Derla* sind etwa 40—50 *Li.* Die Schlucht des *G.*-Berges macht im Norden des Bergrückens einen Umweg von etwa 60—70 *Li.* Wenn man hinunter auf *Karsar* blickt, scheint es vor Augen zu liegen. Aber der Wald am Bergstrom ist so dicht, daß es schwer ist, gerade hinüber zu kommen 54, 47ᵃ. Der Schluchteingang des Berges *G.* ist ein Hauptstützpunkt 59, 44. Wir haben den Nordweg auf dem Rücken an der Schlucht des Berges *G.* geprüft: Es ist ein steiler Abhang. Wenn die Truppe imstande ist, ihn geradeswegs hinabzusteigen, dann kann sie, nördlich der Bergschlucht herunterkommend, den Weg abschneiden. Als ich, General Wznfu, vordem mit der Truppe auf dem *G.* vorgegangen war, hatten wir es so eingerichtet. Aber als die Soldaten sich an gespannten Stricken herabließen, konnten sie, obgleich sie diese auf mehrere hundert Fuß verlängerten, doch nicht auf den Boden kommen. Überdies lag der Schnee auch 10 Fuß tief, so daß es schwer war, aufrecht zu stehen. Deshalb hatten wir die vorher hinuntergelassenen Soldaten wieder hochgezogen und beschlossen, etwas besseres Wetter abzuwarten und dann die Sache noch einmal zu versuchen. Jetzt habe ich aber herausgebracht, daß unterhalb dieses Weges noch ein kleiner Weg läuft, auf dem man schräg (am Berge hin) nach *Samka* gelangen kann. Wenn wir einen Zug abteilen und auf diesem Wege vorschicken, dann kann er mit der Abteilung von *Dajak giyo* zusammen umfassend in den Kampf eingreifen. Der Weg wird aber durch die Bergspalte und den dichten Wald unterbrochen. Wenn wir vorgehen, ohne diesen zu säubern, können wir Überraschungen nicht verhüten. Ich will lieber erst *Dajak giyo* säubern und dann eiligst und in aller Sorgfalt meine Maßnahmen treffen 58, 35ᵇ—37. Wenn man an der Seite des *G.*-Berges bergauf marschiert, hat man dort immer einen kleinen Weg... Dann gibt es weiter einen Weg, auf dem man schräg nach dem Rücken des Berges *Dajak giyo* emporsteigen kann 59, 5/6. Die Schluchtöffnung von *G.* liegt 60—70 *Li* südöstlich von *Mugom* 52, 47ᵃ·ᵇ. Der ganze Weg von *G.* nach *Mugom* weist Höhen, Berge, einen riesigen Bergrücken und tiefe Bäche auf, über eine Strecke von 120 *Li* ist er abschüssig und gefährlich 51, 57ᵃ. Vormarsch von *Buranggo zung* auf *G.*: Östlich von *Z'ula giyok* über die Schlucht, über den Berg hinüber und dann in westlicher Richtung auf der Hauptstraße von *Nio cang* vormarschiert 52, 44. Es finden sich bei *G.* sehr ergiebige Kohlengruben 51, 36ᵃ.

---

[1] d. h. der riesige Berg schien ihm, noch dazu mitten im Winter, nicht recht geheuer.

Gungkar, Ort am Berge *Bang giya* 43, 20[b].

Gungge, Ort nördlich des *Mardik*-Berges[1] 31, 35.

Gung ya, Berg südwestlich von *Minggo zung*. Oben vom Berge G. y. führt ein gerader Weg nach *Meino*. Wo der Felsen dieses Berges *Ning ja* gegenübersteht, dazwischen liegt *Minggo zung* 44, 18 ff. Südlich des Berges G. y. liegen die Berge *Murgulu*, *Giyaba* und *Zi gor ugu* 44, 37[a].

Gung žu, Bergrücken beim Berge *Kaya* 16, 32[a].

Guru, Ort erwähnt bei den Kämpfen um *Meino* 44, 30.

Han nio[2], größte Landschaft im *Zanla*-Lande. Im Osten grenzt sie an *Muping*, im Süden reicht sie nach *Ming jeng*, im Norden unmittelbar nach *Meino*.[3] In der Länge mißt sie über 200 *Li*. Die auf dieser Strecke liegenden Orte *Žung žung* und andere haben sehr gefährliches Gelände. Sie liegen nördlich von *Kaya* und *Da u* 46, 4. Der Weg H. n. ist von *Yoza* 160—170 *Li* entfernt 10, 5[b]. H. n. liegt nördlich des Bergrückens des Lagers von *Kaya* 33, 39[b]. Im Westen von H. n. liegt die große Burg *Sobu* sowie die Orte *Jung nung*, *Kaya*, *Ja wa ko* und *Da u*. Im Nordwesten geht es nach *Meino* 43, 28/29. Von der südlichen Vormarschstraße des Generals AGÔI aus dem VII. Monat des Jahres 1772 wird gesagt, daß hinter dem Rücken der westlichen Berge *Cucin*-Gebiet angrenze, hinter dem Rücken der östlichen Berge H. n.-Gebiet des *Zanla*-Landes 70, 3. Jenseits des Westberges von *Kaya* ist *Cucin*-Land, jenseits des Ostberges ist H. n.-Land 32, 2[a]. Im H. n.-Gebiet im *Zanla*-Lande gibt es einen Abkürzungsweg (nach *Meino?*). Die dortigen Eingeborenen berichten: Wenn man von *Sobu* 2 Tage marschiert, kommt man nach H. n., nach weiteren 2 Tagen kommt man nach *Meino*. Es sind etwas über 300 *Li* 8, 22[b].

Hiyalo, Ort im *Cucin*-Lande, erwähnt 2, 51[b].

Hiyang yang ping (chinesischer Name), Relaisstation auf einer Strecke vom *Tao guwan*-Paß, *Gen da kiyoo*, *O lung guwan*-Paß II. y. p. und *Zi rung* 72, 52[a].

Hiyei ya (chinesischer Name), Ort 60—70 *Li* entfernt von *Giyarlung ba?* 47, 33[b].

Hoor janggu, Stammes- und Ländername, zwischen *Gebžiza* und *Derget*. Erwähnt 39, 30 und 54, 25[b].

Hôwang z´oo ping (chinesischer Name), Ort bei *Siri (Ziri?)*. Erwähnt I, 19[a].

I hi[4], ein wichtiger Engpaß im *Cucin*-Lande 60, 37[a], früher zu *Cosgiyab* gehörig 71, 44 45. Von *Kuan-hsien* bis zum Lager von *I h.* sind es im ganzen 43 Stationen 58, 24[b]. Das Lager von *I h.* ist sehr weit von den Wasserstellen entfernt. Die nächsten Quellen liegen westlich von *Dartu* 52, 7[b]. Die Berge von *I h.* sind hoch, und es wehen dort heftige Winde. Die erste Stelle des Nordweges von *I h.* namens *Ni se gang* liegt oben auf dem Berge. An der Kehrseite des Berges ist dann *Giyomgiyao* 71, 34. *Giyarlung ba* und *Jeng di* waren eigentlich die Wege, auf denen das Heer vorrücken sollte. Aber wenn man vom Lager von *I h.* den Weg dorthin suchen will, braucht man noch 7 Tage, während es von *Zi pang* und *Dartu* nur eine Entfernung von 60—70 *Li* ist 51, 47[b]. General ŠUCANG meldet: Am 12. X. im Lager von *Cosgiyab* angelangt. Brigade General MA HU war am

---

[1] Der Name der Berges wird zwar an dieser Stelle nicht genau genannt. Aber einige Blätter später 43[b] wird anläßlich des Todes des Brigadegenerals FULEHUN, von dem oben die Eroberung des Ortes *Gungge* gemeldet wurde, diesem die Einnahme des Bergrückens *Mardik* nachgerühmt.

[2] Vgl. Pl. II, *I*.

[3] Auf die Karten auf Pl. II paßt diese Orientierung nicht ganz.

[4] Vgl. Pl. II, *I* u. *II*, und IV, 36. Im Text kommen die Schreibungen *Ihi* und *I hi* vor.

10. von *Muc'i* aus vorgerückt, am nächsten Tage um Tagesanbruch östlich von *E po* eingetroffen, hatte sich des Rückens des *I h.*-Berges bemächtigt und 2 Türme sowie 2 Schanzen im Kampfe genommen 41, 24ᵇ. Der Rücken des *I h.*-Berges ist ein wichtiger Angriffsweg gegen *Le'uwei* über *E po* 41, 26ᵇ.

I kar (Ei kar?), Brücke nicht weit vom Berge *Deo u* 42, 3ᵇ.

Jagiyom, Ort bei *Ži jai*, erwähnt 43, 6ᵇ.

Jagungla, Ort im *Zanla*-Lande, erwähnt zusammen mit *Gajung*, *Lamo* und *Žuna*. Nach Einnahme dieser vier Orte schritt man zum Angriff auf *Yoza* 8, 11ᵇ. Östlich vom Flusse 10, 4ᵇ.

Jailung, Burg, erwähnt mit *Layo* 43, 22ᵇ.

Jakar, Burg auf dem Südberge bei *Minggo zung*, in der Nähe des Kleinen Goldflusses, erwähnt mit der Burg *Burak (Bulak)* 43, 30ª; 44, 41ª.

Jako, Ort im *Burakdi*-Lande? Erwähnt 2, 39ᵇ.

Jalma, Ort in der Nähe des Berges *Dugung* 44, 2ª.

Jan, Burg, erwähnt bei *Yamapeng*, in der Nähe des *Kobkioi*-Berges? I, 19ª. Vielleicht bildet das Wort mit *Agiye* zusammen einen Namen: *Agiye jan*.

Jandegu, Ort auf dem Südberge bei *Minggo zung*: General NIU T'IEN-PI stieg heimlich vom Nordberge herab, schlug eine Brücke über den Fluß und rückte dann geradeswegs über die Orte *Burak* und *J.* auf dem Südberge zum Angriff auf den Bergrücken vor 44, 41ª.

Jan dui, untere. Volksstamm, erwähnt 1, 16ª.

Janggu¹, Ort in *Zanla*. *J.* bildet einen Weg, der nach *Zanla* führt (soll wohl heißen nach der Hauptstadt von *Zanla*) 18, 23ᵇ. Das Gebiet des *Mingjeng*-Stammes hat auf eine weite Strecke eine gemeinsame Grenzlinie mit dem von *Zanla* damals besetzten *Gebšiza*-Gebiet. Von *Kaltar* bis nach der Gegend von *Moonio*, *Dunggu*, *Gangca* und *J.* sind es etwa 3—4 Tage Weges 10, 25ᵇ. Von den Straßen nach *Gara'i* die *Marbang*-Straße: führt von *J.* über *Bawang* und *Burakdi* in ungefähr 5—6 Tagemärschen 25, 41ª. Ein Weg von *J.* über *Gidi* nach *Cosgiyab* 46, 35ª. Von *Senio* und *Unggurlung* bis *J.* sind es 5 Tagemärsche. In dem Gebiete dazwischen liegen die Orte *Jeng deng mei liyei*, *Giyarmu*, *Molung*, *Nilung*, *Gargin*, *Yoza*, *Ja wa ko*, *Kaya*, *Bangko* und *Sobu* 70, 42ᵇ. Von *J.* bis *Dandung* sind es 8 Stationen 58, 25ᵇ.

Jang la. Lager erwähnt 3, 32ª: Bei meiner (des Generals Aᴄᴏ̈ɪ) diesmaligen Inspektionsreise an den Grenzen war ich zuerst durch den *Wei-kuan*-Paß gezogen und nach *Zagu nao* gelangt, hatte nacheinander die Lager *Mao jeo*, *Diyei ki*, *Ping fan*, *Sung pan* und *J. l.* besucht ...

Jan gu², Ort im *Cucin*-Lande, erwähnt 2, 47ᵇ.

Jao tung, Name eines Stammes oder Landes? Erwähnt werden die Truppen von *J. t.* und anderen Orten 42, 26ᵇ.

Jarma, Ort, erwähnt bei den Kämpfen um *Unggurlung* und den Nordberg von *Gelukgu* 43, 8ᵇ.

---

¹ = *Rumi janggu (Dschanggu)* s. Pl. I, 4, vgl. oben S. 70.
² Vgl. den gleichnamigen Ort im *Zanla*-Lande. Pl. II, *III*; III, 25.

14. IX, 4.

Ja wa ko, Ort bei *Kaya* und *Giyamu.* An der Mittagsseite des Bergrückens bei *J. w. k.* befindet sich ein steiler Felsen. Als die Feinde sich auf ihrer Flucht von diesem herunterwälzten, stürzten drei ab und blieben in der Schlucht liegen. Der gegenüberstehende hohe Berg heißt *Ayang* 16, 32ᵇ. Der Rücken des Berges *J. w. k.* zeigt überall steile Abhänge. In der Schlucht stehen Türme und Schanzen 24, 28ᵃ. Der Berg von *J. w. k.* liegt östlich vom *Gargin*-Berge 17, 51ᵇ. Er wird genannt in Verbindung mit *Kaya* und *Da u* 43, 29ᵃ, sowie mit dem *Molung*-Berge 32, 12ᵇ. Über *J. w. k.* kommt man an den Saum des *Luyang*-Berges 35, 22.

Je, Burg südlich des Flusses bei *Sengge zung* 64, 41ᵃ.

Jedi, Burg unterhalb und etwa 1—2 *Li* entfernt von *Biyesman* 31, 41ᵇ.

Je lung, wohl als zwei Namen zu lesen.

Jemke, große Burg bei *Dungma,* nahe der Burg *Gologolo* und dem Tempel *Meilo* 30, 22ᵇ.

Jemno, Burg, erwähnt ohne Ortsangabe 50, 35ᵃ. Ein alter Lama Z'ᴜʟᴄɪᴍ Yᴏɴɢʀᴜɴɢ sagt aus: Ich stamme aus der Burg *J.* und wohnte früher im *Narbub*-Tempel auf dem Berge *Mordo* ...

Jemsi, Burg unterhalb und etwa 1—2 *Li* entfernt von *Biyesman* 31, 41ᵇ.

Jeng deng mei liye(1), Ort westlich von *Unggurlung* 68, 40ᵃ, in der Gegend von *Giyamu.* Der Ort hat einen steilen Felsen 43, 7ᵇ. Südlich von dem S. Felsen des *Giyamu*-Berges stehen noch 4 Felsen hintereinander. Der Ort heißt *J. d. m. l.* 41, 7ᵇ.

Jeng diᶥ, Berg im *Cucin*-Lande Wenigstens war das Gebiet, wenn es auch ursprünglich zum *Gebsiza*-Lande gehört hatte, zur Zeit des chinesischen Krieges schon lange von den *Cucin*-Leuten besetzt. Über diesen Berg führte von der Nordburg von *Gidi* ein Vormarschweg auf *Gara'i,* in 4—5 Tagen 25, 41ᵃ. Die Schlucht des Berges bildet einen Durchweg nach *Giyarlung.* Die *Gebsiza*-Leute waren über *J. d.* gegen *Pusj'i gco* vorgerückt 2, 53ᵇ. Von *Giyalu* geht man über den Fluß und kommt nach etwa 3 *Li* an die Schlucht des Berges *J. d.* 41, 13ᵃ. 10 *Li* westlich von *Giyalu* liegt ein Ort *Gejin.* Dort kann man im Bogen den Berg überschreiten und dann nach dem *Giyaza*-Berge bei *J. d.* gelangen 43, 10ᵇ. An der Schlucht des *J. d.*-Berges stehen Türme und Blockhäuser (Holzburgen) 47, 32ᵇ.

Jeoseoᶤ, Länder- und Stammesname, erwähnt 56, 21ᵇ.

Jergiyo, Ort zwischen *Meino* und *Karsar.* Es werden vier Stationen genannt: *J., Cung de, Nio cang* und *Gunggarla* 49, 1ᵃ.

Jio, Burg, erwähnt zusammen mit *Marli* 70, 2ᵃ.

Jiyezung, Ort, erwähnt bei den Kämpfen in der Nähe von *Janggu:* Die eine Truppe ging bei *Janggu* über den Fluß und bemächtigte sich zunächst der Brücke *Gezang;* die andere überschritt den Berg auf dem Wege über *Gozung* und *J.* und ging dann kämpfend hinunter geradeswegs zur Wegnahme von *Mubala* und *Bezu* 23, 9.

Jok, Burg, erwähnt bei *Guru* 44, 29ᵇ.

Jokz'aiᶾ, Stammes- und Ländername. Man durchquert das Land auf dem Wege von der Brücke *El doo kiyoo* (*Erh-tao-ch'iao* = chin. Brücke des zweiten Weges) bei *Wei-chou* im *Damba*-Lande nach *Le'uwei:* über *Somo, J.* und *Zung gak* 25, 39ᵇ.

ᶥ Vgl. Pl. II, *11.*

ᶤ Vgl. Pl. IV, 48.

ᶾ Vgl. Pl. II, *1* u. *III;* III, 1.

Jung nung, Ort westlich von *Hannio*, zusammen mit der großen Burg *Sobu* und den Orten *Kaya*, *Ja wa ko* und *Da u* 43, 29ª. Von *Janggu* bis zum Gebiet von *Nading* liegen *J. n.* und eine große Menge von Burgen und Türmen und Schanzen, die sich bis zu den Bergen von *Voza* hinstrecken 10, 3ᵇ. Erwähnt zusammen mit den Orten Große Burg *Sobu*, *Migang* und *Mari* 8, 11ª.

Jigu šan[1], Berg, erwähnt 65, 23/24: Die Feinde beabsichtigten, auf dem Wege über den Berg *J. š.* die Zufuhrstraße für *I hi* zu unterbrechen.

Kabgiyo, Ort bei den beiden Bergen *Kunser* und *Gokdo?* Erwähnt beim Angriffe auf *Gara'i* I, 19ª.

Kai liyei, Ort, über den einer der drei Hauptwege gegen das *Cucin*-Land führte, neben *Le'uwei* und *Gara'i* 29, 16ᵇ. General AGÔ eroberte die Burgen von *Mila garma* und *K. l.* I, 13ᵇ.

Kaka giyo[2], Ort im *Bawang*-Lande 4, 20ᵇ. Erwähnt zusammen mit *Muki* I, 11ª.

Kaltar, Ort im *Mingjeng*-Lande?, grenzt an das *Gebšia*-Land 10, 27ᵇ. Von *K.* bis in die Gegend von *Moonio*, *Dunggu*, *Gangca* und *Janggu* sind es ungefähr 3—4 Tage Weges 10, 25ᵇ.

Kamser, Burg im *Cucin*-Lande? Diese Burg ist der Platz, an dem die *Cucin*-Leute sich niedergelassen haben. Nachdem die feindliche Besatzung in *Luding zung* bis auf den letzten Mann niedergemacht war, halten sie jetzt diese Burg besetzt 41, 47/48. Ein Bergzug von *Luding zung* steht in einiger Entfernung der Burg *K* gegenüber 38, 50ᵇ. Wir erstiegen den Rücken des Nordberges bei der Burg *K.*, überfielen die große Burg *Murasgo* und nahmen das Dach des Berges *Deo u* ein 42, 1ᵇ.

Kangba da, im *Cucin*-Lande?, ohne Ortsangabe der Lage erwähnt I, 5ª,ᵇ; 5, 16ᵇ.

Kangsar, Ort unweit *Deo u* 38, 36ᵇ.

Kanjo geo, Ort im *Somo*-Lande 38, 13ª. Aus der Gegend von *Zeng teo geo*, *K. g.*, *Muya šan* und *Da ban joo* führen überall Zugänge nach dem *Cucin*-Lande 47, 11ª. Links vom Berge *Dengge* ist ein Weg, auf dem man die feindlichen Schanzen umgehen und sich dann mit der Abteilung von *K. g.* vereinigen kann. Die Zufuhr von *Somo* (nach dem Berge *Guga*) geht am besten über *K.-g.* 38, 49.

Kargo, Ort westlich von *Dimda*. Es heißt 46, 13/14: Als der flüchtige Fürst SENGGE SANG, vor der Burg *Dimda* von dem Häuptling ZEWANG zurückgewiesen, die Kunde hörte, daß der Lama-Tempel von dem chinesischen Heere zerstört sei, und sich an dem westlich gelegenen Orte *K.* auch schon chinesische Truppen befänden, überschritt er bei *Dimda* den Fluß und flüchtete auf dem Nebenwege von *Mei o geo* nach dem *Cucin*-Lande.

Karsar[3], Ort im *Cucin*-Lande. Gegenüber liegt der Ort *Šatu giyo* 60, 4ª. Von *Meino* über *Gunggarla* nach *K.* über 5 Stationen Weges 54, 45ᵇ; 47, 48ª,ᵇ. Von *Si ling* nach *K.* 3 Tagemärsche 51, 9ᵇ. Der Hauptweg zum Angriff auf *Gara'i* geht über *Gunggarla* und gegen *K.* 46, 33ᵇ. Der Weg von *K.* nach *Si ling* ist die Straße, die erst an *Nio cang* und dem Passe von *Gunggarla* vorüber, dann von *K.* in südlicher Richtung vorgeht 52, 45ª. Wenn man auf die Militärlager südlich von *Mugom* hinabblickt, so befindet sich *K.* genau südlich davon. Es ist zwar eine Entfernung von kaum einigen *Li*, aber dazwischen liegt

---

[1] Chinesischer Name.
[2] Vgl. S. 79.
[3] Vgl. S. 77, 79 u. Pl. III, 32.

eine große Schlucht, mit tiefem Wald und dichtem Gebüsch, die man kaum gerade hinabsteigen kann 52, 47. Der eigentliche Vormarsch gegen das *Cucin*-Land geht über *K*. 33, 31 b. Auf der Strecke zwischen *Meino* und *K*. hatte man im ganzen 4 Poststellen eingerichtet: *Jergiyo, Cung dc, Niv cang* und *Gunggarla* 49, 1 a. Zwei gefangene Eingeborene sagen aus, daß sie von ihrem Häuptling nach dem *Cucin*-Lande geschickt worden und danach von dort von *K*. aus an *Gumburi* vorbei entwichen seien 60, 41 a.

Kartar, Ort, erwähnt 38, 57 b: Ein Weg geht über *K*. und *Dandung* nach dem *Cosgiyab*-Lande?

Kasa[1], Ort, erwähnt 17, 15 b: Über diesen Ort führt der eine Einmarschweg nach dem *Cucin*-Lande, der andere geht über *Damba*.

Kasbo, Burg bei *Biyesman* 31, 41 b.

Kasma[2] **lung**, Berg bei *Meino*. Bei *Kodo* auf einer Brücke über den Fluß, auf dem Ostufer vorgerückt, auf einem äußerst schwierigen Wege mit steilen Hängen, dann genau nach Süden, nach dem Grat des Berges *K*. *l*., von dort weiter nach dem Rücken des Berges *Selung* 45, 23;24.

Kaya, wichtiger Engpaß im *Zanla*-Lande, südlich von *Meino*, 19, 11 b; 51, 4 b. Angriff auf *K*.: Es stehen dort feste Türme in einer Reihe. Die Natur der Berge ist steil und abschüssig. *K*. liegt südwestlich von den Orten *Giyamu* und *Gosung*, von denen es durch einen Strom getrennt wird 16, 1. Jenseits der Berge westlich von *K*. ist *Cucin*-Land 32, 2 a. Östlich von *K*. auf der andern Flußseite liegt *Giyamu* (im *Zanla*-Lande). Um von *K*. nach *Giyamu* zu gelangen, muß man seinen Weg über den Bergrücken nördlich seitwärts des Lamatempels nehmen und nach der Rückseite des Berges herumgehen 12, 57 a. Zwei Berge stehen da (bei *K*.) einander umarmend 12, 56 a. Nordöstlich von *K*. liegen 5 Bergrücken in Reihen hintereinander. Dahinter liegen steilabfallende Ränder, so daß es keinen Weg über die Berge gibt 17, 1 b. Wenn man den Berg (von *Yoza?*) überschreitet, so liegt dahinter der Ort *K*. im *Zanla*-Lande 11, 48 b. Auf der Strecke von *K*. bis *Gezung* greifen die Ausläufer (Füße) der beiderseitigen Berge längs des Flusses ineinander, so daß der Weg dort noch schwieriger ist (als auf der Strecke von *Giyamu*) 32, 1. *K*. ist von der Südseite von *Da u* einige Dutzend *Li* entfernt 40, 25 b.

Ke jeo (Kejeo), Ort im *Cucin*-Lande mit 9 Burgen, eine Tagesstrecke südlich von der Burg *Lai jang*, die wieder einen halben Tag südlich von *Sengge zung* liegt. Von *Gara'i* liegt *K. j.* nicht allzu weit entfernt. Der Weg nach *Meino* geht von *K. j.* über *Lai jang* und *Sengge zung* 19, 43. *K. j.* liegt nördlich vom dem Rücken des Berges *Giyarmu* 37, 24 a. Wenn man den Paßübergang des *Danggarla* einnimmt, kann man das ganze *Cucin*-Land von oben her einsehen. Unterhalb dieses Paßüberganges, an einer abschüssigen Stelle steht ein über 20 *Li* breiter dichter Wald. Hier herrscht weithin Schnee und Eis (im Winter). Wenn man dann weiter vorrückt, kommt man zu den 9 Burgen von *K. j.* Der Platz dort ist etwas breiter (eine etwas breitere Fläche) 48, 7. Der Rücken des Berges *Danggarla* mißt in der Länge 20—30 *Li* ... Im Osten geht es nach *Gunggarla* und *Karsar*, im Westen nach den 9 Burgen von *K. j.* 60, 4/5. Genau westlich von der Rückseite des Bergrückens *Danggarla* liegt ein Ort namens *Sengiyab*. Das ist *Burakdi*-Gebiet, stößt aber an die Grenze des *Cucin*-Landes. Wenn man eine Abteilung ausschickte,

---

[1] Vgl. Pl. II, *l* u. *ll*.

[2] Bei *Kasbo* wie *Kasma* haben wir einen mandschurischen Gutturallaut.

die heimlich durch die Schlucht herauskäme, so könnte man die nördlich des Bergrückens liegenden 9 Schanzen von *K. j.* im Kampfe nehmen 61, 29.

Kesgom, kleine Burg, diesseits von *Le u gco* 57, 22ᵃ.

Kiyòn jeng[1], Ort bei *Molung geo.* Aufbruch von *Du u,* am selben Tage in *Molung geo,* am nächsten Tage in *K. j.,* am dritten am Abhange des *Giyarmu*-Berges 41, 1ᵇ. Die ganze Strecke von *Molung geo* (über *K. j.*) bis zum *Giyarmu*-Berge sind über 100 *Li* 40, 26ᵇ.

Kiong šan[2], Berg im *Burakdi*-Lande 2, 39ᵇ.

Kiyoo teo[3], Ort ohne Angabe der Lage erwähnt 36, 21ᵇ.

Kobkioi[4], Berg in der Umgegend von *Ziri* I, 17ᵇ.

Kodo, Ort unweit *Sengge zung. K.* ist der Weg, der von *Meino* nach *Sengge zung* führt 64, 2ᵇ. Von *Sengge zung* muß man, um nach *Meino* zu gelangen, auf dem Westufer entlang gehen nach *K.,* dann eine Brücke schlagen und wieder auf das Ostufer hinüber (weil am Ostufer bei *Sengge zung* der Fuß des Berges dicht an den Fluß stößt) 45, 23ᵃ.

Kos gom[5], Ort, erwähnt 67, 53ᵃ. Es wird erzählt, daß der Häuptling SENGGE SANG von *Zanla* seinen Wohnsitz im VII. Monat des Jahres 37 (1773) dorthin verlegt habe. Demnach müßte es sich um einen Ort im *Cucin*-Lande handeln.

Kunser[6], Berg und Tempel in der Nähe von *Le'uwei.* Der Tempel liegt oberhalb des Lamatempels *Ragu* I, 15ᵇ.

Labisman, Ort im *Cucin*-Lande, wird erwähnt bei dem Einmarsche in dieses Land, nach der Eroberung von 3 Türmen bei *Murjingang* 5, 16ᵇ.

Lagiyom, Ort im *Zanla*-Land? Gelegentlich der Kämpfe um den Berg *Gung ya* südwestlich von *Minggo zung* erwähnt ein Bericht des Generals WENFU die Aussage eines gefangenen Eingeborenen, daß der Häuptling von *Cucin,* SONOM, beabsichtige, von *L.* her die Nordstraße des Heeres abzusperren 44, 20ᵇ.

Lagò o[7], Ort, erwähnt bei *Daudung* und *Udu:* Die in der Nähe dieser beiden Plätze stehenden Truppen sollten über *L. o* vorgehen bei den Kämpfen um *Giyarlung ba, Gidi* und *Jeng di* 40, 21ᵃ.

Lai jang, Burg etwa einen halben Tag südlich von *Sengge zung,* nicht weit von *Gara'i.* Südlich von *L. j.* kommt man in 1 Tage nach den 9 Burgen von *Ke jeo* im *Cucin*-Lande. Der Weg von *Ke jeo* nach *Meino* führt auch über *L. j.* 19, 43.

Lama-Tempel[8], Burg zwischen *Mei mei ka* und *Biyesman,* neben den beiden andern Burgen *Dungma* und *Serkioi* 29, 51ᵃ. Ein Ort mit dem einfachen Namen *L.-T.* ist angeführt bei *Mubo* und *Deng cun* 62, 11ᵃ.

Lamo, Ort im *Zanla*-Lande 8, 11ᵇ.

Langgu, Ort, erwähnt bei *Zisman* I, 19/20.

1—3 Jedenfalls chinesische Namen (*Kiyòn* steht für den chinesischen Laut *ch'ün*).

4 Die Silbe *Ko* ist mit dem mandschurischen Laut geschrieben. Die chinesische Schreibung des Namens lautet *K'o-pu-ch'ü.* Von den Kämpfen um diesen Berg gibt es ein Kupferstichbild im Berliner Museum für Völkerkunde I. D. 31746.

5 Beide Silben sind nach dem mandschurischen Gutturallaut geschrieben.

6 Vgl. hierzu Ostasiatische Zeitschrift, Jahrg. IX, S. 177.

7 Die Silbe *o* ist vielleicht ein chinesischer Bestandteil des Namens = Nest.

8 Vgl. Pl. III, 19.

Layo, Ort mit 7 Burgen, unweit *Jailung* sowie des Berges *Bang giya* 43. 21/22, südlich des Flusses 64, 40ª.

Laza, Burg unterhalb vom Rücken des Berges *Dugung* 44, 2ª.

Lazung, Burg und Turm. Beim Berge *Bang giya?* geht es über den Fluß und geradeswegs auf Burg und Turm *L.* zu, die unterhalb des östlichen Bergrückens gelegen sind 43. 21ª.

Lebo, Ort in der näheren Umgebung von *Meino* und *Sengge zung* 48, 40ᵇ.

Lengiyo, Tempel dicht bei *Le'uwei* I, 16ᵇ.

Leoli, Burg im *Cosgiyab*-Lande, genannt im Zusammenhang mit *Giyaso,* sowie den Burgen *Ge giyang, Giya giyo* und *E po* 3, 51ª.

Le u geo, Ort im *Zanla*-Lande? Erwähnt 57, 22ª.

Le'uwei[1], Hauptort im *Cucin*-Lande. *L.* und *Gara'i* bilden gleichsam Herz und Eingeweide des *Cucin*-Landes 46, 33ᵇ. Der *L.*-Weg führt durch *Cosgiyab*-Land 36, 17ᵇ. Der *Giyaso*-Weg führt von der Nordburg *Meker* im *Cosgiyab*-Lande in 3 Tagemärschen nach *L.* Der *E po*-Weg führt ebenfalls von der Nordburg im *Cosgiyab*-Lande in nur 2 starken Tagemärschen. Der Weg ist näher, der Berg auch sanfter und leichter gangbar 25. 41/42. Von der Brücke *Örh-tao ch'iao* bei der Stadt *Wei-chou* im *Damba*-Lande durch das Gebiet von *Somo, Jok'ai* und *Zung gak* hindurchmarschiert, von dort vorgerückt sind es etwa einige 20 Tagemärsche bis *L.* 25, 39. Der Weg von *Muc'i* nach *L.* führt über *E po:* von *Muc'i* südlich bis zu dem Treffpunkt an der Grenze von *E po* sind es über 70 *Li*, bis *Sedak* = 28 *Li*, dann bis zum *Garma*-Flusse = 20 *Li*, dann bis zum *Ergu*-Flusse = 15 *Li*. Wenn man diesen überschreitet, dann ist man an der Nordschanze von *Le'uwei* im *Cucin*-Lande 40, 24ᵇ.

Lin ka, Ort im *Burakdi*-Lande 64, 37ª.

Litang, der bekannte Ort auf der großen Tibetstraße *Tatsienlu — Batang* 29, 62ᵇ.

Loli, Ort im *Cucin*-Lande? 4, 21ª.

Lorca, Ort unterhalb des Berges *Kiong šan* 2, 39ᵇ.

Luding zung[2], gleichsam das Einfallstor für das *Okši*-Land 48, 55ª. Westlich von *Okši* gelegen 38, 25ᵇ. Der Berg bei *L. z.* ist hoch und die Schlucht breit. Auf der Südseite von *L. z.* laufen 3 Bergzüge, welche etwas schräg abfallen. Der eine Bergzug läuft genau *L. z.* gegenüber. Ein anderer steht schräg nördlich gegenüber *L. z.* Der dritte läuft in einiger Entfernung gegenüber der Burg *Kamser* 38. 50. Die Natur der Berge bei *L. z.*: zwischen 2 Bergen schwillt ein Felsen in die Höhe, der stufenweise steil aufragend an drei Seiten nach dem Flusse abfällt 38, 36ª. Auf der Strecke von *Ziri* nach *Meino* liegen die Orte *Muramba, Okši* »Alte Burg« und *L. z.,* Burg *Munggu* und andere Burgen 15, 38ᵇ. Die ganze Strecke ist kaum einige Dutzend *Li* weit 16, 38ª.

Lung, Burg, vielleicht nicht als selbständiger Name zu lesen, sondern als *Je lung,* vgl. oben 64, 41ª.

Luka, Ort im *Somo*-Lande? 19, 13ᵇ.

---

[1] Vgl. S. 77, 79, Pl. II, *I u. II;* IV, 34. Der Buchstabe *u* ist innerhalb des Wortes mit Ansatzhaken geschrieben, ein Zeichen, daß er selbstlautend und nicht im Diphthong zu lesen ist. Chinesische Schreibung *lo-wu-wei,* tibetische Schreibung *Lho'i.*

[2] Tibetische Schreibung *glub-sling-rdzong.*

Luyang, Berg. Vom Berge *Ja wa ko* an den Abhang des Berges *L.* ... Der Berg fällt steil ab. Es gibt keinen Weg (hinauf) 35, 22 23.

Ma giyo u, große Burg nördlich des Nordberges von *Kamser* 42, 15ᵇ.

Manai, wie *Marbang* ein Ort, wo die Grenzen der Länder *Bawang*, *Burakdi* und *Cucin* zusammenstoßen 47, 34 35; 49, 39; 52, 22/23.

Marbang, Ort im *Burakdi*-Lande, und zwar wie der Ort *Manai*, an einer Stelle, wo jenes mit den Ländern *Bawang* und *Cucin* zusammenstößt 49, 39ª; 47, 34ᵇ; 52, 22ᵇ. Auf dem Wege über diesen Ort war in dem ersten Feldzuge in den Jahren 12 und 13 der Regierung KIENLUNG (1747—48) das chinesische Heer in das *Cucin*-Land einmarschiert. Dieser *M.*-Weg führt von *Janggu* aus durch *Bawang* und *Burakdi* nach *Gara'i*: eine Entfernung von etwa 5—6 Tagemärschen, aber ein sehr schwieriger und enger Weg 25, 41ª. Der Ort muß in der Nähe des Berges *Gazapu* liegen, denn in dem Übersichtsband heißt es, nachdem man sich mit Sappen an diesen Berg herangearbeitet und die feindlichen Werke gesprengt habe, sei nicht nur die feindliche Stellung auf diesem Berge, sondern auch *M.* gleich mitgefallen I, 20 21.

Mardik. Ort und Berg nicht weit von *Gungga*: Auf dem Südberge kommt man von dem Orte *M.* nach *Gungga*. Wenn man dann noch zwei Bergrücken (in südlicher Richtung) überschreitet, liegt da der Ort *Z'ebdan* 41, 14. An den Bergen nördlich der westlichen Marschstraße liegen die Orte *Meimei ka* und *Serkioi*, an den Bergen südlich liegt der Ort *M.* 34, 36ª. Dieser Südberg ist lang und dabei steil aufragend, mit bald hoch bald niedrig wachsendem Walde bestanden. Von oben gesehen, reihen sich auf eine Strecke von über 100 *Li* doppelte Schluchten, aufgetürmte Felsen und wichtige Engpässe einer an den anderen ... Der Berg *M.* ist der Hauptweg für *Oksi* und *Muramba*, ein Ort, um den unbedingt gekämpft werden muß. Auf diesem Wege *M.* ist man von . *Ikamya* aus schon 80—90 *Li* im Bogen vorgedrungen: Auf diesem Wege hat man seit dem 13. V. die sämtlichen feindlichen Schanzen und Burgen der ganzen Gegend im Kampfe genommen, aber die Sperren *Meimei ka* auf dem Nordberge und *Muramba* auf dem Südberge hat man noch nicht genommen 37, 38—41. Aus einem Bericht des Generals WENFU und FENGSENGGE: Auf dem Südberge hat NIU T'IEN-PI sich des Rückens des Berges *Rabcuk* bemächtigt und befindet sich abwärts vorgehend im Kampfe. Wir hatten vordem mit einigen 4000 Mann den Schneeberg auf einem Nebenwege erstiegen und den Rücken des Berges *M.* in Besitz genommen ... Dieser Berg befindet sich einige Dutzend *Li* südlich von *Rabcuk*. Es sollen dort drei Wege sein: Auf dem einen geht es hinab nach *Muramba*, auf dem zweiten hinab nach der alten Burg von *Oksi*, und ein Berg, den man von seitwärts erreichen kann, heißt *Z'ebdan*, dann kann man geradeswegs nach *Meino* gelangen 31, 50.

Margu Dangga, Ort erwähnt beim Berge *Kobkioi* I, 18ᵇ.

Mari, Ort im *Zaula*-Lande? erwähnt mit *Jung nung*, *Sobu*, *Migang* 8, 11ª.

Marli, Burg östlich von der Burg *Žung jai*, nördlich des Kleinen Goldflusses. Genannt in Verbindung mit den Schanzen *Gio (Jio)* 64, 41ᵇ (70, 2ª) und *Mubari* 44, 31ª. An der letztgenannten Stelle heißt es: Nachdem General MINGLIYANG die Eingeborenen aus den Burgen *Sengmuze* u. a. in der Zahl von über 140 Personen gesammelt hatte, kamen von *Burungkaza*, *Taksa*, *M.* und *Mubari* alle nacheinander an und unterwarfen sich. — Eine Schilderung der Kämpfe bei *M.*: In der Burg *Žung jai* am Ufer gegenüber von *Sengge zung* saßen die Feinde noch dichter gedrängt Am 15. VI. überschritten wir den Fluß und kämpften uns allmählich vor, wobei die Feinde sich bis zum letzten Mann wehrten und wir 5o—6o Mann niedermachten, Feuer an die Burgen legten und sie niederbrannten. Jetzt sind auf der Südseite des Flusses nur die beiden Burgen *Je* (und) *Lung* noch unerschüttert und einstweilen noch übriggeblieben. Auf der Nordseite des Flusses von *Sengge zung* bis *Yoza* und auf der Südseite des Flusses von *Kaya* bis zur Burg *Žung jai* haben wir die Feinde alle ausgerottet. Aber östlich von der Burg *Žung jai* stehen immer noch die Burgen *Gio* und *M.*, welche mit den Feinden (den feindlichen Truppen) in engem Verein sich halten. Diese Burgen müssen unbedingt alle zu Fall gebracht werden. Dadurch erst wird der Südweg nach *Meino* geöffnet. Soeben trifft ein Brief von General HAILANCA ein, des Inhalts, daß er die in der Nähe der Burg *Gio* zerstreut gelegenen Burgen einzeln im Kampf genommen und zerstört habe. Und unsere zur Eroberung von *Gio* und *M.* ausgesandte Abteilung ist auch in der Nacht des 16. abmarschiert, und da ich am 17. in der Ferne sehe, wie auf den Bergen eben jener Gegend Rauch aufsteigt, nehme ich an, daß wir dort (den Feind) vernichten und Ordnung schaffen, und wenn wir nach Vereinigung der beiden Heeresabteilungen *Peng lur* und die anderen Burgen nördlich des Stromes einnehmen, das Gebiet von *Meino* westlich des Stromes ebenfalls säubern können 64, 40b—42b.

Marwalji, Ort südlich von *Damba zung.* Nördlich von *Damba zung* liegt der Ort *Biyesman.* Von beiden Orten führen kleine Wege nach *Ziri*, aber alles schmale Wege am Ufer entlang 16, 36a. Südlich von *Damba zung* ist eine Brücke, südlich von dieser an einem großen Berge liegt auch ein Weg (Ort), der nach *Ziri* führt, der heißt *M.* Er ist jedoch voller großer Wälder und Schluchten 15, 34.

Maśao, Burg unterhalb des Berges *Ži gor ugu* (der zwischen *Minggo zung* und *Meino* liegt) am Ufer des (Kleinen Gold-) Flusses 45, 36a.

Mayagang, Ort in der Mitte zwischen der Nordburg *Meker* in *Cosgiyab* und *Le'uwei.* Der *Giyaso*-Weg: Von der Nordburg in *Cosgiyab* bis *Le'uwei* sind es drei Tagemärsche, weiter bis nach *Gara'i* sind es auch drei Tagemärsche. Aber beide (Strecken) sind durch den großen Strom getrennt, und an dem unterwegs liegenden Orte *M.* gibt es eine Menge von Türmen und Burgen 25, 41.

Ma žung, Ort genannt in Verbindung mit *Damba* und *Gezang* 68, 11a; 4, 23b.

Meger[1]**,** Ort erwähnt zusammen mit *Žir Badangga* nach der Einnahme des Berges *I hi* und des Ortes *E po* I, 13b; vgl. *Meker.*

Meidu[2]**,** Lamatempel abwärts vom Berge südlich von *Meino* 65, 28b. Die chinesische Truppe gelangte auf der Verfolgung des Feindes an die Nordseite des Lamatempels *M.* und nahm den Bergrücken in Besitz. Der Platz ist von *Meino* kaum mehr als 3—4 *Li* entfernt. Nun liegt der Lamatempel *M.* nördlich von *Meino* und recht hoch, und die Feinde haben alle ihre Scharen jetzt dort zusammengezogen. Wenn man diesen Tempel einnähme, wäre es eine Leichtigkeit, die feindliche Burg in Besitz zu nehmen. Südlich von dieser Burg führt eine Brücke über den Fluß, die heißt *Samgom* 45, 25.

Mei liyei (Mei liye), nicht als selbständiger Name aufzufassen, s. unter *Jeng deng mei liyei.*

Meilo, Lamatempel und Burg, mit den Burgen *Jemke* und *Gologolo* erwähnt als in der Nähe der Burg *Dungma* (am *Rabcuk*-Berge?) gelegen 30, 22b.

---

[1] Auch im Tung-hua-lu X Monat des Jahres 3 Kienlung in dem betr. Bericht des Generals AGŌI vom Tage Wu-shen findet man den Ort *Meger* (nämlich *Mo-ko-rh*).

[2] Vgl. oben S. 82 Tempel *Sheng-yin-ssr.*

Meimei, Burg auf dem Nordberge von *Da u (Rabcuk)?* 34, 1ª, jedenfalls mit dem folgenden zusammengehörend.

Meimei ka, Ort westlich vom Berge *Purma.* Dieser letztgenannte Platz ist nicht sehr (strategisch) wichtig, aber das westlich gelegene *M. k.* befindet sich oben auf dem Bergübergange. Zu beiden Seiten sind steile Höhen, und zwischen ihnen läuft ein kleiner Weg, auf dem man am Bergrücken entlang schräg hinuntersteigt. Auf dem Nordberge von *Rabcuk (Dersu)* liegt *M. k.* auf dem Südberge *Muramba* 24, 51, 54. Das zweite Wort des Namens wird im Chinesischen durch das Zeichen 卡 *ch'ia* wiedergegeben, welches *Schranke* bedeutet und vielleicht an sich einen chinesischen Bestandteil des Namens darstellt. An einer andern Stelle (31, 37ª) wird der Name *M. k.* noch eigens als *Burg (šancin)* gekennzeichnet.

Meino[1], Hauptstadt im *Zanla*-Lande. Es ist eine »Insel« im *Zanla*-Lande 48, 16ᵇ. Südlich von *M.* liegen *Kaya* und *Yoza* 51, 4ᵇ; südlich und westlich *Ke jeo, Li jang* und Berg *Mordo* 19, 44ª. Südlich der Burg von *M.* ist eine Brücke *Samgom,* über die der Hauptweg nach dem Passe *Gunggarla* im *Cucin*-Lande führt 45, 25. Es führen von dort auch sonst noch viele Wege nach dem *Cucin*-Lande 29, 11ª. Wege: nach *Gunggarla-Buranggo zung.* Westlich von *Daba geo* geht es nach *Gunggarla* 45, 37ª, 44ᵇ. Nach *Ziri* kaum einige Dutzend *Li* 16, 37/38. Nach *Sengge zung* ein äußerst schmaler Bergweg, an dessen schwierigen Stellen man nur unter den Armen gestützt gehen kann. Der Weg führt über die Poststelle *Kodo* 60, 20ᵇ; 64, 2ᵇ. Nach *Karsar,* mit vier Poststellen *Gunggarla, Nio cang, Cung de* und *Jergiyo* 49, 1ª. Nach dem *Balangla* über *Damba* und die drei *Zagu* 65, 65. Nach *Sobu* über *Han nio* in vier Tagen, über 300 *Li.* Nach *Yoza* ist es ein kürzerer Weg, etwa 160—170 *Li.* Nach *Damba zung* etwa 110—120 *Li* 8, 22. 3—4 *Li* nördlich von *M.* liegt ein sehr hoher Tempel namens *Meidu* 45, 25ª.

Mei o, erwähnt als Hauptort für Proviantzufuhr, ohne Angabe der Lage 47, 10ᵇ.

Mei o geo, Ort bei *Dimda* 47, 11ª. Nördlich von der Burg *Daklo.* Der Häuptling von *Zanla,* SENGGE SANG, setzte bei *Dimda* über den Fluß und flüchtete dann über *M.* auf kleinen Wegen in das *Cucin*-Land 46, 12,13. An einer andern Stelle ist es *Mei'o geo* geschrieben 42, 33ᵇ.

Meker, Ort im *Cosgiyab*-Lande: Der *Giyaso*-Weg führt von der Nordburg M. in *Cosgiyab* aus nach *Le'uwei* in drei Tagemärschen, dann nach *Gara'i* in weiteren drei Tagemärschen 25, 41. Vgl. oben *Meger.*

Memurgi, Ort in der näheren Umgebung von *Damba zung* 5, 55ª.

Meng bai la (Meng baila), Gebirgspaß. Im Nordwesten ein Weg nach *Damba,* im Südwesten nach *Cucin,* im Südosten nach *Zanla* 35, 3ᵇ; 39, 12ᵇ.

Meng dung[2], oberes und unteres, Landschaftsname 57, 45ª.

Migang, Ort nördlich des Flusses bei *Janggu?,* erwähnt in Verbindung mit *Jung nung,* der »Großen Burg«, *Sobu* und *Mari* 8, 11ª.

Mila garma, Burg am Berge *I hi,* erwähnt mit der anderen Burg *Kai liyei* und den Orten *Meger* und *Žir Badangga* I, 13ᵇ.

Ming jeng, Stammes- und Landschaftsname, vgl. 49, 38ᵇ und oben S. 72.

---

[1] Nach der Schreibung der tibetischen Inschrift *Mi'ino,* offenbar ein Eingeborenenwort, denn aus dem Tibetischen wäre die zweite Silbe nicht verständlich.

[2] Vgl. Pl. II, *I* u. *IV.*

15. IX, 4.

Minggo zung[1], ein wichtiger Paß im *Zanla*-Lande 48, 55ª. Über den Fuß des Berges *Daksu* vorgehend gelangt man nach *M. z.*, dann nach der Burg *Demda* 43, 2ª, 30ᵇ. Den Rücken des Berges *Daksu* hinunter, die Brücke von *M. z.* besetzt und geradeswegs den Ort *Demda* erobert 44, 42ᵇ. Zur Einnahme von *M. z.*: Wenn man auf dem Südberge (d. h. südlich des Flusses) vorgeht, wird der Weg durch Bergspalten dreimal unterbrochen, so daß es nicht leicht ist hinüberzukommen. Auf dem Nordberge wieder gibt es keinen Verbindungsweg. Man wird den Ort nur dann durch Kampf nehmen können, wenn man den *Daksu*-Berg abwärts vorgeht, den Fluß überschreitet und dann auf dem Hauptwege des Südufers einige Kompanien einsetzt, welche die Feinde überraschen, so daß sie keine Zeit finden, sich gegenseitig zu unterstützen 44, 40. Wenn man von *Meimei ka* nach der Brücke *Žikar* hinabgestiegen ist, findet sich dort ein kleiner Weg, der am Bergrande entlang läuft, der Ort heißt *Deo u*. In der Nähe führt er (der Weg) nach *Kangsar*, in weiterer Entfernung nach *M. z.* 38, 36ᵇ. Auf der Nordseite von *M. z.* liegt der Berg *Ning ja*, auf der Südseite der Berg *Gung ya*. Dort, wo diese beiden Bergwände sich gegenüberstehen, haben die Feinde Türme gebaut, in denen sie sich verteidigen. *M. z.* liegt mitten dazwischen 44, 18ᵇ. Der Weg von *M. z.* nach *Meino* wird durch den Berg *Ži gor ugu* gesperrt, am Flußufer unten am Berg liegt eine Burg *Mašao* 45, 36ª. Ganz nahe bei *M. z.* wie *Meino* befindet sich ein Lamatempel 62, 40ᵇ. Da, nachdem die Feinde an die Flußmündung bei *M. z.* herangekommen sind, unsere Truppen nicht imstande sind, über die Brücke zu debouchieren, so ist es schwer, zum Kampf auf die Gegend des Lamatempels vorzugehen 63, 17ª. Von *M. z.* kann man sehr leicht nach *Si ling* gelangen 61, 22ª.

Molugu, Burg mit Kampfturm zwischen *Da u*, *Dawei* einerseits und *Siri* andererseits I, 18ᵇ.

Molung, nebst *Nilung* und *Da u* ein Ort auf der noch keine 30 *Li* weiten Strecke von *Biyangu* bis *Gezung* 32, 3ᵇ. Als Berg erwähnt 32, 12ᵇ. Vgl. *Molung geo*.

Molung geo, Bergpaß im Norden eines Bergrückens nördlich von *Gargin*. Von dort soll es einen Abkürzungsweg *Da u* geben 19, 8ᵇ. Schneeberge von *M. g.* erwähnt 32, 13. Die ganze Gegend südlich von *Da u* ist voller Schwierigkeiten und sehr hoch gelegen. Doch sind die chinesischen Truppen über *M. g.* vorgedrungen und haben sich des Bergrückens bemächtigt 38, 55ª. Das ganze Gebiet von *M. g.* auf dem Westberge ist zwar steil und hoch, aber wenn man sie bei Ausnützung einer günstigen Gelegenheit in die Hand bekommen könnte, wäre man in den Stand gesetzt, die beherrschende Stellung der Feinde auf dem Ostberge zu Fall zu bringen und danach nach *Sengge zung* vorzustoßen 36, 1ᵇ.

Moonio[2], wichtiger Engpaß im *Mingjeng*-Lande, vom *Gebsiza*-Lande durch einen Berg getrennt, erwähnt zusammen mit den anderen wichtigen Engpässen derselben Landschaft: *Tai mug*, *Dunggu*, *Janggu* und *Gozung* 7, 3ª. An einer andern Stelle wird der Ort der Landschaft *Janggu* untergeordnet und mit *Dunggu* und *Gang ca* zusammengestellt 8, 23ᵇ. Von *Kaltar* bis in die Gegend von *M.*, *Dunggu*, *Gang ca* und *Janggu* sind es etwa 3—4 Tagemärsche 10, 25ᵇ.

Morbiyeji, Burg unterhalb von *Biyesman* 31, 41ᵇ.

---

[1] Vgl. Pl. III, 14, auf Pl. II, *I* den Namen *Menggu* (*Minggo*) und S. 81, der zweite Bestandteil des Namens deutet auf das tibetische *rdsongr*, *Stadt*, *Festung*. Auf der tibetischen Inschrift erscheint der Name in der Schreibung *Mun mgo rdiong*.

[2] Vgl. Pl. I, 5. Die chinesische Schreibung bedeutet »Haar-Rind« (Yak).

Mordo[1], Berg im *Zanla*-Lande, mit einem Tempel *Narbub* 5o, 35[b]. Der Rücken des Berges liegt östlich und in gleicher Höhe des Lamatempels von *Kaya* 14, 51[b]; 15, 17[b]. Wenn man an dem Berge *M.* vom Grenzgebiet des *Bawang*- und *Burakdi*-Landes vorbeigeht, kommt man auch nach dem *Zanla*-Lande. Eine genaue Nachforschung hat ergeben: wo die Grenzen von *Zanla* und *Cucin* sich treffen, sind die Berge mit dichtem Walde bestanden und weisen zahlreiche kleine Wege auf. Ich sehe die Straße, welche die Feinde jetzt über *Ke jeo* und *Lai jang* genommen haben, als ihren Hauptweg an, jedoch muß der Berg *M.* unbedingt auch einen Zugangsweg bilden 19, 44[a].

Moze geo, Ort im *Gebśza*-Lande mit Schwefelquellen. Die Chinesen gruben nach und verwandten den Schwefel zur Pulverbereitung 60, 49[b].

Mubala, Burg im *Gebśza*-Lande, erwähnt mit *Bezu* 23, 14[b].

Mubari, Burg mit Turm, erwähnt zusammen mit den anderen Burgen *Burungkaza*, *Taksa* und *Marli* 44, 31[a].

Mubdo, Ort unweit des Lamatempels *Daido*. Auf der andern Seite die Burg *Daklo* und in weiterer Entfernung *Buranggo zung* 46, 12[b].

Mubo[2], Ort und Burg am Westausgang (der Schlucht) von *Z'ula giyok*, mit Brücke 62, 27[b]. Bei *M.* selbst oder in der Nähe ein Lamatempel, nicht weit von *M.* der Ort *Deng can* 62, 10/11. Nachdem wir von dem Schluchtausgange (von *Z'ula giyok*) nach *M.* hindurchgelangt waren, trafen wir auf den Turm von *Begar giyok* und die große Straße von *Buranggo zung* ... Bei dem Einmarsch ins *Cucin*-Land im Jahre 1747 48 hatte man auf dem *Si ling*-Wege in *M.* und andern Orten Postämter errichtet 52, 57[b]. Ein Weg führt über *Buranggo zung* nach *Si ling*, in 7 Tagemärschen. Das ist der Weg, auf dem man über die Burgen von *M.* u. a. durch die Schlucht von *Z'ula giyok* auf *Mugang* und *Si ling* vorgehen muß 52, 45.

Mucu geo, Ort auf dem Vormarsche gegen *Gara'i* 38, 33[a].

Muc'i, Ort im *Cośgiyab*-Lande. In der Nähe eine Brücke 57, 66[b]. Auf der *Cośgiyab*-Straße ist *M.* der Proviantsammelplatz. Was den Provianttransport von *M.* auf den Rücken des Berges *I hi* anlangt, so läßt man ihn jetzt mit Ula (von den Eingeborenen gestellte Tragtiere) nach dem Orte *Giyongiyao* und von dort mit den reichlich vorhandenen Trägern nach dem Bergrücken schaffen 44, 18[a]. Von *Dandung* nach *M.* sind es 7 Poststellen 39, 38[b]. Südlich von *M.* bis zur Grenzlinie bei *Epo* sind es einige 70 *Li*, dann bis *Sedak* = 28 *Li*, bis zum *G'arma*-Flusse = 20 *Li*, dann bis zum *Ergu*-Fluß = 15 *Li*. Nach Überschreitung dieses Flusses hat man dann die Nordburg von *Le'uwei* im *Cucin*-Lande.

Mudaguwan, Ort in *Cucin*, erwähnt neben *Ośogiyo* und *Doger* 3, 25[b].

Mudui, Ort, 6 Poststellen von *Kuan-hsien* gelegen 58, 25[a].

Mugom[3], Ort gegenüber von *Si ling;* die Schlucht von *Z'ula giyok* hat einen Ostausgang. Wenn man südlich von *Buranggo zung* und westlich von *Begar giyok* allmählich in westlicher Richtung an den Fuß des Berges an der Rückseite des *Gunggarla* gelangt, so nennt man das den Westausgang. (So ist man an dem Westausgang?) Erst wenn man diesen überschritten hat und dann noch einen Berg überstiegen, ist man in *M.* 52, 43[b]. *M.* liegt 60—70 *Li* nordöstlich vom Passe des *Gunggarla*-Berges 52, 47[a]. Wenn man

---

[1] Vgl. S. 81, Pl. II, *I* u. *II.*

[2] Vgl. S. 81 u. Pl. III, 20 *(Mu-p o).*

[3] Vgl. S. 77 u. Pl. II, *I.* Vielleicht ist die chinesische Schreibung *Sui gom* auf Pl. II, *II* ein Fehler für *Mugom.*

morgens von *M.* abmarschiert, ist man zu Mittag in *Z'ula giyok* 53, 40. Vom Passe *T'ao-kuan* bis zum Lager von *M.* sind es insgesamt 29 Stationen 58, 24ª. Nördlich von *M.* liegt ein Berg. Der Aufstieg beträgt etwa 5—6 *Li.* Dann geht es über den Bergrücken. Auf dem rückseitigen Abhang lag (Februar) der Schnee mehrere Ellen tief. Im Nordosten ist dann *Zanla*-Gebiet. Wenn man den Berg überschreitet, kommt man geradeswegs nach *Le u geo* im *Cucin*-Lande, das ist der nach *Le'uwei* durchführende Weg 54, 38ª. Wir haben zwar die drei Vorberge (Bergfüße) südlich von *M.* besetzt, aber unterhalb dieser Vorberge befindet sich eine große Schlucht (die Vorberge werden durch eine große Schlucht getrennt?), die außerordentlich tief und gefährlich ist. Die Bergufer an beiden Seiten sind steile Felsen. An der Schlucht sind Dornsträucher und dergleichen Gestrüpp zu einem undurchdringlichen Dickicht gewachsen 54, 9ª. Die Verpflegung der Truppen in *M.* geht über *Begar giyok* 52, 58ª.

Mugu, Burg zwischen *Marbang* und *Gara'i.* Erwähnt neben den beiden Burgen *Genggete* und *Zengda* I, 21ª.

Muk, Ort im *Cošgiyab*-Lande, Residenz eines Unterhäuptlings *(tuše)*, wahrscheinlich nach der *Cucin*-Grenze zu gelegen, denn der betreffende Unterhäuptling wurde mit einem Einfall ins *Cucin*-Land beauftragt 2, 43ᵇ. An einer andern Stelle wird der Ort im Zusammenhang mit *E po* erwähnt 3, 35ᵇ.

Mukang, Burg im *Cucin*-Lande, erwähnt zusammen mit der Burg *Žusi* und den Burgen auf den Nordbergen von *Ži pang* 3, 50ᵇ.

Muki, Ort erwähnt zusammen mit *Kaka giyo* I, 11ª.

Mulagu, Burg unterhalb *Biyesman.* Vgl. *Adung* 31, 41ᵇ.

Mulozung, Ort im Lande *Zung gak*, erwähnt mit *Garma* 30, 7ᵇ.

Muluzung (Mulu zung), offenbar mit dem vorhergehenden identisch, denn es wird an zwei Stellen mit *Garma* (und *Balang so*) zusammen erwähnt 41, 30ª; 42, 8ª.

Mulzung, vielleicht ebenfalls eine dritte Schreibung für denselben Ort. Ein Eingeborener meldet: Die Leute von *Zanla* hätten die Orte *Okši, Damba zung* (d. h. die Hauptplätze dieser Landschaften), *M.* und *Ziri* belagert 6, 19/20.

Munamba, identisch mit *Muramba?* In einem Kaiserlichen Erlasse findet sich die Stelle: Ein Angehöriger des *Zanla*-Stammes namens Burgiva, der sich unterworfen hatte, erklärte, er wohne an dem Orte *Muramba.* Wenn die chinesischen Truppen nach der Einnahme von *Ziri* nach *Muramba* kämen, hätte seine gesamte Familie keinen Weg (Ort), wo sie leben könne. Wir (der Kaiser) stellen fest, daß in die Karte ein Ort namens *M.* eingezeichnet ist. Das möchte doch wohl eben *Muramba* sein. Jener Ort wird von *Damba zung* nur durch einen Fluß getrennt und ist von *Meino* auch nicht sehr weit entfernt. Wir sagen uns: da einerseits *Ziri* eingeschlossen wird, andererseits eine Truppe auf getrennten Wegen geradezu auf *M.* losgeschickt ist, so ist sie, wenn sie nach *M.* gelangt, dann in den Norden von *Ziri* herumgekommen ... Der in die Karte eingezeichnete Ort *M.* liegt noch innerhalb des *Okši*-Gebietes 18, 41/42.

Muping¹, Stammes- und Ländername östlich von *Mingjeng.* Das Gebiet grenzt im Westen an *Hannio* 46, 4ª. Für den Vormarsch auf *Meino* wurden die beiden Wege über *M.* und *Balangla* gewählt 10, 25ª. Bei dem Wege von *Ch'eng-tu* nach *Meino* über *Ya-chou* und *M.* spart man zwei Stationen (Tage) gegenüber dem Wege von *Ch'eng-tu* nach *Meino* über den Paß *T'ao-kuan.*

¹ Vergl. Pl. II, *II* u. *III.*

Muramba, vgl. auch *Munamba* 18, 42ª, ein Ort auf der Strecke zwischen *Ziri* und *Meino:* auf dieser Strecke, die nur einige Dutzend *Li* mißt, liegen die Orte *M., Okši,* Alte Burg sowie *Luding zung* und Burg *Mungžu* 16, 37'38. *M.* liegt westlich von der Burg *Akamya,* über *M.* hinaus liegt dann die alte Burg von *Okši* 21, 17. Am *Mardik*-Wege liegt am Nordberge *Meimei ka,* am Südberge *M.* 37, 39ᵇ—41.

Murasgo, große Burg auf dem Rücken des Berges nördlich der Burg *Kamser:* nach Eroberung der großen Burg *M.* nahmen wir das Dach des Berges *Deo u* in Besitz 42, 1ᵇ. EsENTEI erstieg auf einem Bogen über den Berg *M.* den Gipfel des Berges *Bolgen* 42, 15ᵇ.

Murgulu. Berg südlich des Berges *Gung ya.* Neben ihm die beiden Berge *Giyaba* und *Ži gor ugu.* Unterhalb der drei Berge befindet sich eine große Schlucht. Überschreitet man diese, so kommt man in südlicher Richtung geradeswegs nach *Meino* 44, 37.

Murjin gang[1], Ort im *Damba*-Lande, steiles und enges Gelände 25, 40ª. Der Ort war zu Anfang des Krieges von den *Cucin*-Leuten besetzt worden 3, 10.

Mur zung[2], wie *Damba zung* und *Ži lung zung* südwestlich von *Balangla* gelegen 6, 51ᵇ. Von *M. z.* geht es nach dem *Biyesman*-Wege . . . Zwischen *M. z.* und *Balangla* liegt die Station *Sung-lin-k'ou* 22, 2.

Mus gunggak, Berg unweit des Berges *Kangsar* I, 14ª.

Muya, Berg oberhalb von *Da ban joo.* Unterhalb von dem Rücken des Berges *Zama* sind die Berge in dem ganzen südwestlichen Gelände sehr langgestreckt, wohl über 40 *Li* weit. Wenn man sie überschritten hat, ist da ein quergelegener Sandberg. Wieder südlich von diesem liegt der Rücken eines Berges, welcher *M.* heißt. Steigt man diesen Berg hinab, so liegt dort *Da ban joo.* Die Berge des Geländes im Südosten haben steile Abhänge und bald hoch, bald niedrig stehenden Wald ohne jeden gangbaren Weg. Aber wenn man geradezu über *Kan jo geo* hinabsteigt und in einem Bogen durch die Schluchtöffnung herauskommt und dann den Fluß überschreitet, dann gelangt man nach *Da ban joo* 39, 10/11. Vom Rücken des Berges *M.* abwärts bis *Da ban joo* höchstens etwa 10—20 *Li* 40, 10/11. Die Orte *Zeng teo geo, Kanjo geo, Muya šan* und *Da ban joo* bieten alle einen Zugang nach dem *Cucin*-Lande 47, 11ª. Abwärts vom Rücken des Berges *M.* ist der Wald zu beiden Seiten sehr dicht 41, 37ª.

Muyang gang, Berg südlich von *Šen kuwan:* Als wir von *Kan jo geo* in südlicher Richtung vorrückten, sahen wir, daß der Rücken des südlich von *Šen kuwan* gelegenen Berges *M. g.* einen wichtigen Vormarschweg für die Truppe darbot. Daher erstürmten wir die unterhalb des Bergrückens gelegenen Steinschanzen und Blockhäuser und dann den Berg *M. g.* selbst. Dort teilten wir die Truppe in zwei Abteilungen, von denen die eine über die Bergübergänge seitwärts des Berges *M. g.* hinabsteigen, die andere auf dem Hauptwege zur Eroberung des Bergrückens *Muya* vorgehen sollte 40, 9/10.

Nading, Ort im *Mingjeng*-Lande, an den das Gebiet von *Bawang* und *Burakdi* angrenzt . . . Er liegt westlich vom Flusse 6, 28ª. Von *N.* über den Fluß an das Ostufer hinüber kommt man zu der großen Burg *Sobu* im *Mingjeng*-Lande 7, 23, 24. Genannt mit *Biyan gu* 7, 52ª. Zwischen *Janggu* und dem Gebiet von *N.* liegt eine große Menge von Burgen, Türmen und Schanzen wie *Jung nung* u. a., die sich bis nach den Bergen von *Yoza* fortsetzen 10, 3ᵇ.

---

[1] Vgl. S. 77.
[2] Die Endung *zung* ist stets *dsong* = Stadt (tibet.).

Naidang, Berg auf der Strecke von *Dugum* nach *Giyaza* I, 20ᵃ.

Najam, Ort, der stets mit *Nawei* zusammen genannt wird, nordwestlich von *Sengge zung* 44, 32ᵃ: Wenn man am Ausgange der Schlucht von *Namgiyor zung* den Berg ersteigt und ca. 40 *Li* weiter marschiert, so kommt man nach *Nawei* und *N.* Und wenn man von dort nordwärts auf den Berg steigt, so liegt da in einer Entfernung von einigen 30 *Li* eine große Bergkette (mit Übergang), die sich in der Ferne in den *Gunggarla* fortsetzt 48, 6ᵇ. Wir wollen nach Eroberung der auf dem Berge südöstlich von *Unggurlung* gelegenen feindlichen Schanzen über *Nawei* und *N.* vorrücken und geradeswegs zum Angriff auf *Sengge zung* marschieren 43, 8ᵇ.

Namdi, Ort erwähnt mit *Se tiyei an:* Wir rückten von *Langgu* aus vor, nahmen den Bergrücken unterhalb von *Zisman* nebst den Orten *N.* und *Se tiyei an*, stießen dann wiederum oberhalb von *Zisman* auf *Giyaso* vor und eroberten *Argu* I, 20ᵃ.

Namgiyor zung, Ort an einer großen Schlucht. Vom Ausgange der Schlucht den Berg hinauf kommt man nach etwa 40 *Li* nach *Nawei* und *Najam* 48, 6ᵇ. Der Ausgang der Schlucht von *N. z.* bietet den großen Weg nach *Nawei* und *Najam* 44, 32ᵇ. Der Schluchtausgang liegt südlich von *Sengge zung* 70, 4ᵃ.

Nara giyo (Naragiyo), Ort bei *Minggo zung* auf dem Südberge 43, 30ᵇ. Vom Nordberge bei *Minggo zung* abwärts geht es über den Fluß nach *N. g.* 44, 41ᵇ. Mit *Z'ula giyok* erwähnt 42, 17ᵃ.

Narbub, Tempel auf dem Berge *Mardo* 50, 35ᵇ.

Narineung, Stammesname, erwähnt zwischen den Stämmen *Hor Janggu* und *Kungsa*, *Maśu* 34, 47ᵃ.

Nawa', Berg, den man halbwegs zwischen *Genda kiyoo* und *Sotang* überschreiten muß. Der Übergang ist schmal und abschüssig und sehr schlüpfrig, nicht anders als der Berg *Tiyan śen śan.* Der General WENFU saß hier persönlich vom Pferde ab und redete den Mannschaften auf diesem schwierigen Wege zu 10, 39ᵇ.

Nawei, Ort bei *Najam*, s. oben.

Na yön da, Ort im *Zaula*-Lande, einen Tagesmarsch von *Meng bai la* 35, 3'4. Westlich davon ist der Weg sehr schmal, mit dichtem Walde … Es gibt dort auch einen kleinen Weg nach dem *Cucin*-Lande … Von dem Bergrücken links von *N. y. d.* gibt es einen Weg, der nach *Da ban jao* führt 38, 26.

Na yum, mit Mauern versehener Platz im *Cucin*-Lande 2, 44ᵇ.

Ni c'i gang, Ort erwähnt 49, 63ᵇ: Der in *Giyomgiyo* sitzende Verpflegungskommissar meldete: als wir gestern abend den halben Weg nach *N. c'. g.* zurückgelegt hatten, machten plötzlich die Feinde aus dem Walde heraus einen Überfall auf uns …

Ni lung, Ort mit Engpaß östlich von *Molung geo* 40, 14ᵃ. In dem Gebiet zwischen *Senio* und *Unggurlung* einerseits und *Janggu* andererseits (5 Tagemärsche Entfernung) aufgeführt neben *Jeng deng mei liyei*, *Giyarmu*, *Molung*, sowie *Gargiu*, *Yoza*, *Ja wa ko*, *Kaya*, *Bangko*, *Sohn* und »Große Burg« 70, 42ᵇ. Von *Biyangu* nach *Gezung*, einer Strecke von nicht über 30 *Li*, liegen die Orte *Molung*, *N. l.* und *Da u* 32, 3ᵇ.

Nio cang², Ort im *Okśt*-Lande. Klein-*N. c.* 58, 15ᵃ. Vor *N. c.* unterhalb von *Gunggarla* liegen 5 große Schanzen 47, 52ᵃ. Unten an der Nordseite des Bergrückens

---

¹ Vgl. Pl. II, *17*

² Chinesisch Rinderstall, vgl. S. 79, 81.

Giyagin da liegt der Ort *N. c.* im *Okši*-Lande 9, 50b. Wenn man von *Meino* über *Cung de* und *N. c.* noch hinausgeht, dann ist man auf der *Karsar*-Straße vom Vormarsch gegen das *Cucin*-Land vom Jahre 1647 46, 1b. Mit *Gungga* zusammen genannt 37, 39 40. Der Ort liegt nahe bei *Bumbur Sanggang* im *Zanla*-Lande 71, 12b. General WENFU führt in einem Berichte aus, er möchte bei dem Wegetreffpunkt südlich der Schlucht *Z'ula giyok* und nördlich des Turmes von *Begar giyok* seinen Weg nehmen, geradeswegs auf *N. c.* vorgehen und dann nach *Meino* (zurück) 47, 12.

Nio jai, Burg, westlich vom *Unggurlung*, erwähnt zusammen mit *Burakni* (und) *Degu* 42, 26a.

Ning ja (ya?), Berg nördlich von *Minggo zung* 44, 18b.

Nirma, Turm unweit *Unggurlung* und *Nio jai* 42, 27a.

Ni se gang, Ort an der Nordeinmarschstraße gegen das *Cucin*-Land, nicht weit von *I hi* 72, 40b.

Niyab giyo, Burg im näheren Umkreise von *Minggo zung*, genannt mit den anderen Burgen *Da i*, *Daksu* und *Gašari* 46, 2b.

Oban, Ort im *Cucin*-Lande. Südlich vom Berge von *Giyomgiyoo* ist *Cucin*-Gebiet. Rechts und links von dem Berge sind zwei Schluchten: die eine führt nach *Že se lo* im *Cucin*-Lande, die andere nach *O.* im *Cucin*-Lande 59, 19a.

Odo, Berg im *Burakdi*-Lande? Die *Burakdi*-Leute steigen von diesem Berge hinab nach *Wasu* im *Bawang*-Lande 2, 54a.

Okši¹, Stammesname.

O lung guwan², Paß innerhalb von *Balangla*, genannt mit Berg *Deng ženg*, *San šen geo* und der Brücke *Gen da kiyoo* 16, 43b; 19, 46a.

Orji, Ort mitten am Südberge von *Daksu* bei *Minggo zung* 44, 24a.

Ošogiyo, Ort im *Cucin*-Lande, mit *Mudaguwan* und *Doger* zusammen genannt 3, 52b.

Penglur, Burg nördlich des Kleinen Goldstromes unweit *Meino* und *Sengge zung* 64, 42b.

Po diyao³, Ort nicht weit von *Minggo zung* 62, 35b.

Pu lunglung, Ort nahe *Damba* 3, 2b. Genannt mit *Zuguding* 2, 38b.

Pung lur (vgl. **Penglur**), 8 Burgen westlich von *Meino* 46, 1a, am Ufer gegenüber der Nordburg von *Meino* 45, 28a. Westlich von *Daba geo* liegt ein Berg namens *P.* 45, 37a.

Purma, Berg mit Burg, nicht weit von *Akamya* und *Mei mei ka* 24, 51b.

Pusj'i geo, Ort im *Cucin*-Lande. Vormarsch dorthin auf dem Wege über *Jeng di* 2, 53b.

Pu sung gang, Ort, von dem aus ein Weg nach *Damba zung* führt. Auf dem Rücken des Berges nordöstlich von *Giyagin da* läuft ein Weg nach *Damba zung*. Wenn man auf dem Bergrücken vorgeht, hat man dort tiefen und dichten Schnee. Ich habe aber festgestellt, daß es (nach *Damba zung* noch) einen Weg über *P. s. g.* gibt, der allerdings durch dichten und weiten Wald führt 13, 29a. Wir gingen auf dem *P. s. g.* genannten kleinen Wege vor und stiegen heimlich den Rücken des Berges hinab südlich und gegenüber von *Damba zung*, auf der anderen Flußseite 17, 26a.

Puteo, Ort an der Grenze von *Somo* 31, 13a.

---

¹ Tibetisch *Og-gži*. Vgl. Pl. II, *I*; Pl. III. Der Stamm nennt sich heute *Wok-shih* und *Wu-ži*.
² Chinesisch »Paß des kauernden Drachen«.
³ Vgl. Pl. III, 16.

Rabcuk, hoher Berg jenseits (nördlich?) vom Berge *Dersu.* Unten am Abhange liegt *Muramba* 24, 51ᵃ. *R.* wird vom Berge *Dersu* durch eine tiefe Schlucht getrennt, die mit dichtem Walde bestanden ist und keinen Verbindungsweg bietet. Sowie *Muramba* am Südberge *(Dersu),* liegt *Mei mei ka* am Nordberge 24, 53,54. Zu beiden Seiten des Berges fehlen die Wege. Am Nordberge liegen die Orte *Zazan, Serkioi* und *Dungma.* Dort kommt ein Weg von *Biyesman* 27, 2. Um nahe an *Muramba* heranzukommen, muß man den Abhang des Berges *R.* hinabsteigend erst alle Orte nehmen, die dicht am Flußufer liegen 26, 30ᵃ. Der Ort *R.* ist sehr abschüssig, aber von allen 4 Seiten zugänglich 35, 5ᵃ.

Ragu, Berg mit Tempel unterhalb des Berges *Kunser,* nahe beim Berge *Gokdo* I, 15/16.

Ramram, Ort erwähnt mit dem Berge *Ži ze* I, 11ᵇ.

Robowa, Berg im *Cucin-*Lande, erwähnt mit *Sepengpu* I, 11ᵃ.

Rumi¹, erwähnt als Stammesname 2, 54ᵇ; 49, 38ᵇ, 42ᵃ.

Sagiya, Berg erwähnt ohne Angabe der Lage 23, 37ᵇ.

Saksagu, Ort genannt neben *Ži pang* I, 14ᵇ.

Salagiyao, Ort erwähnt ohne Angabe der Lage 56, 21ᵇ.

Sala giyo², Ort erwähnt ohne Angabe der Lage 55, 8ᵃ; vgl. das vorige.

Samgom, Brücke südlich der Burg von *Meino.* Sie gibt einen wichtigen Zugangsweg nach *Gunggarla* im *Cucin-*Lande 65, 29ᵃ; 45, 25.

Samka, Ort südlich von *Dajak giyo,* von dem es durch eine Schlucht getrennt wird 56, 33. An der Paßöffnung des Berges *Gunggarla* gibt es einen Weg hinter dem Bergrücken. Unterhalb dieses Weges läuft noch ein kleiner Weg, der schräg (in Serpentinen?) nach *S.* führt. Wenn wir auf diesem Wege vorgehen, können wir mit der Abteilung von *Dajak giyo* zusammen umfassend kämpfen. Aber es liegt eine tiefe Schlucht dazwischen, die mit dichtem Walde bewachsen ist 58, 36.

Sanggang, vgl. *Bumbur sanggang.*

San zang, Lamatempel, ohne Angabe der Lage, erwähnt in einer Reihe mit *Ni c'i gang, Zeri yagu, Salagiyao, Jeoseo, Kiyoo teo, Muc'i, Gan hai ze* und *San yang lu* 56, 22ᵃ.

Sarwai, Burg, genannt neben den anderen Burgen *Agiye* und *Jan* zwischen den Kämpfen um *Seleku zuru, Yamapeng* und den Berg *Kobkioi* andererseits I, 19ᵃ.

Sebser, Ort an der Rückseite des Berges nördlich von *Ziri.* Es steht dort dichter Wald und Unterholz. Der Weg ist eng und schwierig. Geht man auf ihm im Bogen vor, so gelangt man nach der Nordburg von *Okši* 17, 8ᵃ. *S.* liegt an einem Wege, der etwas schräg (in Serpentinen?) nach den Orten *Damba zung* und *Ziri* führt 42, 3ᵇ. Eine Abteilung sollte über *Bumbur sanggang,* eine andere über *S.* vorrücken ... Die *S.*-Abteilung ist immer noch nicht bei der Alten Burg von *Okši* angelangt und lagert jetzt oben auf dem Berge nördlich *Ziri* 19, 36ᵇ.

Sebza, Burg im *Cucin-*Lande, erwähnt 22, 42ᵇ.

Sem sengge, Berg erwähnt bei dem Kampfe um *Minggo zung.* Südlich von *S. s.* kommt man nach *Gesidi* 42, 2ᵃ.

Semze, Ort mit Burg und Turm im *Zanla-*Lande. Unten am Berge südwestlich von *S.* ist ein Weg, den man, wenn man von *Sengge zung* nach *Danggarla* geht, unbedingt nehmen muß, und unten am Berge südöstlich jenes Ortes liegt die Turmburg von *Sengge zung* 64, 1/2.

¹ Vgl. *Rumi janggu* und *Janggu (Dschanggu)* S. 70, 72, 73, 79; Pl. I, 4; II, I.
² Vgl. *Sala* Pl. III, 35.

Sengda, Ort im *Cucin*-Lande, etwa zwischen *Danggarla* und *Šengiyab* gelegen. Genau westlich an der Rückseite des Berges *Danggarla* liegt ein Ort *Šengiyab;* er gehört zum *Burakdi*-Gebiet, an der Grenze des *Cucin*-Landes . . . Auf einem Umwege über *Šengiyab* gelangen wir in die Gegend von *S.* 61, 29. Unterhalb des Bergrückens *Danggarla* liegen die 9 Burgen von *Kejeo.* Wenn man am (Großen Gold-)Flusse entlang in nordöstlicher Richtung vorrückt, gelangt man nach einem Orte *S.* Die 9 Burgen von *Kejeo* liegen an dem Abhange des Nordberges von *Danggarla, S.* dagegen liegt unten am Berge 55, 18,19.

Sengge zung[1], ein wichtiger Engpaß im *Zanla*-Lande, von *Da u* über 60 *Li* entfernt 44, 16ᵃ. Der Ort liegt nordöstlich von *Namgiyor zung* . . . an der Höhe des Berges *Semze.* Wenn man über die Schlucht von *Namgiyor zung* hinausgeht, so hat man im Norden eine ganze Strecke lang Abhänge und Gipfel. Im Süden ist ein großer Strom, an dessen jenseitigem Ufer die Burgen *Dašihi* und *Žung jai* liegen. Die Feinde können von drüben mit ihren Gewehren den Weg an der Nordseite des Flusses bestreichen 72, 22,23. Der Ort *S. z.* liegt nördlich des Ausganges der Schlucht von *Namgiyor zung* und unterhalb des Felsens (Abhanges) des Berges *Semze* 70, 4ᵃ. Vom Rücken des Berges *Giyarma* aus kann man südlich nach *S. z.* hinabsehen, nach Osten hinab *Da u* überfallen 36, 17ᵇ. *S. z.* bietet einen wichtigen Weg von *Danggarla* nach *Janggu* 45, 37ᵇ. Ebenso einen Weg von *Meino* im *Zanla*-Lande nach *Gara'i:* von der Südseite *Meinos* aus vorbei an den 9 Burgen von *Ke jeo* in etwa 6—7 Tagen nach *Gara'i.* Der Weg ist gefährlich und schmal 25, 40. Vom *Gezung*-Passe aus aufwärts sind auf dem Fuße der beiderseitigen Berge Blockhäuser gebaut. Um von dort nach *S. z.* zu kommen, muß man schon einige 1000 Mann detachieren und von den beiden Bergen aus in getrennten Abteilungen vorgehen 32, 2ᵃ. Weg von *Meino* nach dem Gebiete von *S. z.* erwähnt 64, 36ᵇ. Der Fluß bei *S. z.:* auf dem gegenüberliegenden Ufer die Burg *Žung jai.* Südlich des Flusses liegen die beiden Burgen *Je* und *Lung.* Nördlich des Flusses geht es von *S. z.* bis *Yozu,* südlich des Flusses von *Kaya* bis zur Burg *Žung jai,* östlich von dieser Burg liegen noch die beiden Burgen *Gio* und *Marli.* Der Weg südlich des Flusses führt nach *Meino* 64, 40/41. Am Ostufer von *S. z.* stößt der Fuß des Berges unmittelbar in den Lauf des Flusses hinein. Um nach *Meino* zu gelangen, muß man schon zunächst am Westufer nach *Kodo* gehen, eine Brücke schlagen und dann wieder auf das Ostufer hinüber. Es ist dort ein sehr gefährlicher Weg mit steilen Abhängen 45, 23. — Beschreibung eines Übergangs über den Fluß bei *S. z.* durch den General Aᴄôi: Wenn man sich von *Banggiya* aus in die Gegend von *Nawei* und *Najam* begibt, hat man unterwegs einen Ort *Dugung* . . . Die unterhalb des Bergrückens von *Dugung* gelegene Burg *Laza* wurde im Kampfe genommen, ebenso der oberhalb von *Dugung* gelegene Ort *Dan,a* und von einer dritten Abteilung die Turmburgen *Kaya* und *Dangiya.* An der Seite des Ostberges gingen wir am Rande des Flusses vor, nahmen die Burgen *Ze jai* und *Žung jai* und besetzten 3 Bergrücken hintereinander. Von *S. z.* einige *Li* entfernt ist ein Fluß. Die Nordburg von *S. z.* liegt oben auf einem hohen Felsen mit steilen Spitzen an den vier Seiten. Dorthin führt in Windungen ein kleiner Weg . . . Ich gab Auftrag, diesseits des Flusses das Gelände zu erkunden, mit den Häuptlingen von *Bawang* und *Burakdi* Beratung zu pflegen und Abmachungen (für den Flußübergang) zu treffen. Am 19. XI. (1771) zwischen 9 und 11 Uhr abends gingen wir auf Fellbooten über den Fluß und gelangten in aller Stille in zwei Abteilungen an den Fuß des Turmes (der Nordburg von *S. z.?*). Von Westen her kamen die anderen Abteilungen zum Angriff gegen die Nordfront der Nordburg von *S. z.*, griffen an und schnitten gleichzeitig

---

[1] Tibetisch *seng-ge rdsong* »Löwenburg«, vgl. *Sengke zung* Pl. II, *1.*

16. IX, 4.

den Feinden die Zufuhr ab. Diese leisteten zunächst kraftvollen Widerstand. Als sie aber ihre Sache verloren sahen, zerstörten sie die nördliche Steinmauer der Burg und entliefen am Flusse entlang 44, 1—4.

Seng mu ze, Burg erwähnt mit den Türmen *Burungkaza, Taksa, Marli* und *Mubari* 44, 31 a.

Sepengpu, Ort zwischen Berg *Robowa* und *Sunkerzung* I, 11 a.

Serdo, Burg unweit *Mei mei ka?*, genannt mit den anderen Burgen *Purma, Jemsi* und *Kasbo* 31, 41 b.

Serkioi, Burg am Nordberge von *Rabcuk*, nördlich von *Mei mei ka*, genannt mit den Burgen *Zaza*, Lamatempel *Dungma* und *Giyardo* 27, 3.

Serli[1], Burg unweit des Berges *Si ling:* Wenn man den Fuß des Berges *Si ling* ausbiegend überschreitet, kommt man nach der Burg *S.* 57, 31 a. Wenn man von *Si ling* auf geteilten Wegen hinabsteigt, kommt man rechts nach *Le'uwei*, mit nur wenigen kleinen Burgen dazwischen, rechts nach *Gara'i*, mit einem Orte *S.* dazwischen 54, 11 b. Bei der Besprechung des Berges *Dajak giyo:* Wir können geradeswegs auf *Karsar* und den Norden von *S.* vorstoßen 65, 34 a.

Si ling[2], wichtiger Ort im *Cucin*-Lande, nördlich von *Karsar*. Wenn man den nördlichen Bergkamm an der Rückseite des Berges *Gunggarla* übersteigend zwei große Schluchten überschreitet und dann nach Osten geht, so kommt man an den Bergpaß der *Z'ula-giyok*-Schlucht. Geht man am Rande dieses Berges entlang in westlicher Richtung und steigt dann, an das Ende der Schlucht gelangt, wieder oben auf den Berg hinauf, so liegt da der Ort *S. l.* 50, 18 a. *S. l.* liegt nördlich von *Karsar*. Um nach *S. l.* zu gelangen, muß man erst die beiden Wege von *Karsar* und *Gunggarla* in die Hand bekommen haben 50, 39.40. *S. l.* gegenüber liegt *Mugom* 52, 44 a. Von *Karsar* nach *S. l.* etwa 3 Tagemärsche, von *Buranggo zung* 7 Tagemärsche 52, 45 a. Die *S. l.*-Abteilung war über *Zeng teo geo* und *Buranggo zung* vorgegangen 54, 45 b. Die Natur der Berge zeigt steile Abhänge und gefährliche Stellen … Nach Eroberung des Ortes kann man geradeswegs auf *Gara'i* losgehen 52, 32 b. Von *S. l.* aus stiegen wir auf zwei Wegen zu Tal: rechts kann man nach *Le'uwei* gelangen, wird aber unterwegs durch einige kleine Schanzen aufgehalten. Links geht es nach *Gara'i.* Auf diesem Wege liegt ein Ort namens *Serli* 54, 11 b. Unten an dem äußersten Ende des Felsens westlich von *S. l.* liegt die Burg *Serli.* Geht man dort weiter vor, so kommt man nach *Gara'i.* Rechts von *S. l.* ist noch ein Weg, auf dem man nach *Le'uwei* gelangen kann. Aber auf der Rückseite des Berges liegt der Schnee tief, das Bett des Stromes ist dort eng und schmal, Gestrüpp und Sträucher bilden einen dichten Wald.

Sin kiyoo[3], erwähnt zusammen mit *Kodo* 63, 2 a; 64, 16 a.

Siri, Burg, erwähnt bei den Kämpfen um *Gara'i:* In anbetracht des Angriffes auf *Gara'i* habe ich (General Acôi) mir überlegt, daß wir eigentlich erst das Heer teilen, die Burg *S.* nehmen, dann oben auf dem Rücken des Berges *Kobkioi* herumkommen und gegen *Margu* und *Dangga* vorgehen müßten I, 18.

---

[1] Vgl. S. 77, 79.

[2] Nicht etwa chinesisch: Westgebirge, sondern 昔 嶺 *hsi-ling* »altes Gebirge« geschrieben, wahrscheinlich kein chinesischer Name. Vgl. S. 77, 79, Pl. II, *I* u. *II.*

[3] Chinesisch: *hsin ch'iao* Neue Brücke.

Siyoo guwanze'. Von *S. z.* bis nach der Gegend von *Yoo ji* läuft der Weg immer am Rande des Berges. Über *Yoo ji* hinaus kommt man dann nach *Giyagin da* 8, 34.35.

Siyoo nio cang², sehr weit vom *Cucin*-Lande entfernt 55, 31ᵇ. Vgl. oben *Nio cang.*

Sobu³, große Burg im *Ming jeng*-Lande. Die Landschaft *Han nio* stößt im Süden an *Ming jeng*-Gebiet, im Osten an *Zanla*-Gebiet, im Westen liegen die große Burg *S.*, sowie die Orte *Jung nung, Kaya, Ja wa ko* und *Da u.* Im Nordosten geht es dann nach *Meino.* Aber wenn man über den zu *Ming jeng* gehörenden Ort *S.* mit den Truppen (nach *Meino*) vorgeht, hat man einen sehr weiten Weg. Wir wollen daher über *Muping* vorrücken, was auch kein naher Weg ist 43, 28/29. Bei *Nading* gingen wir über den Fluß auf das Ostufer hinüber und eroberten die den *Ming jeng* gehörige, von den *Zanla* besetzte große Burg *S.* 7, 24ª. Der Ort wird einmal erwähnt mit den anderen Orten *Jung nung* sowie *Migang* und *Mari* 8, 11ª, ein andermal mit *Senio, Deli, Unggurlung, Ayang, Kaya, Bangko, Yoza* sowie *Janggu* 67, 24ª.

Solunggu, der höchste Punkt auf dem Rücken des Berges *Kobkioi* I, 19ª.

Somo³, Stammes- und Ländername. Der Weg nach *Le'uwei* im *Cucin*-Lande führt von der Brücke *El doo kiyoo (örh-tao-ch'iao)* bei *Wei-chou* im Lande *Damba* durch das Gebiet von *S.*, *Jokz'ai* und *Zung gak* 28, 39ᵇ.

Suknai, Ort nördlich von *Mugom?* Beim Angriff von *Si ling* überschritt General HAILANCA die nördlichen Gebirge, eroberte zwei Schanzen bei *S.* und besetzte dann den Bergrücken nördlich von *Mugom* 50, 56ª.

Sung lin keo⁵, Ort bei *Cung de:* Wenn man an *Cung de* vorbeigekommen ist, liegt dort im Norden ein Ort namens *S. l. k.* Es steht dort dichter und gefährlicher Wald, der seitwärts bis zu der großen Schlucht von *Z'ula giyok* sich erstreckt 49, 48ᵇ. Die Strecke von *S. l. k.* nach dem Westausgange von *Z'ula giyok* 62, 11ᵇ. Von *Šan šen geo* 5—6 Tage entfernt? 7, 26ª.

Sunkerzung⁶, Ort erwähnt bei den Kämpfen um *Le'uwei*, nördlich des *Galdan*-Tempels und der Burg *Galangga* I, 15ª.

Šaba, Berg, erwähnt nach der Eroberung von *Ži pang*, zusammen mit *Dartu* und *Dereng* I, 14ᵇ.

Šajung, Ort im *Gebšiza*-Lande, erwähnt 1, 29ª.

Šam giyola, Ort außerhalb von *Wei-chou* 11, 20ª, in der Nähe des Berges *Biwangla* 11, 57ᵇ.

Šan gan⁷, Ort, erwähnt mit *Be tu ka* 39, 47ᵇ.

Šan šen geo⁸, wichtiger Engpaß chinesischerseits des *Balangla*, genannt mit dem Berge *Deng ženg* sowie dem Passe *O lung guwan* und der Brücke *Gen da kiyoo* 16, 43ᵇ. *Š. š. g.* liegt 40 *Li* vom Passe *O lung guwan.* Bei *Š. š. g.* gibt es einen besonderen Nebenweg, auf dem man im Bogen nördlich von *Balangla* herauskommen kann ... Wenn man (von *Balangla?*) auf dem Wege über *Š. š. g.* vorgeht, gelangt man in 5 Tagen nach *Damba zung* 7, 1/2. *Š. š. g.* ist von *Deng ženg* kaum einige Dutzend *Li* entfernt 11, 12ª.

---

1 Chinesischer Name.
2 Chinesisch: Kleiner Kuhstall.
3 Vgl. Berg *So-wu*, S. 78, Pl. II, *II*; IV, 31.
4 Pl. II, *I* u. *IV*.
5 Chinesisch: Kiefernwaldpaß, vgl. S. 81.
6 Vgl. Pl. II, *I* u. *III* (= *Sengge zung, Sengke zung?*).
7, 8 Chinesische Namen.

Šan yang lu[1], Ort, erwähnt mit *Gan hai ze* und dem Lamatempel *San zang* 56, 22[a].

Šarni, Ort, erwähnt bei den Kämpfen um *Le'uwei*, unterhalb *Ši jeng ga:* General Mingliyang drang, von *Ši jeng ga* nach abwärts vor und eroberte *Š.* sowie das nördlich der Schlucht liegende *Daslam* und das südlich der Schlucht liegende *Danjam* I, 16.

Šatu giyo, Ort gegenüber *Karsar* 60, 4[a].

Šeci, Tempel, erwähnt bei den Kämpfen um *Gara'i:* Man rückte vom Berge *Kobkioi* über den Paß *Zelang gak*, danach über *Margu* und *Dangga* vor, eroberte die beiden Lamatempel *Š.* und *Yungjung* und schritt dann zur Belagerung von *Gara'i* 1, 19.

Šeleku (zuru), Ort, erwähnt mit *Yamapeng:* Man kam von *Kabgiyo*, eroberte nach der Einnahme der beiden Orte *Š.* und *Yamapeng* die Burgen *Agiye* und *Jan* und erstieg danach geradeswegs den Kamm des Berges *Kobkioi* I, 19[a].

Šelung, Berg zwischen *Kasma lung* und *Meino.* Beim Vormarsch gegen *Meino* heißt es: Die Abteilungen hatten den Auftrag, bei *Kodo* am Westufer des Flusses auf einer Brücke an das Ostufer hinüberzugehen und dann sich weiter vorzukämpfen. Der ganze Weg ist äußerst hoch, abschüssig und, da die Feinde ihn durch Gräben unterbrochen haben, sehr gefährlich. Die Truppen rückten unter großer Mühseligkeit geradeswegs vor, gelangten auf den Kamm des Berges *Kasma lung*, und dann ging es vor gegen den Kamm des Berges *Š.* Danach griffen wir von drei Seiten den Ort *C'imu* an, worauf die Feinde den Widerstand aufgaben und in der Richtung auf *Meino* entflohen 45, 24.

Šengiyab, Ort genau westlich hinter dem Bergrücken des *Danggarla.* Er gehört zum Gebiete von *Burakdi*, liegt aber an der Grenze des *Cucin*-Landes. Wenn man durch die (dortige) Schlucht hindurchgeht, kann man die nördlich des Bergrückens gelegenen 9 Burgen von *Kejeo* wegnehmen ... Wenn man in einem Bogen an *Š.* vorbei vordringt, kommt man in die Gegend von *Sengda* 61, 29.

Šerni, Ort, erwähnt bei den Kämpfen um *Le'uwei:* Als wir von dem Orte *Te lang* u. a. abwärts stiegen, gelang es uns, gegen den Ort *Š.* einen Vorstoß zu machen und im Kampfe mit geteilten Truppen auf der andern Seite des Flusses Vorteile zu erringen (d. h. den Ort zu nehmen) 71, 39 40.

Šetu wangka, Ort, erwähnt beim Angriff auf den Lamatempel *Kunser:* Dieser Tempel liegt oberhalb des Tempels *Ragu*, an einer sehr schwierigen Stelle. General Agôi ging in einem Umweg über *Š. w.* (gegen den erstgenannten Tempel) vor I, 15[b].

Ši jeng ga, Ort, erwähnt kurz vor den Kämpfen um den Tempel *Kunser* I, 15[b].

Šotang, Poststelle am Flusse nicht weit von *Minggo zung* 62, 40[a].

Šozanggar, Ort, erwähnt im Zusammenhange mit *Sebser* 26, 28[b].

Šui jing wan[2], Ort und Weg auf der tibetischen Seite des Passes *Balangla*, Richtung *Ziri.* In einem Berichte von diesem Vormarsche heißt es: Wir dachten daran, daß vordem, als wir am Passe *Balangla* standen, wir erkundet hatten, daß dort ein kleiner Weg namens *Š. j. w.* sich befand, auf dem man die Türme der Feinde umgehen konnte. Da aber an dem besagten Orte zu hoher Schnee lag, haben wir ihn auf unserem Vorgehen und Kämpfen nicht eingeschlagen. Nach Einnahme des Passes *Balangla* haben wir dann auf dem Marsche über die Rückseite des Berges bei der Erkundung des Geländes festgestellt, daß der Weg von *Š. j. w.* sicher unterhalb der feindlichen Türme vorbeiführt 16, 35.

---

[1], [2] Chinesische Namen, der erste vielleicht »Ziegenpfad«.

Sedak, Ort 28 *Li* von *Muc̓i* entfernt, auf der Strecke über die Flüsse *Garma* und *Ergu* nach *Le̓uwei* 40, 24[b].

Se diyei an[1], Ort, von dem aus der Angriff auf *Ziri* und die alte Burg von *Okśi* eingeleitet wird 15, 41[b]. Auf den beiden nördlich und südlich der Brücke bei *Damba zung* nach *Ziri* führenden Wegen, der erste ziemlich weit und gefährlich über hohe Berge in einem Umwege bei *Biyesman* vorbeiführend, der andere über *Marwalji* führend, kann man den Ort *S. d. a.* umgehen 15, 34[b]. Der Bergpaß bei *S. d. a.* ist sehr eng 15, 35[b].

Seduk giyo, Burg auf dem Kamm des Berges *Danggarla* 60, 53[a].

Segen, Ort nahe *Giyarlung ba* 47, 13[a].

Se jai[2], Burg auf dem Berge *Dugnng*, erwähnt mit der Burg *Žung jai:* Nach Einnahme der Turmburgen *Gaca* und *Dangiyan* ging es an der Seite des Ostberges am Rande des Flusses entlang gegen die Burgen *S. j.* und *Žung jai* 44, 2[b].

Senio, Ort südlich von *Unggurlung;* westlich von *Unggurlung* liegt *Jeng deng mei liyei* 68, 40[a].

Tai ning, wichtiger Paß im *Ming jeng*-Lande, erwähnt zusammen mit *Moonio, Dunggu, Janggu, Gozung* 7, 3[a]. Ein andermal erwähnt mit *Janggu* allein 1, 26[a].

Taksa, Turmburg, unweit *Sengge zung*. Erwähnt zusammen mit den anderen Turmburgen *Burungkaza* sowie *Marli* und *Mubari* 44, 31[a].

Tao guwan[3]. Bei dem Wege von *Ch̓eng-tu* nach *Meino* über *Ya-chou* und *Muping* spart man zwei Tage gegenüber dem Wege über den Paß *T. g.* Der letztgenannte Weg geht die ganze Strecke über Land, während man von *Ch̓eng-tu* bis *Ya-chou* Wasserverbindung benutzen kann. (Es handelt sich um die Zufuhr) 47, 22[a].

Tekyur[4], Berg südlich am Flusse gegenüber *Ziri:* Wir haben jetzt den Bergrücken besetzt, sind abwärts an den Strom gelangt und haben die West- und Ostfront von *Ziri* eingeschlossen, aber den Weg, der an dem Berge des Nordufers entlang läuft, haben wir noch nicht sperren können. Es stellte sich heraus, daß jenseits des Berges *T.* noch ein hoher Berg liegt namens *Dersu* 21, 19

Te lang, Ort in der Umgebung von *Le̓uwei*, oberhalb von *Śerni* 71, 39[b].

U du, Ort im *Gebśiza*-Lande. Erwähnt in Verbindung mit *Dandung:* Die in der Nähe von *Dandung* und *U. d.* stehenden Truppen sollten über *Lagô o* (gegen *Giyarlung ba?*) vorrücken 40, 20/21.

Umoi, Stammesname? Erwähnt in Verbindung mit *Gebśiza* 4, 32[a].

Ungguda, großer Berg bei *Daba geo:* Wir haben nördlich von *Begar giyok* und südlich von *Z̓ula giyok* den großen Berg *U.* überschritten und sind dann den Abhang hinabgezogen, wo wir auf *Daba geo* trafen. Der Name der Poststelle ist *Cung de* 49, 48[a].

Unggurlung[5], Ort nördlich von *Senio* und östlich von *Jeng deng mei liyei* 68. 40[a]. Südlich von *U.* steht ein hoher Felsen 43. 21[b]. *U.* ist der Ort, wo sich zwei Felsen treffen 41, 52[b]. Im Osten liegt *U.*, im Westen *Burakni, Degu*, sowie die Burg *Nio jai* 42, 26[a].

Wasu, Ort im Lande *Bawang:* Die Eingeborenen der Stämme *Cucin* und *Burakdi* stiegen vom Berge *Odo* herab und gelangten an den Ort *W.* im Lande *Bawang*, dessen Turmburg sie einschlossen und berannten. Während die Besatzung sich wehrte, erblickten

---

[1], [2], [3] Chinesische Namen.
[4] Vgl. *T̓a-kio-lo* IV, 32.
[5] Vgl. S. 82.

die Verteidigungstruppen von *Elgui* ihre Feuerzeichen, eilten zur Hilfe herbei und sperrten den Rückzugsweg nach *Cucin* ab. Und die Truppen von *Bawang* sowie von *Ming jeng* und *Rumi* kamen auch über den Fluß, griffen in den Kampf ein und brachten den *Cucin*- und *Burakdi*-Leuten eine schwere Niederlage bei; letztere beide ergriffen unter Hinterlassung vieler Toter und Verwundeter die Flucht 2, 54.

Wašu, Ort im *Gebšiza*-Lande, erwähnt 6, 15ª.

Wase[1], Stammesname. Der Berg *Balangla* bildet die Grenze zwischen den Stämmen *W.* und *Okši* 7, 1ª.

Yamapeng, Ort, erwähnt bei den Kämpfen um den Berg *Kobkioi*, zusammen mit den Orten *Seleku* und *Zuru* 1, 19ª.

Yolu, Berg, erwähnt bei den Kämpfen um den Gebirgszug *Danggarla?* 43, 7ᵇ.

Yoo ji, Ort in der Landschaft *Muping*: Wenn man von dem Orte *Y. j.* den Berg nehmend hinabsteigt, so wird man durch einen Strom aufgehalten. Dort ist *Damba zung* 8, 1ª.

Yoza, Ort im *Zaula*-Lande, am Goldstrom. Westlich liegt in den Bergen ein Tempel. Der dorthin führende Weg wird zweimal durch Schluchten unterbrochen 12, 53ª. Mitten durch den Rücken des Berges von *Y.* zieht sich eine Schlucht 10, 2ª. Die Berge bei *Y.* sind sehr langgestreckt und durch den Stromlauf unterbrochen. Wenn man den Rücken des Berges von *Y.* überschreitet, liegt dort *Kaya* 12, 43ª. Westlich von *Sengge zung* geht es nach *Kaya* und *Y.* 64, 6ᵇ. *Y.* liegt südlich des Flusses 64, 41ª. Nach der Einnahme von *Y.* wollen wir einen Weg suchen, den Fluß überschreiten und dann nach Erkundung des Berggeländes auf getrennten Wegen zur Eroberung von *Da u* vorgehen. Dazu haben wir eine Übersichtskarte des *Zaula*-Landes gezeichnet und auf einer Sonderkarte des Gebietes von *Y.* überall Papierzettel mit Erklärungen aufgeklebt 11, 49ª. *Y.* ist von *Ch'eng-tu* über 1400 *Li* entfernt 15, 20ᵇ.

Yubsang, Ort im *Gebšiza*-Lande, erwähnt zusammen mit *Bal*, *Gezang* und *Dabsang* 1, 42ᵇ.

Yungderi, Burg am Berge *Giyarmu?*: Nach Einnahme der Türme und Schanzen auf dem Westberge (des Berges *Giyarmu?*) überschritten wir die Bergschlucht und bemächtigten uns im Kampfe der dortigen Steinschanze. Unterhalb von dieser liegt dann noch eine nach Norden gerichtete Burg *Y.* . . . . Am nächsten Tage schlossen wir diese von drei Seiten ein, nahmen sie im Sturm und eroberten danach noch die Türme *Yung mei* und *Nirma* 42, 26/27.

Yungjung, Lamatempel, erwähnt zusammen mit dem andern Tempel *Seci*, bei dem Angriff auf *Garà'i*: Darauf rückten wir über *Margu* und *Dangga* vor, eroberten die beiden Lamatempel *Seci* und *Y.*, und danach ging es weiter zur Belagerung von *Garà'i* 1, 19ᵇ.

Yung mei, Turm; vgl. oben *Yungderi* 42, 27ª.

Zagu[2], Stammes- und Ländername; vgl. *Zagu nao* 47, 9ᵇ.

Zagu nao[3], Stammes- und Ländername. Von *Kuan-hsien* noch über 300 *Li*; ein Weg, auf dem Tragtiere verkehren können. Von dort zum Heerlager sind es ebenfalls über 300 *Li*, aber abschüssiger Gebirgsweg, der nur von Tragekulis begangen werden kann 37, 13ª.

---

[1] Vgl. *Wasse* Pl. II, *I* u. *III.*
[2] Vgl. Pl. II, *I, III, IV; IV*, 52.
[3] Vgl. Pl. II, *I* u. *IV.*

Zai ze da h'ai [1], Ort, erwähnt bei dem Kampfe um den Tempel *Ragu* auf dem Berge *Kunser* I, 16ª.

Zama [2], Berg im *Zanla*-Lande: Eine Meldung liegt vor, daß der Rücken des Berges Z. besetzt worden sei. Falls man auf diesem Wege in einem Bogen herumkommen könnte, hätten die auf der Kuppe des Berges *Gogar* stehenden Feinde ihre strategische Stellung verloren 38, 49.

Zao po, Ort erwähnt 47, 21ª: Die Zufuhr für die Truppen am Berge *Gunggarla* wird für gewöhnlich auf dem Postwege über *Z. p.* und *Okśi* herangeschafft. Vgl. unten *Z'ao po*.

Zazan, Burg, erwähnt im Zusammenhang mit *Serkioi*, *Dungma*, *Lama-Tempel* und *Giyardo:* Wir wollen zunächst die am Nordberge (von *Rabcuk*) gelegenen Orte Z., *Serkioi* und *Dungma* erobern und den von *Biyesman* herführenden Weg unterbrechen, um den Feinden ihre Verteidigung unmöglich zu machen . . . Ich (General Aɢôi) habe nach Einnahme der Wasserschanze von *Purma* die schweren Geschütze in andere Stellungen gebracht und beschieße jetzt *Meimei ka*. Aber an der Ostseite der Burg befindet sich ein mächtiger steinerner Turm, und an der Nordseite schließen die Burgen Z., *Serkioi*, *Dungma*, *Lama-Tempel* und *Giyardo* sich in schräger Richtung an 27, 2/3.

Zelang gak, Berg in der Nähe des Berges *Kobkioi:* Nachdem wir den Ort *Solunggu*, die höchste Erhebung des Berges *Kobkioi*, vollständig eingenommen hatten, rückten wir gegen die Paßöffnung des Berges Z. g. vor I, 19ᵇ.

Zeng baśigu, Ort, erwähnt im Kampfe um den Ort *Dek* im *Cucin*-Lande 2, 48ᵇ.

Zeng da (Zengda), Burg, erwähnt mit den beiden andern Burgen *Mugu* und *Genggete* nach der Einnahme von *Marbang* I, 21ª. Wenn man die alte Übersichtskarte ansieht, findet man dort nördlich von *Burakdi* einen Ort namens Z. d. Der hat einen Verbindungsweg nach *Gara'i*. Der Ort liegt östlich des Flusses 52, 42/43.

Zeng teo geo, Ort im *Zagu*-Lande. Genannt zusammen mit *Kanjo geo*, *Muya śan* und *Da ban joo*, alles Orte, die eine Verbindung nach dem *Cucin*-Lande haben 47, 11ª.

Zeri Yagu, Ort, genannt mit *Ni c'i gang* sowie *Salagiyao*, *Jeoseo* u. a. 56, 21ᵇ.

Ze lung, Etappenort auf der Zufuhrstraße von *Tatsienlu* nach dem *Cosgiyab*-Lande 59, 16/17; vgl. *Zi lung*.

Zilung (ka), erwähnt zusammen mit *Gallar* 44, 12ᵇ.

Ziri [3], wichtiger Engpaß im *Zanla*-Lande 19, 42ª, um dessen Einnahme zweimal lange gekämpft wurde, das zweitemal über 3 Monate 16, 40—18, 11 und 68, 38. Der Ort liegt an der Paßöffnung, kaum einige Dutzend *Li* von *Meino* entfernt, auf der Strecke die Orte *Muramba*, Alte Burg von *Okśi*, *Luding zung* und Burg *Munggu* 16, 37/38. Gegenüber ein hoher Felsen 18, 7ª. An der Rückseite des Nordberges von Z. liegt *Sebser*, mit dichtem Wald und Unterholz 17, 6ª. Jenseits der Burg *Derunggiyo* am Ende des Südberges ist wieder ein großer Berg. Vom Rücken dieses Berges abwärts kommt man geradeswegs nach der Burg *Akamya* hinunter, jenseits der Burg Z. und diesseits der Nordburg von *Okśi* 19, 20. Der Süd- und Nordberg sind zwar beide wichtige strategische Punkte, aber sie messen doch beide in der Länge und Breite 70—80 *Li* 19. 38. Der Vormarsch auf Z. geht über *Bumbur sanggang* und *Sebser* 19, 38ª. An der Rückseite der Westmauer der

---

[1] Vgl. Ostasiatische Zeitschrift l. c.

[2] Vgl. Pl. III, 24.

[3] Tibetische Schreibung *tse-ri* (*ri* = Berg).

Burg (von Z.) befindet sich eine Quelle 19, 18b. Beschreibung der Befestigungen von Z.: Die Steinmauer ist sehr ausgedehnt. Am Rande derselben sind überall Schießscharten angebracht. In der Erde sind Gräben ausgehoben, in welchen die Feinde sich versteckt halten. Gehen unsere Truppen vor, so kommen sie heraus und eröffnen durch die Schießscharten ein Abwehrfeuer. Im Norden der Burg, auf einem Ort wie ein Schießplatz, ist eine große steinerne Schanze gebaut, die durch einen in den Boden gezogenen Graben mit der Burg in Verbindung steht. Nördlich von dieser Schanze sind 5 weitere steinerne Schanzen hintereinander angelegt, und oben auf einem gegenüberliegenden hohen Felsen liegt noch eine große steinerne Schanze 19, 15/16. Beschreibung der Burg von Z.: Die Burg hat kaum über 100 Räume. In der Mitte erhebt sich ein einzelner hoher Turm wohl über 200 Fuß. An den 4 Ecken stehen 4 andere wohl über 100 Fuß hohe Türme. Ganz um die Burg herum ist eine Steinmauer gebaut, auf der kleine Türme und Bastionen nebeneinander angelegt sind 16, 40.

Zuguding[1], Ort im *Cucin*-Lande 4, 9a, erwähnt zusammen mit *Pu lunglung* 2, 38b.

Zula, s. *Z'ula giyok*.

Zung gak[2], Stammes- und Ländername: Bei *Wei-chou* im *Damba*-Lande geht es über die Brücke *Örh-tao-ch'iao* und dann durch das Gebiet der Länder *Somo*, *Jokz'ai* und *Z.g.* und von dort weiter vor nach *Le'nwei*, im ganzen einige 20 Tagemärsche 25, 39.

Zu u, Burg auf dem *Kaya*-Berge, erwähnt zusammen mit *Deng i*, *Ga gang*, *Gung žu* sowie *Ja wa ko* 16, 32a.

Z'ao po, Ort außerhalb des Gebietes von *Wen-ch'uan*, östlich des *Balangla*. (Von *Ch'eng-tu*?) 12—13 Tagemärsche entfernt 16, 44b. Die Strecke von *San šen geo* und dem Passe *O-lung-kuan* nach *Z'. p.* erwähnt 68, 57a.

Z'ebdan, Ort, der nach *Meino* Verbindung hat, aber nur auf kleinen Wegen, die durch dichten Wald führen 36, 30b. Von *Mardik* nach dem Berge *Gungga* und dann über zwei Bergrücken hinweg, da liegt der Ort *Z'.* 41, 14a.

Z'ebten, Berg nahe *Meino*.

Z'erdan sem, Ort mit Lamatempel, etwa halbwegs zwischen *Sengge zung* und *Da u*, auf einer Strecke von 60—70 *Li* 44, 16a. Der Ort liegt am Strome oder in der Nähe desselben, nicht weit vom Berge *Bang giya* 43, 20. Er stößt an die Grenze vom *Cucin*-Lande, mit den andern Orten *Molung geo*, *Kaya* und *Unggurlung* 67, 22a.

Z'ula, s. *Z'ula giyok*.

Z'ula giyok[3], Schlucht (mit Bergstrom?) westlich von *Buranggo zung*, bildet einen Zugang nach dem Passe *Gunggarla* 46, 17a. Vom Wegetreffpunkt südlich der Schlucht von *Z'. g.* und nördlich von *Begar giyok* geht ein Weg geradezu nach *Niu cang* 47, 12a. Von diesem gleichen (Wegetreff-)Punkte ausgehend überschreitet man einen großen Berg, *Ungguda* und steigt dann am Abhange hinunter. Dort liegt dann *Daba geo*, Poststelle *Cung de* 49, 47'48. Wenn man etwas nördlich von der Paßöffnung des *Gunggarla* den Berg übersteigt, kommt man genau auf den Westauslaß der Schlucht von *Z'. g.* . . . Der hohe Berg am Westauslaß der Schlucht ist das Dach des Berges *Dajak giyo* 57, 31 32. Vom Ostauslaß der Schlucht über einen Berg, dann westwärts auf der Hauptstraße von

---

[1] Vgl. S. 78, Pl. II, *1*.
[2] Vgl. *Sunggak* S. 72.
[3] Vgl. *Z'ula giyok* Pl. II, *1* u. *III*.

Niu cang ... Dieser Auslaß ist von *Buranggo zung* nur 10—20 *Li* entfernt 52, 44. Wenn man hinter dem Berge *Gunggarla* den Rücken des Nordberges nimmt, zwei große Schluchten kreuzt und dann ostwärts geht, kommt man an einen Bergpaß bei der Schlucht von *Zᵗ. g.* Geht man am Rande dieses Berges entlang westwärts bis an das Ende der Schlucht und steigt dann wieder auf die Höhe des Berges, so ist man in *Si ling* 50, 17/18. Der Ort *Zᵗ. g.* wird erwähnt mit *Begar giyok* und *Daba geo* 11, 59ᵇ sowie mit dem Orte *Naragiyo* auf einer Landkarte zu den Operationen um den Berg *Bolgen* und die Burg *Ma giyo u* 42, 17ᵃ.

Že se lo, Ort im *Cucin*-Lande: Vor dem Berge von *Giyomgiyoo* ist *Cucin*-Gebiet. Rechts und links vom Berge sind 2 Schluchten, von denen die eine nach dem Orte *Ž. s. l.* im *Cucin*-Lande führt, die andere nach *Oban* im *Cucin*-Lande.

Ži gor ugu, Berg, der mit den beiden andern Bergen *Murgulu* und *Giyaba* vor dem Berge *Gung ya* gelegen ist 44, 37ᵃ. Auf der Strecke von *Minggo zung* nach *Meino* liegt der Berg *Ž. g. u.* als Hindernis, unterhalb des Berges am Flußufer eine Burg namens *Mašao* 45, 36ᵃ.

Ži gu lu, Ort, mit *Memurgi* in der nahen Umgebung von *Damba zung* gelegen 5, 55ᵃ.

Žiguru, Burg, genannt mit den Burgen *San gio, Marli* sowie *Sengmuze, Burungkaza, Taksa* und *Mubari* 44, 30ᵇ.

Ži jai, Ort (Burg?), erwähnt mit *Jagiyom* 43, 6ᵇ.

Ži kar, Brücke unweit *Meimei ka* 38, 24ᵃ.

Ži lung zung[1], Ort im *Okši*-Lande: Die Orte des *Okši*-Landes, *Damba zung, Mur zung* und *Ž. l. z.,* liegen südwestlich des *Balangla* 6, 51ᵇ.

Žimze, Ort, mit *Jalma (jalam?)* genannt bei den Kämpfen um den Berg *Dugung* 44, 2ᵃ.

Ži pang[2], Berg, gleichsam Tor und Tür für *Cucin,* wie *Dartu* 55, 6ᵃ. Der Berg stößt an die Südostgrenze des *Cosgiyab*-Landes. In der Verlängerung des Bergdaches sind 11 Kampftürme gebaut. Im Westen findet man dichten Wald und steile Felsen. Es ist sehr schwer, dort geradeswegs hochzusteigen 43, 38ᵇ. *Ž. p.* bietet den einen der 3 Vormarschwege gegen *Le'uwei.* Die beiden andern gehen über *E po* und *Giyaso* 41, 26ᵃ. *Ž. p.* ist ein mächtiger Engpaß, über den der Weg nach *Le'uwei* führt 59, 21ᵇ. Im Walde östlich unterhalb des Berges *Ž. p.* läuft etwas schräg ein Weg, den man kriechend ersteigen kann 57, 7ᵃ. Die Gegend bei *Ž. p.* ist leichter gangbar als die bei *Dartu* 52, 11ᵃ. Der Berg von *Ž. p.* ist zwar steil, aber besser zu ersteigen als Berg *Dartu.* Mitten auf dem Bergrücken steht ein großer Turm, links davon eine Steinschanze, rechts ein Blockhaus (Holzburg), außen herum läuft ein über 10 Fuß tiefer Graben 55, 39. *Ž. p.* ist von *Dartu* nur 60—70 *Li* entfernt 51, 47ᵇ. Es werden einmal genannt die Burgen *Mukang* und *Žusi* auf dem Nordberge von *Ž. p.* 3, 50ᵇ. Bei dem Kampfe um *Giyaso* heißt es: Man nahm *Saksagu* und den mächtigen *Ž. p.* und dann nacheinander den Berg *Šaba* sowie die Orte *Dartu* und *Dereng* I, 14ᵇ.

Ži rung[1], Ort wohl mit dem nachgenannten identisch, erwähnt mit den Pässen *Tao guwan* und *O lung guwan,* der Brücke *Gen da kiyoo* und dem Orte *Hiyang yang ping* 72, 52ᵃ, mit *Balangla* 65, 6ᵃ, mit *Ziri* 68, 43ᵃ.

---

[1] Vgl. *Jih-lung-chai* S. 81 und *Žilung kuan* Pl II, *l.*
[2] Vgl. S. 77, 79; Pl. II, *l* u. *ll;* IV, 47.
17. IX, 4.

Ži rung zung, Ort. (50—60 *Li*) westlich von *Balangla*, östlich von *Damba zung*. Nördlich davon führt ein Weg nach *Biwangla*, im Süden geht es nach *Dermi* 22, 2ª. Im Westen des *Balangla* kann man auf allen Wegen von *Ž. r. z.* nach *Damba zung* gelangen 16, 43ª.

Ži ze, Berg westlich des Berges *Ramram* I, 12ª.

Žir badangga[1], Ort. genannt mit *Meger* sowie *Mila garma* I, 13ᵇ. Im *Tung-hua-lu* findet sich ein Bericht des Generals Agôt vom Tage Wu-ch'en V. Monats des 39. Jahres der Regierung KIENLUNG: »Ich habe festgestellt, daß *jih-rh-pa-tang-ka* soviel ist wie *jih-rh-pa tiao* (der Kampfturm *jih-rh-pa*)«. Danach hätten wir also *Žirba dangga* zu lesen. Das zweite Wort würde Kampfturm bedeuten.

Žisman, Ort bei *Langgu:* Von *Langgu* rückt man vor nach dem Rücken des unteren Berges von *Ž.*, nahm diesen und die Orte *Namdi* und *Se diyei an* in Besitz, drang dann wieder von der Seite oberhalb von *Ž.* nach *Giyaso* vor und bemächtigte sich der Feste *Argu* I, 19/20.

Žu na, Ort im *Zanla*-Lande, genannt mit *Gajung*, *Lamo* sowie *Jagungla* 8, 11ᵇ.

Žungbu, Burg, erwähnt mit *Genggete* I, 11ª.

Žung jai, Burg am Flusse gegenüber von *Sengge zung* 64, 40ᵇ. Der Ort *Sengge zung* liegt nordöstlich von *Namgiyor zung*. Wenn man durch die Öffnung der Schlucht von *Namgiyor zung* geht, so sind im Norden eine Strecke Weges lang Abhänge und Felsen. Im Süden ist ein großer Fluß. Und jenseits des Flusses stehen die Burgen *Dašihi* und *Ž. j.* 72, 22ᵇ. Nördlich des Flusses von *Sengge zung* bis *Yoza*, südlich des Flusses von *Kaya* bis zur Burg *Ž. j.* . . . Östlich von der Burg *Ž. j.* liegen noch die Burgen *Gio* und *Marli* 64, 41. Die Burg *Ž. j.* wird einmal erwähnt mit der Burg *Ze jai* 44, 2ᵇ.

Žungsa, Ort im *Cosgiyab*-Lande, erwähnt 2, 46ᵇ.

Žung žung, Ort in sehr wilder Natur. Er liegt mitten im Gebiet von *Hannio*, das in der Länge über 200 *Li* mißt, nördlich von *Kaya* und *Da u* 46, 4.

Žusi, Burg im *Cucin*-Lande, genannt mit der Burg *Mukang* und den Burgen auf den Bergen nördlich von *Ži pang* 3, 50ᵇ.

---

[1] Vgl. *Žir la* S. 81; Pl. II, *I* u. *III*.

2. Bawang.

1. Mit Kriegstürmen befestigtes Tal in Bawang.

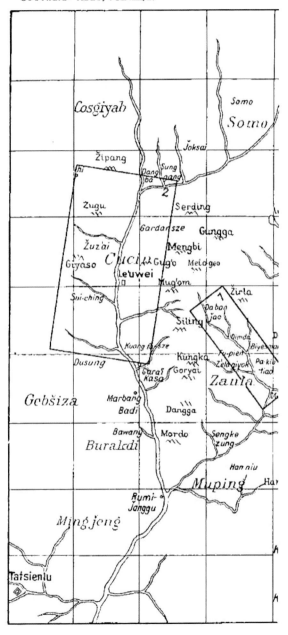

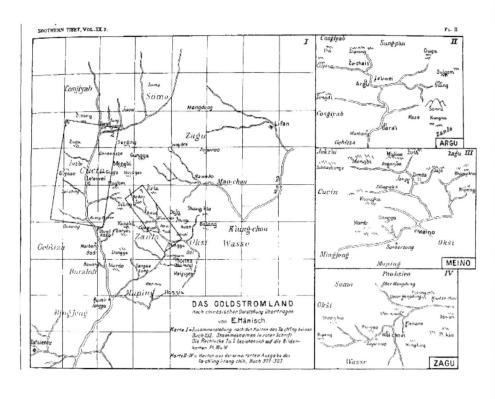

DAS GOLDSTROMLAND
nach chinesischer Darstellung übertragen
von E. Hänisch.

Karte I = Zusammenstellung nach den Karten des Ta-ch'ing hui-tien Buch 232. Stammesnamen in roter Schrift
Die Rechtecke 1a. 2 beziehen sich auf die Bilder-
karten Pl. III u. IV

Karte II–IV = Karten aus der armen Karten Ausgabe des
Ta-ch'ing i-tung chih, Buch 321-323

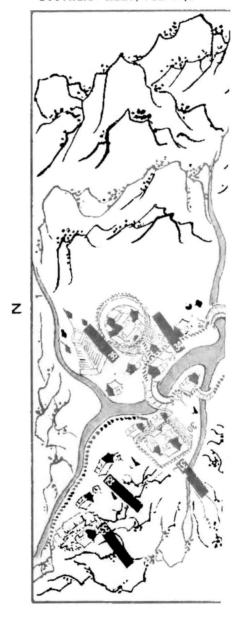

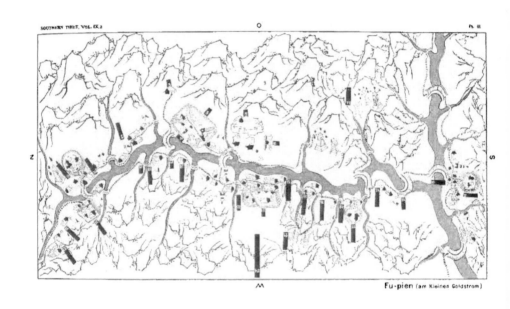

O

N

S

W

Fu-pien (am Kleinen Goldstrom)

Pl. III

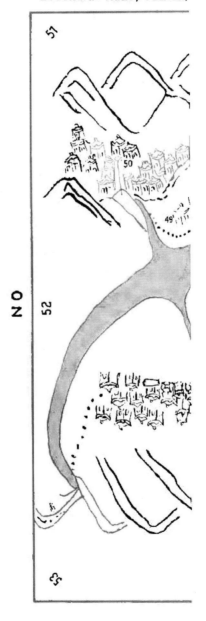

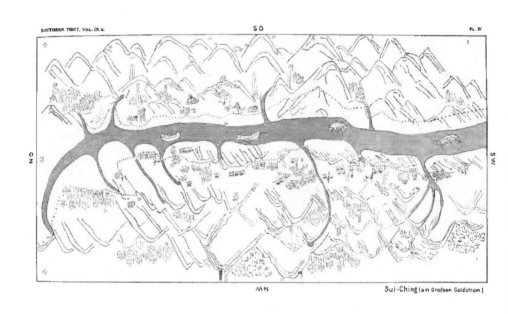

S O

O Z

S W

M N

Sui-Ching (am Grofsen Goldstrom)

NACHTRÄGE.

Balang so, Ort, ursprünglich zum *Cosgiyab*-Lande gehörig, im Jahre 1770 von den *Zanla* in Besitz genommen. Der Ort wird mit den beiden andern Orten *Garma* und *Muluzung* zusammen genannt, die dem *Cosgiyab*-Stamme zur gleichen Zeit von den »Drei *Zagu*« abgenommen wurden 41, 30 ff.

Da poo[1], der bekannte Zugangspaß von *Tatsienlu* nach dem Goldstromlande: Von *Tatsienlu* bis *Janggu* sind es zwar nur einige 400 *Li*, aber die Wegstrecke ist abschüssig und gefährlich und für Menschen und Pferde auch bei großer Anspannung schwer gangbar. Dazu liegt mitten auf dem Wege der Berg *D. p.*, der das ganze Jahr hindurch mit Schnee bedeckt ist. Als ich (General ARTAI) ihn überstieg, lag der Schnee dort 3—4 Ellen hoch, so daß ich erst nach 6 Tagen (in *Janggu?*) ankam 10, 41.

Dek, Ort im *Cucin*-Lande, ohne Angabe der Lage erwähnt 2, 48 b.

Deli[2], Ort, erwähnt bei *Ži jai* und *Jagiyom* 43, 6 b.

Dusung, Ort, erwähnt bei den Kämpfen um *Argu*: Nach der Einnahme von *Argu* stießen wir durch nach dem Rücken des Berges *Naidang*, zerstörten *Giyaza*, eroberten *D.* und versperrten (den Weg nach) *Babu* und *Langgu* I, 20 a.

Ganze, ist jedenfalls dasselbe wie *Hoor ganze.*

Gao ži šan, Berg im *Bawang*-Lande, erwähnt mit dem Berge *Giya gioi* 23, 10 a.

Giya gioi[3], s. das Vorhergehende.

---

[1] Vgl. *Dabo* S. 70, 74.

[2] Vielleicht handelt es sich hier nicht um einen Ortsnamen, sondern um ein mandschurisches Wort: *deli uehe* (*uehe* = Stein) heißt ein steiniges Flußbett. Die Stelle könnte also bedeuten »die Truppe ging im Flußbett vor«.

[3] Die zwei letzten Namen könnten chinesisch sein: der erste ist es sicher. Der zweite würde den chinesischen Silben *kia kü (chia-chü)* entsprechen.

VOL. IX PART V

GENERAL INDEX

ABBREVIATIONS.

Brk.	= Brook	Plt.	= Plateau
Brd.	= Bridge	Pn.	= Plain
Chl.	= Channel	Prov.	= Province
Ctry.	= Country	Ps.	= Pass
Def.	= Defile	Rd.	= Road
Dist.	= District	Rg.	= Region
Dpr.	= Depression	Rit.	= Rivulet
Dst.	= Desert	Riv.	= River
Gl.	= Glacier	Riv. br.	= River branch
Hd.	= Highland	Sh.	= Sheet (concerning Byström's
Hl.	= Hill		map in 1:1 000 000)
Id.	= Island	Sp.	= Spring
Kdm.	= Kingdom	St.	= Station
La.	= Lake	Stm.	= Stream
Mstry.	= Monastery	Tmp.	= Temple
Mt.	= Mountain	Tn.	= Town
Mt.ch.	= Mountain chain	Trb.	= Tribe
Mt.ra.	= Mountain range	Val.	= Valley
Mts.	= Mountains	Vil.	= Village
Pk.	= Peak	Wl.	= Well

PERSONAL NAMES.

1*

GEOGRAPHICAL NAMES.

394

212 II: 154, 164; IV: 366, 368, 424; VI₁: 58, VI₂: 28, 72ff.
213 II: 164; IV: 366.
214 II: 158ff., 164; IV: 366; V: 62ff.; VI₁: 62.
215 II: 155; IV: 367, 425; VI₁: 58.
216 IV: 367, VI₁: 58, 60; VI₂: 28, 72ff.
217 IV: 367; VI₁: 60 ff.
218 II: 156f.; IV: 366ff.; VI₁: 60.
219 II: 153; IV: 368; V: 66; VI₁: 62, 64.
220 II: 152, 165, IV: 308.
221 II: 152f.
222 II: 152f., 165; IV: 308.
223 II: 166, 168; VI₁: 64.
224 II: 168; IV: 369; VI₁: 64
225 II: 166, 168; IV: 366, 425; V: 99; VI₁: 64.
226 IV: 369, 424; V: 101, 103; VI₁: 64; VI₂: 29.
227 IV: 369f., V: 103ff.; VI₁: 64
228 IV: 370, 424; V: 105; VI₁: 64.
229 IV: VI₁: 64.
230 IV: 370, 380f.; VI₁: 64, 66.
231 IV: 371, 375, 422; VI₁: 66.
232 IV: 375, 378, 413; VI₁: 66.
233 IV: 381, 424; VI₁: 68; VI₂: 29, 72ff.
234 IV: 381, 424; V: 109; VI₁: 68; VI₂: 29, 72ff.
235 III: 334; IV: 381, 413; V: 109ff.; VI₁: 68; VI₂: 30, 72ff.; VII: xi.
236 IV: 213; IV: 381, 413; VI₁: v, 68, 70.
237 III: 331; IV: 382, 413; V: 111f.; VI₁: v, 70.
238 III: 332, 334; IV: 382, 413; V: 112; VI₁: v, 70.
239 III: 333; IV: 382, 413; V: 114; VI₁: v, 70; VI₂: 31, 72ff.
240 IV: 382f.; V: 115; VI₁: 70
241 III: 331, 333f., 336; IV: 381ff., 413; V: 115; VI₁: 70; VI₂: 31, 72ff.
242 III: 337; IV: 383, 413; VI₁: 70; VI₂: 32, 72ff.
243 III: 337; IV: x, 383, 413; V: 116f.; VI₁: 70; VI₂: 32, 72ff.
244 III: 337, 342; IV: x, 383, 422; V: 117; VI₁: 70.
245 III: 338, 342; IV: 383, 413, 422, 424; V: 117; VI₁: 70.
246 III: 338, 342; IV: 383, 413; V: 117f.; VI₁: 70, 72; VI₂: 33, 72ff.; VII: 523.
247 III: 339; IV: 384, 413; V: 119, 121; VI₁: 72; VI₂: 33, 72ff
248 III: 339; IV: 384, 413; V: 121; VI₁: 72.
249 III: 341; IV: 384, 413; V: 121; VI₁: 72.
250 III: 250; IV: 384, 413; V: 122; VI₁: 72
251 IV: 382, 384, 413; VI₁: 72; VI₂: 34
252 IV: 383, 413, VI₁: 72

253 IV: 1831, 414, 424, VI₁: 72, VI₂: 31, 76f.
254 IV: 185, 414; VI₁: 72; VI₂: 35, 76f.
255 IV: 186, 414, 424; VI₁: 72.
256 IV: 188, 414; VI₁: 72.
257 IV: 188, 191, 383; V: 122; VI₁: 74, VI₂: 35, 76f.
258 IV: 192; V: 122; VI₁: 74
259 IV: 193, 424; VI₁: 74.
260 IV: 414; VI₁: 74; VI₂: 36, 76f.
261 IV: 194ff., V: 122; VI₁: 74; VII: 521.
262 IV: 195f., 414, 424, V: 122, VI₁: 74; VII: xi.
263 IV: 197; V: 122; VI₁: 74; VI₂: 36, 76f.
264 IV: viii, 198f., 383; V: 122; VI₁: 74; VII: 521
265 IV: 199f., 414, 424; VI₁: 74.
266 IV: 200, 414; VI₁: 74, 76.
267 IV: 201, 414; V: 123; VI₁: 76.
268 IV: 201f., 424; V: 123f.; VI₁: 76.
269 IV: 414; VI₁: 76.
270 VI₁: 76
271 VI₁: 76
272 VI₁: 78.
273 VI₁: 78.
274 VI₁: 78.
275 VI₁: 78.
276 VI₁: 78; VI₂: 37, 76f
277 VI₁: 78.
278 VI₁: 78.
279 IV: 208; VI₁: 78.
280 IV: 207f.; VI₁: 78.
281 IV: 207f., 275; VI₁: 78.
282 IV: 208; VI₁: 78, 80.
283 IV: 208f., 424; VI₁: 80
284 IV: 414; VI₁: 80.
285 IV: 210, 212f., 424; V: 124; VI₁: 80.
286 IV: 210, 414; VI₁: 80.
287 IV: 210, 212, 218; VI₁: 80.
288 IV: 212, 414; VI₁: 80.
289 IV: 212f., 414, 424; V: 124; VI₁: 80.
290 IV: 414; V: 124; VI₁: 80.
291 IV: 213f.; V: 124; VI₁: 80
292 IV: 214; V: 124; VI₁: 80.
293 IV: 214ff., 414; VI₁: 82.
294 IV: 215f., 414; VI₁: 82.
295 IV: 216; V: 124; VI₁: 82; VII: 271.
296 IV: 217f.; V: 124; VI₁: 82; VI₂: 37, 78.
297 IV: 217f.; V: 124; VI₁: 82.
298 IV: 219f.; V: 124; VI₁: 82.
299 IV: 220f.; V: 125; VI₁: 82.
300 IV: 220, 421; V: 125, VI₁: 84; VII: 268, 271.
301 IV: 221f.; VI₁: 10, 12, 84.
302 III: 316; IV: xi, 222, 227, 415; VI₁: 12, 84; VI₂: 38, 56f., 76, 78.
303 IV: 223; VI₁: 84
304 IV: xi, 223f.; V: 125; VI₁: 84

305 IV: 224; VI₁: 84; VI₂: 38, 79f.
306 IV: xi, 224f.; V: 125; VI₁: 84
307 IV: xi, 225, 415; VI₁: 84.
308 IV: 226, 415; V: 125; VI₁: 84
309 IV: xi, 226ff., 424; V: 125; VI₁: 86.
310 IV: xi, 227f.; VI₁: 86.
311 IV: 228, 415; VI₁: 86.
312 IV: xi, 229f., 232; V: 125; VI₁: 86.
313 IV: 232, 424; V: 125, VI₁: 86
314 IV: 232, 415; VI₁: 86.
315 IV: 233, 415; VI₁: 86.
316 IV: 234, 415; VI₁: 86.
317 IV: 234f., 415; VI: v, 88.
318 IV: xi, 235f., 238; VI₁: 88
319 IV: 236f., 422; VI₁: 88.
320 IV: xi, 238f.; V: 125; VI₁: 88.
321 IV: 238; V: 126; VI₁: 88.
322 IV: 239f., 415; VI₁: 88.
323 IV: 240, 422, 441; VI₁: 88. VI₂: 39, 79f.
324 IV: 241ff., 422; V: 126; VI₁: 88.
325 IV: 243f., 422; VI₁: 88.
326 IV: 244f., 422; V: 126; VI₁: 88, 90.
327 IV: 246f., 422; V: 126; VI₁: 90.
328 IV: 246ff., 415; VI₁: 90.
329 IV: 248, 258; V: 126; VI₁: 90.
330 IV: 248ff., 258; V: 126f.; VI₁: v, 90.
331 IV: 249ff.; V: 127; VI₁: 90.
332 IV: 250f.; V: 127; VI₁: 90.
333 IV: xi, 252, 254, 258; V: 127; VI₁: 90.
334 IV: 253ff., 415; VI₁: 90.
335 IV: xi, 254; VI₁: 90; VI₂: 30, 79f.
336 IV: 255ff., 415; VI₁: 90.
337 IV: 257f., 415; VI₁: 92.
338 IV: 258f., 415; VI₁: 92.
339 IV: 258ff.; V: 127; VI₁: 92; VI₂: 40, 80f.
340 IV: 259, 261f.; V: 127; VI₁: 92.
341 IV: 260ff., 416; VI₁: 92.
342 IV: 416; V: 127; VI₁: 92
343 IV: 265; V: 127; VI₁: 92.
344 IV: 265ff., 416; VI₁: 92.
345 IV: 267; V: 128; VI₁: 92.
346 IV: 267f.; VI₁: 94; VI₂: 40, 80f.
347 IV: 269f., V: 128; VI₁: 94.
348 IV: 270f.; VI₁: 94.
349 IV: 271, 273, 275; VI₁: 94.
350 IV: 273, 275; VI₁: 94.
351 IV: 277, 416; VI₁: 94.
352 IV: 277f., 416; VI₁: 94
353 IV: 278, 416; VI₁: 94.
354 IV: 279, 416; VI₁: 94.
355 IV: 280, 416; VI₁: 94.
356 IV: 281, 416; VI₁: 96.
357 IV: 282, 285; V: 128; VI₁: 96. VI₂: 40, 80f
358 IV: 282f., 285; VI₁: 96; VI₂: 41

3

3*

4*

6

6*

7

7*

8

8*

124

10*

INDEX OF SUBJECTS.

11*